# STATISTICAL THEORY IN RESEARCH

# STATISTICAL THEORY IN RESEARCH

I. *Basic Statistical Theory*

II. *Analysis of Experimental Models by Least Squares*

**R. L. ANDERSON**
*Professor, Institute of Statistics, University of North Carolina*

**T. A. BANCROFT**
*Director, Statistical Laboratory, Iowa State College*

NEW YORK TORONTO LONDON
McGRAW-HILL BOOK COMPANY, INC.
1952

STATISTICAL THEORY IN RESEARCH



*Library of Congress Catalog Card Number:* 52-5984

II

THE MAPLE PRESS COMPANY, YORK, PA.

# PREFACE

In 1946, R. L. Anderson was asked to set up a course in mathematical statistics with an applied viewpoint for the Department of Experimental Statistics at North Carolina State College. Since no textbook of this type was then available, a set of notes was prepared in consultation with W. G. Cochran. These notes were mimeographed and later became a part of the Institute of Statistics Mimeo Series. This material borrowed heavily from the notes taken by the author from Professor Cochran at Iowa State College. About the same time, T. A. Bancroft was organizing a set of notes similar to Part I, plus the material on regression in this text, at Iowa State College and in 1948 proposed that the two sets be amalgamated into a textbook.

After numerous rewritings, we have settled on the present version of a combined textbook in mathematical statistics and a reference book for the research worker. This book has been divided into two parts. Part I presents basic statistical theory with some emphasis on research problems; Part II presents the theory of least squares and its use in the analysis of experimental data. Bancroft had the primary responsibility of writing Part I and Anderson of Part II, although there have been frequent consultations between the authors to maintain reasonable continuity throughout the book. At North Carolina State College, this material has been used in three courses: (1) a one-year course in applied mathematical statistics, (2) some of the elementary parts of Chaps. 17 to 24 as supplementary material for a one-quarter course in design of experiments, and (3) the more advanced material in Part II for a one-quarter course in advanced experimental statistics. At Iowa State College, Part I plus the material on regression has been taught in a two-quarter theory course, and selected sections of Part II in a one-quarter advanced methods course.

Many research workers have expressed a need for a convenient reference book on statistical theory pointed to research problems, which could be used in conjunction with their books on general statistical methods, experimental design, and survey sampling. The authors have tried to write a book which would serve this purpose as well as that of a textbook in statistical theory. They realize the difficulties in such an undertaking and will welcome suggestions on methods of improving this book both from a reference and from a text standpoint, without adding materially to the complexity of the material or the length of the book.

If this book is used as a class text, the teacher should make a choice of the topics to be covered. It was not contemplated that all of the material could be covered in a one-year course. Points which must be considered in deciding on topics to be taken up are number of lecture and laboratory hours available, interests of the students, previous training of the students (in mathematics, statistics, and experimentation), and purpose of the course (terminal or part of a sequence). A suggested list of chapters and sections for a one-year course in statistics is presented in the next section. We have postulated that only a good background in differential and integral calculus is required and that the student might use this book as an introduction to statistics. However, a previous or concurrent course in statistical methods is quite helpful. Several specialized topics in matrix algebra and advanced calculus, necessary to an understanding of certain parts of the theory, have been included. Of course, previous work in these or other courses in mathematics would be helpful.

Perhaps the best method of studying the theoretical aspects of statistical techniques is to look at the examples first and then go back to the theory. However, the authors feel that it is best to develop a general theory first, since many research workers will have their own examples in mind when they read this material, and the authors want the theory to be general enough to apply to these examples, not pointed at examples in the text. In lecturing on the material in this book, it may be advisable to present the theory and an example together.

It should be noted that the material in Part II, plus the necessary background material in Part I, could very well form the basis for an introductory course in the theory and methods of experimental design. This course would include the omitted sections in the suggested outline for a first course in statistics, especially Chaps. 19, 23, and 24.

As indicated earlier in this preface, the authors are indebted to Prof. W. G. Cochran for a majority of their early ideas in mathematical and applied statistics. It is understood that they are responsible for the interpretation and amplification of these ideas as presented in this book and for any mistakes in theory or application therein. They wish to express their appreciation to Profs. G. E. Nicholson and H. F. Smith, who made valuable suggestions for improving the presentation after teaching from the original mimeographed materials, and to Om Aggarwal for his help in working through the examples and exercises in Part I. In addition they received many helpful comments from other staff members and graduate students and from the reviewers of the original manuscript. Special thanks are due their typists, Mrs. Jeanne Rathz and Mrs. Margaret Kirwin, who did yeoman service in interpreting the authors' hieroglyphics.

The authors are indebted to Prof. George W. Snedecor and the Iowa State College Press for permission to use the many examples and tables taken from *Statistical Methods*. They are also indebted to Miss Catherine Thompson and Prof. Egon S. Pearson, editor of *Biometrika*, for permission to include Table II in the Appendix, which is an abridged version of a table presented in *Biometrika;* and to Prof. Ronald A. Fisher, Cambridge, Dr. Frank Yates, Rothamsted, and Messrs. Oliver & Boyd, Ltd., Edinburgh and London, for permission to reprint Table III in the Appendix, which is an abridged version of Table III in their book *Statistical Tables for Biological, Agricultural, and Medical Research.* Finally they express their sincere appreciation for permission to use the various sets of experimental data included in their examples and exercises.

R. L. ANDERSON
T. A. BANCROFT

RALEIGH, N. C.
AMES, IOWA
*July*, 1952

# CONTENTS

## Part II—*Analysis of Experimental Models by Least Squares*

# SUGGESTED TOPICS FOR A ONE-YEAR COURSE

*Part* I

1. Use all of the first four chapters, except perhaps to omit cumulants (Sec. 4.6).
2. Perhaps omit the $k$-variate case in Chap. 5 (Sec. 5.9).
3. Emphasize linear forms in Chap. 6 (Sec. 6.4 to 6.7).
4. Perhaps omit the Fisher-Behrens problem in Sec. 7.11.
5. Chapters 8 to 11 are concerned with the fundamental theory of estimation and tests of significance. The teacher may wish to discuss only the applications of these ideas without taking up all of the theoretical details. For example, it may be necessary to discuss the concept of power (Secs. 11.4 to 11.6) in a condensed manner and spend most of the time in Chap. 11 on the methods of setting up the likelihood-ratio criterion (Sec. 11.7).
6. It may be necessary to delete the theoretical parts of Chap. 12 and all of Secs. 12.6 and 12.8.

*Part* II

1. Study all of Chap. 13, but only Sec. 14.1 of Chap. 14, unless matrix-algebra methods are desired.
2. It may be desirable to teach only one method of computation in Chap. 15 and omit either Sec. 15.2 or Sec. 15.3.
3. All of Chap. 16 probably should be omitted except for a short assignment on curve fitting alone, with no theory.
4. A selection of topics from Chaps. 17 to 25 should be made. The following is suggested:
   (*a*) Chapter 17 is a discussion chapter and should be read, but the authors doubt that the student will understand much of it unless he has handled some experiments previously.
   (*b*) One or two examples from each type of design in Chap. 18 should suffice.
   (*c*) Omit Chap. 19 (incomplete-blocks designs).
   (*d*) Use only two or three examples in Chap. 20. Omit Secs. 20.5 and 20.6.

(e) Possibly omit the theory for covariance (Chap. 21). Omit Secs. 21.3 and 21.4.
(f) Since the theory of variance components is quite complicated, it may be necessary to consider only a few simple problems. Omit Sec. 22.4.
(g) It is doubtful that a beginner in statistical theory will be able to understand Chap. 23 (the mixed model), but it might be instructive to go through a few examples to point out the difficulties involved. This chapter was written primarily for research workers, who generally want to use a mixed model. The split-plot design should be pointed out (Sec. 23.2.)
(h) Omit Chap. 24.
(i) In Chap. 25, omit Secs. 25.1 and 25.3, but go over Secs. 25.2 and 25.4.

# SELECTED SYMBOLS AND ABBREVIATIONS

| Symbol | Page first used | Meaning |
|---|---|---|
| $\Sigma$ | 4 | sum of |
| $P(n,r)$ | 10 | permutations of $n$ things taken $r$ at a time |
| $n!$ | 10 | $(n)(n-1)\cdots(2)(1)$ |
| $C(n,r)$ | 10 | combinations of $n$ things taken $r$ at a time |
| $\mathcal{P}$ | 11 | probability of |
| $\Gamma(n)$ | 26 | $\int_0^\infty x^{n-1}e^{-x}\,dx$, the Gamma function |
| $\mathrm{B}(m,n)$ | 27 | $\int_0^1 x^{m-1}(1-x)^{n-1}\,dx$, the Beta function |
| $I_x(n)$ | 26 | incomplete Gamma function |
| $I_x(m,n)$ | 27 | incomplete Beta function |
| $E(x)$ | 31 | expected value of $x$ |
| $\mu_k'$ | 32 | $k$th moment about zero in population |
| $\mu = \mu_1'$ | 32 | population mean value |
| $\mu_k$ | 33 | $k$th moment about $\mu$ in the population |
| $\sigma^2 = \mu_2$ | 33 | population variance |
| $m(t)$ | 34 | moment generating function about zero |
| $M(t)$ | 35 | moment generating function about $\mu$ |
| $\mathrm{K}(t)$ | 36 | cumulant generating function |
| $\kappa_i$ | 36 | $i$th cumulant |
| $\rho$ | 50 | product-moment correlation coefficient |
| $\Pi$ | 52 | product of |
| $\bar{X}$ | 58 | sample mean |
| $s^2$ | 58 | a sample variance, the unbiased estimator of $\sigma^2$ |
| $\{X_i\}$ | 60 | a sample of $X$'s |
| $N(\mu,\sigma^2)$ | 68 | normally distributed with mean $\mu$ and variance $\sigma^2$ |
| NID | 68 | normally and independently distributed |
| $\hat{\theta}$ | 91 | estimated value of $\theta$ |
| $E_f$ | 95 | large sample efficiency |
| $E_f$ | 252 | efficiency factor in incomplete-blocks designs |
| $I$ | 97 | amount of information contained in a given sample (due to R. A. Fisher) |
| $I$ | 236 | relative efficiency of one experimental design compared with another |
| ML | 101 | maximum likelihood |
| $H_0$ | 113 | null hypothesis |
| $H_a$ | 114 | alternative hypothesis |
| $\beta_a$ | 114 | power of an alternative hypothesis |
| $S \in R$ | 114 | sample in a region $R$ |

| *Symbol* | *Page first used* | *Meaning* |
|---|---|---|
| $P_s$ | 125 | likelihood of a sample |
| $\equiv$ | 153 | identically equal to, or is defined to be |
| $\beta_i$ | 153 | a population regression coefficient |
| $\doteq$ | 154 | is estimated by |
| $\epsilon_j$ | 154 | a true error |
| $e_j$ | 154 | a sample residual |
| $b_i$ | 154 | a sample regression coefficient |
| $SX$ | 156 | sum of $X$'s in sample |
| SS | 156 | sum of squares |
| MS | 160 | mean square |
| d.f. | 169 | degrees of freedom |
| $X_{i.}$ | 257 | $\sum_j X_{ij}$ |
| $X_{.j}$ | 257 | $\sum_i X_{ij}$ |
| $\bar{n}_h$ | 278 | harmonic mean |

# Part I
# BASIC STATISTICAL THEORY

# CHAPTER 1

# INTRODUCTION

**1.1. What Is Statistics?** Dissatisfied with attempts at giving a precise formal definition of their subject, mathematicians have on occasion defined mathematics as being those professional activities engaged in by mathematicians. Later in this chapter an attempt will be made to give a more formal definition of the subject of statistics. For the present, however, if in the above definition the words "mathematics" and "mathematician" are replaced by "statistics" and "statistician," a definition of statistics might be written as follows:

*Statistics comprises those professional activities engaged in by statisticians.*

In order to gain some insight into the nature of statistics, then, it remains to present in some detail the steps taken by a statistician in some simple yet representative investigation.

**1.2. A Representative Investigation.** The problem is: Is test material $B$, which is the same as standard material $A$ with one added chemical, a more deadly fly spray than $A$?

*Step a.* A hypothesis, sometimes referred to as a null hypothesis, is set up. In this case a pertinent hypothesis, for which simple techniques for testing are available, is: Test material $B$, with the added chemical, is equally effective as standard material $A$ in killing flies.

*Step b.* An experiment is designed to test the hypothesis. Four batches of 100 randomly selected flies are each sprayed with each spray.

*Step c.* Pertinent data are collected and tabulated. The number of flies killed in each batch are given in the following table:

| $A$ | Rank | $B$ | Rank |
|---|---|---|---|
| 60 | 7 | 68 | 3 |
| 61 | 6 | 69 | 2 |
| 67 | 4 | 64 | 5 |
| 56 | 8 | 71 | 1 |
| 244 | 25 | 272 | 11 |

The numbers killed in the eight batches have been ranked from 1 to 8 and the ranks summed for $A$ and $B$ separately in order to make use of the simple techniques for testing mentioned in step $a$. A low sum indicates a more effective kill.

Now, if $B$ is actually more effective than $A$, we should expect the experiment to give evidence of this, that is, the sum of the ranks, $S$, for $B$ would be expected to be less than that for $A$. The total of the eight ranks is $1 + 2 + \cdots + 8 = 36$; hence, the sum for $A$ is $36 - S$. The possible values of $S$ range from $1 + 2 + 3 + 4 = 10$ to $5 + 6 + 7 + 8 = 26$. In our experiment $S = 11$. A critical question is now in order: Does this low value of $S$, for this one experiment, indicate that $B$ is more effective than $A$, or is there a high probability that one could obtain a value of $S = 11$ or lower by chance when $B$ was actually no more effective than $A$?

*Step d.* The distribution of the data, on the assumption that the null hypothesis is true, is obtained. In order to answer the question posed in step *c*, we assume that the null hypothesis is true, that is, that $A$ and $B$ are equally effective fly killers, and find the probability, $\alpha$, that such a low value (or a lower one) as $S = 11$ could have been obtained under this assumption. If this probability is low, we reject the null hypothesis, knowing that there is a remote possibility (measured by $\alpha$) that the null hypothesis is correct.

To effect the above, we find the number of ways of obtaining the various possible values of $S$. We need to consider only one of the groups, in this instance the $B$ group, since the rank numbers in the $A$ group will be the four not used in $B$. Now, $S = 10$ may be obtained in only 1 way as the sum of 1, 2, 3, 4, while $S = 12$ may be obtained in 2 ways as the sum of either 1, 2, 3, 6 or 1, 2, 4, 5, etc. A table of such values is set out below:

| Sum of ranks, $S$ | 10 | 11 | 12 | 13 | 14 | 15 | 16 | 17 | 18 | 19 | 20 | 21 | 22 | 23 | 24 | 25 | 26 |
|---|---|---|---|---|---|---|---|---|---|---|---|---|---|---|---|---|---|
| Ways to form sums, $N$ | 1 | 1 | 2 | 3 | 5 | 5 | 7 | 7 | 8 | 7 | 7 | 5 | 5 | 3 | 2 | 1 | 1 |

A short-cut method of obtaining the various values of $N$ is given by Wilcoxon.[1] In the next chapter, a short-cut method will also be given for determining the number of ways of dividing 8 quantities into 2 groups of 4 each. For the present we simply note that $\Sigma N = 70$, where the symbol $\Sigma$ is used to mean "the sum of."

Now, there are only 2 possibilities out of a total of 70 in which $B$ could appear as effective as (or better than) it did in the performed experiment. Or, stated another way, if $A$ and $B$ were equally effective, we could expect as good or better showing by $B$ in only 2 out of 70 experiments on the average.

*Step e.* A test of significance is performed. Usually we decide on an acceptable probability level, $\alpha$, before the experiment is conducted, and if the results give a probability $\leq \alpha$, we state that the null hypothesis is rejected at the $\alpha$ significance level. Two commonly used values of $\alpha$ are 0.05 and 0.01. If the null hypothesis is rejected at the $\alpha = 0.05$ level, the results are said to be *significant;* if at the $\alpha = 0.01$ level, *highly significant.*

In our experiment $\alpha = .03$. Hence we might well reject the null hypothesis at the $\alpha = .03$ probability level. In this case, if the null hypothesis was not rejected, we should be forced to accept the happening of an improbable event.

Our experiment is not large enough ever to attain high significance, since even if every $B$ kill was larger than the highest $A$ kill, $\alpha$ could not be greater than $\frac{1}{70} = .014$. In order to have an experiment sensitive enough to detect differences at the $\alpha = .01$ level, more batches of flies must be used. In Chap. 7 we shall present a method of testing the null hypothesis which utilizes the actual number of flies killed. This so-called "$t$ test" is more sensitive to the detection of real treatment differences than our ranking test. However, this new test requires the development of a more complex theoretical background.

In tests like the $t$ test the observations or sample values are *specified* as having been drawn from parent populations of known mathematical form containing one or more unknown *parameters.* In such cases the null hypothesis is a statement concerning the parameter(s). R. A. Fisher[2] has defined the basic theoretical problems underlying modern applied statistics as those of *specification, distribution, estimation,* and *tests* of *hypotheses.* The sample observations are specified as having been drawn from some parent population with unknown parameter(s). Functions of the sample observations are calculated as estimators of these parameters. The mathematical forms of the distributions of these functions obtained from repeated samplings are derived. Properties of estimators are investigated in order that an appropriate estimator may be used in an applied situation. Appropriate test criteria are constructed in order that valid tests of hypotheses may be made.

The representative investigation described above is concerned with an *experiment.* A second large class of investigations involving the use of statistical methodologies is that of the *sample survey.* Either may lead to estimates of *population parameters,* the setting of *confidence limits,* or *tests* of *significance.*

Close inspection of the steps taken by the statistician in the above representative investigation will reveal the fact that most are similar or identical with those taken by workers engaged in many different fields of scientific enquiry. What essential characteristic then is peculiar to the professional activities of the statistician? A careful comparison will reveal that this essential characteristic is the use of the mathematics of probability to calculate from the observations themselves a measure of the fallibility of conclusions and estimates. However, valid and efficient measures of the fallibility of conclusions in terms of exact probability statements are possible only if the earlier steps in the investigation are taken with this end product in mind. Hence, the statistician finds himself vitally concerned with matters not strictly concerned with this main aspect, such as statement of the null hypothesis, design of experiments and sample surveys, questionnaire construction and training and supervision of enumerators, experimental techniques, collection and tabulation of data, specification of the parent population distribution, and interpretation of results.

**1.3. A Formal Definition of Statistics.** With the above discussion in mind, statistics might be given the following formal definition:

*Statistics is the science and art of the development and application of the most effective methods of collecting, tabulating, and interpreting quantitative data in such a manner that the fallibility of conclusions and estimates may be assessed by means of inductive reasoning based on the mathematics of probability.*

**1.4. Probability.** It was stated in the definition that statistics uses inductive reasoning based on the mathematics of probability. In this respect, then, statistics is a branch of applied mathematics whose methodologies stem from the axioms and theorems of probability, which in turn is a branch of pure mathematics. A definition of the probability of the occurrence of an event would appear to be in order. Unfortunately there is no general agreement among workers in the field as to what constitutes a satisfactory definition. For reasons of simplicity the classical definition will be given, which is as follows:

*If an event can occur in $N$ equally likely and mutually exclusive ways, and if $n$ of these ways have an attribute $A$, then the probability of the occurrence of $A$ is $n/N$.*

This is the definition of a priori probability, that is, it assumes that it is possible logically to determine, before trials are made, all the equally likely and mutually exclusive ways that an event may happen and to assign $n$ of these ways to the occurrence of attribute $A$.

**Example 1.1.** What is the probability of obtaining a head with a penny on a single toss? Assuming the coin a "true" coin, we reason that it may fall 2 equally likely ways and that 1 of them must be heads; hence, the probability is $\frac{1}{2}$.

Notice that the classical definition of probability, in using the words "equally likely," assumes a knowledge of probability in order to define the term. Logically, of course, this is certainly undesirable, but a more satisfactory definition must await a higher level of mathematical maturity than that assumed for this text.

In actual practice it would appear that a priori probability might have limited usefulness. It may not be possible in a great many important scientific problems to determine logically, before trials are made, all the equally likely and mutually exclusive ways that an event may happen and to assign $n$ of these ways to the occurrence of attribute $A$. For instance, even in the example, the penny may have a tendency to turn up heads more often than tails, and the probability of heads, then, is no longer $\frac{1}{2}$. But what is the probability of heads now? Suppose the penny is tossed 100 times and 55 heads are noted. The probability of a head might be tentatively set as .55. However, we have only an estimate based on 100 tosses of some unknown postulated "true" probability in a theoretical infinite population of throws. This estimate is called the *empirical probability.*

What then is the connection between a priori probability and the sample estimate of some unknown hypothetical population probability, that is, the *empirical probability?* With the a priori definition and certain postulates the mathematics of probability provides fundamental laws or theorems of probability which in turn make possible the solution of many classes of problems. If the unknown hypothetical population probability and its sample estimates, the *empirical probability,* be assumed to be amenable to the same fundamental laws, then a means becomes available for solving many important problems in the empirical sciences.

## EXERCISES

**1.1.** Using the last three observations for $A$ and $B$ in the data given in step $c$, test the same null hypothesis of step $a$.

**1.2.** Add the two observations $A$ (66), $B$ (70) to the data of step $c$, and test the null hypothesis of step $a$.

**1.3.** Follow the instructions of Exercise 1.2, adding only $A$ (66).

**1.4.** What is the a priori *probability* of obtaining a 7 with a pair of ordinary dice, if the dice are assumed to be "true"? Assuming that the pair of dice are not "true," how could one obtain a reasonable estimate of the unknown probability of obtaining a 7, that is, the *empirical probability?*

**1.5.** Read references cited 1 and 2.

### References Cited

1. Wilcoxon, Frank, "Individual Comparisons by Ranking Methods," *Biometrics Bull.*, **1**:80–82 (1945).
2. Fisher, R. A., *Statistical Methods for Research Workers*, 10th ed., Oliver & Boyd, Ltd., Edinburgh and London, 1948. Chap. I.

### Other Reading

Fisher, R. A., *The Design of Experiments*, 4th ed., Oliver & Boyd, Ltd., Edinburgh and London, 1947. Chaps. I, II.

FISHER, R. A., "Mathematical Foundations of Theoretical Statistics," *Phil. Trans. Roy. Soc. (London)*, **A222**:309–368 (1922).

GOULDEN, C. H., *Methods of Statistical Analysis*, John Wiley & Sons, Inc., New York, 1939. Chap. I.

SNEDECOR, GEORGE W., *Statistical Methods*, 4th ed., Collegiate Press, Inc., of Iowa State College, Ames, Iowa, 1946. Chap. I.

WILCOXON, FRANK, *Some Rapid Approximate Statistical Procedures*, American Cyanamid Co., Stamford, Conn., 1949.

# CHAPTER 2

## PROBABILITY

**2.1. Introduction.** It was stated earlier that statistics concerns itself with inductive reasoning based on the mathematics of probability. In developing statistical methodology the statistician makes use of the definitions, postulates, and theorems of mathematical probability. What can be said of this framework, these "bones," of statistics? The theory of probability had its genesis in the application of mathematics to determining the odds in various games of chance: dice, cards, spun wheels, etc. In particular, the foundations of the science of probability were laid by two seventeenth-century mathematicians, Pascal and Fermat, in their private correspondence concerning questions raised regarding the gambling observations of the French nobleman, Chevalier de Méré. Books on games of chance are still being written by workers in probability and statistics.[1]

Statistics is then no dry-as-dust subject concerning itself with the compilation of innumerable tables and charts. On the contrary, it deals with the development and application of an important methodology based on the fascinating subject of probability. This methodology has become of great importance as a research tool in the physical, biological, and social sciences.

**2.2. Number of Ways an Event Can Occur: Permutations and Combinations.** The number of ways in which an event may occur may be determined by enumeration or by the use of some simple rules from college algebra. The latter method is simpler for more complicated problems. Two fundamental theorems are:

*Rule* 2.1. *If $A$ can happen in $m$ ways and $B$ in $n$ ways independent (the occurrence of one does not affect the chance of the occurrence of the other) of $m$, then both $A$ and $B$ can happen in $mn$ ways.*

**Example 2.1.** If two ordinary dice numbered 1 and 2 are tossed, one may appear face up in 6 ways which are independent of the 6 ways in which the second may appear. Hence, both may appear face up together in 36 different ways.

*Rule* 2.2. *If $A$ can happen in $m$ ways and $B$ in $n$ ways mutually exclusive (the occurrence of one precludes the occurrence of the other) of $m$, then either $A$ or $B$ can happen in $m + n$ ways.*

**Example 2.2.** Either an ace or a king (one card) may be drawn from an ordinary deck of cards in $4 + 4 = 8$ ways.

For multiple arrangements, a rule for *permutations* can be applied. If it be desired to arrange $n$ different objects into sets of $r$ objects per set, the number of such arrangements is called "the number of permutations of $n$ objects taken $r$ at a time" and is indicated by $P(n,r)$. The first of the $r$ positions can be filled in $n$ ways, the second in $(n - 1)$ ways since one object will have been used in the first position, the third in $(n - 2)$ ways, etc. Hence, by Rule 2.1:

*Rule* 2.3. $P(n,r) = n(n-1)(n-2) \cdots (n-r+1) = \dfrac{n!}{(n-r)!}$, *where* $n! = n(n-1) \cdots 2.1.$

It should be noted that, when $r = n$, $P(n,n) = n!$, which implies that $0! = 1$.

**Example 2.3.** The number of different ways of selecting a president, vice-president, and secretary from a suggested slate of 6 is

$$P(6,3) = 6 \cdot 5 \cdot 4 = 120.$$

Suppose that all $n$ objects in the arrangement are used, but certain groups $n_1$, $n_2$, etc., are alike. Any rearrangement of the objects of any $n_i$ group will not change any particular arrangement, hence, the total number of arrangements will be less than if all the objects were different from one another. Now, any group of $n_i$ alike objects can be arranged $n_i!$ ways, and since these $n_i!$ arrangements are alike for every arrangement of the other objects, the total number of different arrangements will be given as below:

*Rule* 2.4. $P(n;n_1,n_2,n_3, \ldots) = \dfrac{n!}{n_1!n_2!n_3! \cdots}$, *where* $P(n;n_1,n_2,n_3, \ldots)$ *represents the total number of permutations, given that* $n_1$ *are alike,* $n_2$ *alike but different from the first group, etc., and* $\Sigma n_i = n$.

**Example 2.4.** How many different 6-flag signals may be made if 3 are red, 2 blue, and 1 yellow? $P(6;3,2,1) = \dfrac{6!}{3!2!1!} = 60.$

If interest lies only in groups of objects and not in the arrangements within the groups, then combinatorial rules apply. The total number of combinations of $n$ objects taken $r$ at a time is denoted symbolically as $C(n,r)$. It is easily seen that

$$P(n,r) = C(n,r)P(r,r),$$

since each combination of $r$ objects may be permuted $P(r,r)$ times. The following rule is now derived:

*Rule* 2.5. $C(n,r) = \dfrac{P(n,r)}{P(r,r)} = \dfrac{n!}{(n-r)!r!}.$

**Example 2.5.** The total number of different bridge hands of 13 cards which can be dealt from a deck of 52 cards is $C(52,13) = \frac{52!}{13!39!}$. Again the total number of sets of 4 bridge hands is

$$C(52,13) \cdot C(39,13) \cdot C(26,13) \cdot C(13,13) = \frac{52!}{(13!)^4}.$$

**2.3. Stirling's Approximation.** The use of the rules of permutations and combinations involves factorials, some with quite large values of $n$. Stirling's formula,

$$n! = \sqrt{2\pi n}\, n^n e^{-n}\left(1 + \frac{1}{12n} + \frac{1}{288n^2} + \cdots\right),$$

may be used to obtain quickly an approximation to $n!$ The first term,

$$n! \sim \sqrt{2\pi n}\, n^n e^{-n},$$

gives a suitable approximation in many cases.

**Example 2.6.** Evaluate 13! by the use of Stirling's formula,

$$13! \sim \sqrt{2\pi(13)}\left\{13^{13}e^{-13}\left[1 + \frac{1}{(12)(13)}\right]\right\},$$

$$\log 13! \sim \tfrac{1}{2}(\log 26 + \log \pi) + 13 \log 13 - 13 \log e + \log \tfrac{157}{156},$$

$$13! \sim 6.2271 \times 10^9,$$

using 5-place logarithm table.

**2.4. Probability and Arrangements.** After obtaining the total number of mutually exclusive and equally likely ways and those which possess attribute $A$ by the use of the rules of permutations and combinations, it is then possible to write the required probability by applying the fundamental definition

$$p = \frac{\text{number of ways that possess attribute } A}{\text{total number of ways}}.$$

**Example 2.7.** A bag contains 4 red and 3 white balls. What is the probability of obtaining exactly 3 red balls when 3 balls are drawn?

$$p = \frac{C(4,3)}{C(7,3)} = \frac{4}{35}.$$

**2.5. Fundamental Laws of Probability**

*Law* 1. *If A and B are two mutually exclusive events (the occurrence of one precludes the occurrence of the other), then the probability of either of them happening is the sum of the respective probabilities. Symbolically,* $\mathcal{P}(A + B) = \mathcal{P}(A) + \mathcal{P}(B)$.

**Example 2.8.** The probability of throwing either a 7 or an 8 with two dice is $\frac{6}{36} + \frac{5}{36} = \frac{11}{36}$.

*Law* 2. *If A and B are two independent events, so that the occurrence of one does not affect the chance of the occurrence of the other, the probability that both happen is the product of their respective probabilities. Symbolically,* $\mathcal{P}(AB) = \mathcal{P}(A) \cdot \mathcal{P}(B)$.

**Example 2.9.** The probability of getting 2 red balls in drawing 1 ball from each of two urns containing 6 red balls and 4 black balls is $\frac{6}{10} \cdot \frac{6}{10} = \frac{9}{25}$.

If $A$ and $B$ are not independent of one another so that the occurrence of one affects the probability of the occurrence of the other, then a definition is needed for the *conditional probability* of $A$ given that $B$ has occurred, which is denoted $\mathcal{P}(A|B)$. Similarly the conditional probability of $B$ given that $A$ has happened is $\mathcal{P}(B|A)$. In such cases fundamental law 2 becomes:

*Law* 3. $\mathcal{P}(AB) = \mathcal{P}(A) \cdot \mathcal{P}(B|A) = \mathcal{P}(B) \cdot \mathcal{P}(A|B)$. *If A and B are independent,* $\mathcal{P}(B|A) = \mathcal{P}(B)$ and $\mathcal{P}(A|B) = \mathcal{P}(A)$.

**Example 2.10.** If both balls were drawn in succession from one of the urns in Example 2.9 without replacement, then the probability of obtaining 2 red balls is $\frac{6}{10} \cdot \frac{5}{9} = \frac{1}{3}$.

*Law* 4. *If two events are not mutually exclusive, then the probability of at least one of them occurring is* $\mathcal{P}(A + B) = \mathcal{P}(A) + \mathcal{P}(B) - \mathcal{P}(AB)$.

*Proof.* Let $\bar{A}$ and $\bar{B}$ represent the nonoccurrence of $A$ and $B$, respectively. Then,

$$\mathcal{P}(A) + \mathcal{P}(B) = \mathcal{P}(AB) + \mathcal{P}(A\bar{B}) + \mathcal{P}(BA) + \mathcal{P}(B\bar{A})$$
$$= \mathcal{P}(AB) + \mathcal{P}(A + B).$$
$$\therefore \mathcal{P}(A + B) = \mathcal{P}(A) + \mathcal{P}(B) - \mathcal{P}(AB),$$

where $\mathcal{P}(A\bar{B})$ is the probability of $A$ occurring and $B$ not occurring, and similarly for $\mathcal{P}(B\bar{A})$.

Law 4 is illustrated in Fig. 2.1, where the outcomes of a chance event are represented by points in a plane. Then the outcomes belonging to either $A$ or $B$ may be represented by the points in $A$ and $B$ less the points common to region $AB$ since $AB$ would be counted twice.

This law may be extended, for example,

$$\mathcal{P}(A + B + C)$$
$$= \mathcal{P}(A) + \mathcal{P}(B) + \mathcal{P}(C) - \mathcal{P}(AB) - \mathcal{P}(AC) - \mathcal{P}(BC) + \mathcal{P}(ABC).$$

**Example 2.11.** In Example 2.9 the probability of obtaining at least one red ball is

$$\mathcal{P}(A + B) = \mathcal{P}(A) + \mathcal{P}(B) - \mathcal{P}(AB) = \tfrac{6}{10} + \tfrac{6}{10} - \tfrac{6}{10} \cdot \tfrac{6}{10} = \tfrac{21}{25}.$$

*Law* 5. *If the probability of an event occurring in a single trial is p, the probability of its occurring r times out of n trials is given by*

$$C(n,r)p^r(1-p)^{n-r} = C(n,r)p^rq^{n-r},$$

*where* $1 - p = q$. This is the $(r+1)$st term of $(q+p)^n$.

*Proof.* If the event occurs $r$ times out of $n$ trials, it will fail to occur $n - r$ times; hence, the probability of the occurrence of any sequence of $r$ successes and $n - r$ failures is $p^r(1-p)^{n-r}$. But the number of possible sequence is given by $C(n,r)$.

**Example 2.12.** The probability of obtaining exactly 3 heads on a single toss of 5 coins is $C(5,3)(\frac{1}{2})^3(\frac{1}{2})^2 = \frac{5}{16}$.

**2.6. A Posteriori Probability.** In the previous sections it was assumed that the casual system was known a priori; hence, exact probabilities of

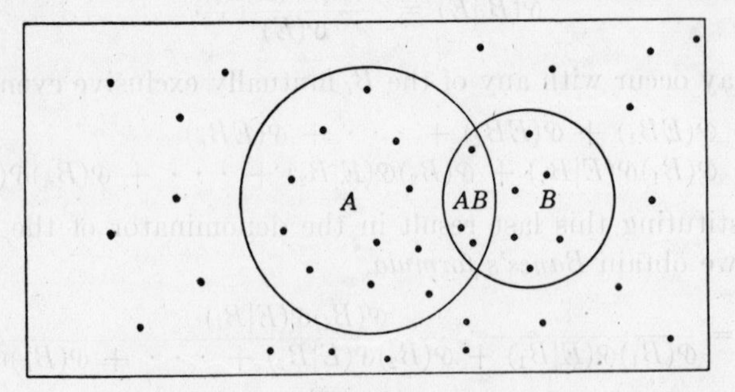


FIG. 2.1.

various results were readily calculated. In tossing a die it was assumed that all 6 faces appeared "equally likely" and that a random toss of the die was made. In such cases the probability of obtaining any number from 1 to 6 was easily seen to be $\frac{1}{6}$. With these same assumptions and use of the fundamental laws of probability it was also easy to state the probability of obtaining a 7 on a single throw, say, with two dice.

In statistics, however, one is often faced with exactly the reverse of this situation. A batch of data resulting from some experiment is at hand, and we wish to state the probability that such data could have been produced by a given casual system. For example, it is noted that two hundred 7's were obtained in tossing two dice 1,000 times. We now wish to know the probability that such a result could have been produced with unbiased dice. Or we may wish to state, on the basis of these results, the expected number of 7's to be obtained on the next 100 tosses of two dice. These problems concern a posteriori probability, probability based on previous occurrences.

A posteriori probabilities, under certain conditions, may be obtained by the use of Bayes's formula. Let $B_1, B_2, \ldots, B_n$ be $n$ mutually exclusive

random events, of which one is certain to occur. Let $\mathcal{P}(B_i)$ be the probability of the occurrence of $B_i$. Let $E$ be an event which can occur only if one of the set of $B$'s occurs. Let $\mathcal{P}(E|B_i)$ be the conditional probability for $E$ to occur, assuming the occurrence of $B_i$. We wish to know how the probability of $B$ changes with the added information that $E$ has actually happened. In other words, we wish the conditional probability $\mathcal{P}(B_i|E)$.

Using law 3,

$$\mathcal{P}(EB_i) = \mathcal{P}(B_i)\mathcal{P}(E|B_i),$$

and

$$\mathcal{P}(EB_i) = \mathcal{P}(E)\mathcal{P}(B_i|E).$$

Equating the right-hand sides of these two equations and solving for $\mathcal{P}(B_i|E)$, we obtain

$$\mathcal{P}(B_i|E) = \frac{\mathcal{P}(B_i)\mathcal{P}(E|B_i)}{\mathcal{P}(E)}.$$

Since $E$ may occur with any of the $B_i$ mutually exclusive events,

$$\begin{aligned}\mathcal{P}(E) &= \mathcal{P}(EB_1) + \mathcal{P}(EB_2) + \cdots + \mathcal{P}(EB_n)\\ &= \mathcal{P}(B_1)\mathcal{P}(E|B_1) + \mathcal{P}(B_2)\mathcal{P}(E|B_2) + \cdots + \mathcal{P}(B_n)\mathcal{P}(E|B_n).\end{aligned}$$

Upon substituting this last result in the denominator of the preceding equation, we obtain *Bayes's formula*,

$$\mathcal{P}(B_i|E) = \frac{\mathcal{P}(B_i)\mathcal{P}(E|B_i)}{\mathcal{P}(B_1)\mathcal{P}(E|B_1) + \mathcal{P}(B_2)\mathcal{P}(E|B_2) + \cdots + \mathcal{P}(B_n)\mathcal{P}(E|B_n)}.$$

If we consider the events $B_1, B_2, \ldots, B_n$ as hypotheses to account for the occurrence of $E$, then Bayes's formula provides a means of calculating probabilities of hypotheses. In this case $\mathcal{P}(B_1), \mathcal{P}(B_2), \ldots, \mathcal{P}(B_n)$ are called a priori probabilities of the hypotheses $B_1, B_2, \ldots, B_n$, and $\mathcal{P}(B_1|E), \mathcal{P}(B_2|E), \ldots, \mathcal{P}(B_n|E)$ are called a posteriori probabilities of the same hypotheses.

**Example 2.13.** Urn I contains 2 white, 1 black, and 3 red balls. Urn II contains 3 white, 2 black, and 4 red balls. Urn III contains 4 white, 3 black, and 2 red balls. One urn is chosen at random, and 2 balls are drawn. They happen to be red and black. What is the probability that both balls came from urn I? urn II? urn III?

We identify $E$ as the event that the 2 balls were, respectively, red and black. To explain this occurrence, we have three hypotheses: the urn was I, II, or III. We identify these hypotheses with $B_1, B_2, B_3$.

Then $\mathcal{P}(B_1) = \mathcal{P}(B_2) = \mathcal{P}(B_3) = \frac{1}{3}$, and $\mathcal{P}(E|B_1) = \frac{3}{6} \cdot \frac{1}{5} + \frac{1}{6} \cdot \frac{3}{5} = \frac{1}{5}$. Similarly, $\mathcal{P}(E|B_2) = \frac{2}{9}$, and $\mathcal{P}(E|B_3) = \frac{1}{6}$. Substituting in Bayes's formula,

$$\mathcal{P}(B_1|E) = \frac{\frac{1}{3} \cdot \frac{1}{5}}{\frac{1}{3} \cdot \frac{1}{5} + \frac{1}{3} \cdot \frac{2}{9} + \frac{1}{3} \cdot \frac{1}{6}} = \frac{18}{53}.$$

Similarly,

$$\mathcal{P}(B_2|E) = \frac{\frac{1}{3}\cdot\frac{2}{9}}{\frac{1}{3}\cdot\frac{1}{5}+\frac{1}{3}\cdot\frac{2}{9}+\frac{1}{3}\cdot\frac{1}{6}} = \frac{20}{53},$$

$$\mathcal{P}(B_3|E) = \frac{\frac{1}{3}\cdot\frac{1}{6}}{\frac{1}{3}\cdot\frac{1}{5}+\frac{1}{3}\cdot\frac{2}{9}+\frac{1}{3}\cdot\frac{1}{6}} = \frac{15}{53}.$$

Note, that the sum, as we should expect, is 1.

**Example 2.14.** (Due to Neyman). Consider the cross of two hybrids $x_1$ and $x_2$ which are heterozygous ($Aa$) and its progeny $y_1$ having the appearance of a dominant, that is, either doubly dominant ($AA$) or heterozygous ($Aa$). Suppose that $y_1$ is crossed with a recessive ($aa$) designated as $y_2$ resulting in $n$ offspring: $z_1, z_2, \ldots, z_n$. Suppose that not one of these offspring is a recessive, that is, either a dominant or a hybrid. It is proposed to find the probability that $y_1$ is ($Aa$).

Let $E$ be the event that $n$ offspring have the appearance of dominants; $B_1$ may be identified with the event that $y_1$ is ($Aa$) and $B_2$ with the event that $y_1$ is ($AA$). Then, $\mathcal{P}(B_1) = \mathcal{P}(y_1 = Aa) = \frac{2}{3}$, and

$$\mathcal{P}(E|B_1) = \mathcal{P}(E|y_1 = Aa) = 1/2^n,$$

and $\mathcal{P}(E|B_2) = \mathcal{P}(E|y_1 = AA) = 1$. Substituting in Bayes's formula,

$$\mathcal{P}(B_1|E) = \mathcal{P}(y_1 = Aa|E) = \frac{\frac{2}{3}\cdot(1/2^n)}{\frac{2}{3}\cdot(1/2^n)+\frac{1}{3}\cdot 1} = \frac{1}{1+2^{n-1}}.$$

Giving $n$ the values 1, 2, 3, 4, 5, we obtain Table 2.1.

TABLE 2.1

A Posteriori Probabilities

| $n$ | $\mathcal{P}(y_1 = Aa\|E)$ |
|---|---|
| 1 | .500 |
| 2 | .333 |
| 3 | .200 |
| 4 | .111 |
| 5 | .059 |

Suppose, however, that we do not know anything about the origin of $y_1$. In that case the a priori probabilities $\mathcal{P}(B_1) = \mathcal{P}(y_1 = Aa)$ and $\mathcal{P}(B_2) = \mathcal{P}(y_1 = AA)$ would be unknown, and we would not have sufficient information to evaluate the right side of Bayes's formula. In the past it has been suggested that since $\mathcal{P}(B_1)$ and $\mathcal{P}(B_2)$ are unknown, and we have no reason to favor one more than another, we should assign one-half to each. Modern statistics provides other ways of attacking such problems which seem more reasonable. These methods will be discussed later.

## EXERCISES

**2.1.** An agronomist is designing an experiment involving the use of 4 varieties, 3 fertilizers, and 3 spacings. How many different treatment combinations, using one from each of the three kinds of treatments, does he have?

**2.2.** In how many different ways may a Jersey or a Holstein be drawn from a mixed herd of 5 Jerseys, 7 Holsteins, 10 Guernseys, and 6 Brahmans?

**2.3.** How many different ways may a horticulturist arrange 5 different potted plants along a line on a greenhouse bench?

**2.4.** How many different ways may a student select a major and a minor from 5 possible fields?

**2.5.** How many different arrangements can be made using the 10 letters from the word "statistics"?

**2.6.** How many signals can be made by hoisting 6 flags of different colors if there are 6 significant positions on the flagpole? Any number of the flags may be hoisted at a time.

**2.7.** An organism has the possibility of having 1, 2, 3, 4, or 5 out of a total of 15 characters. What are the total possible combinations?

**2.8.** An industrial engineer is designing an experiment arranged to measure sources of variation from 4 factors (runs, journeys, cylinders, and pots). If we let $R$, $J$, $C$, and $P$ represent the respective factors, how many 2-factor interactions of the type $RJ$, etc., are there? How many 3-factor interactions? How many 4-factor interactions?

**2.9.** Using the relationship

$$(1 + x)^n = 1 + C(n,1)x + C(n,2)x^2 + \cdots + C(n, n - 1)x^{n-1} + C(n,n)x^n,$$

show that

$$2^n - 1 = C(n,1) + C(n,2) + \cdots + C(n, n - 1) + C(n,n).$$

How many ways can we make a selection of 5 breeds of chickens, taking some or all?

**2.10.** Show that $C(n,r) = C(n, n - r)$.

**2.11.** If $C(n,10) = C(n,6)$, find $C(n,3)$.

**2.12.** If $C(16,r) = C(16, r - 2)$, find $r$.

**2.13.** If $P(56, r + 6)/P(54, r + 3) = 30{,}800$, find $r$.

**2.14.** A random sample of size $n$ from a finite population of $N$ sampling units is one in which every possible combination of size $n$ has an equal chance of being chosen. How many different samples of size 10 may be drawn from a list of 100 names? Use Stirling's approximation to evaluate the factorials.

**2.15.** Suppose that in selecting the sample of size 10 in Exercise 2.14 we draw a number from 1 to 10 at random, say 6, and select every tenth name on our list thereafter, that is, 16, 26, etc. Is this method of selection equivalent to random sampling? Why?

**2.16.** From a pack of 52 cards, 2 are drawn at random; find the probability that one is a queen and the other a king.

**2.17.** There are three events $A$, $B$, $C$, one of which must, and only one can, happen; the probability of $A$ not happening is $\frac{8}{11}$, and the probability of $B$ not happening is $\frac{5}{7}$. Find the probability of $C$ happening.

**2.18.** The probability of $A$ solving a certain problem is $\frac{3}{7}$, and the probability of $B$ solving the same problem is $\frac{5}{12}$. What is the probability that the problem will be solved if both try?

**2.19.** In a family with 6 children, what is the probability that (*a*) all children will be girls; (*b*) all children will be of the same sex; (*c*) the first 5 children will be boys and the sixth a girl? (*d*) That 3 of the children will be boys? Assume the sex ratio is $\frac{1}{2}$.

**2.20.** Show that under the conditions of law 5 the probability that an event happens at least $r$ times in $n$ trials is

$$C(n,r)p^rq^{n-r} + C(n, r+1)p^{r+1}q^{n-r-1} + \cdots + C(n, n-1)p^{n-1}q + p^n$$

or the sum of the last $(n - r + 1)$ terms of the expansion of $(q + p)^n$.

**2.21.** A lady declares that by tasting a cup of tea made with milk she can discriminate whether the milk or the tea infusion was first added to the cup. Eight cups of tea were mixed, 4 in one way and 4 in the other, and the lady was so informed. The cups were then presented, in random order, to her for judgment. She was asked to divide the 8 cups into two sets of 4, agreeing, if possible, with the treatments received. The lady selected 3 right and 1 wrong in each set of the same treatment. On the assumption that the lady cannot discriminate between the two methods, show that the probability of her doing as well or better by chance is $\frac{17}{70}$.

**2.22.** An urn contains 6 balls which are known to be all red or 4 red and 2 black. A ball is drawn and found to be red. What is the probability that all the balls are red?

**2.23.** A male rat is either doubly dominant ($AA$) or heterozygous ($Aa$), and, owing to Mendelian properties, the probabilities of either being true is $\frac{1}{2}$. The male rat is bred to a doubly recessive ($aa$) female. If the male rat is doubly dominant, the offspring will exhibit the dominant characteristic; if heterozygous, the offspring will exhibit the dominant characteristic $\frac{1}{2}$ of the time and the recessive characteristic $\frac{1}{2}$ of the time. Suppose all of 3 offspring exhibit the dominant characteristic, what is the probability that the male is doubly dominant?

**2.24.** Chevalier de Méré's problem was concerned with a certain game of dice. Twenty-four throws of a pair of dice is to be allowed, and the player is permitted to bet even money either on the occurrence or at least one "double six" in the course of the 24 throws or against it. Certain theoretical considerations led De Méré to believe that betting on the double six is advantageous. On the other hand his empirical trials appeared to contradict this conclusion. Pascal's solution stated that, if the dice are "fair," the probability of obtaining at least one double six in 24 throws is .491. Check Pascal's results.

### References Cited

1. BLANCHE, ERNEST, *You Can't Win: Facts and Fallacies about Gambling,* Public Affairs Press, New York, 1949.

### Other Reading

FELLER, WILLIAM, *An Introduction to Probability Theory and Its Applications,* John Wiley & Sons, Inc., New York, 1950.

FRY, T. C., *Probability and Its Engineering Uses,* D. Van Nostrand Company, Inc., New York, 1928.

HALL, H. S., and S. R. KNIGHT, *Higher Algebra,* Macmillan and Company, New York, 1936. Chaps. XI, XXXII.

LEVY, H., and L. ROTH, *Elements of Probability,* Oxford University Press, New York, 1936.

NEYMAN, J., *First Course in Probability and Statistics,* Henry Holt and Company, Inc., New York, 1950.

USPENSKY, J. V., *Introduction to Mathematical Probability,* McGraw-Hill Book Company, Inc., New York, 1937.

WHITWORTH, W. A., *Choice and Chance,* G. E. Stechert & Company, New York, 1942.

# CHAPTER 3

# UNIVARIATE PARENT POPULATION DISTRIBUTIONS

**3.1. Specification.** In Chap. 2, we were interested in obtaining the probability of the occurrence of a single chance event. It will be recalled from Chap. 1 that in order to arrive at the end product, a test of a hypothesis in the representative statistical investigation, we needed the probabilities for a complete set of chance events. In that investigation the chance events were various sums of ranks, $S$. A table of the possible values which a chance event may assume with a corresponding probability for each value is called a *probability distribution* for the parent population. This distribution is given in Table 3.1 for the parent population of values of $S$. In this table, the variable $x$ is used to represent the chance event $S$ and in such cases is called a *chance variable* or *variate*.

TABLE 3.1
Probability Distribution of Sum of Ranks

| $x$ | 10 | 11 | 12 | 13 | 14 | 15 | 16 | 17 | 18 | 19 | 20 | 21 | 22 | 23 | 24 | 25 | 26 |
|---|---|---|---|---|---|---|---|---|---|---|---|---|---|---|---|---|---|
| $(x)$ | $\frac{1}{70}$ | $\frac{1}{70}$ | $\frac{2}{70}$ | $\frac{3}{70}$ | $\frac{5}{70}$ | $\frac{5}{70}$ | $\frac{7}{70}$ | $\frac{7}{70}$ | $\frac{8}{70}$ | $\frac{7}{70}$ | $\frac{7}{70}$ | $\frac{5}{70}$ | $\frac{5}{70}$ | $\frac{3}{70}$ | $\frac{2}{70}$ | $\frac{1}{70}$ | $\frac{1}{70}$ |

Ordinarily, in applied statistics, specification is accomplished by selecting a mathematical function, for example, the normal, binomial, or Poisson, on the basis of theoretical or empirical evidence and stating that the observations form a sample of all possible values of the variate. Quoting from R. A. Fisher:[1] " . . . we may know by experience what forms are likely to be suitable, and the adequacy of our choice may be tested *a posteriori*. We must confine ourselves to those forms which we know how to handle, or for which any tables which may be necessary have been constructed."

**3.2. Discrete Distributions.** Functions like $f(x)$ in Table 3.1 are called *discrete* probability distribution functions to distinguish distributions of this type from *continuous* probability distribution functions, to be discussed later. The various values of $f(x)$ may be thought of as giving the *relative frequencies* of occurrence corresponding to the particular values of $x$. Since some one of the 17 events must occur on any one trial, the sum of all the probabilities is 1 or symbolically

$$\sum_{x=10}^{26} f(x) = 1. \qquad (1)$$

The distinguishing characteristic of the discrete distribution is that the variate $x$ can take only isolated values, that is, in Table 3.1 only the *whole* numbers 10 through 26.

**3.3. The Binomial Distribution.** This discrete distribution is the distribution of successes, $x$, in $n$ repeated independent trials, in which the probability of success on any trial is a constant $p$. It has been named the binomial distribution because the successive probabilities are given by the respective terms of the expansion of the binomial $(q + p)^n$, where $q = 1 - p$. One property of the binomial theorem is that the $(x + 1)$st term of the expansion is

$$f(x) = C(n,x)p^x q^{n-x}, \qquad 0 \leq x \leq n, \tag{2}$$

which by the methods of Chap. 2 also gives the probability of exactly $x$ successes in $n$ trials. On the right side of (2), $x$ is the variate, and $p$

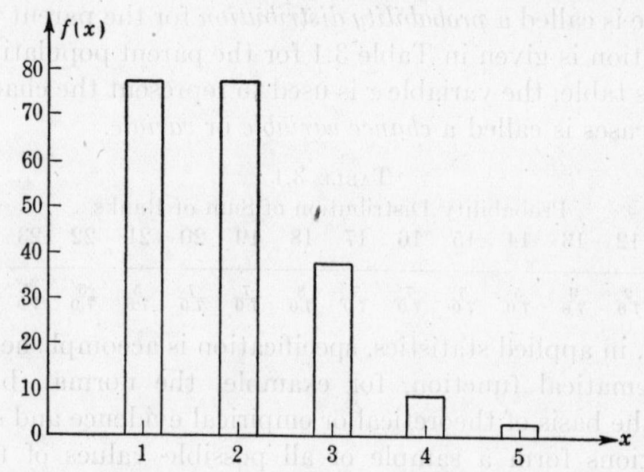


FIG. 3.1. Graph of probabilities of obtaining $x$ tenant farms. [$f(x)$ axis given in parts of 243.]

and $n$ are parameters, that is, for any particular member of this family of distributions special values of $p$ and $n$ must be specified. Since

$$\sum_{x=0}^{n} f(x) = (q + p)^n = 1,$$

this distribution fulfills the requirement that the sum of the probabilities is 1.

Individual terms and partial sums for various numerical values of $p$, $n$, and $x$ for the binomial distribution are given in reference 2.

**Example 3.1.** Given that the probability of drawing a tenant farm in a sample of farms is $\frac{1}{3}$. If samples of 5 farms are drawn, then the respective probabilities of obtaining 0, 1, 2, 3, 4, 5 tenant farms in a single sample are $(\frac{2}{3})^5$; $5(\frac{1}{3})(\frac{2}{3})^4$; $10(\frac{1}{3})^2(\frac{2}{3})^3$; $10(\frac{1}{3})^3(\frac{2}{3})^2$; $5(\frac{1}{3})^4(\frac{2}{3})$; $(\frac{1}{3})^5$ or $\frac{1}{243}$ [32,80,80,40,10,1].

The probabilities $f(x)$ of obtaining $(x = 0,1,2,3,4,5)$ tenant farms may be shown graphically as in Fig. 3.1.

If the probabilities are accumulated and graphed as in Fig. 3.2, then some $F(a)$ value gives the probability of obtaining a value of $x$ less than or equal to $a$, that is, $F(a) = \mathcal{P}(x \leq a)$. This step function is called a *cumulative* distribution or an *ogive*.

Note that points of discontinuity occur for each whole number on the $x$ axis and that $F(5) = \mathcal{P}(x \leq 5) = 1$.

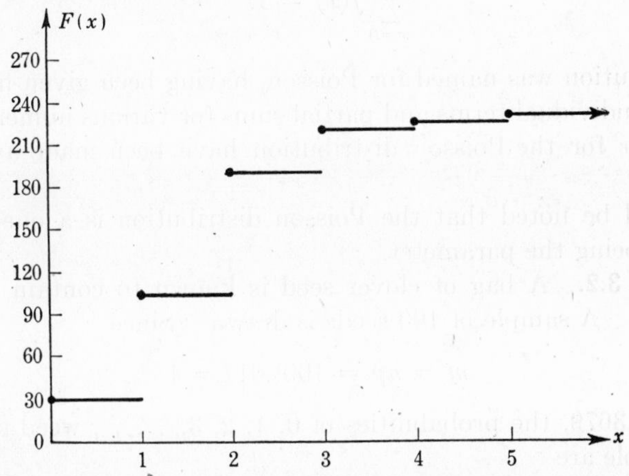


FIG. 3.2. Cumulative distribution of tenant-farm probabilities. [$F(x)$ axis given in parts of 243.]

**3.4. The Poisson Distribution.** Another discrete distribution of importance in applied statistics is the Poisson distribution. The Poisson distribution may be derived as a limiting form of the binomial distribution when $p$ is very small but $n$ is so large that $np$ is a finite constant, equal to $m$, say. To see this, consider the binomial distribution:

$$f(x) = \frac{n(n-1)(n-2)\cdots(n-x+1)}{x!}p^x q^{n-x}.$$

Since $p = m/n$,

$$f(x) = \frac{n(n-1)(n-2)\cdots(n-x+1)}{x!}\left(\frac{m}{n}\right)^x\left(1-\frac{m}{n}\right)^{n-x}$$

$$= \frac{(1-1/n)(1-2/n)\cdots[1-(x-1)/n]m^x(1-m/n)^{n-x}}{x!}.$$

Then

$$\lim_{n\to\infty} f(x) = \frac{m^x e^{-m}}{x!}.$$

Obviously, this function is also a function of $x$; hence the Poisson distribution may be written as

$$f(x) = e^{-m}\frac{m^x}{x!}, \qquad 0 \leq x < \infty.$$

Since

$$\sum_{x=0}^{\infty} \frac{m^x}{x!} = e^m,$$

then

$$\sum_{x=0}^{\infty} f(x) = 1.$$

The distribution was named for Poisson, having been given first by him in 1837. Individual terms and partial sums for various numerical values of $m$ and $x$ for the Poisson distribution have been made available by Molina.[3]

It should be noted that the Poisson distribution is a one-parameter family, $m$ being the parameter.

**Example 3.2.** A bag of clover seed is known to contain 1 per cent weed seeds. A sample of 100 seeds is drawn. Since

$$m = np = 100(.01) = 1$$

and $e^{-1} = .3679$, the probabilities of 0, 1, 2, 3, . . . , weed seeds being in the sample are

| Number of weed seeds | 0 | 1 | 2 | 3 | 4 | 5 | 6 | 7 |
|---|---|---|---|---|---|---|---|---|
| Probability | .3679 | .3679 | .1839 | .0613 | .0153 | .0031 | .0005 | .0001 |

**3.5. Continuous Distributions.** If *measurements* instead of *counts* constitute the data under consideration, then the hypothetical parent population distribution is usually that of a *continuous* variate instead of a *discrete* variate. Snedecor[4] gives the histogram of Fig. 3.3 for the gains in weight of 100 swine. Before powerful mathematical methods may be applied to derive a methodology providing techniques for statistical inferences, it is desirable to "idealize" the histogram into a curve which may be represented by a mathematical function. Such a process takes place in other branches of applied mathematics, for example, in surveying. Before the surveyor can be furnished with a powerful methodology for the solution of his practical problems in mensuration, it is necessary for the geometer to idealize the *physical points, lines,* and *planes.* A geometrical point is defined as having no dimensions but simply an indicator of position. Again, a geometrical line has no width, and a geometrical plane has no thickness. With these idealized definitions and certain assumptions called *axioms* the geometer is able to prove *theorems* concerning relationship and properties of geometrical configurations. These theorems in turn form the bases for a practical surveying methodology.

How shall we idealize a histogram of the type given in Fig. 3.3? First of all, instead of a finite population of possible values of the variate, we assume an infinite population of gains in weight. Next, instead of the class marks differing by 5 pounds, suppose that they are selected closer and closer together. It is not difficult to see that the histogram might reasonably be expected to approach some continuous smooth curve of the type shown in Fig. 3.4.

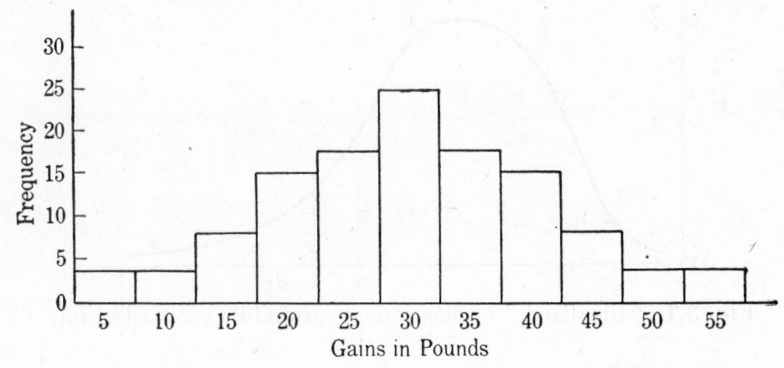


FIG. 3.3. Histrogram showing frequency of gains in weight of 100 swine.

In Fig. 3.1 the probability of obtaining some particular $x$ for the discrete distribution was represented by an ordinate. Here, $x$ represents only whole numbers, but, because of the limitations imposed by measuring devices, the best that can be said concerning the "true" value of some observed $x$ value where $x$ represents a continuous variate is that it lies in some interval $(x, x + dx)$. If the area under the continuous curve be made equal to 1, corresponding to the similar requirement that the sum of the probabilities equal 1 for the discrete distributions, then the probability of $x$ lying in the interval $(x, x + dx)$ will be $f(x)\,dx$. This would be the *theoretical* probability corresponding to the *empirical* probability, say, of a gain of weight lying between 37.5, and 42.5 that is, $\frac{13}{100} = .13$.

The range of $x$ may be thought of as extending from $-\infty$ to $+\infty$, even through the curve may actually contact the $x$ axis at some finite value, since the area under the curve in the contact interval would be zero. As was pointed out, the total probability or area under the curve is 1, symbolically

$$\int_{-\infty}^{\infty} f(x)\,dx = 1. \tag{3}$$

The probability of $x$ being equal to or less than some constant $a$ is expressed as

$$\mathcal{P}(x \leq a) = \int_{-\infty}^{a} f(x)\, dx. \tag{4}$$

Again, the probability of $x$ lying between $a$ and $b$ is given by

$$\mathcal{P}(a \leq x \leq b) = \int_{a}^{b} f(x)\, dx. \tag{5}$$

It is possible to omit the equal signs in the left sides of (4) and (5) since the probability of obtaining any *particular* value of $x$ is equal to the width of a geometrical line which is zero.

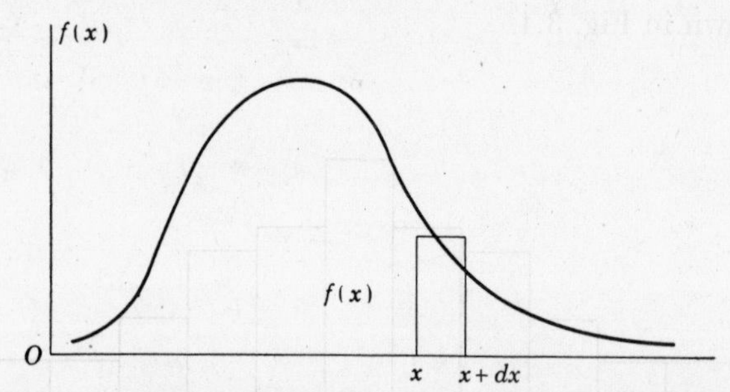


FIG. 3.4. "Idealized," or theoretical, probability distribution.

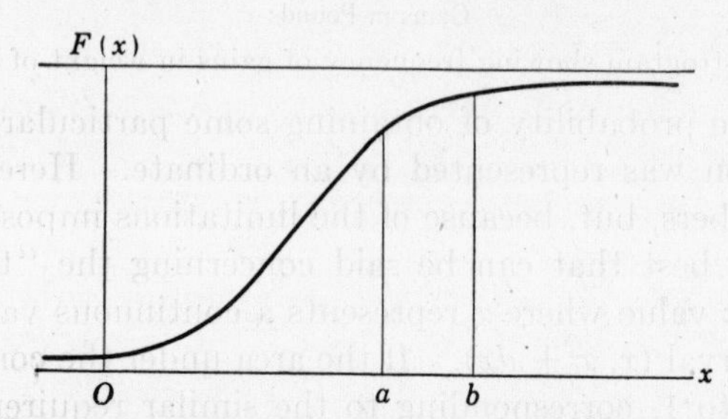


FIG. 3.5. Cumulative probability distribution for a continuous variate.

The *cumulative* probability distribution, or *ogive,* for the continuous variate corresponding to the probability distribution of Fig. 3.4 would appear as in Fig. 3.5. For this curve, $F(a) = \mathcal{P}(x \leq a)$, and hence $F(b) - F(a) = \mathcal{P}(a \leq x \leq b)$.

**3.6. The Normal Distribution.** The most important continuous distribution in applied statistics is the normal distribution. The histogram of Fig. 3.3 and the theoretical distribution of Fig. 3.4 are those for data specified as being normally distributed. Data arising from many different measurements taken on plants and animals are specified as following the normal distribution. There is empirical justification for this assumption. Similarly, distributions of certain data of the physical and social sciences are found to be satisfactorily represented by the normal distribution. It should not be assumed, however, that every continuous distribution representing actual data should be normal. For example, it is known that the distribution of sizes of cumulus clouds should be represented by a U-shaped curve. The mathematical form of the normal curve is defined by

$$f(x)\,dx = \frac{1}{\sigma\sqrt{2\pi}} e^{-(1/2\sigma^2)(x-\mu)^2}\,dx, \qquad -\infty < x < \infty. \tag{6}$$

The curve is symmetrical about $x = \mu$ and bell-shaped as in Fig. 3.4. The inflection points are at $x = \mu \pm \sigma$, and the tails of the curve, although approaching the $x$ axis quite rapidly, extend indefinitely far in both directions. The function (6) represents a two-parameter family, $\mu$ and $\sigma$, of continuous distributions, that is, as $\mu$ and $\sigma$ vary in magnitude a family of distributions is generated.

Since it can be shown for (6) that

$$\int_{-\infty}^{\infty} f(x)\,dx = 1, \tag{7}$$

then the normal probability distribution has this same property in common with the binomial and the Poisson distributions.

Table I in the Appendix gives ordinates and areas for the normal distribution.

**3.7. Probability Distributions as Specialized Mathematical Functions.** We have noticed that theoretical probability distributions are mathematical functions possessing certain requirements. In order to give a complete formal definition of the requirements necessary for a mathematical function to be a probability distribution of statistics, it is convenient and sufficient to consider the *cumulative* distribution function, $F(x)$. It is sufficient since, given the cumulative distribution, it is possible to find the distribution itself by taking the differential, that is,

$$d[F(x)] = f(x)\,dx.$$

A mathematical function, $F(x)$, may be used as a cumulative distribution of a chance variable provided that

(*a*) $F(-\infty) = 0, F(+\infty) = 1$,

(*b*) $F(x)$ is a nondecreasing function, that is, if $x_1 > x_2$, $F(x_1) \geq F(x_2)$,

(*c*) $F(x)$ is defined at every point in a continuous range and is continuous, except possibly at a denumerable number of points.

The following notation should be kept clearly in mind:

$f(x)$ is the frequency function.

$F(x)$ is the cumulative distribution.

**3.8. Some Mathematical Functions Useful as Probability Distributions.** Karl Pearson[5,6] has suggested the differential equation

$$\frac{dy}{dx} = \frac{(d - x)y}{a + bx + cx^2}$$

as a generator of possible parent population distributions useful in applied statistics. For example, if $d = \mu$, $b = c = 0$, and $a = \sigma^2$, then the differential equation becomes

$$\frac{dy}{y} = \frac{(\mu - x)\, dx}{\sigma^2}.$$

Solving for $y$, we have

$$\log_e y = -\frac{(\mu - x)^2}{2\sigma^2} + \log_e c.$$

Then

$$y = ce^{-(x-\mu)^2/2\sigma}.$$

Upon setting the integral between the limits from $-\infty$ to $\infty$ equal to 1, we find

$$c = \frac{1}{\sigma\sqrt{2\pi}}.$$

Hence,

$$y = \frac{1}{\sigma\sqrt{2\pi}} e^{-(x-\mu)^2/2\sigma^2}, \qquad -\infty < x < \infty,$$

which is the normal frequency function. This is Type VII of the Pearson system of frequency functions.[6]

Another method of obtaining a mathematical representation of a frequency function is furnished by the Gram-Charlier series.[6] This latter method will not be discussed here, but the interested reader should consult the reference.

**3.9. The Gamma and Beta Functions.** These are two useful functions in statistics of which extensive use will be made in subsequent chapters. The Gamma function of the positive number $n$ is defined by

$$\Gamma(n) = \int_0^\infty x^{n-1}e^{-x}\, dx, \qquad n > 0.$$

The properties of the Gamma function will be exhibited in Exercises 3.1 to 3.6.

The incomplete Gamma function, defined by

$$\begin{aligned} F(x) = I_x(n) &= \frac{1}{\Gamma(n)} \int_0^x x^{n-1}e^{-x}\, dx, \qquad 0 < x < \infty, \\ &= \frac{\Gamma_x(n)}{\Gamma(n)}, \end{aligned}$$

furnishes a useful cumulative distribution function which will be discussed in Chap. 7.

The Beta function, defined by

$$B(m,n) = \int_0^1 x^{m-1}(1-x)^{n-1}\,dx, \qquad m,\, n > 0,$$

is also of importance in theoretical and applied statistics. The properties of the Beta function will be exhibited in Exercises 3.7 to 3.9.

The cumulative incomplete Beta function is defined by

$$F(x) = I_x(m,n) = \frac{1}{B(m,n)} \int_0^x x^{m-1}(1-x)^{n-1}\,dx, \qquad 0 \le x \le 1,$$
$$= \frac{B_x(m,n)}{B(m,n)}.$$

Both $I_x(n)$ and $I_x(m,n)$ have been tabulated by Karl Pearson and his staff at the Biometric Laboratory, University College, London.

## EXERCISES

**3.1.** Use integration by parts to show that $\Gamma(n+1) = n\Gamma(n)$.

**3.2.** Show that $\Gamma(n+1) = n(n-1) \cdots (n-k)\Gamma(n-k)$, where $k$ is a positive integer less than $n$.

**3.3.** If $n$ is also a positive integer, show that $\Gamma(n+1) = n!$

**3.4.** (*a*) Find $\Gamma(1)$, $\Gamma(2)$, $\Gamma(3)$, and $\Gamma(4)$.

(*b*) Using $\Gamma(n+c) = (n+c-1) \cdots (n+1)n\Gamma(n)$, show that $\Gamma(n)$ becomes infinite when $n = 0$.

**3.5.** Show that $\Gamma(n) = 2\int_0^\infty y^{2n-1}e^{-y^2}\,dy$ by setting $x = y^2$ in the integral defining the Gamma function.

**3.6.** Using the result of Exercise 3.5, show that:

(*a*) $\Gamma(\frac{1}{2}) = 2\int_0^\infty e^{-y^2}\,dy$,

(*b*) $[\Gamma(\frac{1}{2})]^2 = 4\int_0^\infty\int_0^\infty e^{-(x^2+y^2)}\,dx\,dy$,

(*c*) $[\Gamma(\frac{1}{2})]^2 = 4\int_0^{\pi/2}\int_0^\infty e^{-r^2}r\,dr\,d\theta$ in polar coordinates,

(*d*) $\Gamma(\frac{1}{2}) = \sqrt{\pi}$.

**3.7.** By setting $x = \sin^2\theta$ in the integral defining $B(m,n)$, show that

$$B(m,n) = 2\int_0^{\pi/2} \sin^{2m-1}\theta \cos^{2n-1}\theta\,d\theta.$$

**3.8.** By setting $x = 1 - y$ in the integral defining $B(m,n)$ show that $B(m,n) = B(n,m)$.

**3.9.** Show that

(a) $\Gamma(n)\Gamma(m) = 4 \int_0^\infty \int_0^\infty x^{2n-1} y^{2m-1} e^{-(x^2+y^2)}\, dx\, dy,$

(b) $\Gamma(n)\Gamma(m) = 4 \int_0^{\pi/2} \sin^{2m-1}\theta \cos^{2n-1}\theta\, d\theta \int_0^\infty r^{2(m+n)-1} e^{-r^2}\, dr,$

(c) $\Gamma(n)\Gamma(m) = \mathrm{B}(m,n)\Gamma(m+n)$, or

$$\mathrm{B}(m,n) = \frac{\Gamma(m)\Gamma(n)}{\Gamma(m+n)}.$$

**3.10.** Construct a parent population probability distribution for the sum of numbers appearing when two dice are tossed. Give (a) a table of $x$ and $f(x)$, (b) a graph of (a), and (c) the cumulative distribution graph.

**3.11.** If you have a set of random numbers from 0 to 999, how would you set up a sampling scheme to select a random sample of 50 from 490 farms, the farms being numbered 0 to 489?

**3.12.** Follow the instructions in Exercise 3.10 for the binomial distribution with $p = \frac{2}{5}$, $n = 5$.

**3.13.** Follow the instructions in Exercise 3.10 for the Poisson distribution with $p = .002$, $n = 1{,}000$.

**3.14.** Given the frequency function $f(x) = 2x$, $0 \leq x \leq 1$, $f(x) = 0$ for $x < 0$ or $x > 1$. Show that $\int_0^1 f(x)\, dx = 1$. What is the functional form of the cumulative distribution function?

**3.15.** Show that the area under the curve is 1 for the triangular distribution function

$$f(x) = \frac{2(b-x)}{b^2}, \qquad 0 \leq x \leq b.$$

**3.16.** Repeat Exercise 3.15 for the rectangular distribution

$$f(x) = \frac{1}{w}, \qquad 0 \leq x \leq w.$$

**3.17.** Repeat Exercise 3.15 for the Cauchy distribution

$$f(x) = \frac{1}{\pi} \frac{1}{1+x^2}, \qquad -\infty < x < \infty.$$

**3.18.** A random variable $x$, which lies between the limits 0 and 10, has the frequency function $f(x) = Ax^3$. Determine the value of $A$ so that the total probability is 1. What is the probability that $x$ lies between 2 and 5? That $x$ is less than 3?

**3.19.** A random variable follows the normal distribution. Determine the coordinates of the maximum point on the frequency curve, and show that $\mu \pm \sigma$ are the inflexion points. Show that the area under the normal curve is 1.

**3.20.** A variate has the distribution $f(x) = e^{-x}$ in the interval $0 \leq x < \infty$. The probability is $\frac{1}{2}$ that $x$ will exceed what value?

**3.21.** If $\mathcal{P}(x < x_1) = 1 - \frac{1}{1 + x_1^2}$, $x$ being a continuous variate with range $0 \leq x < \infty$, find the frequency function $f(x)$.

**3.22.** May $f(x) = -1/(x - 2)^2$, $0 \leq x \leq 4$, serve as a probability distribution function? Why?

**3.23.** Use the table of areas of the normal curve to determine, for the normal distribution given in Exercise 3.19, the probability of (*a*) $x \geq \mu$, (*b*) $(\mu - \sigma) \leq x \leq (\mu + \sigma)$, (*c*) $x \geq \mu + 2\sigma$.

**3.24.** Give the Poisson approximation to the binomial distribution with $n = 2{,}048$ and $p = 1/1{,}024$. Hence, obtain the probabilities of there being 0, 1, 2, 3, . . . times that 10 tails appear in 2,048 tosses of 10 coins.

**3.25.** It can be shown for large $n$ that the binomial distribution may be approximated by the normal distribution with $\mu = np$ and $\sigma^2 = npq$. If 20 coins are tossed, obtain the approximate probability of obtaining 8 or more heads.

**3.26.** For the distribution $f(x) = 2x$, $0 \leq x \leq 1$, find the number $a$ such that the probability of $x \geq a$ is 3 times the probability of $x \leq a$.

**3.27.** If two values of $x$ are drawn at random from the distribution $f(x) = e^{-x}$, $0 \leq x < \infty$, what is the probability that both are greater than 1?

**3.28.** In Exercise 3.27 what is the probability that at least one value of $x$ is greater than 1?

## References Cited


1. Fisher, R. A., "Mathematical Foundations of Theoretical Statistics," *Phil. Trans. Roy. Soc. (London)*, **A222**:309–368 (1922.)
2. *Tables of the Binomial Probability Distribution*, National Bureau of Standards, Government Printing Office, Washington, D.C., 1950.
3. Molina, E. C., *Poisson's Exponential Binomial Limit*, D. Van Nostrand Company, Inc., New York, 1942.
4. Snedecor, G. W., *Statistical Methods*, 4th ed., Collegiate Press, Inc., of Iowa State College, Ames, Iowa, 1946. Chap. 3.
5. Elderton, W. P., *Frequency Curves and Correlation*, Cambridge University Press, London, 1938.
6. Kendall, M. G., *The Advanced Theory of Statistics*, Charles Griffin & Co., Ltd., London, 1943. Vol. 1, Chaps. I, V, VI.


## Other Reading


Cramer, Harald, *Mathematical Methods of Statistics*, Princeton University Press, Princeton, N.J., 1946. Second part.

Hoel, P. G., *Introduction to Mathematical Statistics*, John Wiley & Sons, Inc., New York, 1947. Chap. III.

Kenney, J. F., and E. S. Keeping, *Mathematics of Statistics*, D. Van Nostrand Company, Inc., New York, 1951. Part II, Chap. III.

*Tables of the Incomplete Beta Function.* Cambridge University Press, London, 1934.

*Tables of the Incomplete Gamma Function*, His Majesty's Stationery Office, London, 1922.

Wilks, S. S., *Mathematical Statistics*, Princeton University Press, Princeton, N.J., 1943. Chaps. II, III.

# CHAPTER 4

## PROPERTIES OF UNIVARIATE DISTRIBUTION FUNCTIONS

**4.1. Introduction.** In this chapter certain important properties of *parent population distributions* will be discussed. The discussion will also apply to similar properties of *derived sampling distributions.* These properties will be found useful in describing parent population distributions and derived sampling distributions.

**4.2. Mathematical Expectation.** The mathematical expectation of any random variable $x$, which can assume values $x_1, x_2, \ldots, x_n$ with probabilities, $p_1, p_2, \ldots, p_n$, respectively, where $\sum_1^n p_i = 1$, is defined to be

$$E(x) = \sum_{i=1}^{n} x_i p_i.$$

For the discrete distribution this becomes

$$E(x) = \sum_{i=1}^{n} x_i f(x_i),$$

for distributions with $p_i = f(x_i)$. For the continuous distribution

$$E(x) = \int_{-\infty}^{\infty} x f(x)\, dx,$$

where as noted before $f(x)$ may vanish over part of the range $(-\infty, +\infty)$.

The term "mathematical expectation" may be shortened to "expected value" or "average value."

The definition of the expected value of any random variable $x$ may be generalized to include functions of $x$. The expected value of any function of $x$, say $\theta(x)$, is

$$E[\theta(x)] = \Sigma\theta(x)f(x) \text{ or } \int \theta(x)f(x)\, dx,$$

over the range of $x$ and depending upon whether $x$ is a discrete or continuous variate.

It is possible, by introducing a generalized form of summation called a "Stieltje's integral," to replace the $\Sigma$ or $\int$ by a single integral sign. Although the concept of the Stieltje's integral simplifies statements concerning probabilities and expected values, the mathematical concepts behind this refinement are beyond the scope of this text. A distinction in all statements will be made between the discrete and continuous distributions.

If the indicated integration, necessary to obtain the expected value, cannot be performed directly, various methods of numerical integration are available.

**Example 4.1.** The expected value of $x$, where $x$ gives the various sums possible to be made by throwing two ordinary dice, may be found from the following table:

| $i$ | 1 | 2 | 3 | 4 | 5 | 6 | 7 | 8 | 9 | 10 | 11 |
|---|---|---|---|---|---|---|---|---|---|---|---|
| $x_i$ | 2 | 3 | 4 | 5 | 6 | 7 | 8 | 9 | 10 | 11 | 12 |
| $36f(x_i)$ | 1 | 2 | 3 | 4 | 5 | 6 | 5 | 4 | 3 | 2 | 1 |

Then,

$$E(x) = \sum_{i=1}^{11} x_i f(x_i) = \frac{2 + 6 + 12 + \cdots + 12}{36} = 7.$$

**Example 4.2.** If $f(x) = 3x^2$, $0 \leq x \leq 1$, then

$$E(x) = \int_0^1 x \cdot 3x^2\, dx = \frac{3}{4}.$$

Also,

$$E(x^2) = \int_0^1 x^2 \cdot 3x^2\, dx = \frac{3}{5}.$$

**4.3. Operations with Expected Values.** The rules stated below will be found useful in operating with expected values.

1. The expected value of a constant is the constant itself. $E(c) = c$.
2. The expected value of a constant times a variable is the constant times the expected value of the variable. $E[c\theta(x)] = cE[\theta(x)]$.
3. The expected value of a sum (or difference) of two variates or functions is the sum (or difference) of the expected values of the separate parts. $E[\theta_1(x) \pm \theta_2(x)] = E[\theta_1(x)] \pm E[\theta_2(x)]$.

The proof of these statements is left as an exercise for the student.

**4.4. Moments.** The expected value of $x^k$ is called the $k$th moment of $x$ about the origin and is represented by the symbol $\mu'_k$. Hence,

$$\mu'_k = E(x^k) = \Sigma x^k f(x) \text{ or } \int x^k f(x)\, dx,$$

over the range of $x$. The first moment of $x$ about the origin is referred to as the *mean* of $x$, and is denoted by $\mu'_1$. To simplify writing let $\mu'_1 = \mu$.

The expected value of $(x - \mu)^k$ is called the $k$th moment of $x$ about the mean and is designated by the symbol $\mu_k$. Hence

$$\mu_k = E(x - \mu)^k = \Sigma(x - \mu)^k f(x) \text{ or } \int (x - \mu)^k f(x)\, dx,$$

over the range of $x$. It is easily seen that

$$\mu_1 = E(x - \mu) = 0.$$

The second moment about the mean, $\mu_2$, is called the *variance* and is usually designated by the symbol $\sigma^2$. Hence,

$$\sigma^2 = \mu_2 = E(x - \mu)^2 = \Sigma(x - \mu)^2 f(x) \text{ or } \int (x - \mu)^2 f(x)\, dx,$$

over the range of $x$. The formula for $\sigma^2$ may be written as follows:

$$\sigma^2 = E(x - \mu)^2 = E(x^2) - 2\mu E(x) + (\mu)^2 = E(x^2) - (\mu)^2 = \mu_2' - (\mu)^2.$$

The square root of $\sigma^2$, or $\sigma$, is referred to as the *standard deviation*.

The third moment about the mean, $\mu_3$, furnishes a measure of *skewness*, or departure from symmetry about the mean of the distribution. One of the most generally accepted measures of skewness is the nondimensional quantity

$$\alpha_3 = \frac{\mu_3}{\sigma^3}.$$

It is seen that $\alpha_3$ will be zero for a symmetric distribution.

A measure of the relative flatness or peakedness of the distribution, called the *kurtosis*, is given by the nondimensional quantity

$$\alpha_4 = \frac{\mu_4}{\sigma^4}.$$

**Example 4.3.** Using the table of values of Example 4.1, we see that $\mu = 7$. Also,

$$\mu_2' = \frac{4 + 18 + 48 + \cdots + 144}{36} = \frac{1{,}974}{36}.$$

Hence,

$$\sigma^2 = \frac{1{,}974}{36} - 49 = \frac{35}{6}.$$

**Example 4.4.** Using the distribution function of Example 4.2, that is, $f(x) = 3x^2$, $0 \leq x \leq 1$,

$$\mu = \tfrac{3}{4}, \qquad \sigma^2 = \tfrac{3}{5} - \tfrac{9}{16} = \tfrac{3}{80},$$

and

$$\mu_3 = \int_0^1 \left(x - \frac{3}{4}\right)^3 \cdot 3x^2\, dx = -\frac{1}{160}.$$

**Example 4.5.** In order that the function,

$$f(x)\,dx = ke^{-c(x-m)^2}\,dx, \qquad -\infty < x < \infty,$$

represent a probability distribution, it is necessary that

$$\int_{-\infty}^{\infty} f(x)\,dx = 1.$$

Hence, we find $k = \sqrt{c/\pi}$. Also,

$$\mu = \int_{-\infty}^{\infty} xf(x)\,dx = m, \qquad \text{and} \qquad \sigma^2 = \int_{-\infty}^{\infty} (x-\mu)^2 f(x)\,dx = \frac{1}{2c}.$$

Substituting these values in the original function, we find

$$f(x)\,dx = \frac{1}{\sigma\sqrt{2\pi}} e^{-(x-\mu)^2/2\sigma^2}\,dx, \qquad -\infty < x < \infty,$$

which is the normal distribution.

**Example 4.6.** For the binomial distribution,

$$f(x) = C(n,x)p^x q^{n-x},$$

$$\mu = \sum_{x=0}^{n} x \frac{n!}{(n-x)!x!} p^x q^{n-x}$$

$$= np \sum_{x=1}^{n} \frac{(n-1)!}{(n-x)!(x-1)!} p^{x-1} q^{n-x}$$

$$= np(q+p)^{n-1}.$$

$$\therefore \mu = np.$$

**4.5. Moment Generating Functions.** The expected value of $e^{tx}$ often provides a convenient short cut in evaluating the moments of $x$. Since

$$e^{tx} = 1 + \frac{tx}{1!} + \frac{(tx)^2}{2!} + \frac{(tx)^3}{3!} + \cdots = \sum_{i=0}^{\infty} \frac{t^i}{i!} x^i,$$

then

$$E(e^{tx}) = \sum_{i=0}^{\infty} \mu_i' \frac{t^i}{i!}, \qquad \text{where } \mu_0' = 1.$$

We set, say,

$$m(t) = E(e^{tx})$$

and designate $m(t)$ *the moment generating function* of $x$. If $m(t)$ be differentiated $k$ times with respect to $t$ and then evaluated at $t = 0$, we note that

$$\left.\frac{\partial^k m(t)}{\partial t^k}\right|_{t=0} = \mu_k'.$$

To obtain the moment generating function of $x - \mu$, we consider

$$e^{t(x-\mu)} = 1 + \frac{t(x-\mu)}{1!} + \frac{t^2(x-\mu)^2}{2!} + \frac{t^3(x-\mu)^3}{3!} + \cdots.$$

Then,

$$E[e^{t(x-\mu)}] = 1 + \sum_{i=1}^{\infty} \mu_i \frac{t^i}{i!}.$$

If we set $M(t) = E[e^{t(x-\mu)}]$, then

$$\mu_k = \left.\frac{\partial^k M(t)}{\partial t^k}\right|_{t=0}.$$

In general the moment generating function of any function $\theta(x)$ may be defined as

$$E[e^{t\theta(x)}].$$

**Example 4.7.** For the distribution,

$$f(x)\,dx = e^{-x}\,dx, \qquad 0 \leq x < \infty,$$

$$m(t) = \int_0^\infty e^{-(1-t)x}\,dx = (1-t)^{-1} = \sum_{i=0}^{\infty} t^i.$$

Hence,

$$\mu_k' = k!.$$

**Example 4.8.** For the binomial distribution

$$m(t) = \sum_{x=0}^{n} e^{tx} C(n,x) p^x q^{n-x} = \sum_{x=0}^{n} C(n,x)(pe^t)^x q^{n-x} = (q + pe^t)^n.$$

Then,

$$\mu_1' = \mu = npe^t(q + pe^t)^{n-1}\Big|_{t=0} = np,$$

$$\mu_2' = np[e^t(n-1)(q + pe^t)^{n-2}pe^t + (q + pe^t)^{n-1}e^t]\Big|_{t=0} = np[(n-1)p + 1].$$

Hence,

$$\mu_2 = \sigma^2 = \mu_2' - (\mu)^2 = np(1-p) = npq.$$

We may obtain the following relation between $M(t)$ and $m(t)$:

$$M(t) = E[e^{t(x-\mu)}] = e^{-t\mu}[E(e^{tx})]$$

$$\therefore M(t) = e^{-t\mu} m(t).$$

Besides furnishing a simple method of obtaining the moments in certain cases, the moment generating function is of use in deriving distribution functions and in comparing distributions. These latter two uses follow from Theorems 4.1 and 4.2 of Sec. 4.7.

The expected value of $e^{tx}$ may not exist for real values of $t$ for many discrete and continuous distributions, for example, for the Cauchy distribution

$$f(x)\,dx = \frac{1}{\pi}\frac{dx}{1+x^2}, \qquad -\infty < x < \infty.$$

A more general function, which can be proved always to exist, is the characteristic function defined as $E(e^{itx})$, where $t$ is real. The characteristic function for the Cauchy distribution is $e^{-|t|}$. However, the evaluation of the integral, necessary to obtain the characteristic function, makes use of more advanced mathematical methods than are assumed for this course. Our uses of Theorems 4.1 and 4.2 will be confined to the moment generating function, which will be assumed to exist in such cases.

**4.6. Cumulants.** Suppose that we define

$$\log m(t) = \mathrm{K}(t) = \kappa_1 t + \kappa_2 \frac{t^2}{2!} + \cdots + \kappa_r \frac{t^r}{r!} + \cdots. \tag{1}$$

But

$$\log m(t) = t\mu + \log M(t)$$

and

$$\log M(t) = \log\left[1 + \sum_{i=1}^{\infty} \mu_i \frac{t^i}{i!}\right].$$

Hence

$$\log m(t) = t\mu + \log\left[1 + \left(\mu_2\frac{t^2}{2!} + \mu_3\frac{t^3}{3!} + \cdots\right)\right].$$

Since

$$\log(1+x) = x - \tfrac{1}{2}x^2 + \tfrac{1}{3}x^3 - \cdots,$$

then

$$\log m(t) = t\mu + \left(\mu_2\frac{t^2}{2!} + \mu_3\frac{t^3}{3!} + \cdots\right) - \frac{1}{2}\left(\mu_2\frac{t^2}{2!} + \mu_3\frac{t^3}{3!} + \cdots\right)^2 + \cdots$$

$$= \mu t + \mu_2\frac{t^2}{2!} + \mu_3\frac{t^3}{3!} + (\mu_4 - 3\mu_2^2)\frac{t^4}{4!} + \cdots. \tag{2}$$

Hence, equating coefficients of like powers of $t$ in (1) and (2), we find $\kappa_1 = \mu$, $\kappa_2 = \mu_2$, $\kappa_3 = \mu_3$, $\kappa_4 = \mu_4 - 3\mu_2^2$, etc. The function $\mathrm{K}(t)$ is called the *cumulant generating function.*

**Example 4.9.** For the normal distribution

$$f(x) = \frac{1}{\sigma\sqrt{2\pi}} e^{-(x-\mu)^2/2\sigma^2}\,dx, \qquad -\infty < x < \infty,$$

$$m(t) = \frac{1}{\sigma\sqrt{2\pi}} \int_{-\infty}^{\infty} e^{tx-(x-\mu)^2/2\sigma^2}\,dx.$$

Let $x = \mu + y$, then

$$m(t) = \frac{e^{t\mu}}{\sigma\sqrt{2\pi}} \int_{-\infty}^{\infty} e^{ty-(y^2/2\sigma^2)}\,dy$$

$$= \frac{e^{t\mu}}{\sigma\sqrt{2\pi}} \int_{-\infty}^{\infty} e^{-(y-t\sigma^2)^2/2\sigma^2} e^{t^2\sigma^2/2}\,dy.$$

$$\therefore m(t) = e^{t\mu+(t^2\sigma^2/2)}.$$

Now, in order to read off the moments, we need the expansion of $m(t)$ in series, but this is not very simple. However, the cumulants may be found quite simply, since for this case

$$\mathrm{K}(t) = \log m(t) = t\mu + \frac{t^2\sigma^2}{2}.$$

But

$$\mathrm{K}(t) = \kappa_1 t + \kappa_2 \frac{t^2}{2!} + \kappa_3 \frac{t^3}{3!} + \cdots.$$

Hence, for the normal distribution

$$\kappa_1 = \mu, \qquad \kappa_2 = \sigma^2, \qquad \kappa_i = 0 \qquad \text{for } i > 2.$$

It is important to remember that all cumulants after and including $\kappa_3$ for the normal distribution are zero.

Hence, for the normal distribution, it is simpler to read the cumulants, $\kappa_i$, for the cumulant generating function, $\mathrm{K}(t)$. If the moments are desired, they may be obtained easily from the cumulants. Hence the use of either the moment generating function or the cumulant generating function depends on the form of the distribution function.

**4.7. An Inverse Problem.** It was seen that, if we are given the theoretical distribution, then we may obtain a set of moments ($\mu$, $\mu_2'$, $\mu_3'$, . . . ). In applied work we may have a large sample of observations and wish to determine from the data some evidence regarding an appropriate theoretical function to represent the assumed parent population distribution.

From the table of values giving the empirical frequency distribution it would be possible to obtain sample moments for the large sample. If it be assumed that these *sample* moments are "good" estimates of the corresponding moments of some *theoretical* distribution, then we have the inverse problem of determining uniquely a theoretical distribution having given the moments. This problem is discussed in texts on advanced mathematical statistics and is beyond the scope of this course. The "Pearson system of curves" is an assumed set of continuous functions whose parameters may be expressed in terms of the moments. Hence, estimates of these parameters may be obtained from a large sample and some one of the theoretical curves "fitted" to the empirical frequency distribution. A test of "goodness of fit" may then be accomplished by the use of chi-square (see Chap. 12).

Closely related to the moment problem mentioned above is the inverse relation of the characteristic function or the moment generating function to a possible corresponding distribution function. Two theorems from advanced theoretical statistics will be stated without proof and made use of in subsequent derivations.

*Theorem* 4.1. *A distribution function is uniquely determined by its characteristic function or, where it exists, the moment generating function.*

*Theorem* 4.2. *If a distribution function has a characteristic function (moment generating function) which approaches the characteristic function (moment generating function) of another distribution, the two distributions approach each other.*

## EXERCISES

**4.1.** Find the mathematical expectation for the following distribution:

| $y$ | 10 | 20 | 30 | 40 |
|---|---|---|---|---|
| $p$ | .1 | .3 | .5 | .1 |

**4.2.** Given the following probability laws, find $\mu$, $\sigma^2$ for each:
(*a*) $f(x) = 10x^9,\ 0 \le x \le 1$,
(*b*) $f(x) = x/50,\ 0 \le x \le 10$.

**4.3.** A random variable can assume only two values 1 and 2. Its mathematical expectation is $\frac{3}{2}$. Find $p_1$ and $p_2$.

**4.4.** A random variable has the distribution function $f(x) = A + Bx$, $0 \le x \le 1$. The mathematical expectation is $\frac{1}{2}$. Find the constants $A$ and $B$.

**4.5.** Express $\mu_3$ and $\mu_4$ in terms of moments about zero.

**4.6.** Use the cumulants for the normal distribution to determine the first four moments about the mean.

**4.7.** Two other measures of skewness and kurtosis, or departure from normality, are $\gamma_1 = \kappa_3/(\kappa_2)^{\frac{3}{2}}$ and $\gamma_2 = \kappa_4/\kappa_2^2$. Show that $\gamma_1 \equiv \alpha_3$ and $\gamma_2 \equiv \alpha_4 - 3$. Find $\gamma_1$ and $\gamma_2$ for the normal distribution.

**4.8.** Determine the first four cumulants for the binomial distribution. Verify that $\kappa_{r+1} = pq(d\kappa_r/dp)$, $r > 1$, for the cumulants obtained.

**4.9.** Show that $E(x - x_1)^2$ is a minimum if $x_1 = E(x)$.

**4.10.** If $x$ has the distribution function $f(x) = \frac{1}{2}$ on the interval (0,2), find the moment generating function of $x$, and determine the variance of $x$. This is called a *rectangular distribution.*

**4.11.** An unbiased penny is tossed 64 times. Find (*a*) the expected number of heads, (*b*) the theoretical standard deviation.

**4.12.** A pair of dice is thrown 60 times. Find (*a*) the expected number of times that the sum 10 appears, (*b*) the expected value of the square of the standard deviation.

**4.13.** There are 6 urns containing, respectively, 1 white, 9 black; 2 white, 8 black; 3 white, 7 black; 4 white, 6 black; 5 white, 5 black; 4 white, 6 black balls. One ball is to be drawn from each urn. What is the expected number of white balls taken? Let $x_i$ be a variable which assumes the values 1 or 0 according as to whether the trial results in success or failure. Then, $m = x_1 + x_2 + \cdots + x_n$ is the number of successes in $n$ trials. But $E(x_i) = p_i \cdot 1 + (1 - p_i) \cdot 0 = p_i$ for $i = 1, 2, \ldots, n$. Hence $E(m) = p_1 + p_2 + \cdots + p_n$.

**4.14.** An urn contains $a$ red balls and $b$ black balls, and $c$ balls are drawn simultaneously. What is the expected number of red balls drawn?

**4.15.** An urn contains $r$ tickets numbered from 1 to $r$, and $s$ tickets are drawn at a time. What is the expected sum of the numbers on the tickets drawn? Let $x_i$ be the variable attached to the $i$th ticket which may assume any of the values $1, 2, \ldots, r$. Then,

$$E(x_i) = \left(\frac{1}{r}\right)(1 + 2 + \cdots + r).$$

Set $m = x_1 + x_2 + \cdots + x_s$, and complete the solution by finding $E(m)$.

**4.16.** Find the moment generating function $m(t)$ for the triangular distribution sketched in the accompanying figure.

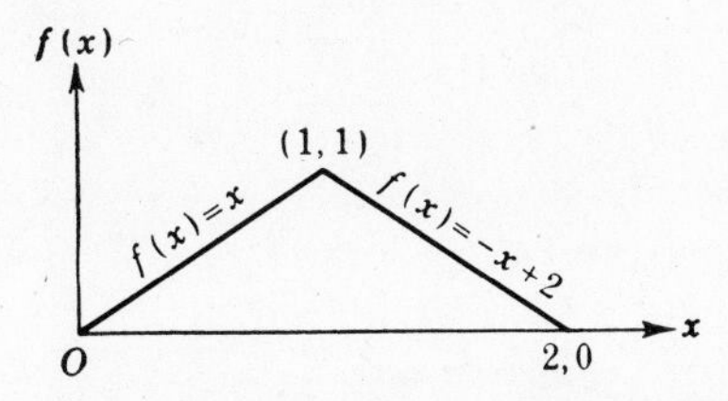


**4.17.** Find the moment generating function $m(t)$ for the rectangular distribution $f(x) = 1/w$, $0 \leq x \leq w$. Verify that when $w = 1$, the square of the moment generating function of the rectangular distribution equals the moment generating function of the triangular distribution in Exercise 4.16.

**4.18.** Find $\mu'_2$, $\mu'_3$, $\mu'_4$ for the binomial distribution using the formulas for the definitions of these moments. NOTE: $x^2 = x(x-1) + x$,

$$x^3 = x(x-1)(x-2) + 3x^2 - 2x,$$

and $x^4 = x(x-1)(x-2)(x-3) + 6x^3 - 11x^2 + 6x$.

**4.19.** Find $\alpha_3$ and $\alpha_4$ for the binomial distribution.

**4.20.** Find $\mu$, $\sigma^2$, $\alpha_3$, and $\alpha_4$ for the following binomials: $(\frac{1}{6} + \frac{5}{6})^7$, $(\frac{1}{3} + \frac{2}{3})^{18}$.

**4.21.** Show that the moment generating function for the Poisson distribution is $m(t) = e^{m(e^t-1)}$.

**4.22.** Show that $\kappa_i = m(i = 1, 2, 3, \ldots)$ for the Poisson distribution.

**4.23.** Find $\mu$, $\mu'_2$, $\mu'_3$, $\mu'_4$ for the Poisson distribution, (*a*) using the formulas for the definitions of the moments, (*b*) using the moment generating function.

**4.24.** Find $\mu_2$, $\alpha_3$, and $\alpha_4$ for the Poisson distribution.

**4.25.** Prove the general formula connecting the moments about $\mu$ with the moments about the origin:

$$\mu_k = \mu'_k - k\mu\mu'_{k-1} + \frac{k(k-1)}{2!}\mu^2\mu'_{k-2} - \cdots.$$

Use the formula to obtain

$$\mu_1 = 0,$$
$$\mu_2 = \mu'_2 - (\mu)^2,$$
$$\mu_3 = \mu'_3 - 3\mu\mu'_2 + 2(\mu)^3,$$
$$\mu_4 = \mu'_4 - 4\mu\mu'_3 + 6(\mu)^2\mu'_2 - 3(\mu)^4.$$

# CHAPTER 5

## BIVARIATE AND MULTIVARIATE DISTRIBUTIONS AND THEIR PROPERTIES

**5.1. Introduction.** In the previous chapters single-variate, or univariate, distributions and their properties have been discussed. It is proposed now to extend the discussion to cases of two or more variates, that is, *bivariate and multivariate distributions.* The discussion will apply alike to bivariate and multivariate *parent population* distributions and bivariate and multivariate *derived sampling* distributions. The latter distributions will be discussed in Chap. 6.

**5.2. Discrete Bivariate Distributions.** Suppose that for every value of a given variate, $x$, we also know the values which a second variate, $y$, can take. Then it will be possible to construct a joint probability distribution, from which can be obtained the probability that any combination of $x$ and $y$ will occur in random draws. The bivariate frequency function will be represented symbolically by $f(x,y)$. The conditions required for a mathematical function $F(x,y)$ to be used as a *cumulative joint probability* distribution are analogous to those in Sec. 3.7 for the univariate case. These conditions imply the following conditions for $f(x,y)$:

(*a*) $f(x,y)$ is nonnegative over the $(x,y)$ plane.

(*b*) $\sum_{W} f(x,y) = 1$, where $W$ is the entire $(x,y)$ region.

(*c*) $\sum_{w} f(x,y)$ can be computed for any subregion, $w$, of $W$.

**Example 5.1.** Consider the two-dice problem. Let $x$ represent the number of spots showing on die 1 and $y$ the number on die 2 in any one toss of the two dice. The joint probability distribution is given by Table 5.1 ($p = \frac{1}{36}$). The frequency function is $f(x,y) = \frac{1}{36}$ for any pair of values, $(x,y)$, for $x$ or $y = 1, 2, \ldots, 6$. Note that $\Sigma f(x,y) = 1$ over the ranges of both variates, $1 \leq x \leq 6$, $1 \leq y \leq 6$. The probability that $x$ and $y$ lie, at the same time, in ranges $a \leq x \leq b$, $c \leq y \leq d$ is given by

$$\mathcal{P}(w) = \sum_{w} f(x,y), \tag{1}$$

where $w$ is the subregion defined by $a \leq x \leq b$, $c \leq y \leq d$. In the two-dice problem

$$\mathcal{P}(1 \leq x \leq 3, 2 \leq y \leq 4) = \tfrac{9}{36} = \tfrac{1}{4}.$$

We may define a *cumulative distribution function* for the bivariate case in a manner similar to that for $\mathcal{P}(w)$ in (1) above. If $F(b,d)$ represents the probability that $x \leq b$, $y \leq d$, then,

$$F(b,d) = \sum_{w} f(x,y), \tag{2}$$

where $w$ is the subregion $(x \leq b, y \leq d)$. For the two-dice problem

$$F(3,2) = (\tfrac{6}{36}) = \tfrac{1}{6}.$$

If the subregion $w$ is allowed to assume all possible values, the $x$ and $y$ will assume all possible pairs of values and (2) in three dimensions becomes analogous to the two-dimension step function of Sec. 3.3 and may be written as

$$F(x,y) = \sum_{w} f(x,y), \tag{3}$$

over the range of values of the subregion $w$. The function defined by (3) is the *cumulative bivariate distribution function.*

TABLE 5.1

Joint Probability Distribution in Two-dice Problem

| $y$ \ $x$ | 1 | 2 | 3 | 4 | 5 | 6 | Total |
|---|---|---|---|---|---|---|---|
| 1 | $p$ | $p$ | . | . | . | $p$ | $6p$ |
| 2 | $p$ | $p$ | . | . | . | $p$ | $6p$ |
| 3 | . | . | . | . | . | . | . |
| 4 | . | . | . | . | . | . | . |
| 5 | . | . | . | . | . | . | . |
| 6 | $p$ | $p$ | . | . | . | $p$ | $6p$ |
| Total | $6p$ | $6p$ | . | . | . | $6p$ | $36p$ |

Suppose we extend this process. Add all of the probabilities for a given value of $x$, say $x_1$; then the range of values of the subregion $w$ is simply the linear range of $y$, and hence we may write

$$\sum_{y} f(x_1,y) = g(x_1),$$

which is the probability that $x = x_1$. If this be thought of as being done for all values of $x$, then we may write the frequency function of $x$ as

$$g(x) = \sum_{y} f(x,y), \tag{4}$$

which is called the *marginal distribution of x*. Similarly, the *marginal distribution of y* is

$$h(y) = \sum_x f(x,y). \tag{5}$$

As can be seen from the border totals in Table 5.1, the distributions (4) and (5) may be exhibited as in Table 5.2.

TABLE 5.2
Marginal Distributions of $x$ and $y$ in Two-dice Problem

| $x = y$ | 1 | 2 | 3 | 4 | 5 | 6 |
|---|---|---|---|---|---|---|
| $g(x) = h(y)$ | $\frac{1}{6}$ | $\frac{1}{6}$ | $\frac{1}{6}$ | $\frac{1}{6}$ | $\frac{1}{6}$ | $\frac{1}{6}$ |

Finally, the marginal distribution and the joint distribution may be used to define the *conditional distribution*, corresponding to the *conditional probability* discussed in Sec. 2.5. Using the notation $f(y|x)$ to mean the probability of $y$, given $x$, we know that

$$f(y|x) = f(x,y)/g(x), \qquad g(x) \neq 0, \tag{6}$$

since

$$f(x,y) = g(x)f(y|x)$$

by law 3 of Sec. 2.5. The distribution (6) is called the *conditional distribution* of $y$. Similarly, the *conditional distribution* of $x$ is

$$f(x|y) = f(x,y)/h(y), \qquad h(y) \neq 0. \tag{7}$$

Now, if $f(y|x)$ does not depend on $x$, then $y$ and $x$ are said to be independent variates, since

$$f(x,y) = g(x) \cdot h(y). \tag{8}$$

This is true for the two-dice problem since for any $x = x_1$, $f(y|x_1) = \frac{1}{6}$. Hence, by (8),

$$f(x,y) = \tfrac{1}{6} \cdot \tfrac{1}{6} = \tfrac{1}{36},$$

for $x, y = 1, 2, \ldots, 6$.

**5.3. Continuous Bivariate Distribution.** In the case of two continuous variates, $x$ and $y$, the probability that $x$ is in the interval $(x, x + dx)$ and $y$ in the interval $(y, y + dy)$ is

$$f(x,y)\, dx\, dy. \tag{9}$$

The graph of $z = f(x,y)$ is called the *frequency surface*. The frequency function $f(x,y)$ is nonnegative, but it may be zero over certain subregions of the $(x,y)$ plane.

The probability that $(x,y)$ will fall in some subregion $w$ of the $(x,y)$ plane $W$ is given by

$$\mathcal{P}(w) = \iint_w f(x,y)\,dx\,dy, \tag{10}$$

since

$$\iint_W f(x,y)\,dx\,dy = 1. \tag{11}$$

The cumulative distribution function is given by

$$F(x,y) = \int_{-\infty}^{x} \int_{-\infty}^{y} f(x,y)\,dy\,dx. \tag{12}$$

The marginal distribution of $x$ is given by

$$g(x) = \int_{-\infty}^{\infty} f(x,y)\,dy,$$

and similarly for $h(y)$.

Finally, the conditional probability that $y$ lies in the interval $(y, y + dy)$, given that $x$ is in the interval $(x, x + dx)$, is

$$f(y|x)\,dy = \frac{f(x,y)\,dy\,dx}{g(x)\,dx} = \frac{f(x,y)\,dy}{g(x)}. \tag{13}$$

Again, if $f(y|x)$ is independent of $x$, that is, if the right side of (13) does not contain $x$ after algebraic simplification, then $x$ and $y$ are said to be independent variates and

$$f(x,y) = g(x) \cdot h(y).$$

**Example 5.2.** Given $f(x,y)\,dx\,dy = e^{-x-y}\,dx\,dy$, $(x, y \geq 0)$.

(*a*) $F(x,y) = \int_0^x \int_0^y e^{-x-y}\,dy\,dx.$ For $x = x_1 = 1$, $y = y_1 = 1$,

$$F(x_1,y_1) = \mathcal{P}(x, y \leq 1) = (1 - e^{-x_1})(1 - e^{-y_1}) = \left(\frac{e-1}{e}\right)^2 = .3996.$$

(*b*) $g(x) = \int_0^\infty e^{-x-y}\,dy = e^{-x}.$

(*c*) $f(y|x) = \dfrac{e^{-x-y}}{e^{-x}} = e^{-y}$ (independent of $x$).

**Example 5.3.** The normal bivariate distribution with means of $x$ and $y$ both zero is

$$f(x,y)\,dy\,dx = \frac{1}{2\pi\sigma_x\sigma_y\sqrt{1-\rho^2}}\, e^{-\frac{1}{2(1-\rho^2)}\left[\frac{x^2}{\sigma_x^2} + \frac{y^2}{\sigma_y^2} - \frac{2\rho xy}{\sigma_x\sigma_y}\right]}\,dy\,dx,$$

where $-\infty < x < \infty$, $-\infty < y < \infty$.

(a) $g(x) = \int_{-\infty}^{\infty} f(x,y)\, dy = \frac{1}{\sigma_x \sqrt{2\pi}} e^{-x^2/2\sigma_x^2}.$

(b) $f(y|x) = \frac{f(x,y)}{g(x)} = \frac{1}{\sigma_y \sqrt{2\pi(1-\rho^2)}} e^{-\frac{1}{2(1-\rho^2)}\left[\frac{y}{\sigma_y} - \frac{\rho x}{\sigma_x}\right]^2}.$

If $\rho = 0$,

$$f(y|x) = \frac{1}{\sigma_y \sqrt{2\pi}} e^{-y^2/2\sigma_y^2} = h(y);$$

hence, in *this case*, $x$ and $y$ are independent. Hence, $\rho$ may be used as a measure of relationship between $x$ and $y$. It is, in fact, the population *correlation coefficient* between $x$ and $y$.

**5.4. Distribution of Functions of Discrete Variates.** In order to obtain certain properties of bivariate and multivariate discrete or continuous distributions, such as expected values, moments, and moment generating functions, it is sometimes necessary to make transformations of the variates so that the summations or integrals may be evaluated. The discrete case will be considered first.

The distribution of a function of $x$, say $z = \psi(x)$, given the distribution of $x$, is simple if there is a one-to-one correspondence between $x$ and $z$, that is, if for every value of $x$ there is only one value of $z$, and vice versa. In this case, the same probabilities hold for $z$ as for $x$. For example, consider a single die with $f(x) = \frac{1}{6}(x = 1,2, \ldots ,6)$. Suppose $z = x^2$. In general, there is not a one-to-one correspondence between $x$ and $z$, because $x = \pm \sqrt{z}$, resulting in two values of $x$ for each $z$. However, in our die problem, $x$ must be positive; hence $x = +\sqrt{z}$ only. Therefore, $f(z) = \frac{1}{6}$, for $z = 1, 4, \ldots, 36$.

On the other hand, suppose $z = (x - 1)(x - 2)$, or $x = (3 \pm \sqrt{1 + 4z})/2$. Then, even for $x$ always positive, there is not a one-to-one correspondence between $x$ and $z$, since, say, for $z = 0$, $x = 1$ or 2. Hence, in this case

$$f(z) = \begin{cases} \frac{1}{3} & \text{for } z = 0, \text{for two integral values of } x \text{ in the range } 1 \le x \le 6. \\ \frac{1}{6} & \text{for } z = 2, 6, 12, 20, \text{for one integral value of } x \text{ in the range } 1 \le x \le 6. \\ 0 & \text{elsewhere, no integral value of } x \text{ in the range } 1 \le x \le 6. \end{cases}$$

Again, if $z = (x - 1)(x - 2) \cdots (x - 6)$,

$$f(z) = \begin{cases} 1 & \text{for } z = 0, \text{for six values of } x \text{ in the range } 1 \le x \le 6. \\ 0 & \text{elsewhere, no values of } x \text{ in the range } 1 \le x \le 6. \end{cases}$$

If we consider a bivariate distribution, such as that of the two-dice problem, the distribution of a function of the two variates is still simple.

For example, consider the distribution $f(w)$, where $w = xy$; then

$$\begin{aligned}
f(1) &= f(1,1) &&= \tfrac{1}{36}.\\
f(2) &= f(2,1) + f(1,2) &&= \tfrac{2}{36}.\\
f(3) &= f(3,1) + f(1,3) &&= \tfrac{2}{36}.\\
f(4) &= f(4,1) + f(2,2) + f(1,4) &&= \tfrac{3}{36}.\\
&\ldots\ldots\ldots\ldots\ldots\ldots\ldots\\
f(7) & &&= 0.\\
&\ldots\ldots\ldots\ldots\ldots\ldots\ldots\\
f(36) &= f(6,6) &&= \tfrac{1}{36}.
\end{aligned}$$

Here again $\Sigma f(w) = 1$ over the possible range.

**5.5. Distributions of Functions of Continuous Variates.** The distribution of $x$ is $f(x)\,dx$, $x$ defined in the range $x_1$ to $x_2$. We seek the distribution of $z = z(x)$. If there is a one-to-one correspondence between $x$ and $z$ and $x$ can be solved uniquely in terms of $z$, then $x = \psi(z)$, $dx = \psi'(z)\,dz$, $f(x) = f[\psi(z)]$, and the limits are $z_1 = z(x_1)$, $z_2 = z(x_2)$. The probability distribution of $z$, with these conditions, will be $f[\psi(z)][\psi'(z)]\,dz$ over the range $z_1$ to $z_2$.

**Example 5.4.** If $f(x)\,dx = 2(1 - x)\,dx$ for $0 \leq x \leq 1$, we find the distribution of $z$, where $z = x^2$, as follows:

Since $z$ is always positive, there is a one-to-one correspondence between $z$ and $x$, that is, $x = +\sqrt{z}$; hence

$$f(z)\,dz = 2(1 - \sqrt{z})\frac{1}{2\sqrt{z}}\,dz,$$

or

$$f(z)\,dz = (z^{-\frac{1}{2}} - 1)\,dz, \qquad 0 \leq z \leq 1.$$

**Example 5.5.** If $f(x)\,dx = \dfrac{1 - x}{2}\,dx$, $-1 \leq x \leq 1$, then $x = \pm\sqrt{z}$ for $z = x^2$. For positive values of $x$, $x = +\sqrt{z}$, and for negative values of $x$, $x = -\sqrt{z}$. In this case

$$f(z)\,dz = \begin{Bmatrix} \dfrac{1}{4}(z^{-\frac{1}{2}} - 1)\,dz, & x \geq 0 \\ \dfrac{1}{4}(z^{-\frac{1}{2}} + 1)\,dz, & x \leq 0 \end{Bmatrix} 0 \leq z \leq 1.$$

If we wish, we may add the two functions to obtain a single function

$$f(z)\,dz = \tfrac{1}{2}z^{-\frac{1}{2}}\,dz, \qquad 0 \leq z \leq 1,$$

but this is not possible in all cases.

The distribution of a function of *two* continuous variates, $x$ and $y$, is more complex mathematically. We wish to derive the simultaneous distribution of $u$ and $v$, $f(u,v)\,du\,dv$, where $u = u(x,y)$ and $v = v(x,y)$. In case we wish only the distribution of $u$, then $v$ is integrated out between its limits of integration, leaving some $f(u)\,du$. In such cases it is necessary in general to assume a one-to-one correspondence between $(x,y)$ and $(u,v)$. It will then be possible to make the inverse solution:

$$x = x(u,v), \qquad \text{and} \qquad y = y(u,v).$$

The probability distribution of $f(x,y)\,dx\,dy$ then becomes

$$f[x(u,v),\, y(u,v)]|J|\,du\,dv,$$

where $J$ is the Jacobian of the transformation, that is,

$$J = \begin{vmatrix} \dfrac{\partial x}{\partial u} & \dfrac{\partial y}{\partial u} \\ \dfrac{\partial x}{\partial v} & \dfrac{\partial y}{\partial v} \end{vmatrix}, \qquad \text{or} \qquad \frac{1}{J} = \begin{vmatrix} \dfrac{\partial u}{\partial x} & \dfrac{\partial u}{\partial y} \\ \dfrac{\partial v}{\partial x} & \dfrac{\partial v}{\partial y} \end{vmatrix}.$$

This implies, of course, that these partial derivatives exist. If the second form is used, then $J$ must be evaluated at $x = x(u,v)$, $y = y(u,v)$.

The limits for $u$ and $v$ must be determined individually for each problem. The limits for the first variable in the integral may be functions of the second variable.

**Example 5.6.** Let us find $f(u,v)\,du\,dv$, where $f(x,y)\,dx\,dy = e^{-x-y}\,dx\,dy$, $0 \le x < \infty$, $0 \le y < \infty$, $u = x + y$, $v = x/y$.

Then,

$$x = \frac{uv}{1+v}, \qquad y = \frac{u}{1+v}$$

and

$$J = \begin{vmatrix} \dfrac{v}{1+v} & \dfrac{1}{1+v} \\ \dfrac{u}{(1+v)^2} & \dfrac{-u}{(1+v)^2} \end{vmatrix} = \frac{-u}{(1+v)^2},$$

or

$$\frac{1}{J} = \begin{vmatrix} 1 & 1 \\ \dfrac{1}{y} & -\dfrac{x}{y^2} \end{vmatrix} = -\frac{(x+y)}{y^2} = -\frac{(1+v)^2}{u}.$$

$$\therefore f(u,v)\,du\,dv = e^{-u}\frac{u}{(1+v)^2}\,du\,dv.$$

Since, if $u$ is fixed, $v$ can assume any value, then the limits of integration for $u$ and $v$ are $0 \le u < \infty$, $0 \le v < \infty$.

To find the distribution of $u$, we have

$$f(u)\,du = \left[ue^{-u}\int_0^\infty \frac{1}{(1+v)^2}\,dv\right]du = ue^{-u}\,du, \qquad 0 \le u < \infty.$$

Similarly,

$$f(v)\,dv = \frac{1}{(1+v)^2}\,dv, \qquad 0 \le v < \infty.$$

Note that $u$ and $v$ are independent in this case.

**Example 5.7.** Find $f(u,v)\,du\,dv$, where

$$f(x,y)\,dx\,dy = \frac{2e^2}{(1-e)^2}\,e^{-x-y}\,dx\,dy,$$

$0 \le x \le y$, $0 \le y \le 1$, $u = x + y$, and $v = x - y$.

We find easily $dx\,dy = \frac{1}{2}\,du\,dv$, and hence

$$f(x,y)\,dx\,dy = \frac{e^2}{(1-e)^2}\,e^{-u}\,du\,dv.$$

However, the assignment of limits for $u$ and $v$ in this case is more involved. First, we plot as in Fig. 5.1 the region on the $(x,y)$ plane with the following boundaries: $x = y$, $y = 1$, and $x = 0$.

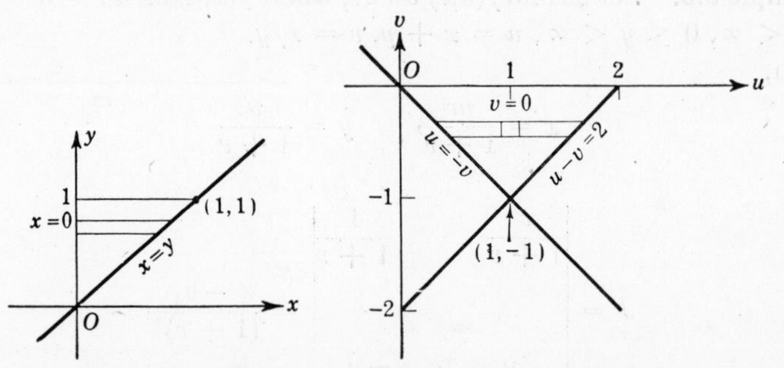


Fig. 5.1. Regions of integration for Example 5.7.

Since $x = (u + v)/2$, $y = (u - v)/2$, then the boundary $x = y$ becomes $v = 0$; $y = 1$ becomes $u - v = 2$; and $x = 0$ becomes $u = -v$. We now plot the new region determined by these new boundaries on the $(u,v)$ plane as in Fig. 5.1. In the new region, $u$ varies from $-v$ to $v + 2$, and $v$ varies from 0 to $-1$. Hence the new limits are $-v \le u \le v + 2$, $-1 \le v \le 0$.

**5.6. Expected Values for Bivariate Distributions.** For any bivariate frequency function, $f(x,y)$, the expected value of any function of $x$ and $y$, say $\psi(x,y)$, is

$$E[\psi(x,y)] = \sum_W\sum \psi(x,y)f(x,y) \text{ or } \iint_W \psi(x,y)f(x,y)\,dx\,dy,$$

where $W$ is the entire region of $(x,y)$. The following specializations of $\psi(x,y)$ will enable us to derive some simple rules for operating with expected values. Continuous variates will be used in the derivations, but similar rules will hold for discrete variates.

(1) $E(c) = c$, where $c$ is a constant.

(2) $E(cx) = c\int_{-\infty}^{\infty} x\left[\int_{-\infty}^{\infty} f(x,y)\,dy\right]dx = c\int_{-\infty}^{\infty} xg(x)\,dx = cE(x).$

(3)
$$E(x+y) = \int_{-\infty}^{\infty} x\left[\int_{-\infty}^{\infty} f(x,y)\,dy\right]dx + \int_{-\infty}^{\infty} y\left[\int_{-\infty}^{\infty} f(x,y)\,dx\right]dy$$
$$= \int_{-\infty}^{\infty} xg(x)\,dx + \int_{-\infty}^{\infty} yh(y)\,dy = E(x) + E(y).$$

(4) $E(xy) = \int_{-\infty}^{\infty} x\left[\int_{-\infty}^{\infty} yf(x,y)\,dy\right]dx = \int_{-\infty}^{\infty} xh_1(x)\,dx,$

where

$$h_1(x) = \int_{-\infty}^{\infty} yf(x,y)\,dy.$$

Note that $E(xy)$ can be evaluated, if the integrations can be performed, even though $x$ and $y$ are not independent.

(5) If $x$ and $y$ are independent, then $f(x,y) = g(x)\cdot h(y)$ and hence

$$E(xy) = \int_{-\infty}^{\infty} xg(x)\,dx \int_{-\infty}^{\infty} yh(y)\,dy = E(x)E(y).$$

**5.7. Moments.** The product moment $x^ry^s$ about the origin is given by

$$\mu'_{rs} = E(x^ry^s) = \int_{-\infty}^{\infty}\int_{-\infty}^{\infty} x^ry^sf(x,y)\,dx\,dy.$$

Let the mean of $x$ be $\mu'_{10}$ and the mean of $y$ be $\mu'_{01}$; then

$$\mu_{rs} = E[(x-\mu'_{10})^r(y-\mu'_{01})^s] = \int_{-\infty}^{\infty}\int_{-\infty}^{\infty} (x-\mu'_{10})^r(y-\mu'_{01})^sf(x,y)\,dx\,dy.$$

**Example 5.8.** To find $\sigma_x^2$, defined as equal to $\mu_{20}$, we have

$$\mu_{20} = E(x-\mu'_{10})^2 = \mu'_{20} - (\mu'_{10})^2.$$
$$\therefore \sigma_x^2 = \mu'_{20} - (\mu'_{10})^2.$$

Similarly,

$$\sigma_y^2 = \mu_{02} = \mu'_{02} - (\mu'_{01})^2.$$

**Example 5.9.** To find $\sigma_{xy}$, defined as equal to $\mu_{11}$ and called the *covariance* of $x$ and $y$, we have

$$\mu_{11} = E[(x - \mu'_{10})(y - \mu'_{01})] = E(xy) - \mu'_{10}\mu'_{01}.$$
$$\therefore \sigma_{xy} = \mu'_{11} - \mu'_{10}\mu'_{01}.$$

If $x$ and $y$ are independent, $E(xy) = \mu'_{11} = \mu'_{10}\mu'_{01}$, hence $\sigma_{xy} = 0$ for this condition. The correlation, $\rho_{xy}$, between $x$ and $y$ is defined as the nondimensional quantity

$$\rho_{xy} = \frac{\sigma_{xy}}{\sigma_x \sigma_y}.$$

It can be shown that $-1 \leq \rho \leq 1$. Also, if $\sigma_{xy} = 0$, then $\rho_{xy} = 0$.

**Example 5.10.** To find the variance of $(x + y)$, we have

$$\sigma^2_{x+y} = E[x - \mu'_{10} + y - \mu'_{01}]^2 = \sigma_x^2 + \sigma_y^2 + 2\sigma_{xy}$$
$$= \sigma_x^2 + \sigma_y^2 + 2\rho\sigma_x\sigma_y.$$

If $x$ and $y$ are independent, that is, $\sigma_{xy} = 0$, then $\sigma^2_{x+y} = \sigma_x^2 + \sigma_y^2$.

**Example 5.11.** To find $E(xy)$ for the bivariate normal distribution, with $\mu'_{10} = 0$, $\mu'_{01} = 0$, we have

$$E(xy) = k \int_{-\infty}^{\infty} \int_{-\infty}^{\infty} xye^{-\theta}\,dx\,dy,$$

where

$$k = \frac{1}{2\pi\sigma_x\sigma_y\sqrt{1 - \rho^2}}$$

and

$$\theta = \frac{1}{2(1 - \rho^2)}\left[\frac{x^2}{\sigma_x^2} + \frac{y^2}{\sigma_y^2} - \frac{2\rho xy}{\sigma_x\sigma_y}\right].$$

Note that for the bivariate normal, $\rho_{xy}$ has been abbreviated to $\rho$.

The function $\theta$ may be written

$$\theta = \frac{1}{2(1 - \rho^2)}\left[\frac{x^2}{\sigma_x^2} - \frac{2\rho xy}{\sigma_x\sigma_y} + \frac{\rho^2 y^2}{\sigma_y^2}\right] + \frac{y^2}{2\sigma_y^2}$$
$$= \frac{1}{2}\left[\frac{t^2}{1 - \rho^2} + \frac{y^2}{\sigma_y^2}\right], \qquad \text{where } t = \frac{x}{\sigma_x} - \frac{\rho y}{\sigma_y}.$$

Then, using the methods of Sec. 5.5,

$$E(xy) = k \int_{-\infty}^{\infty} y \left[\int_{-\infty}^{\infty} \frac{\sigma_x^2(t\sigma_y + \rho y)}{\sigma_y} e^{-\frac{t^2}{2(1-\rho^2)}}\,dt\right] e^{-y^2/2\sigma_y^2}\,dy$$
$$= \frac{\rho\sigma_x}{\sqrt{2\pi}} \int_{-\infty}^{\infty} \frac{y^2}{\sigma_y^2} e^{-y^2/2\sigma_y^2}\,dy = \rho\sigma_x\sigma_y.$$

**Example 5.12.** Consider

$$f(x,y)\,dx\,dy = e^{-x-y}\,dx\,dy, \qquad 0 \le x < \infty, 0 \le y < \infty.$$

Then,

$$E(x) = \mu'_{10} = \int_0^\infty e^{-y}\left[\int_0^\infty xe^{-x}\,dx\right]dy = 1,$$
$$E(y) = \mu'_{01} = 1,$$
$$\mu'_{20} = \mu'_{02} = 2,$$
$$\sigma_x^2 = \sigma_y^2 = 1,$$
$$\mu'_{11} = \int_0^\infty xe^{-x}\,dx \int_0^\infty ye^{-y}\,dy = 1,$$
$$\sigma_{xy} = \mu'_{11} - \mu'_{10}\mu'_{01} = 0,$$

and

$$\rho_{xy} = 0.$$

**Example 5.13.** Consider the following discrete bivariate distribution with $p = \frac{1}{12}$:

| $x$ \ $y$ | 0 | 1 | 2 | Total |
|---|---|---|---|---|
| 0 | $2p$ | $2p$ | $2p$ | $6p$ |
| 1 | $p$ | $4p$ | $p$ | $6p$ |
| Total | $3p$ | $6p$ | $3p$ | $12p$ |

Then,

$$\mu'_{10} = \sum_0^2\sum_0^1 xf(x,y) = .5, \qquad \mu'_{01} = \sum_0^2\sum_0^1 yf(x,y) = 1.0,$$
$$\mu'_{20} = \sum_0^2\sum_0^1 x^2f(x,y) = .5, \qquad \mu'_{02} = \sum_0^2\sum_0^1 y^2f(x,y) = 1.5,$$
$$\sigma_x^2 = .5 - .25 = .25, \qquad \sigma_y^2 = 1.5 - 1.0 = .5,$$
$$\mu'_{11} = \sum_0^2\sum_0^1 xyf(x,y) = .5, \qquad \sigma_{xy} = .5 - .5 = 0,$$

and

$$\rho = 0.$$

Note that we cannot state that $x$ and $y$ are independent in this case even though $\rho = 0$, since $f(x|y)$ is not the same for all values of $y$. It can be seen that $f(x|y = 0) = \frac{2}{3}, \frac{1}{3}$; $f(x|y = 1) = \frac{1}{3}, \frac{2}{3}$; and

$$f(x|y = 2) = \tfrac{2}{3}, \tfrac{1}{3}.$$

**5.8. Moment and Cumulant Generating Functions.** For the bivariate case, the moment generating function about the origin is defined to be $m(t_x,t_y) = E(e^{xt_x+yt_y})$. The moment generating function about $\mu'_{10}$ and

$\mu'_{01}$ is defined as

$$M(t_x,t_y) = E(e^T) = \int\int e^T f(x,y)\,dx\,dy,$$

where $T = (x - \mu'_{10})t_x + (y - \mu'_{01})t_y$ and the double integration is performed over the ranges of $x$ and $y$.

Then,

$$M(t_x,t_y) = \sum_{r,s=0}^{\infty} \mu_{rs} \frac{t_x^r t_y^s}{r!s!},$$

and

$$\mu_{rs} = \left. \frac{\partial^{r+s} M(t_x,t_y)}{\partial t_x^r\, \partial t_y^s} \right|_{t_x=t_y=0}.$$

Note that $\mu_{00} = 1$, $\mu_{01} = \mu_{10} = 0$.

The cumulant generating function in this case is given by

$$\mathrm{K} = \log m(t_x,t_y) = \log M(t_x,t_y) + \mu'_{10}t_x + \mu'_{01}t_y = \sum_{r,s=0}^{\infty} \kappa_{rs} \frac{t_x^r t_y^s}{r!s!}$$

and

$$\kappa_{rs} = \left. \frac{\partial^{r+s} \mathrm{K}}{\partial t_x^r\, \partial t_y^s} \right|_{t_x=t_y=0}.$$

If $f(x,y) = g(x) \cdot h(y)$, the moments of $x$ and $y$ may be computed separately. In this case

$$M(t_x,t_y) = \int e^{T_x} g(x)\,dx \cdot \int e^{T_y} h(y)\,dy = M(t_x) \cdot M(t_y),$$

where

$$T_x = (x - \mu'_{10})t_x, \qquad T_y = (y - \mu'_{01})t_y$$

and the two integrations are taken over the respective ranges of $x$ and $y$. Hence, we have the following theorem:

*Theorem* 5.1. *The moment generating function about the origin of the sum of two independent variates is the product of the moment generating function of each.*

*Proof:*

$$m(t)_{x+y} = E[e^{t(x+y)}] = E(e^{tx})E(e^{ty}) = m(t_x) \cdot m(t_y).$$

The theorem is also true for the moment generating function about the mean of the sum of two independent variates.

For the bivariate distribution

$$\mathrm{K} = \log m(t_x) + \log m(t_y) = K(t_x) + K(t_y).$$

**5.9. Extension to $k$ Variates.** Let

$$f\{x_i\} \prod_{i=1}^{k} dx_i$$

represent the joint probability distribution of the $k$ variates, $x_1, x_2, \ldots,$ $x_k$, where $f\{x_i\}$ is the *frequency function* of the $k$ variates and

$$\prod_{i=1}^{k} dx_i = dx_1\, dx_2 \cdots dx_k.$$

The following properties are those for the continuous case, but they can be applied equally well to discrete variates:

(a) $\mathcal{P}(w) = \int_w \cdots \int f\{x_i\} \prod_{i=1}^{k} dx_i,$

where $w$ is a subregion in the $k$-dimensional space, $W$.

(b) $g(x_1) = \int_w \cdots \int f\{x_i\} \prod_{i=2}^{k} dx_i,$

(c) $f(x_1|x_2, \cdots, x_k) = \dfrac{f\{x_i\}}{f(x_2, \cdots, x_k)},$

where

$$f(x_2, \ldots, x_k) = \int f\{x_i\}\, dx_1$$

over the range of $x_1$.

(d) For a transformation

$$u_i = u_i\{x_i\}, \qquad i = 1, 2, \ldots, k$$

$$\frac{1}{J} = \begin{vmatrix} \dfrac{\partial u_1}{\partial x_1} & \dfrac{\partial u_1}{\partial x_2} & \cdots & \dfrac{\partial u_1}{\partial x_k} \\ \cdot & \cdot & \cdots & \cdot \\ \dfrac{\partial u_k}{\partial x_1} & \dfrac{\partial u_k}{\partial x_2} & \cdots & \dfrac{\partial u_k}{\partial x_k} \end{vmatrix}.$$

(e) $E[\theta\{x_i\}] = \int_W \cdots \int \theta\{x_i\} f\{x_i\} \prod_{i=1}^{k} dx_i.$

(f) $E[e^{\theta\{x_i\}}] = \int_W \cdots \int e^{\theta\{x_i\}} f\{x_i\} \prod_{i=1}^{k} dx_i.$

**Example 5.14.** The multinomial distribution is a generalization of the binomial distribution. Any one of the events $y_1, y_2, \ldots, y_k$ can occur with respective probabilities $p_1, p_2, \ldots, p_k$ on a single trial, $\sum_{i=1}^{k} p_i = 1.$ If $n$ trials are made, the probability that $y_1$ occurs $x_1$ times, $y_2$ occurs $x_2$ times, etc., $\sum_{i=1}^{k} x_i = n$, is given by

$$f\{x_i\} = \frac{n!}{\prod_{i=1}^{k} x_i!} \prod_{i=1}^{k} p_i^{x_i}.$$

This is the general term of the expansion of

$$(p_1 + p_2 + \cdot \cdot \cdot + p_k)^n.$$

For example, a single die can show the number 1, 2, . . . , 6 on the upper face with equal probabilities, $p_i = \frac{1}{6}$.

In this case the moment generating function about the origin is

$$m\{\theta_i\} = E(e^{\Sigma_1^k \theta_i x_i}) = \sum_x \frac{n!}{\prod_1^k x_i!} e^{\Sigma_1^k \theta_i x_i} \prod_1^k p_i^{x_i},$$

where the symbol $\sum_x$ is to be interpreted as meaning the summation over all values of $x$, such that $\Sigma x_i = n$,

$$\therefore m\{\theta_i\} = \sum_x \frac{n!}{\prod_1^k x_i!} \prod_{i=1}^{k} (p_i e^{\theta_i})^{x_i} = (p_1 e^{\theta_1} + p_2 e^{\theta_2} + p_3 e^{\theta_3} + \cdot \cdot \cdot + p_k e^{\theta_k})^n.$$

Then

$$\mu'_{1i} = \left.\frac{\partial m\{\theta_i\}}{\partial \theta_i}\right|_{\{\theta_i\}=0} = np_i,$$

$$\mu'_{2i} = \left.\frac{\partial^2 m\{\theta_i\}}{\partial \theta_i^2}\right|_{\{\theta_i\}=0} = np_i + n(n-1)p_i^2,$$

and

$$\sigma_i^2 = \mu'_{2i} - (\mu'_{1i})^2 = np_i - np_i^2 = np_i(1 - p_i).$$

Also,

$$\mu'_{ij} = \left.\frac{\partial^2 m\{\theta_i\}}{\partial \theta_i \, \partial \theta_j}\right|_{\{\theta_i\}=0} = n(n-1)p_i p_j.$$

Hence,

$$\sigma_{ij} = \mu'_{ij} - \mu'_{1i}\mu'_{1j} = n(n-1)p_i p_j - n^2 p_i p_j = -np_i p_j.$$

## EXERCISES†

**5.1.** The marginal distribution of $x$ for a bivariate distribution function $f(x,y)$ is

$$g(x) = \int f(x,y)\, dy.$$

† The following exercises contain important theory which will be referred to subsequently and hence should be worked by all students: 5.1, 5.2, 5.4, 5.5, and 5.6.

The limits for $y$ must be determined by the region $W$ within which $f(x,y)$ is defined. If $W$ includes the entire $(x,y)$ plane, the limits are $(-\infty,\infty)$. However, consider a problem of this nature: $f(x,y) = kxy$ for $x \leq y$, $0 \leq y \leq 1$; then

$$g(x) = \int_x^1 kxy\,dy, \qquad 0 \leq x \leq 1,$$

and

$$h(y) = \int_0^y kxy\,dx, \qquad 0 \leq y \leq 1.$$

Find the explicit values of $g(x)$ and $h(y)$.

**5.2.** Given a continuous bivariate frequency function $f(x,y)$ and the corresponding marginal distributions, $g(x)$ and $h(y)$. Set up the integrals for the following: ($a$) mean and variance for $y$ for a given $x$, $(\mu_{y|x},\sigma^2_{y|x})$; ($b$) mean and variance of $x$ for a given $y$.

**5.3.** Given the bivariate frequency function $f(x,y) = 2/a^2$, $0 \leq x \leq y$, $0 \leq y \leq a$. Show that ($a$) $\int\int f(x,y)\,dx\,dy = 1$, over the respective ranges of $x$ and $y$; ($b$) $g(x) = 2(a - x)/a^2$; ($c$) $h(y) = (2/a^2)y$;

$$(d)\ f(x|y) = \frac{1}{y};$$

($e$) $\mu'_{10} = a/3$, $\mu'_{01} = 2a/3$; ($f$) $\rho = \frac{1}{2}$; ($g$) $\mu_{y|x} = (a + x)/2$; ($h$) $\mu_{x|y} = y/2$.

**5.4.** In Exercise 5.2($a$) the mean value of $y$ for a given $x$ $(\mu_{y|x})$ is a function of $x$ and hence defines a curve in the $(x,y)$ plane called the *curve of regression of y on x*. If the regression of $y$ on $x$ is linear $(\mu_{y|x} = \alpha + \beta x)$, then

$$\mu_{y|x} = \int_{-\infty}^{\infty} y\,\frac{f(x,y)\,dy}{g(x)} = \alpha + \beta x$$

or

$$\int_{-\infty}^{\infty} yf(x,y)\,dy = \alpha g(x) + \beta x g(x).$$

By integrating each side of the last equation with respect to $x$, show that

$$\mu'_{01} = \alpha + \beta\mu'_{10}.$$

Before integrating, as above, multiply both sides by $x$, and show that

$$\mu'_{11} = \alpha\mu'_{10} + \beta\mu'_{20}.$$

Hence, find the values of $\alpha$ and $\beta$ in terms of the moments of the original distribution, and show that

$$\mu_{y|x} = \mu'_{01} + \rho\,\frac{\sigma_y}{\sigma_x}\,(x - \mu'_{10}).$$

**5.5.** In Exercise 5.3($a$) if the variance of $y$ for a given $x$ is averaged over all values of $x$, we have

$$\sigma^2_{y\cdot x} = \int_{-\infty}^{\infty}\int_{-\infty}^{\infty} g(x)\left[(y - \mu_{y|x})^2\frac{f(x,y)}{g(x)}\,dy\right]dx$$
$$= \int_{-\infty}^{\infty}\int_{-\infty}^{\infty} (y - \mu_{y|x})^2 f(x,y)\,dy\,dx.$$

If $\mu_{y|x} = \alpha + \beta x$, as given in Exercise 5.4, show that

$$\sigma^2_{y\cdot x} = \sigma^2_y(1 - \rho^2).$$

**5.6.** Work Exercises 5.3($a$), 5.4, and 5.5 for a normal bivariate distribution.

**5.7.** As an example of the distribution of a function of two variables for a discrete bivariate distribution, consider the distribution of the sum of two independent Poisson variates, $x$ and $y$. The joint distribution of $x$ and $y$ is

$$f(x,y) = e^{-m_1}\frac{m_1^x}{x!}e^{-m_2}\frac{m_2^y}{y!}.$$

Let $z = x + y$, or $x = z - y$; then

$$f(z,y) = e^{-(m_1+m_2)}\frac{m_1^{(z-y)}m_2^y}{(z-y)!y!}.$$

Sum out the variable $y$ over the range $0 \leq y \leq z$, and show that

$$f(z) = e^{-(m_1+m_2)}\frac{(m_1 + m_2)^z}{z!}.$$

Hence, show that the sum of two independent Poisson variates is distributed as a single Poisson variate with a mean equal to the sum of the two single means ($m = m_1 + m_2$).

**5.8.** Given $f(x,y) = 6(1 - x - y)$ for $(x,y)$ contained within the triangle bounded by $x = 0$, $y = 0$, $x + y = 1$.

($a$) Find the means and variances of $x$ and $y$ and the covariance of $x$ and $y$.

($b$) Find the equation of the regression line of $y$ on $x$ and $\sigma^2_{y\cdot x}$.

**5.9.** Given $f(x,y) = kxy(1 - x - y)$ over the same triangle as in Exercise 5.8.

($a$) Find the value of $k$ which makes $f(x,y)$ a frequency distribution.

($b$) Find the marginal distribution $g(x)$.

($c$) Find $\mu_{y|x}$.

**5.10.** If $x$ is a discrete variate having the Poisson distribution

$$g(x) = \frac{m^x e^{-m}}{x!}, \qquad y \leq x < \infty,$$

and $y$ is another discrete variate having the binomial distribution

$$f(y|x) = C(x,y)p^y q^{x-y}, \qquad 0 \le y < \infty,$$

show that the marginal distribution of $y$ is

$$\frac{(mp)^y e^{-mp}}{y!}.$$

**5.11.** Given that $x$ and $y$ are normally distributed with zero means and variances $\sigma_x^2$ and $\sigma_y^2$. Find the distribution of $z = x + y$.

**5.12.** If $x$ and $y$ represent the number of dots appearing on dice $A$ and $B$, respectively, what is the probability that in throwing the two dice $x + 2y \le 6$?

**5.13.** Given $f(x|y) = y^x e^{-y}/x!$ and $h(y) = e^{-y}$, where $x$ is discrete $(x = 0, 1, \ldots)$ and $y$ continuous $(y \ge 0)$. Show that $g(x) = (\frac{1}{2})^{x+1}$.

**5.14.** Given two continuous variates $x$ and $y$ $(x, y \ge 0)$ with the frequency distribution $f(x,y) = 2(1 + x + y)^{-3}$. Find $g(u)$ and $\mathcal{P}(u \le 1)$, where $u = x + y$.

**5.15.** Given $f(x,y) = 1$ over the square $(0 \le x, y \le 1)$. Show that $\mathcal{P}(xy > u) = 1 - u + u \log u$.

**5.16.** Show that the joint moment generating function of $x_1$ and $x_2$ from the bivariate normal distribution with means $\mu_1$ and $\mu_2$, variances $\sigma_1^2$ and $\sigma_2^2$, and correlation $\rho$ is given by

$$m(t_1,t_2) = e^{t_1\mu_1 + t_2\mu_2 + \frac{1}{2}(t_1^2\sigma_1^2 + 2\rho t_1 t_2 \sigma_1\sigma_2 + t_2^2\sigma_2^2)}.$$

**5.17.** Use the results of Exercise 5.16 to find the variances and covariance of $x_1$ and $x_2$.

# CHAPTER 6

## DERIVED SAMPLING DISTRIBUTIONS AND ORTHOGONAL LINEAR FUNCTIONS

**6.1. Introduction.** For the sequence of the statistical method—*specification, distribution, estimation,* and *tests* of *hypotheses*—we have considered certain parent populations and their properties which are usually specified in applied statistical investigations. After problems of specification it would seem logical to discuss problems of estimation next in order. Such problems involve determining what functions of the sample observations should be used to "best" estimate the parameters of the specified population distribution, where "best" must be defined in some exact manner. For example, if $X_1, X_2, \ldots, X_n$ is a sample of $n$ observations, specified as having been drawn in some manner from a normal distribution with mean, $\mu$, and variance, $\sigma^2$, what two functions of the observations should be used to "best" estimate $\mu$ and $\sigma^2$? A function of the observations used to estimate a population parameter is called an *estimator*. The numerical value obtained by using the estimator is called an *estimate.* It seemed appropriate to earlier workers in statistics to use the sample mean, $\bar{X} = \Sigma X/n$, and the sample variance, $(s')^2 = \Sigma(X - \bar{X})^2/n$, as estimators of the two populations parameters $\mu$ and $\sigma^2$. However, as will be shown later, in cases where the sample is a *random sample,* the "best" sample estimate of $\sigma^2$ is $s^2 = \Sigma(X - \bar{X})^2/(n - 1)$. A *random sample* is a sample drawn in such a manner that the probability of obtaining any member is independent of the probability of obtaining any other member.

A less restrictive method of estimating the value of a parameter, $\theta$, is a method which derives limits $c_1$ and $c_2$ which are functions of the sample values $(X_1,X_2, \ldots ,X_n)$. The interval $(c_1,c_2)$ will contain the parameter $\theta$ a certain percentage of the time. The limits are thus functions of the sample and this percentage, which is called the *confidence probability.* It is understood that in each repeated sample a new set of confidence limits is determined. The concepts of confidence limits were introduced by Neyman.[1]

Various methods of estimating the confidence interval will be discussed in later chapters. Fisher[2] uses the term *fiducial limits* to indicate essentially the same concept.

In the chronological development of modern statistical methodology, however, the distribution of estimators and the distributions of certain functions of these estimators used in making tests of hypotheses and setting confidence limits did not wait upon the development of a sound theory of estimation. In this chapter, then, we shall assume, for the time being, that certain estimators are the "best" estimates of the corresponding population parameters and that certain functions of these estimators used in making tests of hypotheses and setting confidence limits are the "best" such functions.

**6.2. Derived Sampling Distribution Problems.** In a typical applied statistical investigation, for example, a *sample survey* or an *experiment*, we specify that the observations obtained by some sampling process are drawn from some particular parent population distribution. We then calculate certain functions of the observations as estimates of the parameters of the specified population. Now, in order to set confidence limits for the population parameters or to make tests of hypotheses concerning the population parameters, it is necessary to know the probability distributions of the estimators, for example, of $\bar{X}$ and $s^2$ for a normal parent population, and of certain functions of the statistics, for example, of $\chi^2$, $t$, and $F$. Mathematically these probability distributions are *derived* from the specified parent population distributions and hence are called *derived sampling distributions.*

**6.3. Random and Systematic Samples.** In applied statistics two kinds of samples are in common use, (*a*) the random sample as defined above, and (*b*) the systematic sample. In the latter the first member *may* be chosen at random, but subsequent members depend upon the position or value of the preceding members (a systematic sample after a random start), or all members of the sample may be chosen systematically, including the first member.

Soil sampling—to study nutritive[3] and other components[4] of the soil—in most cases makes use of some form of systematic sampling. Soil samples are selected from various spots in a field, and chemical determinations are made to determine what nutrients are required to bring the soil up to a suitable productive capacity. It would be possible to lay a grid down on the field and select the samples at random from the grid. This method, however, presents many practical difficulties such as the exact determination of the selected sample point and the excessive time consumed in finding these points, especially if the field is irregular in both boundary and contour. It is much easier to select the first point at random by selecting two random numbers to determine the two coordinates of the starting point and then proceed a certain numbers of paces from this point to the next one by a predetermined route.

Another systematic method is to predetermine a definite route and collect samples only along this path. This latter method is used quite extensively in sampling forest stands[5] to estimate the amount of usable timber.

Most economic data are far from random but have been analyzed in many instances in the past as though they were random because of lack of techniques for analyzing nonrandom data. More exact methods of analyzing this type of nonrandom data have been devised. The chief obstacle to the use of the more exact techniques is computational. The rapid development of electronic computers may overcome this difficulty.

The derived sampling distributions obtained in the next chapter will assume a *random* sample of $n$ observations unless otherwise stated. Randomness in the sample must be ensured by the use of an objective method of selection. Tables of random numbers provide such a means and have been made available by Tippett,[6] Fisher and Yates,[7] Snedecor,[8] and others.

**6.4. Linear Functions.** In the derivations of sampling distributions in the next chapter it will frequently be necessary to know the distribution of some linear functions of the members of a sample. Let such a linear function be given by

$$l = a_1X_1 + a_2X_2 + \cdots + a_nX_n = \sum_{i=1}^{n} a_iX_i,$$

where $a_i$ is some fixed constant and the sample, here not necessarily random, is represented by $X_1, X_2, \ldots, X_n$ or $\{X_i\}$. In order to obtain some general results, in the discussion following, each $X_i$ is assumed to be drawn from a population with mean $\mu_i$ and variance $\sigma_i^2$.

**6.5. Properties of Linear Functions.** It follows that

$$E(l) = \sum_{i=1}^{n} a_iE(X_i) = \sum_{i=1}^{n} a_i\mu_i.$$

Also,

$$\sigma_l^2 = E[l - E(l)]^2 = E\left[\sum_{i=1}^{n} a_i(X_i - \mu_i)\right]^2 = \sum_{i=1}^{n} a_i^2\sigma_i^2 + 2\sum_{i<j}\sum a_ia_j\sigma_{ij}.$$

If $\{X_i\}$ is a random sample, then $\sigma_{ij} = 0$ and

$$\sigma_l^2 = \sum_{i=1}^{n} a_i^2\sigma_i^2,$$

but this will not be true for a systematic sample since $\sigma_{ij}$ will not be zero in that case.

Finally, if all $\mu_i = \mu$ and all $\sigma_i^2 = \sigma^2$, then

$$E(l) = \mu \sum_{i=1}^{n} a_i$$

and

$$\sigma_l^2 = \sigma^2 \sum_{i=1}^{n} a_i^2.$$

**Example 6.1.** If each $a_i = 1/n$, then $l = (1/n) \sum_{i=1}^{n} X_i$, which is the sample mean, $\bar{X}$. Further, for any sample

$$E(\bar{X}) = \frac{1}{n}(n\mu) = \mu.$$

Also, if the sample be random,

$$\sigma_{\bar{X}}^2 = E(\bar{X} - \mu)^2 = n\sigma^2 \cdot \frac{1}{n^2} = \frac{\sigma^2}{n}.$$

In Sec. 6.1 mention was made of a "best" estimator of a population parameter. One property usually desired in a "best" estimator is that of being *unbiased*. An estimator of a population parameter is said to be unbiased if its expected value is equal to the population parameter. It follows from Example 6.1 that $\bar{X}$ is an unbiased estimator of $\mu$ whether the sample is random or systematic. However, using an analogous method to that for a random sample for obtaining an estimate of the variance of a systematic sample does not lead to an unbiased estimate.

**Example 6.2.** Let $l = \sum_{i=1}^{n} a_i(X_i - \mu)$, for a random sample from a population with $\mu_i = \mu$, $\sigma_i^2 = \sigma^2$; then

$$E(l) = \sum_{i=1}^{n} a_i E(X_i - \mu) = 0.$$

Also,

$$\sigma_l^2 = E[l - E(l)]^2 = E\left[\sum_{i=1}^{n} a_i^2(X_i - \mu)^2 + 2\sum\sum_{i<j} a_i a_j (X_i - \mu)(X_j - \mu)\right]$$

$$= \sigma^2 \sum_{i=1}^{n} a_i^2.$$

**Example 6.3.** To find $E(S)$ where $S = \sum_{i=1}^{n} (X_i - \bar{X})^2$, under conditions given in Example 6.2, we find

$$S = \sum_{i=1}^{n} [(X_i - \mu) - (\bar{X} - \mu)]^2 = \sum_{i=1}^{n} (X_i - \mu)^2 - n(\bar{X} - \mu)^2.$$

But

$$E\left[\sum_{i=1}^{n} (X_i - \mu)^2\right] = n\sigma^2.$$

Also,

$$E(\bar{X} - \mu)^2 = \frac{\sigma^2}{n}$$

by Example 6.1. Hence,

$$E(S) = n\sigma^2 - \sigma^2 = (n - 1)\sigma^2.$$

Now, if we set $s^2 = S/(n - 1)$, then $E(s^2) = \sigma^2$ and therefore $s^2$ is an unbiased estimate of $\sigma^2$ for a random sample.

For a discussion of the above problems for systematic samples, consult W. G. Madow and Lillian Madow,[9] Lillian Madow,[10] and Cochran.[11]

**6.6. Orthogonal Linear Forms.** Consider the two linear forms $l_1 = \sum_{i=1}^{n} a_i X_i$ and $l_2 = \sum_{i=1}^{n} b_i X_i$. Since $E(l_1) = \sum_{i=1}^{n} a_i \mu_i$ and $E(l_2) = \sum_{i=1}^{n} b_i \mu_i$, then $E(l_1 \pm l_2) = \sum_{i=1}^{n} (a_i \pm b_i)\mu_i$.

Now, if $\{X_i\}$ is a random sample with $\mu_i = \mu$, $\sigma_i^2 = \sigma^2$, then

$$\sigma_{l_1}^2 = \sigma^2 \sum_{i=1}^{n} a_i^2, \qquad \sigma_{l_2}^2 = \sigma^2 \sum_{i=1}^{n} b_i^2, \qquad \text{and} \qquad \sigma_{12} = \sigma^2 \sum_{i=1}^{n} a_i\, b_i.$$

Hence the condition that would make $l_1$ and $l_2$ uncorrelated is that $\sum_{i=1}^{n} a_i b_i = 0$. Two uncorrelated linear forms are said to be *orthogonal.*

**Example 6.4.** For a random sample of 5 drawn from a normal population with mean, $\mu$, and variance, $\sigma^2$, the mean value and variance of

$$l_1 = X_1 + X_2 + X_3 + X_4 + X_5 = 5\bar{X}$$

are, respectively,

$$E(l_1) = \mu + \mu + \mu + \mu + \mu = 5\mu,$$
$$\sigma_{l_1}^2 = 5\sigma^2.$$

For a second linear form

$$l_2 = -2X_1 - X_2 + X_4 + 2X_5,$$

we obtain

$$E(l_2) = -2\mu - \mu + \mu + 2\mu = 0$$

and also

$$\sigma_{l_1 l_2} = [(1)(-2) + (1)(-1) + (1)(1) + (1)(2)] = 0.$$

For a third linear form

$$l_3 = 2X_1 - X_2 - 2X_3 - X_4 + 2X_5,$$

we obtain

$$E(l_3) = 2\mu - \mu - 2\mu - \mu + 2\mu = 0,$$

also

$$\sigma_{l_1 l_3} = \sigma^2[(1)(2) + (1)(-1) + (1)(-2) + (1)(-1) + (1)(2)] = 0,$$

and

$$\sigma_{l_2 l_3} = \sigma^2[(-2)(2) + (-1)(-1) + (0)(-2) + (1)(-1) + (2)(2)] = 0.$$

Notice that the sum of the coefficients of $l_2$ and $l_3$, respectively, is zero and that $l_2$ and $l_3$ are uncorrelated with $l_1$, illustrating the theory in the paragraph above.

**Example 6.5.** To determine a fourth orthogonal linear form,

$$l_4 = b_1X_1 + b_2X_2 + b_3X_3 + b_4X_4 + b_5X_5,$$

to $l_1$, $l_2$, and $l_3$ of Example 6.4, we find

$$\begin{aligned} l_1l_4&: \quad b_1 + b_2 + b_3 + b_4 + b_5 = 0, \\ l_2l_4&: \quad -2b_1 - b_2 + b_4 + 2b_5 = 0, \\ l_3l_4&: \quad 2b_1 - b_2 - 2b_3 - b_4 + 2b_5 = 0. \end{aligned}$$

Eliminating $b_3$ from the first and third equations and then $b_2$ from the remaining two equations, we find

$$b_1 + b_4 + 3b_5 = 0.$$

This condition will be satisfied if we let $b_5 = 1$, $b_4 = -2$, and $b_1 = -1$. Then, we find $b_2 = 2$ and $b_3 = 0$. Hence a fourth orthogonal form desired is

$$l_4 = -X_1 + 2X_2 - 2X_4 + X_5.$$

There are an infinite number of such functions.

**6.7. Linear Forms with Normally Distributed Variates.** Suppose that the $X_i$ in the linear form $l = \sum_{i=1}^{n} a_iX_i$ each follows a normal parent population distribution with mean, $\mu_i$, and variance, $\sigma_i^2$. Then, the probability of getting the particular $X_i$'s in a random sample of $n$ will be

$$\frac{1}{(2\pi)^{n/2}} \frac{1}{\prod_{i=1}^{n} \sigma_i} e^{-\sum_{i=1}^{n}[(X_i-\mu_i)^2/2\sigma_i^2]} \prod_{i=1}^{n} dX_i.$$

It is desired to find the distribution of $[l - E(l)]$.

The moment generating function of $[l - E(l)]$ is

$$M(t) = E[e^{t\{l-E(l)\}}]$$

$$= \frac{1}{(2\pi)^{n/2}} \frac{1}{\prod_{i=1}^{n} \sigma_i} \int_{-\infty}^{\infty} \cdots \int_{-\infty}^{\infty} e^{-\{\sum_{i=1}^{n}(X_i-\mu_i)^2/2\sigma_i^2 - t[\sum_{i=1}^{n}a_i(X_i-\mu_i)]\}} \prod_{i=1}^{n} dX_i$$

$$= \prod_{i=1}^{n} \frac{1}{\sigma_i\sqrt{2\pi}} \int_{-\infty}^{\infty} e^{-(X_i-\mu_i)^2/2\sigma_i^2 + ta_i(X_i-\mu_i)}\, dX_i.$$

By completing the square of the exponent we have

$$-\frac{1}{2\sigma_i^2}[(X_i - \mu_i)^2 - 2\sigma_i^2 ta_i(X_i - \mu_i) + \sigma_i^4 t^2 a_i^2] + \frac{\sigma_i^2 t^2 a_i^2}{2}$$

$$= -\frac{1}{2\sigma_i^2}[(X_i - \mu_i) - \sigma_i^2 ta_i]^2 + \frac{\sigma_i^2 t^2 a_i^2}{2}.$$

Hence,

$$M(t) = \prod_{i=1}^{n} e^{\sigma_i^2 t^2 a_i^2/2} = e^{(t^2/2)\sum_{i=1}^{n} a_i^2\sigma_i^2}.$$

Now, the moment generating function for the normal distribution

$$\frac{1}{\sigma\sqrt{2\pi}} e^{-y^2/2\sigma^2}\, dy, \qquad -\infty < y < \infty,$$

is

$$M(t) = \frac{1}{\sigma\sqrt{2\pi}} \int_{-\infty}^{\infty} e^{-y^2/2\sigma^2 + ty}\, dy = e^{t^2\sigma^2/2}.$$

Hence, we may say that $l$ is normally distributed with mean $E(l) = \sum_{i=1}^{n} a_i\mu_i$ and variance $\sigma_l^2 = \sum_{i=1}^{n} a_i^2\sigma_i^2$. This result is analogous to that found in Sec. 6.6 for the mean and variance for nonspecified parent population distributions.

## EXERCISES

**6.1.** Determine a fifth linear form orthogonal to the form in Examples 6.4 and 6.5. How many linear forms make a complete set for a sample of $n$?

**6.2.** Given a random sample of $N$, all members being drawn from the same population. Determine the relationship between the cumulants for the total of the sample and the cumulants for a single member of the sample. HINT:

$$m_{\Sigma X}(t) = [m(t)]^N.$$

**6.3.** Use the results of Exercise 6.2 to determine the first three cumulants for the total of $N$ from a binomial distribution. ($N$ represents the number of samples and $n$ the number of independent trials per sample.)

**6.4.** What happens to Exercise 6.2 if each member of the random sample is drawn from different populations? HINT: Show that

$$K_{\Sigma X}(t) = \sum_{i=1}^{N} K_i(t)$$

and the $r$th cumulant for the sum is hence

$$\kappa_r = \sum_{i=1}^{N} \kappa_{ri}.$$

Consider this problem for Poisson distributions with unlike means and binomial distributions with unlike values of $n$ and $p$.

**6.5.** Given two independent estimates of $Y$, $X_1$ and $X_2$, with variances $\sigma_1^2$ and $\sigma_2^2$, respectively. If we desire to estimate $Y$ as an unbiased linear function of the $X$'s, find the coefficients of the $X$'s which will minimize the variance of the estimate. HINT: $E(X_i) = Y$. Let $Y = l_1X_1 + l_2X_2$.

**6.6.** If the $X_i$ in the linear form $l = \Sigma a_iX_i$ are normally and independently distributed with means $\mu_i$ and variances $\sigma_i^2$ and all $a_i = 1/n$, $\mu_i = \mu$, and $\sigma_i = \sigma$, then $l = \bar{X}$. Show that the mean of a normal sample is normally distributed with mean $\mu$ and variance $\sigma^2/n$.

**6.7.** Suppose that $\bar{X}_1$ represents the mean of a sample of $n_1$ taken from a normal population with mean $\mu_1$ and variance $\sigma_1^2$ and $\bar{X}_2$ the mean of a sample of $n_2$ taken from another normal population with mean $\mu_2$ and variance $\sigma_2^2$. Let $l = \bar{X}_1 - \bar{X}_2$. Show that $l$ is normally distributed with mean $\mu_1 - \mu_2$ and variance

$$\frac{\sigma_1^2}{n_1} + \frac{\sigma_2^2}{n_2}.$$

**6.8.** Consider the following applied problem: The effect of a nitrogen top-dressing on a crop is to be determined. In addition it is desired to discover at what time during the growing season the top-dressing, if beneficial, should be applied. The experiment was designed as follows: Use four plots, one with no nitrogen, one with nitrogen applied early, one applied in the middle of the growing season, and one applied later. Naturally, this entire experiment would be repeated several times, say $r$, in order to discover how consistent the differences were from replication to replication. The totals of the $4r$ plots are indicated as follows:

| | Nitrogen applied | | |
|---|---|---|---|
| No N | Early | Middle | Late |
| $T_0$ | $T_1$ | $T_2$ | $T_3$ |

$$T_0 = X_{01} + X_{02} + \cdots + X_{0r},\ T_1 = \sum_{j=1}^{r} X_{1j}, \text{ etc.}$$

Suppose $X_{ij}$ is $N(\mu_i,\sigma^2)$, where $\mu_i$ is the mean effect of the $i$th treatment. Three pertinent independent linear forms are: $l_1 = 3T_0 + T_1 + T_2 + T_3$, for determining the effect of nitrogen; $l_2 = T_3 - T_1$, for determining the linear effect; $l_3 = T_1 - 2T_2 + T_3$, for determining the quadratic effect. Find a fourth linear form to complete the set, and determine the variance of each.

### References Cited


1. Neyman, J., "On the Problem of Confidence Intervals," *Ann. Math. Stat.*, **6**:111–116 (1935).
2. Fisher, R. A., *Design of Experiments*, 4th ed., Oliver & Boyd, Ltd., Edinburgh and London, 1947. Pp. 186–205.
3. Rigney, J. A., and J. F. Reed, "Some Factors Affecting the Accuracy of Soil Sampling," *Proc. Soil Sci. Soc. Am.*, **10**:257–259 (1945).
4. Finney, D. J., "Field Sampling for the Estimation of Wireworm Populations," *Biometrics Bull.*, **2**:1–7 (1946).
5. Schumacher, F. X., "Statistical Methods in Forestry," *Biometrics Bull.*, **1**:29–32 (1945).
6. Tippett, L. H. C., "Random Sampling Numbers," *Tracts for Computers*, XV, Cambridge University Press, London, 1927.
7. Fisher, R. A., and F. Yates, *Statistical Tables*, Oliver & Boyd, Ltd., Edinburgh and London, 1938.
8. Snedecor, George W., *Statistical Methods*, 4th ed., Collegiate Press, Inc., of Iowa State College, Ames, Iowa, 1946.

9. MADOW, W. G., and L. MADOW, "On the Theory of Systematic Sampling," *Ann. Math. Stat.*, **15**:1–24 (1944).
10. MADOW, L., "Systematic Sampling and Its Relation to Other Sampling Schemes," *J. Am. Stat. Assoc.*, **41**:204–217 (1946).
11. COCHRAN, W. G., "Relative Accuracy of Systematic and Stratified Random Samples for a Certain Class of Populations," *Ann. Math. Stat.*, **27**:164–177 (1946).

# CHAPTER 7

## DERIVED SAMPLING DISTRIBUTIONS: NORMAL PARENT POPULATION

**7.1. Introduction.** In this chapter we shall consider only random samples of $n$ drawn from a normal parent population with mean $\mu$ and variance $\sigma^2$, that is, from $N(\mu,\sigma^2)$. If it is desired to indicate that two or more variates are also independently normally distributed with mean $\mu$ and variance $\sigma^2$, we shall denote this by

$$\text{NID}(\mu,\sigma^2).$$

The derived sampling distributions which will be discussed here are of importance in applied statistics in making tests of hypotheses and setting confidence limits. As pointed out earlier, we shall assume in these discussions of distribution theory that certain estimators of population parameters and certain test criteria are the "best," and we shall be interested here in obtaining their probability distributions. In later chapters on tests of hypotheses and estimation, a discussion will be given of what properties a "best" estimator or an "appropriate" test criterion should have.

Methods of obtaining test criteria and setting confidence limits will now be explained in order that an understanding of the uses of these important statistical methods may be obtained simultaneously with the derivations of the related sampling distributions. The methods described below do not take into account important considerations described in detail in subsequent chapters on estimation and tests of hypotheses, but for the cases presented the corresponding techniques will be the same.

If it be possible to find the sampling distribution of a function of an estimator and its corresponding population parameter which is independent of the parameter and all other unknown parameters, then hypotheses specifying numerical values of these parameters may be tested. Such a hypothesis is often called a null hypothesis, and the function called a *test criterion*.

By making probability statements regarding the test criterion in the form of inequalities, and then solving these inequalities for the population parameter, one may set confidence limits for the particular parameter.

Illustrations for the techniques described in the above two paragraphs will be presented in subsequent sections of this chapter.

If the specified parent population distribution is not normal, then the derived sampling distributions may become unduly complicated. Nonrandomness in the sample presents additional difficulties. Consequences of the relaxation of such assumptions regarding the parent population and the sample have been studied to some extent, and further investigations may be expected in the future.

**7.2. Distribution of the Sample Mean, $\bar{X}$.** In Sec. 6.7 it was shown, for a random sample of size $n$, with each $X_i$ from a parent population $N(\mu_i,\sigma_i^2)$, that the distribution of $l = \sum_{i=1}^{n} a_i X_i$ is $N\left(\sum_{i=1}^{n} a_i\mu_i, \sum_{i=1}^{n} a_i^2\sigma_i^2\right)$. If $a_i = \frac{1}{n}$, $\mu_i = \mu$, and $\sigma_i^2 = \sigma^2$, then $\sum_{i=1}^{n} a_i X_i = \bar{X}$, $\sum_{i=1}^{n} a_i\mu_i = \mu$, and $\sum_{i=1}^{n} a_i^2\sigma_i^2 = \frac{\sigma^2}{n}$. Therefore the distribution of $\bar{X}$ is $N(\mu, \sigma^2/n)$.

Let

$$T = \frac{\bar{X} - \mu}{\sigma/\sqrt{n}}.$$

The sampling distribution of $T$ is $N(0,1)$, which is symmetrical about zero. Then, if $\sigma$ be known, $T$ fulfills the requirements set out in Sec. 7.1 for a test criterion which may be used to test a hypothesis specifying a numerical value for $\mu$, say $\mu = \mu_0$.

Suppose a random sample of size $n$ is drawn from the assumed population, $N(\mu_0,\sigma^2)$. The sample mean, $\bar{X}$, and a corresponding value of $T$, called $T_0$, are calculated, where

$$T_0 = \frac{\bar{X} - \mu_0}{\sigma/\sqrt{n}}.$$

It is possible, using Table I*b* in the Appendix, to find the probability of $T$ being greater in absolute value than the calculated $T_0$. Should this probability be as small as or smaller than some preassigned small numerical value, $\alpha$, we say that we have evidence that the hypothesis being tested is not true, or we should be forced to accept the occurrence of a very unlikely event. This $\alpha$ is called the *significance probability*, and the entire testing procedure a *test of significance* or a *test of the hypothesis* that $\mu = \mu_0$. A more precise mathematical treatment of tests of hypotheses will be presented in Chap. 11.

The validity of the procedure set out in the above paragraph may be checked empirically by constructing a simulated population, $N(\mu_0,\sigma^2)$, drawing a large number of samples of size $n$, and finding the empirical distribution of the values of $T_0$ obtained from these samples of size $n$. It would be found that approximately $\alpha$ of the calculated $T_0$ values would lie outside of the corresponding tabular $T$ values (usually denoted as $-T_\alpha$ and $T_\alpha$).

The probability, $1 - \alpha$, that $T$ lies between $-T_\alpha$ and $T_\alpha$ may be expressed as $\mathcal{P}[-T_\alpha < T < T_\alpha] = 1 - \alpha$, or $\frac{1}{\sqrt{2\pi}} \int_{-T_\alpha}^{T_\alpha} e^{-y^2/2}\, dy = 1 - \alpha$. It follows that

$$\mathcal{P}[T < T_\alpha] = 1 - \frac{\alpha}{2},$$

or

$$\mathcal{P}\left[\frac{\bar{X} - \mu}{\sigma/\sqrt{n}} < T_\alpha\right] = 1 - \frac{\alpha}{2}.$$

Solving for $\mu$, we find

$$\mathcal{P}\left[\frac{\bar{X} - T_\alpha \sigma}{\sqrt{n}} < \mu\right] = 1 - \frac{\alpha}{2}.$$

Similarly,

$$\mathcal{P}\left[\mu < \frac{\bar{X} + T_\alpha \sigma}{\sqrt{n}}\right] = 1 - \frac{\alpha}{2}.$$

Hence,

$$\mathcal{P}\left[\frac{\bar{X} - T_\alpha \sigma}{\sqrt{n}} < \mu < \frac{\bar{X} + T_\alpha \sigma}{\sqrt{n}}\right] = 1 - \alpha. \tag{1}$$

The symbol $\mathcal{P}[T < T_\alpha]$ is read "the probability of $T$ being less than $T_\alpha$."

The inequality set out in (1) above provides a confidence interval for $\mu$ at the $(1 - \alpha)$ *confidence probability level*. The validity of the procedure described may be checked in a similar manner as that suggested for the test criterion in preceding paragraphs. It should be noted that $\mu$ is a population parameter and does not have a sampling distribution but is some fixed though unknown quantity. For some sample in hand, (1) above is not an a priori probability statement but indicates an average outcome to be expected in repeated sampling. This kind of probability is called a confidence probability. A more precise mathematical formulation of these concepts will be presented in Chap. 10.

Values of $(1 - \alpha/2)$ are given in Table I*b* in the Appendix for $y$ ranging from 0 in steps of .01 to 3.49. The reader must interpolate in order to determine $y = T_\alpha$ for a specified value of $\alpha$ (see the section on Explanation of the Tables preceding the tables). Values of $T_\alpha$ are given at the bottom of Table I*b* in the Appendix for a few selected values of $\alpha$.

**Example 7.1.** Given a normal population of yields with variance $\sigma^2 = 90$. The following nine sample values were obtained from this population: 65, 45, 43, 40, 64, 58, 52, 56, 63. The mean of this sample is $\bar{X} = 54$. On the basis of previous experience it was believed that the true mean, $\mu$, was 50. Using a significance probability of $\alpha = .05$, does the sample contradict this presumption? We find that

$$T_0 = \frac{54 - 50}{\sqrt{10}} = 1.26.$$

From Table I*b*, we see that $T_{.05} = 1.96$. Since $T_0$ is less than $T_{.05}$, we cannot contradict the presumption that $\mu = 50$ on the basis of this sample.

On the basis of this sample, in the absence of any knowledge of $\mu$, we could set up confidence limits for $\mu$. The 95 per cent confidence limits are

$$54 - (1.96)(3.16) < \mu < 54 + (1.96)(3.16),$$

or

$$47.8 < \mu < 60.2.$$

This states that from our sample of nine values, we infer that the true mean lies between 47.8 and 60.2 with a confidence probability of 95 per cent.

**7.3. Law of Large Numbers.** In the preceding section it was shown, for a random sample of $n$ from an arbitrary parent population, that $E[\bar{X}] = \mu$ and $\sigma_{\bar{X}}^2 = \sigma^2/n$. It follows that whatever the form of the parent population distribution (provided the variance is finite), the distribution of the sample mean becomes more and more concentrated about the population mean as the size of the sample increases. It is evident then that as the size of the sample is increased, the more confident we can be that the sample mean provides a "good" estimate of the population mean. Essentially this is the meaning of the *law of large numbers*. A more precise statement of this property is provided by *Tchebysheff's inequality*, which will be derived in Chap. 8.

**7.4. The Central-limit Theorem.** This theorem states that:

*If an arbitrary population distribution has a mean $\mu$ and finite variance $\sigma^2$, then the distribution of the sample mean approaches the normal distribution with mean $\mu$ and variance $\sigma^2/n$ as the sample size $n$ increases.*

The proof of this important theorem is beyond the scope of this text except for a distribution possessing a moment generating function. Now, if $Y$ is distributed as $N(\mu,\sigma^2)$ and $u = (Y - \mu)/\sigma$, then

$$
\begin{aligned}
m_u(t) &= E[e^{t\left(\frac{Y-\mu}{\sigma}\right)}] \\
&= e^{-t\mu/\sigma}E[e^{(t/\sigma)Y}] \\
&= e^{-t\mu/\sigma} \cdot e^{\mu(t/\sigma)+\frac{1}{2}t^2} \\
&= e^{\frac{1}{2}t^2}. \\
\therefore \mathrm{K}_u(t) &= \tfrac{1}{2}t^2.
\end{aligned}
$$

If X has an arbitrary distribution, and $v = (X - \mu)/\sigma$, then

$$m_v(t) = E[e^{t\left(\frac{X-\mu}{\sigma}\right)}] = e^{-\frac{\mu t}{\sigma}}E[e^{X\frac{t}{\sigma}}].$$

Also, the moment generating function of $w = (\bar{X} - \mu)/(\sigma/\sqrt{n})$ is

$$
\begin{aligned}
m_w(t) &= E[e^{t\left(\frac{\bar{X}-\mu}{\sigma/\sqrt{n}}\right)}] = e^{-\mu\frac{t\sqrt{n}}{\sigma}}E[e^{\frac{t}{\sigma\sqrt{n}}(X_1+X_2+\cdots+X_n)}] \\
&= \{e^{-\mu(t/\sigma\sqrt{n})}E[e^{(tX/\sigma\sqrt{n})}]\}^n \\
&= \left[m_v\left(\frac{t}{\sqrt{n}}\right)\right]^n.
\end{aligned}
$$

It follows that

$$
\begin{aligned}
\log m_w(t) &= n \log \left[m_v\left(\frac{t}{\sqrt{n}}\right)\right]. \\
\therefore \mathrm{K}_w(t) &= n \log \left[1 + \frac{1}{n}\left(\frac{t^2}{2} + \frac{1}{3!\sqrt{n}}\frac{\mu_3}{\sigma^3}t^3 + \cdots\right)\right]
\end{aligned}
$$

Since

$$\log (1 + X) = X - \tfrac{1}{2}X^2 + \tfrac{1}{3}X^3 - \cdots,$$

we have

$$
\begin{aligned}
\mathrm{K}_w(t) = n \Bigg[\frac{1}{n}\left(\frac{t^2}{2} + \frac{1}{3!\sqrt{n}}\frac{\mu_3}{\sigma^3}t^3 + \cdots\right) \\
- \frac{1}{2}\cdot\frac{1}{n^2}\left(\frac{t^2}{2} + \frac{1}{3!\sqrt{n}}\frac{\mu_3}{\sigma^3}t^3 + \cdots\right)^2 + \cdots\Bigg].
\end{aligned}
$$

$$\therefore \lim_{n\to\infty} \mathrm{K}_w(t) = \frac{t^2}{2}.$$

Hence, $\mathrm{K}_w(t)$ approaches $\mathrm{K}_u(t)$, and it follows that the distribution of $\bar{X}$ approaches the normal distribution with mean $\mu$ and variance $\sigma^2/n$ as the sample size $n$ increases.

**7.5. Chi-square Distribution.** An important distribution that enters into the theory of derived sampling distributions is the chi-square distribution, defined as

$$f_\nu(\chi^2)\,d(\chi^2) = \frac{1}{2^{\nu/2}\Gamma(\nu/2)}(\chi^2)^{(\nu/2)-1}e^{-\chi^2/2}\,d(\chi^2), \qquad 0 \leq \chi^2 < \infty,$$

where $\nu$ is called the *degrees of freedom*. It is easy to see that

$$\mathcal{P}(\chi^2 \leq \chi^2_\alpha) = \int_0^{\chi_\alpha^2} f_\nu(\chi^2)\, d(\chi^2) = \frac{1}{\Gamma(\nu/2)} \int_0^{y_\alpha} y^{(\nu/2)-1} e^{-y}\, dy$$

$$= \frac{\Gamma_{y_\alpha}(\nu/2)}{\Gamma(\nu/2)}$$

which is the incomplete Gamma function, $I_{y_\alpha}(\nu/2)$, with $y_\alpha = \chi^2_\alpha/2$. This function has been tabulated in the form $I(u,p)$ by Karl Pearson[1] for various values of $u = y_\alpha/\sqrt{p+1} = \chi^2_\alpha/2\sqrt{p+1}$ and $p = (\nu/2) - 1$. In this form, $\mathcal{P}(\chi^2 > \chi^2_\alpha) = 1 - I(u,p)$. These tables are described and their uses in statistics explained in detail by Bancroft.[2]

Catherine M. Thompson[3] gives values of $\chi^2_\alpha$ for $\alpha = .995, .990, .975, .950, .900, .750, .500, .250, .100, .050, .025, .010$, and $.005$ and $\nu = 1\ (1)\ 30$, where $\alpha = \mathcal{P}(\chi^2 > \chi^2_\alpha)$. These values are presented in Table II in the Appendix.

**7.6. Properties of the Chi-square Distribution.** The moment generating function for $\chi^2$ is

$$m(t) = \frac{1}{\Gamma(\nu/2)} \int_0^\infty \left(\frac{\chi^2}{2}\right)^{(\nu/2)-1} e^{-(1-2t)(\chi^2/2)}\, d\left(\frac{\chi^2}{2}\right) = (1-2t)^{-\nu/2}.$$

It follows that the cumulant generating function is

$$\mathrm{K}(t) = -\frac{\nu}{2} \log(1-2t) = \frac{\nu}{2} \sum_{i=1}^{\infty} \frac{(2t)^i}{i},$$

whence

$$\kappa_i = (i-1)!2^{i-1}\nu.$$

The $\chi^2$ distribution has mean $\nu$ and variance $2\nu$.

Consider a new variable $y = (\chi^2 - \nu)/\sqrt{2\nu}$, for which $\mu = 0, \sigma^2 = 1$. The cumulant generating function for this new variable is

$$\mathrm{K}(t) = \frac{\nu}{2} \sum_{i=2}^{\infty} \frac{(2t)^i}{i(2\nu)^{i/2}},$$

and

$$\kappa_i = \left(\frac{2}{\nu}\right)^{\frac{i-2}{2}} (i-1)!, \qquad i \geq 2.$$

Then

$$\kappa_3 = \frac{2\sqrt{2}}{\sqrt{\nu}}, \qquad \kappa_4 = \frac{12}{\nu}, \qquad \text{etc.}$$

Also, for $i > 2$

$$\lim_{\nu \to \infty} \kappa_i = 0.$$

But this is a property of the normal distribution, indicating that the $\chi^2$ distribution approaches the normal distribution for large $\nu$.

**7.7. Distribution of a Sum of Squares of Deviations.** Given a sample $\{X_i\}$ of $n$ from the population of $X$'s which are NID$(\mu,\sigma^2)$. Set

$$u_i^2 = (X_i - \mu)^2/\sigma^2.$$

We wish to find the distribution of

$$u^2 = \frac{\sum_{i=1}^{n} (X_i - \mu)^2}{\sigma^2} = \sum_{i=1}^{n} u_i^2.$$

Now, since the $X$'s are independent,

$$m_{u^2}(t) = m_1(t) \cdot m_2(t) \cdots m_n(t),$$

where $m_i(t) = m_{u_i^2}(t)$. Hence, since all the $X$'s have the same distribution function,

$$m_{u^2}(t) = [m_i(t)]^n.$$

Now

$$m_i(t) = \frac{1}{\sqrt{2\pi}} \int_{-\infty}^{\infty} e^{tu_i^2} e^{-u_i^2/2}\, du_i = (1 - 2t)^{-\frac{1}{2}}.$$

Hence,

$$m_{u^2}(t) = (1 - 2t)^{-n/2}.$$

But this is the moment generating function of a $\chi^2$ with $\nu = n$ degrees of freedom; hence

$$\frac{\sum_{i=1}^{n} (X_i - \mu)^2}{\sigma^2}$$

is distributed as $\chi^2$ with $\nu = n$ degrees of freedom. In this case each $X$ furnishes a single degree of freedom; hence, the number of degrees of freedom is the number of independent values which make up $\chi^2$. The number of degrees of freedom in general is the total number of observations less the number of independent restraints imposed on the observations in forming the distribution.

This $\chi^2$ distribution can be used to test hypotheses and to set up confidence intervals concerning the population variance, $\sigma^2$, assuming the population mean, $\mu$, is known. A sample value of $\chi^2$ is computed from a sample of $n$ as follows:

$$\chi_0^2 = \frac{\sum_{i=1}^{n} (X_i - \mu)^2}{\sigma_0^2}.$$

A significance probability, say $\alpha$, is decided upon, and $\chi_0^2$ is then compared with the corresponding tabular value, $\chi_\alpha^2$, where

$$\mathcal{P}(\chi^2 > \chi_\alpha^2) = \alpha.$$

If $\chi_0^2$ is greater than $\chi_\alpha^2$, we conclude that $\sigma^2$ is greater than the assumed $\sigma_0^2$. It should be noted here that we can only test the hypothesis $\sigma^2 = \sigma_0^2$ against the alternative that $\sigma^2 > \sigma_0^2$. If it is not known that $\sigma^2$ is at least as large as $\sigma_0^2$, a more general testing procedure is needed; this will be discussed in later chapters.

The construction of confidence interval for $\sigma^2$ is complicated by the fact that the $\chi^2$ distribution is not symmetrical. Hence it is not clear that an equal amount of probability should be put outside each confidence limit. This problem is discussed in detail in Chap. 10. If the same amount of probability ($\alpha/2$) is put outside each confidence limit, the confidence limits for $\sigma^2$ are

$$\frac{n(s')^2}{\chi_2^2} < \sigma^2 < \frac{n(s')^2}{\chi_1^2},$$

where $n(s')^2 = \sum_{i=1}^{n} (X_i - \mu)^2$. $\mathcal{P}(\chi^2 > \chi_2^2) = \alpha/2$, and $\mathcal{P}(\chi^2 < \chi_1^2) = \alpha/2$.

**Example 7.2.** Suppose in Example 7.1 that the true mean of the population was $\mu = 50$ but that $\sigma^2$ was unknown. In this case

$$9(s')^2 = \Sigma(X_i - \mu)^2 = 868.$$

If we want to test the hypothesis that $\sigma^2 = 90$, we use the test criterion

$$\chi_0^2 = \tfrac{868}{90} = 9.64,$$

to be compared with $\chi_\alpha^2$ for 9 degrees of freedom. If we use $\alpha = .05$, $\chi_\alpha^2 = 16.9$. Hence we cannot conclude that $\sigma^2$ is greater than 90 on the basis of this sample. We see that the 95 per cent confidence limits are

$$\frac{868}{19.0} < \sigma^2 < \frac{868}{2.70}, \quad \text{or} \quad 46 < \sigma^2 < 321.$$

**7.8. Reproductive Property of the Chi-square Distribution.** Using the relationship

$$\chi^2 = \frac{\sum_{i=1}^{n} (X_i - \mu)^2}{\sigma^2},$$

we may prove that the sum of $n$ variates, each independently distributed as $\chi^2$ with $\nu_i$ degrees of freedom, is itself distributed as $\chi^2$ with $\nu = \sum_{i=1}^{n} \nu_i$ degrees of freedom. Suppose

$$\chi_1^2 = \frac{\sum_{i=1}^{\nu_1} (X_{1i} - \mu_1)^2}{\sigma_1^2}$$

and

$$\chi_2^2 = \frac{\sum_{i=1}^{\nu_2} (X_{2i} - \mu_2)^2}{\sigma_2^2}.$$

Then $\chi^2 = \chi_1^2 + \chi_2^2$ has the moment generating function
$m_{\chi^2}(t) = [m_{\chi_1^2}(t)][m_{\chi_2^2}(t)] = (1 - 2t)^{-\nu_1/2}(1 - 2t)^{-\nu_2/2} = (1 - 2t)^{-(\nu_1+\nu_2)/2}$.
But this is the moment generating function for a chi-square with $(\nu_1 + \nu_2)$ degrees of freedom; hence, $\chi_1^2 + \chi_2^2$ is distributed similarly. This result may be extended to $n$ variates.

**7.9. Simultaneous Distribution of the Sample Mean $\bar{X}$ and Variance Estimate, $s^2$.** It was shown in Sec. 7.7 that

$$\frac{\sum_{i=1}^{n} (X_i - \mu)^2}{\sigma^2}$$

is distributed as chi-square with $\nu = n$ degrees of freedom. We shall now obtain the simultaneous distribution of two parts of this sum when expressed as

$$\sum_{i=1}^{n} \frac{(X_i - \mu)^2}{\sigma^2} = \sum_{i=1}^{n} \frac{(X_i - \bar{X})^2}{\sigma^2} + \frac{n(\bar{X} - \mu)^2}{\sigma^2} = \frac{(n-1)s^2}{\sigma^2} + \frac{n(\bar{X} - \mu)^2}{\sigma^2},$$

where it will be recalled that $\bar{X}$ is an unbiased estimate of $\mu$ and $s^2$ is an unbiased estimate of $\sigma^2$.

In order to simplify the notation in the following derivation, let $u_i = (X_i - \mu)/\sigma$, so that $u_i$ is $N(0,1)$ and $\bar{u} = (\bar{X} - \mu)/\sigma$. Let $\gamma^2 = s^2/\sigma^2$.

The derivation will be accomplished by making use of orthogonal linear forms as discussed in Sec. 6.6. To this end we set up the following orthogonal linear transformation:

$$y_1 = \frac{u_1 + u_2 + \cdots + u_n}{\sqrt{n}},$$

$$y_2 = \frac{u_1 - u_2}{\sqrt{2}},$$

$$y_3 = \frac{u_1 + u_2 - 2u_3}{\sqrt{6}},$$

$$\cdots\cdots\cdots\cdots$$

$$y_n = \frac{u_1 + u_2 + \cdots + u_{n-1} - (n-1)u_n}{\sqrt{n(n-1)}}.$$

It is easily seen that each $y_i$ is orthogonal to each $y_j$ $(i \neq j)$. Also the denominators have been chosen to make the variances of the $y$'s equal unity. This type of transformation is called *completely orthogonal,* and these requirements may be designated as

$$E(y_i y_j) = \begin{cases} 0 & i \neq j. \\ 1 & i = j. \end{cases}$$

From Sec. 6.7 we know that the $y_i$'s are NID(0,1); hence, the simultaneous distribution of the $\{y_i\}$ is identical with that of the $\{u_i\}$, and $\sum_{i=1}^{n} y_i^2 = \sum_{i=1}^{n} u_i^2$. Also, since $y_1^2 = n\bar{u}^2$, then

$$\sum_{i=2}^{n} y_i^2 = (n-1)\gamma^2.$$

Since $y_1$ is independent of the other $y$'s, $\bar{u}$ is independent of $\gamma^2$. Hence

$$f(\bar{u},\gamma^2)\, d\bar{u}\, d(\gamma^2) = f_1(\bar{u}) f_2(\gamma^2)\, d\bar{u}\, d(\gamma^2).$$

We know that

$$f_1(\bar{u})\, d\bar{u} = \sqrt{\frac{n}{2\pi}}\, e^{-n\bar{u}^2/2}\, d\bar{u}.$$

It is also known that

$$\sum_{i=2}^{n} y_i^2$$

is distributed as chi-square with $(n-1)$ degrees of freedom since there are $(n-1)$ independent normal variates. Now, $\chi^2 = (n-1)\gamma^2$; hence

$$f_2(\gamma^2)\, d(\gamma^2) = \frac{\left(\dfrac{n-1}{2}\right)^{(n-1)/2} (\gamma^2)^{(n-3)/2} e^{-(n-1)\gamma^2/2}}{\Gamma\left(\dfrac{n-1}{2}\right)}\, d(\gamma^2).$$

Using the original $X$'s, which were $N(\mu,\sigma^2)$, the simultaneous distribution of $\bar{X}$ and $s^2$ is

$$f(\bar{X},s^2)\, d\bar{X}\, d(s^2) = \frac{\sqrt{\dfrac{n}{2\pi}} \left(\dfrac{n-1}{2}\right)^{(n-1)/2}}{\sigma^3 \Gamma\left(\dfrac{n-1}{2}\right)} \left(\frac{s^2}{\sigma^2}\right)^{\frac{n-3}{2}} e^{-\frac{n(\bar{X}-\mu)^2+(n-1)s^2}{2\sigma^2}}\, d\bar{X} d(s^2).$$

**7.10. Distribution of $t$.** It is now proposed to obtain the distribution of a test criterion, independent of $\sigma^2$, to be used in testing the hypothesis that a sample $\{X_i\}$ was drawn from a normal population with a specified mean $\mu$. The distribution must be independent of $\sigma^2$, if it is to be of practical use, since we seldom know the value of $\sigma^2$.

One proposed test criterion of this hypothesis is

$$t = \frac{\bar{X} - \mu}{s/\sqrt{n}},$$

where $\bar{X}$ and $s$ are computed from a random sample of $n$ from the parent population $N(\mu,\sigma^2)$. Two properties of $t$ should be noted: (i) $t$ is the ratio between a normal deviate and the square root of an unbiased estimate of its variance. (ii) $t^2$ is the ratio between the square of a variate, $y = \sqrt{n}\,(\bar{X} - \mu)/\sigma$, which is $N(0,1)$, and a variate $s^2/\sigma^2$, which is distributed as $\chi^2/\nu$ with $\nu$ degrees of freedom. Note that $\sigma^2$ cancels in the derivation of $t$. We shall take (ii) as the definition of $t$.

From Sec. 7.7

$$f(\bar{X},s^2)\,d\bar{X}\,d(s^2) = k\left(\frac{s^2}{\sigma^2}\right)^{(n-3)/2} e^{-[n(\bar{X}-\mu)^2+(n-1)s^2]/2\sigma^2}\,d\bar{X}\,d(s^2),$$

$$-\infty < \bar{X} < \infty,\ 0 < s^2 < \infty,$$

where

$$k = \frac{\sqrt{\dfrac{n}{2\pi}}\left(\dfrac{n-1}{2}\right)^{(n-1)/2}}{\sigma^3\Gamma\left(\dfrac{n-1}{2}\right)}.$$

Writing $f(\bar{X},s^2)$ as a function of $t$ and $s^2$, we obtain,

$$f(t,s^2)\,d(s^2)\,dt = k'(s^2)^{\frac{n-2}{2}} e^{-\frac{(n-1)s^2\left(1+\frac{t^2}{n-1}\right)}{2\sigma^2}}\,d(s^2)\,dt.$$

Let

$$u = \frac{(n-1)s^2\left(1+\dfrac{t^2}{n-1}\right)}{2\sigma^2}, \qquad t = t;$$

then

$$f_{n-1}(t)\,dt = k''\left(1+\frac{t^2}{n-1}\right)^{-n/2} dt \int_0^\infty u^{(n/2)-1}e^{-u}\,du$$

$$= k''\Gamma\left(\frac{n}{2}\right)\left(1+\frac{t^2}{n-1}\right)^{-n/2} dt, \qquad -\infty < t < \infty.$$

Since the area under the curve must be unity for a probability distribution and because of symmetry, we have

$$k''\Gamma\left(\frac{n}{2}\right)\int_0^\infty\left(1+\frac{t^2}{n-1}\right)^{-n/2} dt = \frac{1}{2}.$$

Let

$$t^2 = (n - 1)v;$$

then

$$k''\Gamma\left(\frac{n}{2}\right)(n-1)^{\frac{1}{2}}\int_0^\infty (1+v)^{-n/2}v^{-\frac{1}{2}}\,dv = 1.$$

Let

$$y = \frac{v}{1+v};$$

then

$$k''\Gamma\left(\frac{n}{2}\right)(n-1)^{\frac{1}{2}}\int_0^1 y^{\frac{1}{2}-1}(1-y)^{\frac{n-1}{2}-1}\,dy = 1.$$

Hence

$$k''\Gamma\left(\frac{n}{2}\right)(n-1)^{\frac{1}{2}}\mathrm{B}\left(\frac{1}{2}, \frac{n-1}{2}\right) = 1,$$

and

$$k'' = \frac{1}{\sqrt{\pi(n-1)}\,\Gamma\left(\dfrac{n-1}{2}\right)}.$$

The distribution becomes

$$f_{n-1}(t)\,dt = \frac{\Gamma(n/2)}{\sqrt{\pi(n-1)}\,\Gamma\left(\dfrac{n-1}{2}\right)}\left(1+\frac{t^2}{n-1}\right)^{-n/2} dt,$$

$$-\infty < t < \infty.$$

Since $s^2$ has $(n-1)$ degrees of freedom, $f_{n-1}(t)\cdot dt$ is designated as the distribution of $t$ for $(n-1)$ degrees of freedom. The distribution for $n$ degrees of freedom is

$$f_n(t)\,dt = \frac{\Gamma\left(\dfrac{n+1}{2}\right)}{\sqrt{\pi n}\,\Gamma(n/2)}\left(1+\frac{t^2}{n}\right)^{-(n+1)/2}, \qquad -\infty < t < \infty.$$

It should be noted that

$$\mathcal{P}[|t| \geq t_\alpha] = 2\int_{t_\alpha}^\infty f_n(t)\,dt = \alpha.$$

If it is assumed that $\{X_i\}$ is a random sample of $n$ from a normal population, we can test the hypothesis that the true mean of this population is $\mu_0$ by use of $t$ at, say, the $\alpha$ significance probability level. We compute

$$t_0 = \sqrt{n}\,(\bar{X} - \mu_0)/s,$$

where $\bar{X} = \Sigma X_i/n$ and $s = \sqrt{\Sigma(X_i - \bar{X})^2/(n-1)}$. Then a tabular value of $t_\alpha$ is obtained for $(n-1)$ degrees of freedom, and $|t_0|$ is compared with $t_\alpha$. If $|t_0|$ is greater than $t_\alpha$, there is evidence that the true mean, $\mu$, is different from $\mu_0$. If $|t_0|$ is less than $t_\alpha$, there is no evidence that $\mu$ is different from $\mu_0$.

Similarly if $\bar{X}$ is used as an estimate of $\mu$ and

$$s^2 = \sum_{i=1}^{n} (X_i - \bar{X})^2/(n-1)$$

as an estimate of $\sigma^2$, the two-tailed confidence limits for $\mu$ are

$$\bar{X} - t_\alpha \frac{s}{\sqrt{n}} < \mu < \bar{X} + t_\alpha \frac{s}{\sqrt{n}},$$

at the $(1-\alpha)$ confidence probability level.

Values of $t_\alpha$ are given for various values of $\alpha$ and various degrees of freedom in Table III in the Appendix. For the location of other tables and methods of obtaining exact values, see Bancroft.[2] Note that the tabular values are for a two-tailed test. If it is desired to use $\mathcal{P}(t > t_0)$, the tabular probabilities must be divided by 2.

**7.11. Test of the Difference between Two Means.** Another important use of the $t$ distribution is in testing a hypothesis concerning the difference of two population means. Suppose that we have two random samples $\{X_{1i}\}$ and $\{X_{2i}\}$ from populations $N(\mu_1,\sigma_1^2)$ and $N(\mu_2,\sigma_2^2)$, respectively, with $\sigma_1^2 = \sigma_2^2 = \sigma^2$. We wish to test the hypothesis that $\mu_1 = \mu_2$. The procedure in constructing a suitable test criterion will be to (i) find a function of the observations whose distribution is independent of $\sigma^2$ and which involves the difference between the population means $\mu_1$ and $\mu_2$, and (ii) find the sampling distribution of the function on the assumption that the hypothesis tested is true, for example, in this case, $\mu_1 = \mu_2$.

Let the samples have the following characteristics:

| Sample | Size | Mean | Variance |
|---|---|---|---|
| $\{X_{1i}\}$ | $n_1$ | $\bar{X}_1$ | $s_1^2$ |
| $\{X_{2i}\}$ | $n_2$ | $\bar{X}_2$ | $s_2^2$ |

Now, $(n_1 - 1)s_1^2/\sigma_1^2$ is distributed as chi-square with $(n_1 - 1)$ degrees of freedom, and $(n_2 - 1)s_2^2/\sigma_2^2$ is distributed as chi-square with $(n_2 - 1)$ degrees of freedom. Since $\sigma_1^2 = \sigma_2^2 = \sigma^2$,

$$\frac{(n_1 - 1)s_1^2}{\sigma_1^2} + \frac{(n_2 - 1)s_2^2}{\sigma_2^2} = \frac{[(n_1 - 1)s_1^2 + (n_2 - 1)s_2^2]}{\sigma^2}.$$

By the reproductive property of chi-square, assuming the two samples are independently drawn, this quantity is distributed as chi-square with $(n_1 + n_2 - 2)$ degrees of freedom. But

$$s^2 = \frac{(n_1 - 1)s_1^2 + (n_2 - 1)s_2^2}{n_1 + n_2 - 2}$$

is an unbiased estimate of $\sigma^2$ since its expected value is $\sigma^2$. Also the variance of $(\bar{X}_1 - \mu_1) - (\bar{X}_2 - \mu_2)$ is

$$\frac{\sigma_1^2}{n_1} + \frac{\sigma_2^2}{n_2} = \sigma^2\left(\frac{1}{n_1} + \frac{1}{n_2}\right).$$

The quantity

$$\frac{(\bar{X}_1 - \mu_1) - (\bar{X}_2 - \mu_2)}{s\sqrt{(1/n_1) + (1/n_2)}} = \frac{(\bar{X}_1 - \bar{X}_2) - (\mu_1 - \mu_2)}{s\sqrt{(1/n_1) + (1/n_2)}}$$

is the ratio of a normal deviate to the square root of an unbiased estimate of its variance. Writing the square of the quantity as

$$\frac{[(\bar{X}_1 - \bar{X}_2) - (\mu_1 - \mu_2)]^2/\sigma^2\left(\frac{1}{n_1} + \frac{1}{n_2}\right)}{s^2/\sigma^2},$$

we see that it is now the ratio of the square of a variate which is $N(0,1)$ and a variate which is distributed as $\chi^2/(n_1 + n_2 - 2)$ with $(n_1 + n_2 - 2)$ degrees of freedom. But the second property is the definition of a quantity distributed as $t$. Hence, the test criterion on the assumption that the hypothesis tested $(\mu_1 = \mu_2)$ is true is

$$t = \frac{\bar{X}_1 - \bar{X}_2}{s\sqrt{(1/n_1) + (1/n_2)}}.$$

The two-tailed confidence limits for the true difference between the two means, $\mu_1 - \mu_2 = \delta$, are given by $d - t_\alpha s_d < \delta < d + t_\alpha s_d$, where $d = \bar{X}_1 - \bar{X}_2$ and $s_d = s\sqrt{(1/n_1) + (1/n_2)}$.

If $\sigma_1^2 \neq \sigma_2^2$, then the variance of $(\bar{X}_1 - \mu_1) - (\bar{X}_2 - \mu_2)$ is

$$\frac{\sigma_1^2}{n_1} + \frac{\sigma_2^2}{n_2},$$

for which

$$\frac{s_1^2}{n_1} + \frac{s_2^2}{n_2}$$

is an unbiased estimate. Hence the first property of $t$ is met by

$$t' = \frac{(\bar{X}_1 - \bar{X}_2) - (\mu_1 - \mu_2)}{\sqrt{(s_1^2/n_1) + (s_2^2/n_2)}}$$

but not the second, since the square of the denominator is not distributed as $\chi^2/\nu$, with $\nu$ degrees of freedom.

We know that $(n_1 - 1)s_1^2/\sigma_1^2$ is distributed as chi-square with $(n_1 - 1)$ degrees of freedom and similarly for $(n_2 - 1)s_2^2/\sigma_2^2$. Hence a denominator analogous to that of $t^2$ is

$$\frac{(n_1 - 1)s_1^2/\sigma_1^2 + (n_2 - 1)s_2^2/\sigma_2^2}{n_1 + n_2 - 2}$$

and an analogous numerator is

$$\frac{[(\bar{X}_1 - \bar{X}_2) - (\mu_1 - \mu_2)]^2}{(\sigma_1^2/n_1) + (\sigma_2^2/n_2\ )}.$$

If we set

$$t = \frac{(\bar{X}_1 - \bar{X}_2) - (\mu_1 - \mu_2)}{\sqrt{(\sigma_1^2/n_1) + (\sigma_2^2/n_2)}} \Bigg/ \sqrt{\frac{(n_1 - 1)s_1^2/\sigma_1^2 + (n_2 - 1)s_2^2/\sigma_2^2}{n_1 + n_2 - 2}}$$

and let $\lambda = \sigma_2^2/\sigma_1^2$ and $l = s_2^2/s_1^2$, then

$$t' = \frac{t\sqrt{(n_1 - 1) + (n_2 - 1)l/\lambda}}{\sqrt{n_1 + n_2 - 2}} \quad \frac{\sqrt{(1/n_1) + (\lambda/n_2)}}{\sqrt{(1/n_1) + (l/n_2)}}$$

is an analogous expression to the ordinary $t$. The exact distribution of $t'$ is not known and even if known would be of little practical use since it would undoubtedly involve the population parameters $\sigma_1^2$ and $\sigma_2^2$. Two methods have been devised for using $t'$ to make the desired test. They are described by Bartlett[4,5] and Welch.[6]

Several other methods have been suggested for testing the difference between two means when the population variances are unequal. One of the oldest methods is the Fisher-Behrens test,[7] which is based on Fisher's concept of *fiducial probability*. Sukhatme[8] has prepared tables to be used in connection with this test. Since there is considerable controversy regarding the validity of this test, it will not be presented here.

Two approximate tests have become quite popular. One by Cochran and Cox[9] utilizes a weighted mean of the tabular $t$ values for the two samples, weighted by the two sample variances. Compute $d = \bar{X}_1 - \bar{X}_2$ and

$$s_d = \sqrt{\frac{s_1^2}{n_1} + \frac{s_2^2}{n_2}}.$$

The approximate tabular value for $t' = d/s_d$ is

$$t'_\alpha = \frac{(w_1 t_{\alpha_1} + w_2 t_{\alpha_2})}{(w_1 + w_2)},$$

where $w_i = s_i^2/n_i$ and $t_{\alpha_i}$ is $t_\alpha$ for $(n_i - 1)$ degrees of freedom.

Another approximate test was suggested by Smith[10] and further expanded by Satterthwaite.[11] The test criterion is also $t'$, but the approximate tabular value is $t_\alpha$ with $f$ degrees of freedom, where

$$f = \frac{s_d^4}{\dfrac{(s_1^2/n_1)^2}{n_1 - 1} + \dfrac{(s_2^2/n_2)^2}{n_2 - 1}}.$$

Dixon and Massey[12] have a slightly different value of $f$:

$$f = \frac{s_d^4}{\dfrac{(s_1^2/n_1)^2}{n_1 + 1} + \dfrac{(s_2^2/n_2)^2}{n_2 + 1}} - 2.$$

A method will be presented in the next section to test whether $\sigma_1^2 = \sigma_2^2$, using $s_1^2$ and $s_2^2$.

**7.12. Distribution of $F$.** Another very useful statistic in making tests of hypotheses involves the ratio of two chi-squares. Let $\chi_1^2$ and $\chi_2^2$ be independently distributed with $n_1$ and $n_2$ degrees of freedom, respectively. Then their simultaneous or joint distribution is

$$f(\chi_1^2,\chi_2^2)\, d(\chi_1^2)\, d(\chi_2^2)$$
$$= \frac{1}{4\Gamma(n_1/2)\Gamma(n_2/2)} \left(\frac{\chi_1^2}{2}\right)^{(n_1/2)-1} \left(\frac{\chi_2^2}{2}\right)^{(n_2/2)-1} e^{-(\chi_1{}^2+\chi_2{}^2)/2}\, d(\chi_1^2)\, d(\chi_2^2).$$

Let

$$F = \frac{n_2\chi_1^2}{n_1\chi_2^2} \quad \text{or} \quad \chi_1^2 = \frac{n_1F\chi_2^2}{n_2}.$$

Then

$$f(F,\chi_2^2) = \frac{(n_1/n_2)^{n_1/2}}{2\Gamma(n_1/2)\Gamma(n_2/2)} F^{\frac{n_1}{2}-1} \left(\frac{\chi_2^2}{2}\right)^{\frac{n_1+n_2-2}{2}} e^{-\frac{\chi_2{}^2\left(1+\frac{n_1}{n_2}F\right)}{2}},$$

and

$$f(F)\, dF = \left[\int_0^\infty f(F,\chi_2^2)\, d(\chi_2^2)\right] dF$$
$$= CF^{(n_1/2)-1}\left(1 + \frac{n_1}{n_2}F\right)^{-(n_1+n_2)/2} dF, \qquad 0 < F < \infty.$$

Since $n_1$ and $n_2$ are degrees of freedom,

$$\chi_1^2 = \frac{n_1s_1^2}{\sigma_1^2} \quad \text{and} \quad \chi_2^2 = \frac{n_2s_2^2}{\sigma_2^2},$$

where $s_1^2$ and $s_2^2$ are two independent sample estimates of $\sigma_1^2$ and $\sigma_2^2$, respectively. Then

$$F = \frac{s_1^2}{s_2^2} \cdot \frac{\sigma_2^2}{\sigma_1^2}.$$

This function provides a test of the hypothesis $\sigma_1^2 = \sigma_2^2 = \sigma^2$. Then

$$F = F_0 = \frac{s_1^2}{s_2^2},$$

which is the ratio of the independent sample estimates of two assumed equal variances.

A tabular value, $F_\alpha$, is obtained for $n_1$ and $n_2$ degrees of freedom, such that

$$\mathcal{P}(F \geq F_\alpha) = \int_{F_\alpha}^{\infty} f(F)\, dF = \alpha.$$

$\alpha$ is the probability that a value of $F$ as large as or larger than $F_\alpha$ could have been obtained from two random samples from two normal populations with the same variances. For a fixed $\alpha$, $F_0$ is compared with $F_\alpha$. If $F_0$ is greater than $F_\alpha$, this is evidence that $\sigma_1^2 > \sigma_2^2$. If $F_0$ is less than $F_\alpha$, there is insufficient evidence to state that $\sigma_1^2 > \sigma_2^2$. It should be reemphasized that there is always a chance of being wrong in stating that $\sigma_1^2 > \sigma_2^2$ when $F_0 > F_\alpha$. If we make a large number of such tests, we would expect to be wrong less than $100\alpha$ per cent of the time. If we further protect ourselves from such mistakes by decreasing $\alpha$, we shall unfortunately reduce the number of times real differences are indicated. A further discussion of this problem will be taken up in Chap. 11.

In the above discussions we have been assuming that the only alternative to $\sigma_1^2 = \sigma_2^2$ is that $\sigma_1^2 > \sigma_2^2$. Of course, even if $\sigma_1^2 > \sigma_2^2$, the sample $F_0$ might be less than 1. Under certain conditions of an applied problem it may not be valid to assume that the only alternative to the hypothesis $\sigma_1^2 = \sigma_2^2$ is $\sigma_1^2 > \sigma_2^2$. If $\sigma_1^2$ may also be less than $\sigma_2^2$, then the alternative hypothesis is $\sigma_1^2 \neq \sigma_2^2$, and it becomes necessary to consider both tails of the $F$ distribution in testing the hypothesis. In this case, we compute $F_0$ as the larger mean square divided by the smaller and compare it with $F_{\alpha/2}$ instead of $F_\alpha$, if we wish to test at the $\alpha$ significance probability level. Or, conversely, we can use $F_\alpha$ as the tabular value and test at the $2\alpha$ probability level.

In Sec. 7.11 it was shown that $t$ may be used to test the hypothesis that $\mu_1 = \mu_2$ on the assumption that $\sigma_1^2 = \sigma_2^2$. Suppose that for the two samples $\{X_{1i}\}$ and $\{X_{2i}\}$ there is some reason to believe that the population variances are not equal but that there is no a priori reason for one to be larger than the other. In this case it is necessary to use the two-tailed F test in testing for the significance of the difference between the two variances. On the other hand, in applying the $F$ test to an analysis-of-variance table, to be explained later, the usual alternative hypothesis is $\sigma_1^2 > \sigma_2^2$, and a single-tailed F test is used.

Tabular values of $F_{.05}$ and $F_{.01}$ are presented in Table IV in the Appendix for various values of $n_1$ and $n_2$. Norton has computed values of $F_{.20}$ and Colcord and Deming of $F_{.001}$. All of these tables may be found in reference 14. See Bancroft[2] for a complete description of where such tables can be found.

## EXERCISES

**7.1.** (*a*) Set up the joint probability distribution of the sample of size $n$ from a bivariate normal distribution $(X_1,X_2)$ with means $\mu_1$ and $\mu_2$, variances $\sigma_1^2$ and $\sigma_2^2$, and correlation $\rho$. (*b*) Show that the simultaneous distribution of $\bar{X}_1$ and $\bar{X}_2$ is

$$\frac{n}{2\pi\sigma_1\sigma_2\sqrt{1-\rho^2}}\,e^{-\theta}\,d\bar{X}_1\,d\bar{X}_2$$

where

$$\theta = \frac{n}{2(1-\rho^2)}\left[\frac{(\bar{X}_1-\mu_1)^2}{\sigma_1^2} + \frac{(\bar{X}_2-\mu_2)^2}{\sigma_2^2} - \frac{2\rho(\bar{X}_1-\mu_1)(\bar{X}_2-\mu_2)}{\sigma_1\sigma_2}\right],$$
$$-\infty < \bar{X}_1 < \infty,\ -\infty < \bar{X}_2 < \infty.$$

**7.2.** Given a normal population with $\sigma^2 = 25$. A sample of 12 produced the following values: 24, 30, 26, 33, 21, 24, 20, 32, 24, 30, 33, 34.

(*a*) Test the hypothesis that the true mean of the population is 24, using the $\alpha = .05$ significance probability.

(*b*) Make the same test as (*a*) if $\alpha = .01$.

What is the difference between the two tests?

(*c*) Set up a 95 per cent confidence interval for the true mean.

(*d*) What is the connection between the test of (*a*) and the confidence interval of (*c*)?

**7.3.** Given the distribution of $\chi^2$ as in the Sec. 7.5, find the distribution

$$y = \frac{\chi^2}{1+\chi^2}.$$

**7.4.** Given the two functions

$$u = a_1\chi_1^2 + a_2\chi_2^2,$$
$$v = \chi_1^2 + \chi_2^2.$$

Find the distribution of $w = u/v$. What effect would the provision $a_1 > a_2 > 0$ have on the results?

**7.5.** If $X_1$ and $X_2$ are NID(0,1), show that the variables $r$ and $\theta$ defined as follows,

$$X_1 = r\sin\theta, \qquad X_2 = r\cos\theta,$$

are independently distributed and that $r^2$ is distributed as $\chi^2$ with 2 degrees of freedom.

**7.6.** Given the bivariate normal distribution with means zero and variances $\sigma_1^2$ and $\sigma_2^2$ and correlation $\rho$. Show that

$$\theta = \frac{1}{1-\rho^2}\left\{\frac{X_1^2}{\sigma_1^2} + \frac{X_2^2}{\sigma_2^2} - \frac{2\rho X_1 X_2}{\sigma_1\sigma_2}\right\}$$

is distributed as chi-square with 2 degrees of freedom. HINT: Show that the moment generating function of $\theta$ is the same as that of $\chi^2$ with 2 degrees of freedom.

**7.7.** Using the result in Exercise 7.6, find the probability that $\theta \leq c^2$.

**7.8.** In Exercise 7.6 let $\sigma_1^2 = \sigma_2^2 = 1$ and $\rho = 0$. Find the equation of the circle with center at the origin which would contain 99 per cent of a large number of samples of $X_1$ and $X_2$.

**7.9.** A random sample of $n$ individuals $\{X_i\}$ is drawn from a $N(0,1)$ population. Suppose the sample is subdivided into $r$ subclasses with two or more in each ($n_1,n_2, \ldots ,n_r$ being the numbers in the subclasses). The sum of squares $q_i$ ($i = 1,2, \ldots ,r$) of deviations from the subclass mean is computed for each subclass. What is the distribution of $\sum_{i=1}^{r} q_i$?

**7.10.** Compute the 1 per cent and 5 per cent tabular values of $\chi^2$ for $\nu = 1$, 2, and 4. Check with the results in Table II in the Appendix.

**7.11.** Given $(s')^2/\sigma^2 = 2$ with $n = 4$. What is the probability of obtaining a value this large or larger? Check your results by interpolating with the tabled values.

**7.12.** Use the data in Exercise 7.2 to test the hypothesis that $\sigma^2 = 25$, assuming $\mu = 30$ and $\alpha = .05$. Also set up 95 per cent confidence limits for $\sigma^2$.

**7.13.**† (*a*) Show that the results of Sec. 7.7 can now be extended to test hypotheses and to set up confidence limits for $\sigma^2$ without assuming $\mu$ known, where $s^2$ replaces $(s')^2$.

(*b*) Use the data in Example 7.1 to test the hypothesis that $\sigma^2 = 90$, when no assumption is made concerning $\mu$. Set up 95 per cent confidence limits for $\sigma^2$.

(*c*) Repeat Exercise 7.12 when no assumption is made concerning $\mu$.

(*d*) What is the advantage of the use of $s^2$ instead of $(s')^2$ in making statements concerning $\sigma^2$?

**7.14.** Show that the distribution of $s^2$ approaches normality for large $n$. What are the skewness and kurtosis of $s^2$?

**7.15.** Find the moment generating function of $\log_e s$, where $s^2$ is an unbiased estimate of variance. Show that the distribution of $\log_e s$ is independent of $\sigma^2$ apart from its mean value.

† Exercise 7.13 should be worked by everyone.

**7.16.** Given $s^2/\sigma^2 = 2$ with $n = 5$, where $s^2 = \sum_{i=1}^{n} (X_i - \bar{X})^2/(n-1)$. What is the probability of obtaining a value this large or larger? Check your results by interpolating with the tabular values.

**7.17.** The distribution of $t$ for 1 degree of freedom is the so-called "Cauchy distribution." What about its mean and variance? Compute the tabular values of this $t$ for $\alpha = .01$ and $.05$, using the two-tailed test.

**7.18.** (*a*) Given a random sample of $n$ paired observations ($A$ and $B$). The sample mean of the $A$'s is $\bar{X}_a$, and that of the $B$'s is $\bar{X}_b$. The $A$'s and $B$'s come from normal populations with the same variance. It is desired to test whether the population means are equal. The value of the $i$th members of $A$ and $B$ may be represented, respectively, as

$$A_i = \mu_a + p_i + e_{ai},$$
$$B_i = \mu_b + p_i + e_{bi},$$

where $\mu_a$ and $\mu_b$ are the population mean effects of $A$ and $B$, $p_i$ represents the effect common to the two paired observations, assumed $N(0,\sigma_p^2)$. The $e_{ai}$ and $e_{bi}$ represent residual effects for each observation not explained by the $\mu$'s and $p_i$ and independent of them. The $e_{ai}$ and $e_{bi}$ are assumed $N(0,\sigma_e^2)$.

If

$$\bar{X}_a = \frac{\sum_{i=1}^{n} A_i}{n}, \qquad \bar{X}_b = \frac{\sum_{i=1}^{n} B_i}{n}$$

and

$$s^2 = \frac{\sum_{i=1}^{n} [(A_i - B_i) - (\bar{X}_a - \bar{X}_b)]^2}{n-1},$$

show that

$$\frac{(\bar{X}_a - \bar{X}_b)\sqrt{n}}{s}$$

follows the $t$ distribution with $(n - 1)$ degrees of freedom.

(*b*) Compare $s^2$ in (*a*) with that obtained by pooling the two sample sums of squares of deviations.

**7.19.** Show that the $t$ distribution approaches normality for large $n$.

**7.20.** The distribution of the correlation coefficient $r$ in samples of $n$ from a normal bivariate population with $\rho = 0$ is

$$f(r)\,dr = \frac{1}{\mathrm{B}\left(\frac{n-2}{2}, \frac{1}{2}\right)} (1 - r^2)^{(n-4)/2}\,dr, \qquad -1 < r < 1.$$

Show that

$$r\sqrt{\frac{n-2}{1-r^2}}$$

is distributed as $t$ with $(n - 2)$ degrees of freedom.

**7.21.** Compute the 5 per cent tabular value of $t$ (two-tailed test) for 2 degrees of freedom. What is the probability that $|t| > 3$?

**7.22.** In a certain test, given to the 45 members of a class in statistics, 20 women students had an average score of 40 with a variance of 16, while 25 men students had an average of 46 with a variance of 16. What is the probability of obtaining such results if both groups were equally well prepared for the test? What assumptions are made in obtaining this probability value? On the basis of this sample and the validity of the assumptions is there much evidence that both groups are not equally well prepared? What are the 95 per cent confidence limits for the difference between the two means?

**7.23.** Given the following data on the gains (in pounds) by 27 hogs, in individual and similar pens, 12 fed ration $A$ and 15 ration $B$. Test the hypothesis that the population mean gains are the same, and set up 99 per cent confidence limits for the difference between the two means.

$A$: 25, 30, 28, 34, 24, 25, 13, 32, 24, 30, 31, 35
$B$: 44, 34, 22, 8, 47, 31, 40, 30, 32, 35, 18, 21, 35, 29, 22

**7.24.** In a certain school 34 girl beginners in the first grade were selected and paired on the basis of IQ, socioeconomic rating of family, general health, and family size. One member of each pair had attended one year of kindergarten, while the other had not. On a certain first-grade readiness test given to all 34 pupils the scores were:

| Kindergarten | 65 | 68 | 70 | 63 | 64 | 62 | 73 | 75 | 72 | 78 | 64 | 73 | 79 | 80 | 67 | 74 | 82 |
|---|---|---|---|---|---|---|---|---|---|---|---|---|---|---|---|---|---|
| No kindergarten | 63 | 68 | 68 | 60 | 65 | 60 | 72 | 75 | 73 | 70 | 66 | 70 | 77 | 78 | 63 | 74 | 78 |

Is there significant evidence from this investigation that kindergarten is of benefit in preparing for the first grade? In making use of the $t$ test what null hypothesis is made concerning $\mu = \mu_1 - \mu_2$? How many degrees of freedom do you use here? What must be true concerning the distribution of the paired differences? Set up 95 per cent confidence limits for $\mu$.

**7.25.** Cochran[13] presents an example of an experiment with a control and six chalk and lime treatments on the number of mangolds per plot,

Suppose we compare the control numbers with those having a large amount of chalk or lime. The numbers of mangolds per plot were:

| | | Total |
|---|---|---|
| Control | 140, 142, 36, 129, 49, 37, 114, 125 | 772 |
| Treated | 117, 137, 137, 143, 130, 112, 130, 121 | 1027 |

(*a*) Calculate the sample mean and variance for each group.

(*b*) Assume that the two population variances are equal, and test for the difference between the two population means.

(*c*) Assume that the two population variances are unequal. Test for the difference between the two population means by the Cochran and Cox, Smith-Satterthwaite, and Dixon and Massey tests.

**7.26.** Show that in Sec. 7.12

$$C = \frac{(n_1/n_2)^{n_1/2}}{B(n_1/2,\ n_2/2)}.$$

**7.27.** Show that

$$\int_0^\infty f(F)\,dF = 1.$$

**7.28.** When $n_1 = 1$, show that $F = t^2$.

**7.29.** Let $F(n_1,n_2)$ be the distribution of $F$ with $n_1$ degrees of freedom for the numerator and $n_2$ for the denominator. (*a*) Derive the distribution of

$$F' = F(n_2,n_1) = \frac{1}{F(n_1,n_2)}.$$

(*b*) Hence show that

$$\mathcal{P}\left[F(n_2,n_1) < \frac{1}{X}\right] = \mathcal{P}[F(n_1,n_2) > X].$$

(*c*) Use this result to show why we can use $F_\alpha$ as a tabular value to test at the $2\alpha$ probability level for a two-tailed $F$ test.

**7.30.** Show that $\mathcal{P}(F > F_\alpha)$ is an incomplete Beta function. Set up this function. HINT: Let $X = \dfrac{n_1F/n_2}{1 + (n_1F/n_2)}$.

**7.31.** Use the result in Exercise 7.30 to determine a general formula for $\mu_i$ of F.

**7.32.** Determine the 5 per cent tabular value for $F$ if (*a*) $n_1 = 2, n_2 = 4$, and (*b*) $n_1 = 4,\ n_2 = 4$.

**7.33.** What is $\mathcal{P}(F > 4)$ for $n_1 = 4,\ n_2 = 4$?

**7.34.** Given $s_1^2 = 40$ and $s_2^2 = 10$, each based on 4 degrees of freedom. Determine the probability that sample variances as divergent as these could be estimates of the sample population variance with an alternative hypothesis that $\sigma_1^2 \neq \sigma_2^2$.

**7.35.** Given that one mean square, 80, with 4 degrees of freedom, is an estimate of $\sigma_2^2 + 5\sigma_1^2$, while another mean square, 10, with 20 degrees of freedom, is an estimate of $\sigma_2^2$. Use an $F$ table to test the hypothesis that $\sigma_1^2 = 0$.

**7.36.** Test the hypothesis that the two population variances in Exercise 7.25 were equal.

**7.37.** R. A. Fisher first considered the problem of the ratio of two variances as the difference between the logarithms of the two variances. If we let

$$z = \tfrac{1}{2} \log_e F,$$

we obtain his $z$ distribution, which is more nearly normal than the $F$ distribution. Show that

$$f(z)\, dz = 2Ce^{n_1 z}\left(1 + \frac{n_1}{n_2} e^{2z}\right)^{-(n_1+n_2)/2} dz, \qquad -\infty < z < \infty.$$

**7.38.** Show that $f(z)$ is symmetrical if $n_1 = n_2$.

### References Cited

1. Pearson, Karl, *Tables of the Incomplete* Γ *function*, H.M. Stationery Office, London, 1922.
2. Bancroft, T. A., "Probability Values for the Common Tests of Hypotheses," *J. Am. Stat. Assoc.*, **45**:211–217 (1950).
3. Thompson, C. M., "Tables of Percentage Points of the Incomplete Beta Function and of the Chi-square Distribution," *Biometrika*, **32**:151–181, 187–191(1941).
4. Bartlett, M. S., "Complete Simultaneous Fiducial Distribution," *Ann. Math. Stat.*, **10**:129*ff.* (1939).
5. Bartlett, M. S., "The Information Available in Small Samples," *Proc. Cambridge Phil. Soc.*, **32**:560*ff.* (1936).
6. Welch, B. L., "Significance of the Difference between Two Means When the Population Variances Are Unequal," *Biometrika*, **29**:350–362 (1937).
7. Fisher, R. A., "The Fiducial Agreement in Statistical Inference," *Ann. Eugenics*, **6**:391–398 (1935).
8. Sukhatme, P. V., "On the Fisher-Behrens Test of Significance for the Difference in Means of Two Normal Samples," Sankhyā, **4**:39*ff.* (1938).
9. Cochran, W. G., and G. M. Cox, *Experimental Designs*, John Wiley & Sons, Inc., New York, 1950.
10. Smith, H. F., "The Problem of Comparing the Results of Two Experiments with Unequal Errors." *J. Sci. Ind. Research* (*India*), **9**:211–212 (1936).
11. Satterthwaite, F. E., "An Approximate Distribution of Estimates of Variance Components," *Biometrics Bull.*, **2**:110–114 (1946).
12. Dixon, W. J., and F. J. Massey, Jr., *Introduction to Statistical Analysis*, McGraw-Hill Book Company, Inc., New York, 1951.
13. Cochran, W. G., "Some Consequences When the Assumptions for the Analysis of Variance Are Not Satisfied," *Biometrics*, **3**:22–38 (1947).
14. Fisher, R. A., and F. Yates, *Statistical Tables*, Oliver & Boyd., Ltd., Edinburgh and London, 1938.

## CHAPTER 8

# INTRODUCTION TO POINT ESTIMATION AND CRITERIA OF "GOODNESS"

**8.1. Introduction.** A worker in animal husbandry may wish to estimate the mean gain in weight of swine, of the same breed, sex, and age, fed on the same ration and managed similarly for a period of 20 days. To this end the following sample set of gains in pounds was obtained: 27, 28, 28, 29, 29, 29, 30, 30, 30, 30, 31, 31, 31, 32, 32, 33. Now, if it be assumed that these observations are a random sample from a population of such gains which are normally distributed with mean, $\mu$, then we must decide what function of the sample observations must be used to obtain a "good" or "best" estimate of $\mu$. We must, of course, define "good" or "best" in some technical sense. As will be shown later, it turns out that the sample mean, $\bar{X} = 30$, is a "good" estimate of $\mu$. Our investigation concerned itself then with drawing a sample from some population of specified mathematical form for the purpose of estimating a parameter of the population. In subsequent discussions the function of the observations chosen to estimate the population parameter, in this case $\bar{X}$, will be called an *estimator*, while the particular numerical value obtained in an application will be called an *estimate*.

**8.2. The Problem of Point Estimation.** A sample $X_1, X_2, \ldots X_n$ is specified as having been drawn from a common population with distribution function $f(X; \theta_1,\theta_2, \ldots ,\theta_k)$, where $X$ is the variate and $\theta_1,\theta_2 \ldots, \theta_k$ are population parameters. We wish to find functions of the observations, say $\hat{\theta}_1(X_1,X_2, \ldots ,X_n)$, $\hat{\theta}_2 (X_1,X_2, \ldots ,X_n), \ldots, \hat{\theta}_k(X_1,X_2, \ldots ,X_n)$, such that the distribution of these functions will be concentrated closely about the respective true values of the parameters. By saying that the distribution of $\hat{\theta}_i(X_1,X_2, \ldots ,X_n)$ will be concentrated closely about the true value we can mean one of several conditions, such as

(*a*) The probability that the estimator falls within a short distance of the true value shall be large regardless of the fact that this requirement may be satisfied only by an estimator which is distributed in such a way that there is a possibility (though small) of a very large deviation from the parameter.

(*b*) The probability that the estimator falls more than a specified distance from the parameter shall be negligible, or even zero, regardless of how the estimator is distributed inside this region.

(*c*) Or we may be willing to have the estimator deviate in one direction from the parameter but may wish to minimize the change of large deviations in the other direction.

These three conditions may be represented by estimators which are distributed as shown in Fig. 8.1 ($\theta$ is the parameter).

There are other considerations which might influence one in deciding whether or not a given estimator is a "good" one. For example, is the estimator appropriate for small samples as well as large? It also might be possible to set down a cost of a given deviation of an estimator from the parameter, the cost presumably being an increasing function of the size of the deviation. Then, if we could determine this cost function for

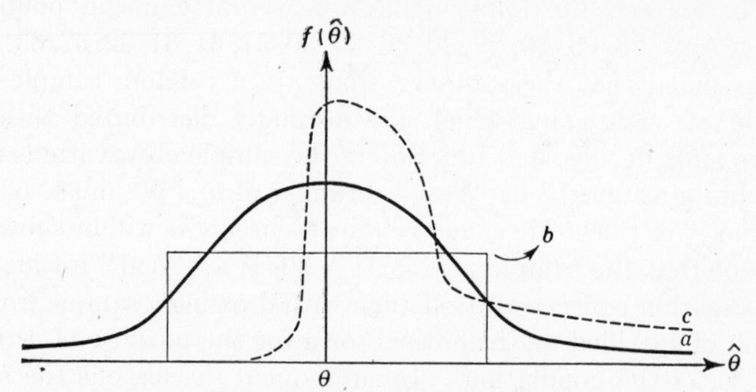


Fig. 8.1. Distributions of estimators.

various proposed estimators, it would be possible to estimate the total cost for each and adopt that estimator which produced a minimum cost.

Most of these problems of estimation are resolved if all the estimators are normally distributed. In this case, the best estimator can reasonably be assumed to be that one which has the minimum variance. However, it is difficult to say which estimator is superior if one is distributed normally and the other uniformly, for example. Although most common estimators are asymptotically normally distributed ($n$ large), few are normal for small samples and many are far from normal in this case. On the whole we can advance only a few guiding principles to be used in deciding whether an estimator is "good" or not. While these principles have yielded fruitful results, much work remains to be done, especially regarding nonnormally distributed estimators and nonrandom samples.

In the following sections we shall define certain characteristics of a "good" estimator and introduce a method which sometimes yields an estimator which satisfies all of these characteristics. Much of the philosophy and theory of estimation are a result of the work of R. A. Fisher (see reference 1).

**8.3. Unbiasedness.** An estimator $\hat{\theta}$ is said to be unbiased if $E(\hat{\theta}) = \theta$. It is said to be positively or negatively biased, respectively, according as to whether $E(\hat{\theta}) \gtrless \theta$. Unbiasedness is a desirable but not necessarily an indispensable property of a "good" estimator. If the amount of bias is small compared with the standard deviation of the estimator, the estimator though biased may be entirely satisfactory.

**8.4. Consistency.** An estimator $\hat{\theta}$ is said to be a consistent estimator of $\theta$ if $\hat{\theta}$ converges stochastically to $\theta$ as $n$ approaches $\infty$. Symbolically $\hat{\theta}$ will converge stochastically to $\theta$ as $n$ approaches $\infty$, if for two arbitrarily

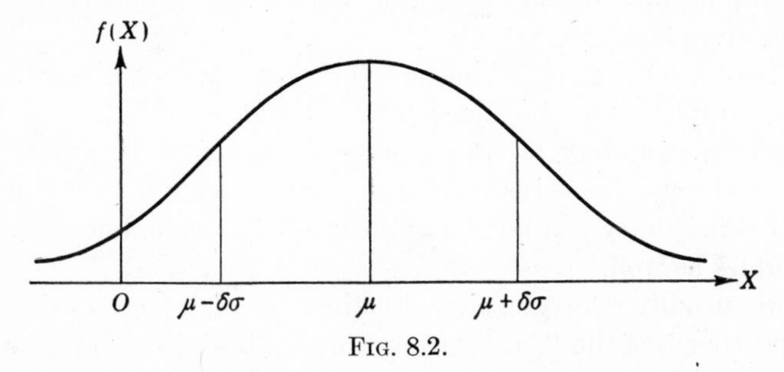


FIG. 8.2.

small positive numbers, $\epsilon$ and $\eta$, a large enough sample can be taken so that

$$\mathcal{P}[|\theta - \hat{\theta}| > \epsilon] < \eta.$$

A useful relation for proving consistency is furnished by *Tchebysheff's inequality:* Given a random variate $X$ with distribution function $f(X)$, mean $\mu$, and variance $\sigma^2$ assumed to exist, then for a given $\delta(>0)$

$$\mathcal{P}[|X - \mu| > \delta\sigma] \leq \frac{1}{\delta^2}.$$

The *inequality* may be established from Fig. 8.2. It follows that

$$\begin{aligned}\sigma^2 &= \int_{-\infty}^{\infty} (X - \mu)^2 f(X)\, dX \\ &= \int_{-\infty}^{\mu-\delta\sigma} (X - \mu)^2 f(X)\, dX + \int_{\mu-\delta\sigma}^{\mu+\delta\sigma} (X - \mu)^2 f(X)\, dX \\ &\qquad + \int_{\mu+\delta\sigma}^{\infty} (X - \mu)^2 f(X)\, dX.\end{aligned}$$

Also, since the second integral is positive,

$$\sigma^2 \geq \int_{-\infty}^{\mu-\delta\sigma} (X - \mu)^2 f(X)\, dX + \int_{\mu+\delta\sigma}^{\infty} (X - \mu)^2 f(X)\, dX.$$

Since, in the range of integration, $|X - \mu| \geq \delta\sigma$, the factor $(X - \mu)^2$ may be replaced by $\delta^2\sigma^2$ and

$$\sigma^2 \geq \delta^2\sigma^2 \int_{-\infty}^{\mu-\delta\sigma} f(X)\, dX + \delta^2\sigma^2 \int_{\mu+\delta\sigma}^{\infty} f(X)\, dX.$$

It is now evident that

$$\frac{1}{\delta^2} \geq \mathcal{P}(|X - \mu| > \delta\sigma),$$

or

$$\mathcal{P}[|X - \mu| > \delta\sigma] \leq \frac{1}{\delta^2}.$$

It should be noted that this inequality holds for any distribution but is not very efficient for a normal distribution. For example, if $X$ is $N(\mu,\sigma^2)$, then the exact probability, $\alpha$, for $\delta = 2$ is .05, while Tchebyscheff's inequality gives $\alpha \leq .25$.

In the limit a consistent estimator will necessarily be unbiased although for finite sample sizes the consistent estimator may be biased. An unbiased estimator may or may not be consistent. It can be proved (Cramer[2]) that an unbiased estimator will be consistent if $\sigma^2_{\hat{\theta}} \rightarrow 0$ as $n \rightarrow \infty$. Note that consistency is a large sample criterion, while bias is applied to small samples as well.

There are usually many consistent estimators of $\theta$; hence, other criteria are needed to select the "best" from among those with the property of consistency. In general, consistency is a desirable property of an estimator.

**Example 8.1.** Since $E(\bar{X}) = \mu$, the sample mean, $\bar{X}$, is an unbiased estimator of the population mean, $\mu$. Also, if $\sigma^2$ exists, $\sigma^2_{\bar{X}} = \sigma^2/n$ and then, by Tchebysheff's inequality,

$$\mathcal{P}\left[|\bar{X} - \mu| > \frac{\delta\sigma}{\sqrt{n}}\right] \leq \frac{1}{\delta^2}.$$

Now, if we set $\epsilon = \delta\sigma/\sqrt{n}$ and $\eta = 1/\delta^2$, then $\bar{X}$ will converge stochastically to $\mu$, if we choose $n \geq \delta^2\sigma^2/\epsilon^2$. Hence $\bar{X}$ is a consistent estimator for $\mu$.

**Example 8.2.** It can be shown that the distribution of the median, $m$, for a random sample of $n$ from $N(\mu,\sigma^2)$ approaches $N(\mu,\sigma_m^2)$ for $n$ large, with $\sigma_m^2 = \pi\sigma^2/2n$. Hence, for large $n$, $m$ may be taken as unbiased and is also a consistent estimator of $\mu$ for normally distributed data. [It can be shown in general that $\sigma_m^2 = 1/4nf^2(m)$ if $f(m) \neq 0$. $\sigma_m^2$ is the asymptotic variance.]

**8.5. Efficiency.** Since there are usually many consistent estimators of a given parameter $\theta$, we require some additional criterion to use in deciding which of these consistent estimators is the "best." Also, there might be cases in which it is desirable to use an estimator for which the limiting value deviates by a small amount from the parameter, that is, an inconsistent estimator, if such an estimator were superior in other respects. Another criterion advanced by R. A. Fisher is that the estimator shall have a minimum variance in large samples. An estimator possessing this property is said to be *efficient.*

*Definition.* $\hat{\theta}$ *is an efficient estimator of* $\theta$ (i) *if* $\sqrt{n}\,(\hat{\theta} - \theta)$ *approaches* $N(0,\sigma^2)$ *as* $n \to \infty$, (ii) *for any other estimator* $\theta'$ *for which* $\sqrt{n}\,(\theta' - \theta)$ *approaches* $N(0,\sigma'^2)$, $\sigma'^2 \geq \sigma^2$.

The efficiency of $\theta'$ is given by $E_f = \sigma^2/\sigma'^2$.† We shall consider later an estimation method which provides an estimator with minimum variance.

**Example 8.3.** Consider two consistent estimators of $\mu$ furnished by a random sample of $n$ taken from $N(\mu,\sigma^2)$, that is, the mean $\bar{X}$, and the median, $m$. We know that $\sigma_{\bar{X}}^2 = \sigma^2/n$ and also for large samples that $\sigma_m^2 = \pi\sigma^2/2n$. The efficiency of the median relative to the mean is given by

$$E_f = \frac{\sigma^2/n}{\pi\sigma^2/2n} = .64.$$

**Example 8.4.** Consider the mid-range, MR, as an estimator of $\mu$. MR is the average of the largest $X$ and the smallest $X$ in the sample. It can be shown that if the $n$ members of the sample $\{X_i\}$ are $N(\mu,\sigma^2)$, then $E(\text{MR}) = \mu$ and

$$\sigma_{\text{MR}}^2 = \frac{\pi^2\sigma^2}{24 \log n} + O\left(\frac{1}{\log^2 n}\right).$$

Hence, the efficiency of MR using the first term only of $\sigma_{\text{MR}}^2$ relatively to the mean, $\bar{X}$, is given by

$$E_f = \frac{\sigma^2/n}{\pi^2\sigma^2/24 \log n}$$

But, $\lim_{n\to\infty} E_f = 0$. Hence, although MR is an unbiased and consistent estimator for $\mu$, it is decidedly *inefficient* in large samples as compared with the mean, $\bar{X}$.

**Example 8.5.** Consider the efficiencies of $\bar{X}$, $m$, and MR as estimators of $\mu$ from a sample of $n$ from the rectangular distribution: $f(X) = 1/w$, $0 \leq X \leq w$, $w < \infty$, $\mu = w/2$, and $\sigma^2 = w^2/12$. All three estimators are unbiased. The variances are

$$\sigma_{\bar{X}}^2 = \frac{\sigma^2}{n} = \frac{w^2}{12n}, \qquad \sigma_m^2 = \frac{3\sigma^2}{n}, \qquad \sigma_{\text{MR}}^2 = \frac{6\sigma^2}{(n+1)(n+2)}.$$

Hence each estimator is consistent. If MR were asymptotically normally distributed, we could infer that the efficiency, $E_f$, of the mean or the median relative to mid-range would be zero. However, MR is not so

† We shall use the symbol $E_f$ to represent *efficiency* to distinguish it from $E$, which stands for *expected value of.*

distributed: hence, we cannot use the criterion of efficiency in making such a comparison. The efficiency of $m$ relative to $\bar{X}$ is $\frac{1}{3}$.

**8.6. Sufficiency.** Another criterion which is useful for small samples is *sufficiency.*

*Definition.* *$\hat{\theta}$ is said to be a sufficient estimator for estimating $\theta$ if the joint distribution of the sample $\{X_i\}$ of $n$ observations may be put in the form*

$$\prod_{i=1}^{n} f(X_i;\theta) = g(X_1,X_2, \ldots ,X_n|\hat{\theta}) \cdot h(\hat{\theta};\theta),$$

*where $g(X_1,X_2, \ldots ,X_n|\hat{\theta})$ does not involve $\theta$.*

In words, it must be possible to subdivide the joint distribution of the sample into the conditional distribution of $(X_1,X_2, \ldots ,X_n)$ given $\hat{\theta}$ multiplied by the joint distribution of $\hat{\theta}$ and $\theta$ in such a way that the conditional distribution does not involve $\theta$.

In the factored form it is easy to see that no other estimator, say $\theta'$, can provide any information about $\theta$. For the distribution of $\theta'$ for a fixed $\hat{\theta}$ will be determined by $g(X_1,X_2, \ldots ,X_n|\hat{\theta})$ and will involve $\hat{\theta}$ but not $\theta$. Hence $\theta'$ will provide information about $\hat{\theta}$ but not $\theta$. But, for any given problem, $\hat{\theta}$ is known, so that this information is of no value. In the language of R. A. Fisher, a sufficient estimator is one which exhausts all of the information in the sample.

It should be emphasized that sufficiency is not an asymptotic property; it does not require that $n$ be increased without limit or that $\hat{\theta}$ be distributed normally for large $n$. In view of the above discussion it would appear appropriate to consider a sufficient estimator as the "best" estimator. Certainly if an estimator of $\theta$ is not a function of $\theta$, it can be of no use in estimating $\theta$. Conversely, if an estimator exhausts all the information in a sample, it seems useless to consider any other estimator. Unfortunately there is no sufficient estimator for many parameters.

**8.7. Amount of Information and a Measure of Efficiency for Small Samples.** The minimum variance for $\hat{\theta}$ is given by

$$\sigma_{\hat{\theta}, \min}{}^2 = \frac{1}{nE\left(\dfrac{\partial \log f}{\partial \theta}\right)^2},$$

where $f(X;\theta)$ has been abbreviated to $f$. This minimum variance can be achieved only if $\hat{\theta}$ is an unbiased sufficient estimator of $\theta$ and if

$$\frac{\partial \log h(\hat{\theta};\theta)}{\partial \theta} = k(\hat{\theta} - \theta),$$

where $k$ may be a function of $\theta$ but is independent of $\hat{\theta}$, and $h(\hat{\theta};\theta) > 0$.

R. A. Fisher has designated the reciprocal of $\sigma_{\hat{\theta},\min}{}^2$ the *amount of information in the sample of n*, that is,

$$I = n \int_{-\infty}^{\infty} \left( \frac{\partial \log f}{\partial \theta} \right)^2 f(X;\theta)\, dX.$$

Now, if $\hat{\theta}$ is the estimator with minimum variance, then the efficiency of any other estimator will be measured by

$$E_f = \frac{1}{I\sigma_{\theta'}^2}.$$

If the estimator $\hat{\theta}$ is asymptotically normally distributed so that

$$\log\,[h(\hat{\theta};\theta)] = \text{constant} - \frac{(\hat{\theta} - \theta)^2}{2\sigma_{\hat{\theta}}{}^2},$$

then

$$\frac{\partial \log h}{\partial \theta} = \frac{\hat{\theta} - \theta}{\sigma_{\hat{\theta}}{}^2}.$$

Hence, in this case the second requirement for minimum variance is met with $k = 1/\sigma_{\hat{\theta}}{}^2$, provided $\sigma_{\hat{\theta}}{}^2$ exists.

**8.8. Other Forms of $I$.** We can write the integrand of $I$ in several additional ways. Since

$$\frac{\partial \log f}{\partial \theta} = \frac{1}{f}\frac{\partial f}{\partial \theta},$$

the integrand may be written as

$$\frac{1}{f}\left(\frac{\partial f}{\partial \theta}\right)^2.$$

Also,

$$\frac{\partial^2 \log f}{\partial \theta^2} = \frac{1}{f}\frac{\partial^2 f}{\partial \theta^2} - \frac{1}{f^2}\left(\frac{\partial f}{\partial \theta}\right)^2.$$

Hence

$$-n \int_{-\infty}^{\infty} \left(\frac{\partial^2 \log f}{\partial \theta^2}\right) f\, dx = n \int_{-\infty}^{\infty} \frac{1}{f}\left(\frac{\partial f}{\partial \theta}\right)^2 dX - n \int_{-\infty}^{\infty} \frac{\partial^2 f}{\partial \theta^2}\, dX.$$

But the last integral on the right is zero; hence

$$I = -n \int_{-\infty}^{\infty} \left(\frac{\partial^2 \log f}{\partial \theta^2}\right) f\, dX = -nE\left(\frac{\partial^2 \log f}{\partial \theta^2}\right).$$

**Example 8.6.** Consider a random sample of $n$ from $N(\mu,\sigma^2)$. The joint frequency distribution is

$$\prod_{i=1}^{n} f(X_i;\mu,\sigma^2) = \frac{1}{(\sqrt{2\pi}\sigma)^n} e^{-\frac{1}{2\sigma^2}\Sigma_{i=1}^n (X_i-\mu)^2}.$$

Since $\sum_{i=1}^{n} (X_i - \mu)^2 = \sum_{i=1}^{n} (X_i - \bar{X})^2 + n(\bar{X} - \mu)^2$, then

$$\prod_{i=1}^{n} f(X_i;\mu,\sigma^2) = \frac{1}{(\sqrt{2\pi}\sigma)^n} e^{-\frac{n(\bar{X}-\mu)^2}{2\sigma^2}} \cdot e^{-\frac{1}{2\sigma^2}\Sigma_{i=1}^n (X_i-\bar{X})^2}.$$

Then we may make the identifications:

$$h(\hat{\theta};\theta) = h(\bar{X};\mu) = e^{-n(\bar{X}-\mu)^2/2\sigma^2},$$

and

$$g(X_1,X_2, \ . \ . \ . \ ,X_n|\hat{\theta}) = g(X_1,X_2, \ . \ . \ . \ ,X_n|\bar{X}) = e^{-\frac{1}{2\sigma^2}\Sigma_{i=1}^n (X_i-\bar{X})^2}.$$

But the function $g$ is independent of $\mu$; hence, $\bar{X}$ is a sufficient estimator of $\mu$.

Also since

$$\log [f(X;\mu)] = \log (\sigma \sqrt{2\pi}) - \frac{(X - \mu)^2}{2\sigma^2},$$

then

$$I = n \int_{-\infty}^{\infty} \frac{(X - \mu)^2}{\sigma^4} f(X;\mu) \, dX = \frac{n}{\sigma^2}.$$

Hence the minimum variance is $\sigma^2/n$, which is the variance of $\bar{X}$.

**Example 8.7.** Suppose that the sample of $n$ is taken from a Poisson population so that

$$f(X;m) = e^{-m} \frac{m^X}{X!}.$$

The probability of obtaining the sample, that is, the joint frequency function, is

$$\prod_{i=1}^{n} f(X_i;m) = e^{-nm} m^{\Sigma_{i=1}^n X_i} \frac{1}{\prod_{i=1}^{n} X_i!}.$$

Since we may set

$$h(\bar{X};m) = (m^{\bar{X}} e^{-m})^n,$$

$\bar{X} = \sum_{i=1}^{n} X_i/n$ is a sufficient estimator for $m$. Also, $\bar{X}$ is unbiased, since $E(\bar{X}) = \sum_{i=1}^{n} E(X_i)/n = m$. Again, since

$$\log [f(X;m)] = X \log m - m - \log X!,$$

$$I = n \sum_{X=0}^{\infty} \frac{(X-m)^2}{m^2} f(X;m) = \frac{n}{m}.$$

Hence the minimum variance is $m/n$, which is the variance of $\bar{X}$.

## EXERCISES

**8.1.** Show that $(s')^2 = \Sigma(X - \bar{X})^2/n$ is a biased estimator for $\sigma^2$.

**8.2.** Given a random sample of $n$ from $N(0,\sigma^2)$.

(*a*) Show that $s^2 = \Sigma X^2/n$ is an unbiased estimator for $\sigma^2$. HINT: $s^2 = (\sigma^2/n)\chi^2$.

(*b*) Show that $\sigma^2_{s^2} = 2\sigma^4/n$. HINT:

$$\sigma^2_{s^2} = E[(s^2 - \sigma^2)^2] = E[(s^2)^2] - (\sigma^2)^2.$$

Use $E[(s^2)^2] = (\sigma^4/n^2)E[(\chi^2)^2]$ to complete the demonstration.

(*c*) Is $s^2$ also consistent? HINT: Use the results of (*b*) and Tchebysheff's inequality.

(*d*) Using the concept of information, $I$, show that the minimum variance of $s^2$ is $2\sigma^4/n$. Is $s^2$ efficient in small samples?

(*e*) Is $s^2$ a sufficient estimator for $\sigma^2$?

**8.3.** (*a*) Show that $h(\bar{X};m)$ for a sample from a Poisson distribution meets the conditions given for minimum variance. HINT: From Example 8.7, $h(\bar{X};m) = (m^{\bar{X}}e^{-m})^n$. Now, show that $\dfrac{\partial \log [h(\bar{X};m)]}{\partial m} = \dfrac{n}{m}(\bar{X} - m)$.

(*b*) Is $\bar{X}$ consistent in this case?

**8.4.** Suppose $N$ experiments consisting of $n$ trials each are conducted with data assumed binomially distributed with constant probability $p$. That is,

$$f(X;p) = C(n,X)p^X q^{n-X}, \qquad 0 \le X \le n.$$

We estimate $p$ by $\bar{X} = \Sigma X/Nn$. Discuss this estimator as to:

(*a*) Sufficiency, by showing that $h(\bar{X};p) = [p^{\bar{X}}(1-p)^{1-\bar{X}}]^{Nn}$.

(*b*) Bias.

(*c*) Information, by showing $I = Nn/pq$.

(*d*) Consistency, by using $\sigma^2_{\bar{X}} = pq/Nn$ and Tchebysheff's inequality.

**8.5.** Given a sample of $n$ taken from the Cauchy distribution

$$f(X;\mu) = \frac{1}{\pi[1 + (X-\mu)^2]}.$$

(*a*) It can be shown that $\bar{X}$ has the same distribution as $X$. Hence what can be said about the usefulness of $\bar{X}$ as an estimate of $\mu$ in this case?

(*b*) Using the concept of information, show that the minimum variance of $\hat{\mu}$ is $2/n$.

(*c*) Show that the asymptotic variance of the median for this distribution is $\pi^2/4n$. What is its asymptotic efficiency?

(*d*) Is the median consistent in this case?

**8.6.** R. A. Fisher has shown that

$$\sigma^2_{s^2} = \frac{1}{n}\left(\mu_4 - \frac{n-3}{n-1}\sigma^4\right),$$

where $s^2 = \Sigma(X - \bar{X})^2/(n - 1)$ and the sample is from an arbitrary universe. Show that $s^2$ is a consistent estimator for $\sigma^2$.

**References**

1. Fisher, R. A., *Statistical Methods for Research Workers*, 10th ed., Oliver & Boyd, Ltd., Edinburgh and London, 1946. Chap. IX.
2. Cramer, Harald, *Mathematical Methods of Statistics*, Princeton University Press, Princeton, N.J., 1946. P. 253.

# CHAPTER 9

## PRINCIPLES OF POINT ESTIMATION: MAXIMUM LIKELIHOOD

**9.1. Introduction.** Several principles of estimation, leading to routine mathematical procedures, have been proposed for obtaining "good" estimators. These include *the principle of moments, minimum chi-square, the method of least squares,* and *the principle of maximum likelihood.* The application of these principles in particular cases will lead to estimators which may differ and hence possess different attributes of "goodness." A principle much in use, yielding estimators with many desirable attributes of "goodness" obtained by easily applied routine mathematical procedures, is that of *maximum likelihood* devised by R. A. Fisher. In this chapter we shall discuss this important principle of estimation in detail.

**9.2. Basic Theory.** The procedure for determining the maximum-likelihood (ML) estimator for a population parameter $\theta$ is as follows:

(*a*) Determine the distribution function of the sample, $f(X_1,X_2, \ldots, X_n;\theta)$. This is the probability of obtaining the particular sample for discrete variates and is this probability without the differentials for continuous variates. R. A. Fisher has called this the *likelihood* of the sample.

(*b*) Determine $L = \log f(X_1,X_2, \ldots ,X_n;\theta)$.

(*c*) Determine the value of $\theta$ which will maximize $L$ by solving the equation

$$\frac{\partial L}{\partial \theta} = 0.$$

This will also maximize the likelihood. From the previous chapter we recall that a sufficient estimator for $\theta$ exists when the joint distribution of the sample may be put in the form

$$f(X_1,X_2, \ldots ,X_n;\theta) = g(X_1,X_2, \ldots ,X_n|\hat{\theta})\cdot h(\hat{\theta};\theta),$$

where $g(X_1,X_2, \ldots ,X_n)|\hat{\theta})$ does not involve $\theta$. Hence the ML equation reduces to

$$\frac{\partial \log [h(\hat{\theta};\theta)]}{\partial \theta} = 0.$$

But any solution of this equation can depend only on $\hat{\theta}$; hence, this ML solution must be the sufficient estimator, as it depends on no other estimator.

**9.3. Maximum-likelihood and Efficient Estimators in Small Samples.** If an efficient estimator for small samples exists (has minimum variance), the ML estimator, adjusted for bias if necessary, will be efficient.

In order that $\hat{\theta}$ have minimum variance, we know from the previous chapter that $\hat{\theta}$ must be an unbiased sufficient estimator and also that

$$\frac{\partial[h(\hat{\theta};\theta)]}{\partial\theta} = k(\hat{\theta} - \theta).$$

But to obtain the ML estimator we set this, or what amounts to the same thing,

$$\frac{\partial \log [h(\hat{\theta};\theta)]}{\partial\theta} = 0.$$

Hence, $\hat{\theta}$, the unbiased ML estimator, is an efficient estimator in small samples. It follows from the previous chapter that the minimum variance that an *unbiased ML* estimator can have is $1/I(\theta)$. If the ML estimator, $\hat{\theta}$, is biased in such a way that $E(\hat{\theta}) = \theta + b(\theta)$, the minimum variance is

$$\left(1 + \frac{d[b(\theta)]}{d\theta}\right)^2 \Big/ I(\theta).$$

If the ML estimator is biased, we may adjust it for bias and the minimum variance of the adjusted $\hat{\theta}$ will be $1/I(\theta)$.

**9.4. Maximum-likelihood Estimators for Two or More Parameters.** If there are $h$ parameters for which estimators are desired, we solve the set of $h$ equations

$$\frac{\partial L}{\partial\theta_i} = 0, \qquad i = 1, 2, \ldots, h.$$

In the case of two parameters, $\theta_1$ and $\theta_2$, Cramer[1] has shown that the minimum variance for $\theta_i$ is

$$\frac{1}{1-\rho} \cdot \frac{1}{I(\theta_i)},$$

where

$$\rho^2 = n^2 \left[ E\left( \frac{\partial \log f}{\partial\theta_1} \cdot \frac{\partial \log f}{\partial\theta_2} \right) \right]^2 \Big/ I(\theta_1)I(\theta_2).$$

The joint efficiency in small samples is given by Cramer[1] as

$$\frac{1}{(1-\rho^2)^2} \cdot \frac{1}{I(\theta_1)I(\theta_2)\sigma_1^2\sigma_2^2}.$$

The asymptotic efficiency $E_f$ is given by the limiting value of this joint small-sample efficiency as $n \to \infty$. Similar formulas may be derived for $h > 2$.

## 9.5. Examples Using the Principle of Maximum Likelihood

**Example 9.1.** Consider a random sample of $n$ for $N(\mu,\sigma^2)$. In this case

$$L = \log f(X_1,X_2, \ldots ,X_n;\mu,\sigma^2)$$

$$= -\frac{1}{2}\left[n(\log 2\pi + \log \sigma^2) + \frac{\sum_{i=1}^{n}(X_i - \mu)^2}{2\sigma^2}\right].$$

Let us study the following three cases:

(a) *$\sigma^2$ known*

$$\frac{\partial L}{\partial \mu} = 0: \sum_{i=1}^{n} (X_i - \hat{\mu}) = 0, \qquad \hat{\mu} = \frac{\sum_{i=1}^{n} X_i}{n} = \bar{X},$$

and

$$\sigma_{\bar{X}}^2 = \frac{\sigma^2}{n} \text{ (the minimum variance).}$$

(b) *$\mu$ known*

$$\frac{\partial L}{\partial(\sigma^2)} = 0: \frac{n}{\widehat{\sigma^2}} = \frac{\sum_{i=1}^{n}(X_i - \mu)^2}{(\widehat{\sigma^2})^2}.$$

$$\therefore \sigma^2 = \frac{\sum_{i=1}^{n}(X_i - \mu)^2}{n},$$

$$\sigma_{\widehat{\sigma^2}}^2 = \frac{2\sigma^4}{n} \text{ (also the minimum variance).}$$

Note that $s^2 = \frac{\sum_{i=1}^{n}(X_i - \bar{X})^2}{n - 1}$ in this case is not completely efficient in small samples since

$$\sigma_{s^2}^2 = \frac{2\sigma^4}{n - 1}.$$

(c) *Both $\mu$ and $\sigma^2$ unknown*

$$\hat{\mu} = \bar{X}, \qquad \widehat{\sigma^2} = \frac{\sum_{i=1}^{n}(X_i - \bar{X})^2}{n}.$$

In case $c$, $\widehat{\sigma^2}$ is biased, and we would use $s^2$ as the unbiased estimator for $\sigma^2$. It has previously been shown that $\bar{X}$ and $s^2$ are independently distributed. The two estimators $\bar{X}$ and $s^2$ are sufficient since

$$f(X_1,X_2, \ldots ,X_n;\mu,\sigma^2) = g(X_1,X_2, \ldots ,X_n) \cdot h_1(\bar{X};\mu,\sigma^2) \cdot h_2(s^2;\mu,\sigma^2),$$

where $g(X_1,X_2, \ldots ,X_n)$ is independent of $\mu$ and $\sigma^2$ (in this case, also independent of $\bar{X}$ and $s^2$).

We see that $\bar{X}$ is still efficient in small samples with $\sigma_{\bar{X}}^2 = \sigma^2/n$. However, $s^2$ is not quite efficient, since $\sigma_{s^2}^2 = 2\sigma^4/(n-1)$ and the minimum variance in small samples is still $2\sigma^4/n$ ($\bar{X}$ and $s^2$ are independently distributed). Hence the efficiency of $s^2$ is $(n-1)/n$, which approaches 1 as $n \to \infty$. The *joint* small-sample efficiency is also $(n-1)/n$.

To show that the minimum variance of $s^2$ is $1/I(\sigma^2)$, consider the following:

$$E(\widehat{\sigma^2}) = (n-1)\frac{\sigma^2}{n} = \sigma^2 - \frac{\sigma^2}{n}.$$

Then $\sigma^2 - (\sigma^2/n)$ is of the form $\theta + b(\theta)$, with $db(\theta)/d\theta = -1/n$. But $s^2 = n\widehat{\sigma^2}/(n-1)$, and hence the minimum variance of $s^2$ is

$$\left(1 - \frac{1}{n}\right)^2 \cdot \frac{\left(\dfrac{n}{n-1}\right)^2}{I(\sigma^2)} = \frac{1}{I(\sigma^2)}.$$

**Example 9.2.** Given $N$ random samples consisting of $n$ trials each from a population assumed binomially distributed with constant probability, $p$, so that

$$f(x;p) = C(n,x)p^x(1-p)^{n-x}.$$

Then,

$$f(x_1,x_2, \ldots ,x_n;p) = \prod_{i=1}^{n} C(n,x_i)p^{\sum_{i=1}^N x_i}(1-p)^{\sum_{i=1}^N (n-x_i)}$$

and

$$L = \sum_{i=1}^{N} \log C(n,x_i) + \sum_{i=1}^{N} x_i \log p + \sum_{i=1}^{N} (n - x_i) \log (1-p).$$

Hence

$$\frac{\partial L}{\partial p} = 0: \hat{p} = \frac{\sum_{i=1}^{N} x_i}{\sum_{i=1}^{N} (n-x_i) + \sum_{i=1}^{N} x_i} = \frac{\sum_{i=1}^{N} x_i}{Nn} = \bar{x}.$$

## EXERCISES

**9.1.** Determine the ML estimator for $m$ in the Poisson distribution.

**9.2.** Given the Pearson Type III distribution

$$f(X;\alpha) = \frac{1}{\alpha^\lambda \Gamma(\lambda)} X^{\lambda-1} e^{-X/\alpha}, \qquad 0 \leq X < \infty,$$

where $\lambda$ is some fixed positive constant. (*a*) Show that the ML estimator for $\alpha$ for a sample of $n$ is $\hat{\alpha} = \bar{X}/\lambda$. (*b*) It can be shown that $\sigma^2_{\hat{\alpha}} = \sigma^2/n\lambda$. Using the concept of information, show that the minimum variance is also given by $\sigma^2/n\lambda$. (*c*) Is the estimator consistent? (*d*) Is the estimator efficient in small samples? (*e*) Show that $E(X) = \alpha\lambda$, hence that $E(\hat{\alpha}) = \alpha$ and $\hat{\alpha}$ is unbiased. (*f*) Show that

$$f(X_1,X_2, \ldots ,X_n;\alpha) = \frac{\prod_{i=1}^{n} X_i^{\lambda-1} \cdot e^{-n\lambda\hat{\alpha}/\alpha}}{[\Gamma(\lambda)]^n \alpha^n}$$

and hence $\hat{\alpha}$ is a sufficient estimator for $\alpha$.

**9.3.** Derive for random samples of $n$ the ML estimators of $\mu$, $\beta$, and $\sigma^2$ in the regression equation $Y = \mu + \beta x + \epsilon$, where $\epsilon$ is $N(0,\sigma^2)$. (*a*) What are the variances of $\hat{\mu}$ and $\hat{\beta}$? (*b*) Are these efficient? (*c*) Is the ML estimator for $\sigma^2$ unbiased?

**9.4.** Given the bivariate normal distribution with parameters: $\mu_x$, $\mu_y$, $\sigma^2_x$, $\sigma^2_y$, $\rho_{xy}$. (*a*) Find the ML estimators for each parameter for random samples of $n$. (*b*) Show that $(\hat{\rho})^2 = (\hat{\beta})^2 \cdot \widehat{\sigma^2_x}/\widehat{\sigma^2_y}$, where $\hat{\beta}$ is obtained from Exercise 9.3. (*c*) Is there any difference between $\widehat{\sigma^2_y}$ above and the $\widehat{\sigma^2}$ of Exercise 9.3?

### Reference Cited

1. CRAMER, HARALD, *Mathematical Methods of Statistics*, Princeton University Press, Princeton, N.J., 1946. Pp. 490–495.

# CHAPTER 10

## INTERVAL ESTIMATION

**10.1. Introduction.** In Sec. 6.1 we introduced a method of estimating the value of a parameter, $\theta$, which is less restrictive than that of point estimation. This method, called *interval estimation*, derives limits $c_1$ and $c_2$ which are functions of the sample values $\{X_i\}$ or functions of the sample values and known population parameters. We recall that the interval $(c_1,c_2)$ is called the *confidence interval*, which is determined so that, in repeated sampling from the same population, the interval will contain the parameter $\theta$ a certain percentage of the time. Symbolically $c_1$ and $c_2$ are determined so that

$$\mathcal{P}(c_1 < \theta < c_2) \geq 1 - \alpha,$$

that is, the probability of the interval $(c_1,c_2)$ containing the population parameter $\theta$ is greater than or equal to $1 - \alpha$. The value $\alpha$ is a small positive number less than 1. The probability holds only for a large number of similarly drawn samples, where $c_1$ and $c_2$ are recalculated for each sample. The value $(1 - \alpha)$ is called the *confidence probability*. In Chap. 7 methods and examples were given introducing confidence-interval construction in connection with the derivations of certain important sampling distributions.

These concepts were introduced by Neyman.[1] R. A. Fisher uses the terms *fiducial interval* and *fiducial probability* to indicate substantially the same concepts, though he restricts his results to sufficient statistics.

**10.2. Intervals for Sufficient Estimators.** If $\hat{\theta}$ is a sufficient estimator such that

$$\prod_{i=1}^{n} f(X_i;\theta) = g(X_1,X_2, \ldots ,X_n|\hat{\theta}) \cdot h(\hat{\theta};\theta),$$

then the problem of estimating the confidence limits becomes one of finding the limits $\gamma_1(\theta)$ and $\gamma_2(\theta)$ such that

$$\int_{\gamma_1(\theta)}^{\gamma_2(\theta)} h(\hat{\theta};\theta)\, d\hat{\theta} = 1 - \alpha.$$

It follows that

$$\mathcal{P}[\gamma_1(\theta) < \hat{\theta} < \gamma_2(\theta)] = 1 - \alpha.$$

We then solve the equations $\gamma_1(\theta) = \hat{\theta}$ and $\gamma_2(\theta) = \hat{\theta}$ for $\theta$ and obtain the solutions $c_2$ and $c_1$, respectively.

Let us consider the problem graphically. In Fig. 10.1 the curves $\gamma_1(\theta)$ and $\gamma_2(\theta)$ are drawn so that $\mathcal{P}[\gamma_1(\theta) < \hat{\theta} < \gamma_2(\theta)] = 1 - \alpha$ if $f(X_i;\theta)$ is continuous, and $\mathcal{P} \geq 1 - \alpha$ if $f(X_i;\theta)$ is discrete. Let $c_1$ and $c_2$ be the intersections of the straight line $\hat{\theta} = \hat{\theta}_0$ with the curves $\gamma_2(\theta)$ and $\gamma_1(\theta)$, respectively (note the interchange of subscripts). $\hat{\theta}_0$ is the particular value of $\hat{\theta}$ obtained from the sample. The line segment $(c_1,c_2)$ will

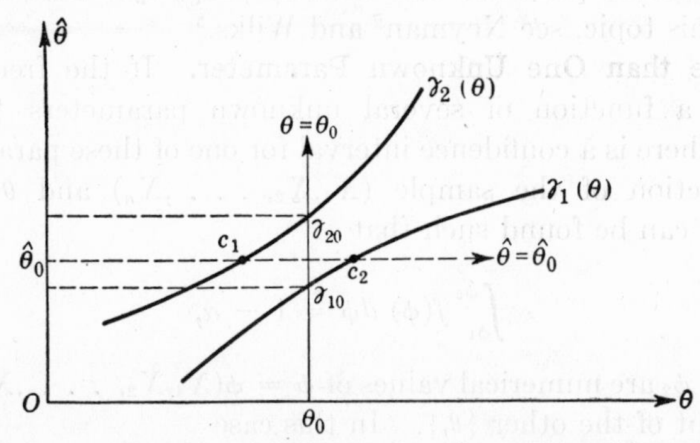


FIG. 10.1. Graphical representation of confidence interval.

intersect the line $\theta = \theta_0$ (the true value of the parameter) only if $\hat{\theta}$ falls between $\gamma_{10}$ and $\gamma_{20}$. But the probability of the latter event is

$$\mathcal{P}(\gamma_{10} < \hat{\theta} < \gamma_{20}) = 1 - \alpha.$$

Hence, $1 - \alpha$ is also the probability that the variable interval $(c_1,c_2)$ includes $\theta_0$.

We may summarize as follows:

$$1 - \alpha = \mathcal{P}(\gamma_{10} < \hat{\theta} < \gamma_{20}|\theta = \theta_0) = \mathcal{P}(c_1c_2 \text{ intersects } \theta = \theta_0) = \mathcal{P}(c_1 < \theta_0 < c_2).$$

This does *not* imply that $\theta$ has a distribution or that on a given trial there is a probability that the true value $\theta_0$ lies between $c_1$ and $c_2$. What *is* meant is that, if a series of trials are made, in about $100(1 - \alpha)$ per cent of these trials the *variable* interval $(c_1,c_2)$ will include $\theta_0$, the true value of $\theta$.

**10.3. Shortest Confidence Interval.** It is clear that there are an infinity of possible limits $(\gamma_1,\gamma_2)$ such that $\mathcal{P}(\gamma_1 < \hat{\theta} < \gamma_2) = 1 - \alpha$. For example, we might take $\gamma_1 = -\infty$ so that $\mathcal{P}(\hat{\theta} > \gamma_2) = \alpha$, or we might take $\mathcal{P}(\hat{\theta} > \gamma_2) = \mathcal{P}(\hat{\theta} < \gamma_1) = \alpha/2.$† In determining which of the infinity of possible limits $(\gamma_1,\gamma_2)$ to use, we shall usually wish to make the confidence interval as small as possible. If we consider only unbiased estimates which are asymptotically normally distributed, this interval

† It will be convenient, in general, to let $\mathcal{P}(\hat{\theta} > \gamma_2) = \alpha_2$ and $\mathcal{P}(\hat{\theta} < \gamma_1) = \alpha_1$, where $\alpha_1 + \alpha_2 = \alpha$.

can be made as small as possible by choosing the $\hat{\theta}$ with the smallest variance and selecting the limits $(\gamma_1,\gamma_2)$ such that

$$\alpha_1 = \alpha_2 = \frac{\alpha}{2}.$$

The ML estimator possesses this desired property. For detailed discussions of this topic, see Neyman[2] and Wilks.[3]

**10.4. More than One Unknown Parameter.** If the frequency distribution is a function of several unknown parameters $\{\theta_i\}$, $i = 1, 2, \ldots, h$; there is a confidence interval for one of these parameters, say $\theta_1$, if a function of the sample $(X_1,X_2, \ldots ,X_n)$ and $\theta_1$, $\phi(X_1,X_2, \ldots ,X_n;\theta_1)$, can be found such that

$$\int_{\phi_1}^{\phi_2} f(\phi)\, d\phi = 1 - \alpha,$$

where $\phi_1$ and $\phi_2$ are numerical values of $\phi = \phi(X_1,X_2, \ldots ,X_n;\theta_1)$ and $\phi$ is independent of the other $\{\theta_i\}$. In this case

$$\mathcal{P}[\phi_1 < \phi(X_1,X_2, \ldots ,X_n;\theta_1) < \phi_2] = 1 - \alpha.$$

By reversing the inequalities $\phi < \phi_2$ and $\phi > \phi_1$ we can find values of $c_1$ and $c_2$ such that

$$\mathcal{P}[c_1 < \theta_1 < c_2] = 1 - \alpha,$$

where $c_1$ and $c_2$ are functions of $(X_1,X_2, \ldots ,X_n)$ and also $\phi_2$ and $\phi_1$, respectively.

The problem of finding a function $\phi$ which is independent of the other parameters is often quite difficult. The use of the usual $t$, used in $t$ tests, to solve the Behrens-Fisher problem is an example of this. Hotelling introduced the term *nuisance parameters* to apply to these other parameters which appear in the distribution of the statistic but which we wish to eliminate when making statements concerning confidence limits for one of the parameters.

**Example 10.1.** It is desired to estimate the 95 per cent confidence interval ($\alpha = .05$) for the mean $\mu$ of a $N(\mu,\sigma^2)$ population by use of a random sample of $n$. We consider the following cases:

(*a*) $\sigma^2$ *known.* The ML estimation of $\mu$ is $\bar{X} = \sum_{i=1}^{n} X_i/n$. Since $\bar{X}$ is $N(\mu, \sigma^2/n)$, it is evident that the shortest interval will be obtained by letting $\alpha_1 = \alpha_2 = .025$, that is,

$$\int_{-\infty}^{\gamma_1} N\left(\mu, \frac{\sigma^2}{n}\right) d\bar{X} = \int_{\gamma_2}^{\infty} N\left(\mu, \frac{\sigma^2}{n}\right) d\bar{X} = .025.$$

This is true because of the concentration of the probability, or area under the curve, about $\mu$ for the symmetrical normal distribution.

Now, the integral on the right above becomes

$$\sqrt{\frac{n}{2\pi\sigma^2}} \int_{\gamma_2}^{\infty} e^{-n(\bar{X}-\mu)^2/2\sigma^2}\, d\bar{X} = .025.$$

Let $T = \sqrt{n}\,(\bar{X} - \mu)/\sigma$, and the integral becomes

$$\int_{\frac{\sqrt{n}(\gamma_2-\mu)}{\sigma}}^{\infty} N(0,1)\, dT = .025.$$

The value of the lower limit of this integral may be obtained from a table of areas for the normal curve. It will be found that

$$\frac{\sqrt{n}\,(\gamma_2 - \mu)}{\sigma} = 1.96,$$

and hence,

$$\gamma_2 = \mu + \frac{1.96\sigma}{\sqrt{n}}.$$

Similarly,

$$\gamma_1 = \mu - \frac{1.96\sigma}{\sqrt{n}}.$$

It follows that

$$\mathcal{P}\left[\mu - \frac{1.96\sigma}{\sqrt{n}} < \bar{X} < \mu + \frac{1.96\sigma}{\sqrt{n}}\right] = .95.$$

Reversing the positions of $\mu$ and $\bar{X}$, we have

$$\mathcal{P}\left[\bar{X} - \frac{1.96\sigma}{\sqrt{n}} < \mu < \bar{X} + \frac{1.96\sigma}{\sqrt{n}}\right] = .95.$$

Note that $c_1 = \bar{X} - (1.96\sigma/\sqrt{n})$ corresponds to $\gamma_2 = \mu + (1.96\sigma/\sqrt{n})$; and similarly for $c_2$ and $\gamma_1$; that is, if

$$\bar{X} < \gamma_2 = \mu + \frac{1.96\sigma}{\sqrt{n}},$$

then

$$\mu > \bar{X} - \frac{1.96\sigma}{\sqrt{n}} = c_1.$$

Unless the nuisance parameter $\sigma$ is known, these confidence limits are of little use. This result is the same as that obtained in Sec. 7.2.

(*b*) $\sigma^2$ *unknown*. In this case we are concerned with two unknown parameters, $\mu$ and $\sigma^2$. It is known that $t = \sqrt{n}\,(\bar{X} - \mu)/s$ is distributed as Student's $t$ with $(n - 1)$ degrees of freedom. Hence $t$ is a function of only $\mu$ and the sample values $n$, $\bar{X}$, and $s$. It is possible then to find numerical values $t_1$ and $t_2$ such that

$$\mathcal{P}[t_1 < t < t_2] = .95.$$

Since $t$ has a symmetrical distribution with its maximum density in the center, the shortest confidence interval with $\alpha = .05$ will result from setting

$$\mathcal{P}(t > t_2) = \mathcal{P}(t < t_1) = .025.$$

In this case $t_1 = -t_2$. Since the values of $t_1$ and $t_2$ depend on $n$, we cannot find unique confidence limits as in (*a*) above. For $n = 4$ (3 degrees of freedom), $t_1 = t_2 = 3.182$, and for $n = 20$ (19 degrees of freedom), $t_1 = t_2 = 2.093$.

The reverse limits are obtained as follows: For $t = \sqrt{n}\,(\bar{X} - \mu)/s < t_2$, $\mu > \bar{X} - t_2 s/\sqrt{n}$, and similarly for $t > t_1$ we obtain $\mu < \bar{X} + t_1 s/\sqrt{n}$. Hence

$$\mathcal{P}\left[\frac{\bar{X} - t_2 s}{\sqrt{n}} < \mu < \frac{\bar{X} + t_1 s}{\sqrt{n}}\right] = .95,$$

where .95 is the confidence probability. The confidence limits are now independent of the nuisance parameter $\sigma$ since $t$ was used instead of $T$, as in Sec. 7.10.

**Example 10.2.** In Example 10.1(*b*), determine a 95 per cent confidence interval for $\sigma^2$. We know that $\chi^2 = (n - 1)s^2/\sigma^2$ is distributed as chi-square with $(n - 1)$ degrees of freedom. Let $\chi_1^2$ and $\chi_2^2$ be values of $\chi^2$ such that

$$\int_{\chi_1^2}^{\chi_2^2} f(\chi^2)\,d(\chi^2) = .95.$$

Then

$$\mathcal{P}[\chi_1^2 < \chi^2 < \chi_2^2] = .95,$$

and for $\chi^2 = (n - 1)s^2/\sigma^2 < \chi_2^2$, $\sigma^2 > (n - 1)s^2/\chi_2^2$. Similarly, for $\chi^2 > \chi_1^2$, $\sigma^2 < (n - 1)s^2/\chi_1^2$. Hence, the confidence interval for $\sigma^2$ is

$$\frac{(n - 1)s^2}{\chi_2^2} < \sigma^2 < \frac{(n - 1)s^2}{\chi_1^2}.$$

As for Example 10.1(*b*), the values of $\chi_1^2$ and $\chi_2^2$ depend on $n$ (see Exercise 7.13).

In this case the problem of selecting values of $\chi_1^2$ and $\chi_2^2$ in order to obtain the shortest confidence interval is more complicated because of the skewness of the $\chi^2$ distribution. It is clear that the interval is proportional to

$$\frac{1}{\chi_1^2} - \frac{1}{\chi_2^2}.$$

Let us illustrate the difficulty in selecting values of $\chi_1^2$ and $\chi_2^2$ in order to obtain the shortest confidence interval for the case $n = 3$ (2 degrees of freedom). We have

$$\int_{\chi_1^2}^{\chi_2^2} e^{-\chi^2/2}\, d\left(\frac{\chi^2}{2}\right) = .95.$$

(*a*) If we select $\chi_1^2$ and $\chi_2^2$ so that $\alpha_1 = \alpha_2 = .025$, then $\chi_2^2 = 7.38$, and $\chi_1^2 = .05066$. Hence

$$\frac{1}{\chi_1^2} - \frac{1}{\chi_2^2} = 19.8 - 0.1 = 19.7,$$

and the confidence interval is $0.2s^2 < \sigma^2 < 39.6s^2$.

(*b*) If we select $\chi_1^2$ and $\chi_2^2$ so that $\alpha_1 = .05$ and $\alpha_2 = 0$, then $\chi_2^2 = \infty$ and $\chi_1^2 = .1026$. Hence

$$\frac{1}{\chi_1^2} - \frac{1}{\chi_2^2} = 9.7.$$

The confidence interval now becomes

$$0 < \sigma^2 < 19.4s^2,$$

which is much shorter than that obtained in (*a*) above.

(*c*) By minimizing $1/\chi_1^2 - 1/\chi_2^2$ subject to the relation

$$\int_{\chi_1^2}^{\chi_2^2} f(\chi^2)\, d(\chi^2) = 1 - \alpha,$$

it is possible to show that the values $\chi_1^2$ and $\chi_2^2$ should satisfy the following relationship in order to provide the shortest confidence interval for $\sigma^2$:

$$\chi_1^4 f(\chi_1^2) = \chi_2^4 f(\chi_2^2).$$

## EXERCISES

**10.1.** Given a sample of $n$ from a binomial population with constant probability $p$. If we let $\alpha_1 = \alpha_2 = .025$ and assume that the sample estimate of $p$, $\bar{x}$, is approximately $N(p, p(1 - p)/n)$, show that the confidence interval is $(p_1 < p < p_2)$, where $p_1$ and $p_2$ are solutions of the quadratic equation

$$n(\bar{x} - p)^2 = (1.96)^2(p - p^2).$$

**10.2.** Find the shortest confidence interval for the difference between the means of two normal populations with the same variance, $\sigma^2$, with a sample of $n_1$ from the first population and of $n_2$ from the second population.

**10.3.** (*a*) Show that the confidence interval for the ratio of the variance of two normal populations

$$\theta = \sigma_1^2/\sigma_2^2$$

is given by

$$F_0/F_2 < \theta < F_0/F_1,$$

where

$$\int_{F_1}^{F_2} f(F)\, dF = 1 - \alpha$$

and $F_0 = s_1^2/s_2^2$ with $(n_1 - 1)$ and $(n_2 - 1)$ degrees of freedom, respectively,

(*b*) Given $n_1 = 12$ and $n_2 = 25$ and $\alpha = .10$, determine values of $F_1$ and $F_2$ if $\alpha_1 = \alpha_2$. Suppose $s_1^2 = 20$ and $s_2^2 = 10$, what are the 90 per cent confidence limits?

**10.4.** Use the data in Exercise 7.35 to set up 90 per cent confidence limits for the following ratios, used in statistical genetics:

(*a*) $\dfrac{\sigma_2^2 + 5\sigma_1^2}{\sigma_2^2}$.

(*b*) $\dfrac{\sigma_1^2}{\sigma_2^2}$.

(*c*) $\dfrac{\sigma_1^2}{\sigma_1^2 + \sigma_2^2}$.

**10.5.** (For students who have studied advanced calculus.) Derive condition *c* of Example 10.2.

**10.6.** Using condition *c*, derive the shortest confidence interval for Exercise 7.13(*c*).

**10.7.** (*a*) Derive the general confidence limits for a linear function of the sample values, that is,

$$l = \sum_{i=1}^{n} a_i X_i,$$

where the $X$'s are NID$(\mu,\sigma^2)$.

(*b*) Apply your result to $l_1$ and $l_2$ in Exercise 6.8, assuming $r = 4$, $T_0 = 50$, $T_1 = 105$, $T_2 = 95$, and $T_3 = 70$, and $s^2 = 12$.

**References Cited**

1. Neyman, J., "On the Problem of Confidence Intervals," *Ann. Math. Stat.*, **6**:111*ff*. (1935).
2. Neyman, J., "Outline of a Theory of Statistical Estimation Based on the Classical Theory of Probability," *Phil. Trans. Roy. Soc. (London)*, **236**:333–380 (1937).
3. Wilks, S. S., "Shortest Average Confidence Intervals for Large Samples," *Ann. Math. Stat.*, **9**:166–175 (1938).

## CHAPTER 11

## TESTS OF HYPOTHESES

**11.1. Introduction.** Statistical inference concerns itself in general with two types of problems: *estimation of population parameters* and *tests of hypotheses.* In the preceding three chapters, we have considered problems of estimation. Desirable properties of a "good" estimator were discussed; and a principle of estimation, the maximum-likelihood method, was presented as a technique which in many cases may be easily used to obtain estimators possessing many of these desirable properties.

In this chapter, we propose to discuss the general problem of tests of hypotheses and present a principle, the *likelihood-ratio criterion*, which in many cases will provide a "good" *test criterion* to be used in testing hypotheses concerning population parameters. In discussing derived sampling distributions in Chap. 7, it will be recalled that the distributions of $\chi^2$, $t$, and $F$ were obtained and their uses in applied statistics in testing hypotheses were pointed out and illustrated. In this discussion we wish to investigate the theoretical justification for selecting a particular test criterion for a particular problem in hand.

**11.2. The General Problem.** In order to test whether a given hypothesis ($H_0$, the *null hypothesis*) is supported by a given set of data, we must devise a rule of procedure, depending on the outcome of calculations obtained from the sample, to decide whether to reject or not to reject $H_0$. For example, in testing whether or not a given sample supports the hypothesis that the observations were randomly selected from $N(0,1)$ we calculate $T = \bar{X}$ and consider it a normal deviate with unit variance. After a choice of an allowable error or probability of rejecting $H_0$ when it is true, say $\alpha$, we find two regions such that, if $\bar{X}$ is in one region, we reject $H_0$ and, if in the other region, we do not reject $H_0$. The first region will be called the *region of rejection*, $R$, and is defined so that the probability of the sample falling in $R$ is $\alpha$, if $H_0$ is true. Designate $T$ the *test criterion* and $\alpha$ the *significance level.*

As indicated in Sec. 11.1 there are many different criteria for judging the truth of a given hypothesis. For example, if we wish to test whether or not a given sample could have been drawn from NID(0,1), we could use any one of the following tests (and probably many more):

(i) $T = \bar{X}$, a normal deviate with unit variance.

(ii) $t = \sqrt{n}\, \bar{X}/s$, Student's test.

(iii) $\chi^2 = (n - 1)s^2/1$, the $\chi^2$ test for the agreement of sample and population variance.

(iv) Tests for skewness or kurtosis in the distribution (evidence of nonnormality).

(v) Tests for serial correlation in the observations.

The likelihood-ratio criterion, mentioned earlier, may be used to indicate which of the possible test criteria to use. Actually the likelihood ratio defines a region of rejection $R$, which involves computing some test criterion such as one of those mentioned above.

The observations in the sample $(X_1,X_2, \ldots ,X_n)$ may be thought of as representing the coordinates of a point, $S$, in $n$-dimensional space. The space is divided into two regions—the region of rejection $R$ and the region of nonrejection. If $S$ falls in $R$, we shall reject $H_0$; otherwise accept it. The region $R$ corresponds to the region outside the confidence interval discussed in the previous chapter and is defined so that the probability of rejecting a true hypothesis (the probability of $S$ falling in $R$ when $H_0$ is true) is the significance level $\alpha$ (for example, $\alpha = .05$ or $.01$). This will be indicated symbolically as

$$\mathcal{P}(S \in R|H_0) = \alpha,$$

where $S \in R$ means that the sample point $S$ is contained in $R$.

As with confidence intervals, there may be a large number of possible regions $R$ which satisfy this probability statement. For purposes of making tests of significance, it seems reasonable to select that $R$ for which $\mathcal{P}(S \in R)$ is maximized if the true hypothesis is not $H_0$. That is, we want to reject the null hypothesis as often as possible when it is not true. Hence, we are led to consider the possible alternatives to $H_0$. Designate all alternatives as $H_a$. Symbolically we wish to maximize $\mathcal{P}(S \in R|H_a)$ for a fixed $\mathcal{P}(S \in R|H_0) = \alpha$. In future discussions we shall let $\mathcal{P}(S \in R|H_a) = \beta_a$. The quantity $\beta_a$ is called the *power* of the test, since it measures how powerful the test is in indicating a true difference from $H_0$ when such a difference actually exists. In most cases there will be an infinity of possible alternatives $H_a$, and $\beta_a$ will be different for each $H_a$. Hence, in general, it will not be possible to maximize the power for all alternative hypotheses. However, in certain cases, such a test can be found and is called a *uniformly most powerful* test. It can be shown that the likelihood ratio criterion will produce a uniformly most powerful test if one exists.

An *unbiased* test is one for which the power is a minimum for $H = H_0$; that is, we reject $H_0$ the least number of times when $H_0$ is the true hypothesis. In case there is no over-all uniformly most powerful test, it would appear that we should at least choose an unbiased test and, if possible, select the uniformly most powerful test from among the unbiased ones.

The theory of tests of hypotheses under discussion was introduced by Neyman and Pearson.[1,2,3] Tests of significance are considered from the point of view of errors of the first and second kind. In making a test of $H_0$, two types of errors may be committed: (I) we may reject $H_0$ when it is true; (II) we may accept $H_0$ when it is false. It follows that

$$\mathcal{P}(\mathrm{I}) = \alpha, \qquad \mathcal{P}(\mathrm{II}) = 1 - \beta_\alpha.$$

Maximizing the power corresponds to minimizing the probability of committing a Type II error for a fixed probability of committing a Type I error.

The importance of taking into account the Type II error or the power of a test may be illustrated as follows: It is desired to determine whether or not a new variety of corn yields more than some accepted variety. Suppose account is taken of a Type I error only and that the significance probability is fixed at $\alpha = .05$, which guarantees that, if there is no real difference between the new variety and the standard, significance shall be indicated only 5 per cent of the time. In this case it would not be necessary to perform an experiment at all. It would suffice to draw a bead at random from a bowl whose composition is 19 white and 1 red. If it is white, we accept $H_0$ (no difference between the varieties); if red, we reject $H_0$. Using the procedure, we shall always reject $H_0$ 5 per cent of the time, and this will be done whether $H_0$ is true or not. The defect in this procedure is now apparent. If there is a real difference, we shall recognize this only 5 per cent of the time, which also, in this case, is the power of the test. It is now clear that we need a different testing procedure in order that the probability of detecting true differences when they exist may be large. The $t$ test may be shown to maximize the power of the test under certain conditions. This will be discussed later.

Cramer[4] has summarized the problem of selecting a "good" test criterion as follows: "In order that a test of the hypothesis $H_0$ should be judged to be good, we should accordingly require that the test has a small probability of rejecting $H_0$ when this hypothesis is true, but a large probability of rejecting $H_0$ when it is false. Of two tests corresponding to a probability $\alpha$ of rejecting $H_0$ when it is true, we should thus prefer the one that gives the largest probability of rejecting $H_0$ when it is false."

**11.3. Types of Hypotheses.** A hypothesis, $H_0$, which specifies the values of all parameters in the population distribution is called a *simple hypothesis*; in other words, a simple hypothesis specifies that the distribution is one specific member of a family of distributions. If $H_0$ does not specify the values of all population parameters, it is called a *composite* *hypothesis*. The hypothesis $H_0$ must be taken from a set of admissible hypotheses, $\Omega$, which usually depend upon the form of the distribution. For the normal parent distribution, $N(\mu,\sigma^2)$, $\Omega$ is $-\infty < \mu < \infty$, $0 < \sigma^2 < \infty$. A composite hypothesis then states that a distribution belongs to some subspace of the parameter space.

**11.4. Simple Hypothesis for a One-parameter Distribution.** In order to illustrate the method of determining the power curve for a test, consider the problem of testing some hypothesis concerning the value of the mean, $\mu$, of a normal population with unit variance, $N(\mu,1)$. The sample observations may be $n$ differences obtained from $n$ pairs of observations such as in the corn-variety problem mentioned earlier. In this case the population of differences would be assumed to have unit variance. Set up the null hypothesis $H_0$: $\mu = \mu_0$. The set of admissible hypotheses is $-\infty < \mu < \infty$, $\sigma^2 = 1$. The sample mean of the differences, $\bar{X}$, is to be used to test $H_0$ against some alternative $H_a$.

From the discussion on confidence intervals, we know that the probability of committing a Type I error is given by

$$\mathcal{P}(\mathrm{I}) = 1 - \sqrt{\frac{n}{2\pi}} \int_{\gamma_1}^{\gamma_2} e^{-n(\bar{X}-\mu_0)^2/2}\, dX = \alpha,$$

where $\gamma_2 = \mu_0 + T_2/\sqrt{n}$ and $\gamma_1 = \mu_0 + T_1/\sqrt{n}$. It will be shown later that, for this particular problem, $\bar{X}$ is the "best" test criterion. If $\alpha = .05$, the shortest confidence interval was shown to result when $T_2 = -T_1 = 1.96$.

The integration is simplified by setting $T_0 = \sqrt{n}\,(\bar{X} - \mu_0)$ so that

$$\alpha = 1 - \frac{1}{\sqrt{2\pi}} \int_{T_1}^{T_2} e^{-T_0^2/2}\, dT_0.$$

Hence, if the calculated $\bar{X}$ is greater than $\gamma_2$ or less than $\gamma_1$ or, what amounts to the same thing, if the value of $T_0$ for a particular problem is greater than $T_2$ or less than $T_1$, then we say that we have evidence that $H_0$ is false.

In order to evaluate the power of this test to detect real differences, that is, $\mu = \mu_a \neq \mu_0$, we obtain the power function. The power function will give the probability of rejecting $H_0$ when $\mu = \mu_a \neq \mu_0$. The function should increase as the difference between $\mu_a$ and $\mu_0$ increases, since in such cases it would be increasingly desirable to reject $H_0$. The problem then is to determine the probability $\beta_a$ of obtaining $\bar{X} > T_2$ or $\bar{X} < T_1$ from $N(\mu_a,1)$ for fixed $\alpha$. Note that the power, $\beta_a$, equals $\alpha$ for $\mu_a = \mu_0$.

Now,

$$\beta_a = 1 - \sqrt{\frac{n}{2\pi}} \int_{\gamma_1}^{\gamma_2} e^{-n(\bar{X}-\mu_a)^2/2}\, d\bar{X}$$
$$= 1 - \frac{1}{\sqrt{2\pi}} \int_{T_1}^{T_2} e^{-[T_0-\sqrt{n}\,(\mu_a-\mu_0)]^2/2}\, dT_0$$
$$= \frac{1}{\sqrt{2\pi}} \int_{-\infty}^{T_{1a}} e^{-T_a^2/2}\, dT_a + \frac{1}{\sqrt{2\pi}} \int_{T_{2a}}^{\infty} e^{-T_a^2/2}\, dT_a,$$

where $T_a = \sqrt{n}\,(\bar{X} - \mu_a) = T_0 - \sqrt{n}\,(\mu_a - \mu_0)$,

$T_{2a} = T_2 - \sqrt{n}\,(\mu_a - \mu_0)$,

and $T_{1a} = T_1 - \sqrt{n}\,(\mu_a - \mu_0)$.

To illustrate the computations, let us compute $\beta_a$ for $n = 25$, $\alpha = .05$ and (i) $T_1 = -\infty$, $T_2 = 1.645$ and (ii) $T_2 = -T_1 = 1.96$. We see that the value of the sum of the two integrals giving $\beta_a$ may be obtained from Table I*b* in the Appendix for given $(\mu_a - \mu_0)$ as set out in Table 11.1.

TABLE 11.1

| $5(\mu_a - \mu_0)$ | (i) | | (ii) | | |
|---|---|---|---|---|---|
| | $T_{2a}$ | $\beta_a$ | $T_{2a}$ | $T_{1a}$ | $\beta_a$ |
| −3.0 | 4.645 | .0000 | 4.960 | 1.040 | .8508 |
| −2.0 | 3.645 | .0001 | 3.960 | .040 | .5160 |
| −1.0 | 2.645 | .0041 | 2.960 | − .960 | .1700 |
| .0 | 1.645 | .0500 | 1.960 | −1.960 | .0500 |
| 1.0 | .645 | .2594 | .960 | −2.960 | .1700 |
| 2.0 | − .355 | .6387 | − .040 | −3.960 | .5160 |
| 3.0 | −1.355 | .9123 | −1.040 | −4.960 | .8508 |
| 4.0 | −2.355 | .9907 | −2.040 | −5.960 | .9793 |

It might be helpful if these results were illustrated graphically as in Fig. 11.1. Let us consider the difference between the power for $5(\mu_a - \mu_0) = d = 0$ and the power for $d = 1$. The small shaded area is the rejection region for $d = 0$, with $\alpha = .05$. The upper shaded area is the added amount to the rejection area for $d = 1$. The sum of the two shaded areas gives the *power* $(\beta_a)$ for rejecting the hypothesis that $\mu_a = \mu_0$ when $\mu_a$ is actually $\mu_0 + .2$, since $1 = 5(\mu_a - \mu_0)$. In this case $\beta_a = .2594$.

Graphs of various power functions for the above example, depending on the values of $T_1$ and $T_2$, with fixed $\mathcal{P}(\mathrm{I}) = \alpha$, and on the position of the minimum point are set out in Fig. 11.2.

(i) $T_1 = -\infty$; $T_2 = 1.645$.

(ii) Minimum at $\mu_a = \mu_0$; $T_2 = 1.96$, $T_1 = -1.96$.

(iii) $T_2 = \infty$; $T_1 = -1.645$.

(iv) Minimum at $\mu_a < \mu_0$, for example, $T_2 = 1.75$, $T_1 = -2.33$.
(v) Minimum at $\mu_a > \mu_0$, for example, $T_2 = 2.33$, $T_1 = -1.75$.

From the definition of $\beta_a$, we see that the minimum point is reached when

$$T_2 - \sqrt{n}\,(\mu_a - \mu_0) = -[T_1 - \sqrt{n}\,(\mu_a - \mu_0)]$$

or

$$T_1 + T_2 = 2\sqrt{n}\,(\mu_a - \mu_0).$$

This relation is found by differentiating $\beta_a$ with respect to $\mu_a$ and setting the derivative equal to zero. It follows that if $\mu_a = \mu_0$, the minimum point is at $T_1 = -T_2$.

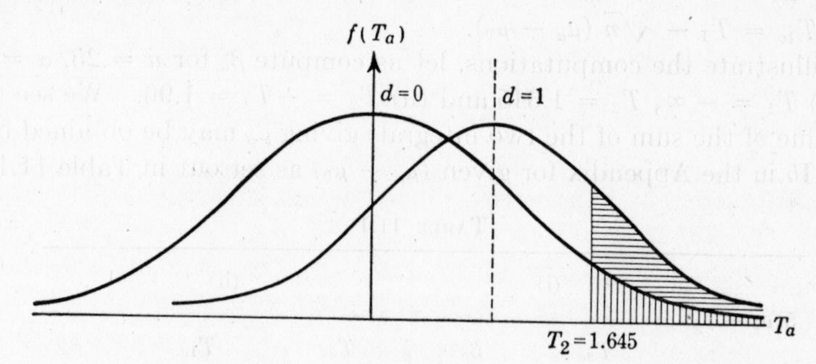


FIG. 11.1.

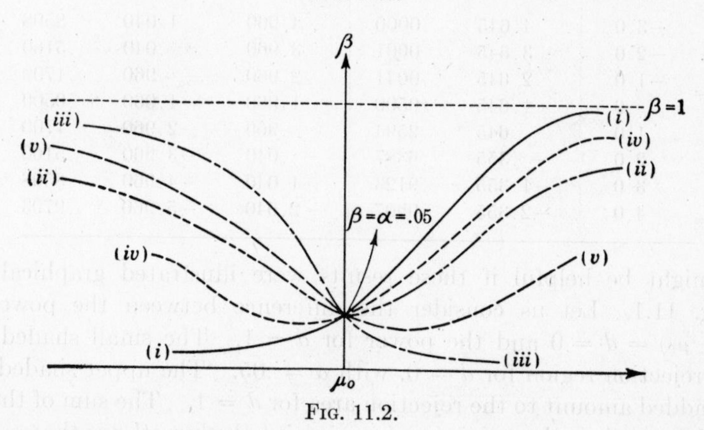


FIG. 11.2.

It is instructive to examine these *power curves* from the standpoint of the following types of alternative hypotheses:

(i) If $H_a$ asserts $\mu_a > \mu_0$, power curve (i) is *uniformly most powerful*, since its power is greater than that of any other curve for all such $H_a$. In this case we are willing to accept $H_0: \mu = \mu_0$ even though the true hypothesis is $\mu < \mu_0$. Hence, the region of rejection is $T > 1.645$ for $\alpha = .05$.

(iii) Similarly power curve (iii) is uniformly most powerful for testing the hypothesis $\mu = \mu_0$ against the alternatives $\mu_a < \mu_0$. The region of rejection is $T < -1.645$ for $\alpha = .05$.

(ii) There is no uniformly-most-powerful test for testing $H_0$ against the alternative $H_a$: $\mu_a \neq \mu_0$. This result is evident from a study of (i) and (iii). Each of these is uniformly most powerful on opposite sides of $\mu = \mu_0$ but has practically no power on the other side. No other single test can be as powerful as (i) on the right or (iii) on the left. For $H_a$: $\mu_a \neq \mu_0$ we must adopt some compromise rejection region. Neyman and Pearson have suggested using an *unbiased* test, which in this case would lead to the use of power curve (ii). For this curve $T_1 = -T_2$. It should be noted that curves (iv) and (v) are more powerful than (ii) on one tail but give a power less than $\alpha$ for some alternatives. It should be emphasized that the Type I error (probability of rejecting $H_0$ when $\mu = \mu_0$) is constant for all of these power curves.

**11.5. Composite Hypotheses.** The theory of tests of composite hypotheses has not been completed. Some methods will be illustrated by use of the single-tailed $t$ test. Given a sample of $n$ from $N(\mu,\sigma^2)$, it is desired to test the null hypothesis, $H_0$: $\mu = 0$, $0 < \sigma^2 < \infty$, against the alternative hypothesis, $H_a$: $\mu > 0$, $0 < \sigma^2 < \infty$. The admissible hypotheses are $\Omega$: $-\infty < \mu < \infty, 0 < \sigma^2 < \infty$. The null hypothesis is composite since it does not specify the value of $\sigma^2$.

From our study of confidence intervals, it seems reasonable to use $-\infty < \bar{X} < t_2 s/\sqrt{n}$ as the acceptance region, where

$$\int_{t_2}^{\infty} f(t)\,dt = \alpha.$$

The rejection region is $t = \bar{X}\sqrt{n}/s > t_2$. (If $H_a$ was $\mu < 0$, we should use the acceptance region $t > t_1 = -t_2$ or rejection region $t < t_1$. Both of these yield uniformly-most-powerful tests. However, if $H_a$ was $\mu \neq 0$, no uniformly-most-powerful test is available. In this case we might make use of the unbiased test with acceptance region $t'_1 < t < t'_2$, where $t'_1 = -t'_2$ and $\alpha_1 = \alpha_2 = \alpha/2$.) A more rigorous treatment of this problem is beyond the scope of this text.

The determination of the power for a composite test is, in general, quite complicated owing to the nonspecificity of certain of the parameters by the null hypothesis. In using the $t$ test, $H_0$ does not specify the value of $\sigma^2$, hence, we must make use of $s^2$, the estimate of $\sigma^2$, from the sample. We must determine the probability that $t = \bar{X}\sqrt{n}/s > t_2$, if the sample has been drawn from a population with mean $\mu \neq 0$. Now, when $t > t_2$, we reject $H_0$; and if $\mu$ is actually greater than zero, a correct decision has been made. The probability of making this correct decision is called the power of the test for a given $\mu(\neq 0)$ and $\alpha$. It will be recalled that $\alpha$ is the probability of stating $\mu \neq 0$ when it actually is zero.

To evaluate the power of the $t$ test, we recall the joint distribution of $\bar{X}$ and $s^2$ from Chap. 7.

$$f(\bar{X},s^2) = f_1(\bar{X}) \cdot f_2(s^2),$$

where

$$f_1(\bar{X}) = \sqrt{\frac{n}{2\pi}} \cdot \frac{1}{\sigma} e^{-n(\bar{X}-\mu)^2/2\sigma^2}$$

and

$$f_2(s^2) = \frac{\left(\frac{n-1}{2}\right)^{(n-1)/2}}{\sigma^2\Gamma\left(\frac{n-1}{2}\right)} \left(\frac{s^2}{\sigma^2}\right)^{(n-3)/2} e^{-(n-1)s^2/2\sigma^2}.$$

Now, the power of the $t$ test to detect a true mean, $\mu = \mu_a$, is given by $\mathcal{P}[t = \bar{X}\sqrt{n}/s > t_2 | \mu = \mu_a, \mathcal{P}(\text{I}) = \alpha] = \beta_a$, where

$$\mathcal{P}(\text{I}) = \mathcal{P}(t > t_2 | \mu = 0) = \alpha.$$

It will be recalled that the $t$ distribution was obtained from that of $\bar{X}$ and $s^2$ in Chap. 7. Since $\mathcal{P}(t > t_2) = \mathcal{P}(\bar{X} > st_2/\sqrt{n})$, we may find the power of the test from

$$\beta_a = \int_0^\infty f_2(s^2)\, d(s^2) \int_{t_2/\sqrt{n}}^\infty \sqrt{\frac{n}{2\pi}} \cdot \frac{1}{\sigma} e^{-n(\bar{X}-\mu_a)^2/2\sigma^2}\, d\bar{X},$$

where it is understood that we first determine $t_2$ so that $\mathcal{P}(\text{I}) = \alpha$ and then $\beta_a$.

Let $\mu_a\sqrt{n}/\sigma = t_a$ ( known value) and $\bar{X}\sqrt{n}/\sigma = t_a + y$; then

$$\beta_a = \int_0^\infty f_2(s^2)\, d(s^2) \int_{y_2=(st_2/\sigma)-t_a}^\infty N(0,1)\, dy.$$

But, $s^2/\sigma^2 = \chi^2/(n-1)$, and hence

$$\beta_a = \int_0^\infty f(\chi^2)\, d(\chi^2) \int_{y_2=(\chi t_2/\sqrt{n-1})-t_a}^\infty N(0,1)\, dy.$$

The evaluation of $\beta_a$ must be accomplished by some form of numerical integration over the region $y > (\chi t_2/\sqrt{n-1}) - t_a$ and $\chi^2 > 0$. If we let

$$p = \int_0^{\chi^2} f(u)\, du,$$

then

$$\frac{dp}{d\chi^2} = f(\chi^2).$$

Since $p = 0$ when $\chi^2 = 0$ and $p = 1$ when $\chi^2 = \infty$, we may change to a $(p,y)$ system where $0 < p < 1$. We may now compute the power of the test to detect a given value of $t_a \neq 0$ for a fixed $t_2$ and $n$. In order to compute the power for $t = t_a$, we proceed as follows:

(i) Set down successive values of $p$.

(ii) Ascertain the values of $\chi$ corresponding to each $p$.

(iii) Compute the value of $y_2$ for each $\chi$.

(iv) Determine the area, $P$, under the normal curve between $y_2$ and $\infty$.

If we plot the values of $P$ as ordinates with the corresponding $p$ values as the abscissas, then $\beta_a$ is given by the area under this curve as illustrated in Fig. 11.3. This area may be computed by some method of numerical integration, such as the trapezoidal rule or Simpson's rule.

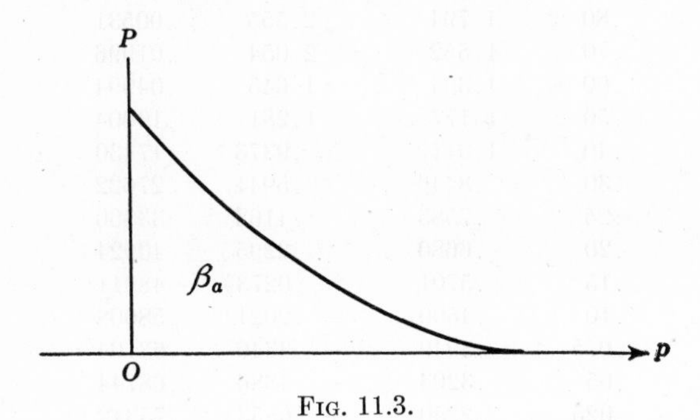


FIG. 11.3.

Neyman and Tokarska[5] have published values of $t_a$ for $\beta_a$† = .99, .95, .90(.10).10. Using the procedure outlined above, let us calculate $\beta_a$ for $t_a = 1.15$, which is the value of $t$ given in the Neyman and Tokarska tables, corresponding to $\alpha = .05$, $\beta_a = .20$, and $n$† = 3. If $\alpha = .05$, then $t_2 = 2.920$ and $y_2 = 2.065\chi - 1.15$. We now obtain the entries in Table 11.2.

Using the trapezoidal rule, we obtain $\beta_a = .2017$ as compared with the actual value of .20 mentioned earlier.

**11.6. Use of Power-function Tables in Planning Experiments.** In case the experimenter has in advance some knowledge of the size of the *coefficient of variation*, that is, the standard deviation of any observation expressed as a per cent of the general mean, it will then be possible to make use of the tables of Neyman and Tokarska in the planning of experiments.

**Example 11.1.** (Due to Neyman and Tokarska.) A plant breeder wishes to compare a new variety, $V_1$, with an established standard $V_0$.

† $\beta_a$ may be found from the tables of Neyman and Tokarska by the relationship, $\beta_a = 1 - P_{\text{II}}$. The $n$ of the tables is the degrees of freedom.

Let $\mu_1$ and $\mu_0$ denote the true mean yields of $V_1$ and $V_0$ per some unit of area, respectively. The hypothesis to be tested is $H_0: \mu_1 \leq \mu_0$, and the alternative hypothesis is $H_a: \mu_1 > \mu_0$. In other words, the plant breeder will consider his problem of producing a better variety as successfully accomplished whenever he obtains evidence that $H_0$ is not true and therefore that $\mu_1 > \mu_0$. It is desired to reduce the probability of an unjust rejection of $H_0$ to $\alpha = .01$. In a completely randomized experiment each variety is repeated $n' = 8$ times, and hence the pooled experimental-error

TABLE 11.2

| $p$ | $\chi$ | $y_2$ | $P$ |
|---|---|---|---|
| .90 | 2.146 | 3.282 | .00052 |
| .80 | 1.794 | 2.555 | .00531 |
| .70 | 1.552 | 2.054 | .01996 |
| .60 | 1.354 | 1.645 | .04994 |
| .50 | 1.177 | 1.281 | .10004 |
| .40 | 1.011 | .9373 | .17430 |
| .30 | .8446 | .5941 | .27622 |
| .25 | .7585 | .4163 | .33860 |
| .20 | .6680 | .2295 | .40924 |
| .15 | .5701 | .0273 | .48911 |
| .10 | .4590 | − .2021 | .58008 |
| .075 | .3949 | − .3346 | .63104 |
| .05 | .3203 | − .4886 | .68744 |
| .025 | .2250 | − .6853 | .75342 |
| .020 | .2010 | − .7349 | .76880 |
| .015 | .1739 | − .7910 | .78553 |
| .010 | .1418 | − .8572 | .80433 |
| .005 | .1001 | − .9433 | .82724 |
| .0025 | .07075 | −1.0039 | .84229 |
| .00 | .00 | −1.1500 | .87493 |

degrees of freedom is 14. According to previous experience the standard deviation of any single yield is expected to be $\sigma_0 = 6$ per cent of the general mean yield. The experimenter now wishes to know the size of differences between the mean yields of varieties $V_0$ and $V_1$ (in favor of the new variety $V_1$) which he is likely to detect in his experiment in case they in fact exist.

Now, in order to use Table II from Neyman and Tokarska, we find the standard deviation of the difference of the two means as

$$\sigma = \sigma_0 \sqrt{2/n'} = 6 \sqrt{\tfrac{2}{8}} = 3 \text{ per cent of the general mean.}$$

But $\Delta = \rho\sigma = 3\rho$ per cent of the general mean, where $\Delta = \mu_1 - \mu_0$ and $\rho = (\mu_1 - \mu_0)/\sigma$ by definition. Then, entering Table II opposite $n = 14$ degrees of freedom, we multiply the tabled values of $\rho$ by 3 to obtain the entries in Table 11.3. The first pair of entries means that if the true difference in mean yield of $V_1$ over $V_0$ is as large as 15.54 per cent of the general mean yield, then the experiment described will detect this difference in 99 per cent of the cases. From the table it may be seen that a reasonable probability of detection such as .90 or .80 corresponds to true differences in yields exceeding 10 per cent of the general mean and that differences under 5 per cent have a probability of only .20 of being detected. The experimenter now possesses information enabling him to judge the adequacy of the proposed experiment. The experiment would be judged satisfactory if it is desired to discover differences over 10 per cent. On the other hand, if the process of improving the particular varieties is well advanced, a difference as large as 5 per cent may be as large as could be expected. In the latter case the proposed experiment is not satisfactory, and some modification is in order. Increased precision may be obtained by (i) increasing the number of repetitions and thereby increasing the degrees of freedom, (ii) improving the experimental techniques and thereby decreasing the standard deviation of any single plot yield, or (iii) increasing the size of $\alpha$.

TABLE 11.3

Level of Significance $\alpha = 0.01$

| Size of real differences in average yields in percentages of the acreage yield | 15.54 | 13.26 | 12.03 | 10.53 | 9.48 | 6.87 | 5.97 | 4.92 | 3.45 |
|---|---|---|---|---|---|---|---|---|---|
| Probability of detection | .99 | .95 | .90 | .80 | .70 | .40 | .30 | .20 | .10 |

**Example 11.2.** Tang[6] has obtained the functional form of the power function of the analysis-of-variance tests, and tables with illustrations of their uses. While the derivations are beyond the scope of this text, it is instructive to consider one of Tang's examples illustrating the use of his tables in planning experiments. A randomized-blocks experiment is planned to compare four treatments ($k = 4$), replicated five ($n = 5$) times. Let $\delta_i$ be the difference between the true $i$th-treatment effect and the true general mean, so that $\sum_{i=1}^{k} \delta_i = 0$. Suppose that for the experiment the $\delta_i$ have values $-5$, $-4$, 3, 6, expressed as percentages of the mean yield per plot. Further, suppose from past experience that the true standard deviation per plot, $\sigma$, is 10 per cent of the general mean. In order to enter Tang's tables we calculate

$$\phi = \sqrt{\frac{1}{k}\sum_i \delta_i^2} \Big/ \frac{\sigma}{\sqrt{n}} = \sqrt{\frac{25 + 16 + 9 + 36}{4}} \Big/ \frac{10}{\sqrt{5}} = 1.04.$$

Entering Table II from Tang, with degrees of freedom $f_1 = 3$, $f_2 = 12$, and $\phi = 1.04$, we find $P_{11} = .7$ roughly. This means that true treatment differences, such as those given above, would be significant at the 5 per cent level in about 3 experiments out of 10 only.

In practice the true treatment differences are not known, but use may be made of the fact that if $\phi$ were as large as some specified value $\phi_0$, say, the probability $P_{11}$ of failing to detect the existence of treatment differences may be obtained from Tang's tables.

In a second example Tang considers a randomized-blocks experiment with $k = 6$ treatments and $n = 7$ blocks. Then $f_1 = 5$, $f_2 = 30$, and Table II, appropriate when using the 5 per cent significance level, shows $P_{11} = .262$ for $\phi = 1.5$. In this case we would fail to detect the presence of treatment differences in about one in four times when $\phi$ is as large as 1.5 or when

$$\sqrt{\frac{1}{6}\sum_i \delta_i^2} = \frac{\sigma}{\sqrt{7}} \times 1.5 = 0.567\sigma.$$

Assuming the standard deviation of a plot to be about 10 per cent of the mean yield, then $\sqrt{\frac{1}{6}\sum_i \delta_i^2} = 5.67$ per cent of the mean yield per plot. Now, there will be an unlimited number of sets of six values of $\delta_i$ whose sum will be zero and having 5.67 as standard deviation. In order to obtain upper and lower bounds for at least one value of the $\delta_i$, we consider the two extreme sets

(a) $\delta_1 = \delta_2 = \delta_3 = \delta_4 = \delta_5 = -\delta_6/5$,
(b) $\delta_1 = \delta_2 = \delta_3 = -\delta_4 = -\delta_5 = -\delta_6$.

For (a) we find

$$\delta_6 = \sqrt{k-1}\sqrt{\frac{1}{k}\sum_i \delta_i^2} = 12.68$$

and for (b)

$$\delta_6 = \sqrt{\frac{1}{k}\sum_i \delta_i^2} = 5.67.$$

It may be proved, for this example, that there must be at least one $\delta$, say $\delta_6$, whose value lies between 12.68 and 5.67.

**11.7. The Likelihood-ratio Criterion.** In Sec. 9.2 the method of maximum likelihood was presented as a general method, involving routine mathematical procedures, for obtaining an estimator of a population parameter possessing many desirable properties. In an analogous manner the *likelihood-ratio criterion* will now be presented as a general method, involving routine mathematical procedures, for obtaining a "good" test criterion.

The procedure for obtaining a likelihood-ratio criterion to be used in testing the hypothesis that $f(X;\theta_1,\theta_2, \ldots ,\theta_k)$ belongs to the subspace $\omega$ of the entire parameter space $\Omega$ on the basis of the random sample $\{X_i\}$ drawn from the population of $(X;\theta_1,\theta_2, \ldots ,\theta_k)$ is set out below.

Let the likelihood of the sample be

$$P_s = \prod_{i=1}^{n} f(X_i;\theta_1,\theta_2, \ldots ,\theta_k).$$

This likelihood will usually have a maximum as the parameters vary over the entire parameter space $\Omega$. Denote this maximum value by

$$P_s(\hat{\theta}_1,\hat{\theta}_2, \ldots ,\hat{\theta}_k)$$

or briefly as $P_s(\hat{\Omega})$. Similarly, $P_s$ will usually have a maximum value in $\omega$ which shall be denoted as $P_s(\hat{\omega})$. Then the likelihood-ratio criterion for the hypothesis to be tested is

$$\lambda = \frac{P_s(\hat{\omega})}{P_s(\hat{\Omega})}.$$

The estimators $\hat{\theta}_i$ of the population parameters $\theta_i$, which are obtained as quantities to be substituted in $P_s$ determining $P_s(\hat{\omega})$ and $P_s(\hat{\Omega})$, are derived by the method of maximum likelihood. It follows that $\lambda$ is a function of the sample observations only, that is, it does not involve any population parameters.

Since $P_s$ is positive as a result of being the product of density functions and $P_s(\hat{\omega})$ is less than or at most equal to $P_s(\hat{\Omega})$ because we are more restricted in maximizing $P_s$ in $\omega$ than in $\Omega$, $\lambda$ will be a positive fraction. Its range will be from 0 to 1.

In order to use $\lambda$ as a test criterion in applied statistics, it is necessary that we obtain the sampling distribution of $\lambda$ on the assumption that the hypothesis being tested is true. We note that $\lambda$ will be small, if $P_s(\hat{\omega})$ is smaller than $P_s(\hat{\Omega})$. We shall wish to reject the hypothesis to be tested in case $\lambda$ is small.

We now find a $\lambda_\alpha$ such that $\mathcal{P}(\lambda \leq \lambda_\alpha) = \alpha$ on the assumption that the hypothesis to be tested is true. If the calculated value $\lambda_0$ is less than or equal to $\lambda_\alpha$, that is, if $\lambda_0 \leq \lambda_\alpha$, we reject the hypothesis; otherwise we accept it. It should be noted that any monotonic function of $\lambda$ may be used in place of $\lambda$ as the test criterion.

As indicated earlier, a "good" test criterion is one which determines a region which maximizes the power of detecting true deviations from the null hypothesis for a given probability of committing a Type I error. In general it will not be possible to find a region of rejection which will maximize the power for all alternatives to the null hypothesis. However for the simple case of only one alternative, $H_1$, and when both $H_0$ and $H_1$ are simple hypotheses, it can be shown that the likelihood-ratio test defines a *best critical region*. In this case the whole parameter space $\Omega$ contains only two points. If the alternative hypotheses $H_a$ specify the entire parameter space $\Omega$ other than $\omega$ to be a range of values on a line, then it is possible to choose a best critical region for each $H_a$. If this region is the same for each $H_a$, then the test is said to be uniformly most powerful.

**Example 11.3.** Given a random sample of $n$ from $N(\mu,1)$. The null hypothesis to be tested is $H_0: \mu = \mu_0$, which states that $\omega$ is a point while $\Omega$ is the whole $\mu$ axis. The likelihood of the sample is

$$P_s = \left(\frac{1}{\sqrt{2\pi}}\right)^n e^{-\frac{1}{2}\Sigma(X-\mu)^2}$$

or

$$P_s = \left(\frac{1}{2\pi}\right)^n e^{-\frac{1}{2}\Sigma(X-\bar{X})^2-(n/2)(\bar{X}-\mu)^2}.$$

Since the ML estimator for $\mu$ is $\bar{X}$, we find the maximum value of $P_s$ in $\Omega$ to be

$$P_s(\hat{\Omega}) = \left(\frac{1}{2\pi}\right)^n e^{-\frac{1}{2}\Sigma(X-\bar{X})^2}.$$

Also,

$$P_s(\hat{\omega}) = \left(\frac{1}{2\pi}\right)^n e^{-\frac{1}{2}\Sigma(X-\bar{X})^2-(n/2)(\bar{X}-\mu_0)^2}.$$

The likelihood ratio becomes

$$\lambda = e^{-(n/2)(\bar{X}-\mu_0)^2}.$$

If $\bar{X}$ is close to $\mu_0$ in value, then the sample is reasonably consistent with the null hypothesis $H_0$ and $\lambda$ will be close to 1 in value. Conversely, the sample will not be reasonably consistent with $H_0$, and $\lambda$ will ordinarily be close to zero.

Now, suppose for the above example, or in general, the distribution of $\lambda$ when $H_0$ is true is $g(\lambda)$ and $\mathcal{P}(\mathrm{I}) = \alpha$; then $\lambda_\alpha$ is determined so that

$$\int_0^{\lambda_\alpha} g(\lambda)\, d\lambda = \alpha.$$

If the calculated $\lambda$, say $\lambda_0$, be less than $\lambda_\alpha$, we would reject $H_0$, and vice versa.

From the discussion in the above paragraph it follows that the likelihood-ratio method as described may not always lead to a unique test. If $H_0$ is a simple hypothesis, a unique distribution of $\lambda$ may be obtained. On the other hand, if $H_0$ is a composite hypothesis, it will not in general be possible to obtain a unique distribution for $\lambda$ and hence no unique test.

**Example 11.4.** Given a sample of $n$ from $N(\mu,\sigma^2)$. The null hypothesis to be tested is $H_0: \mu = 0$, $\sigma^2$ is unspecified. The entire parameter

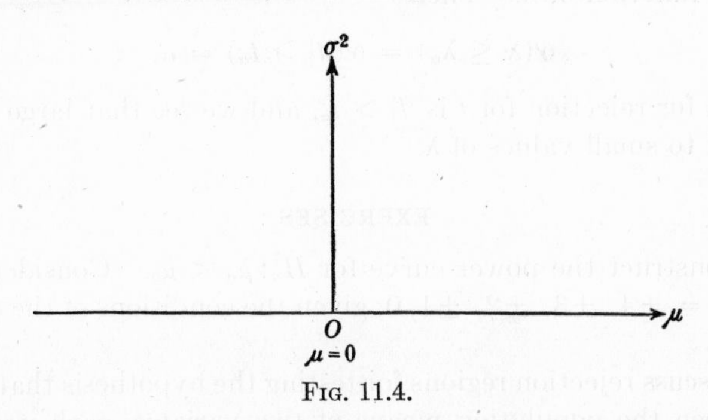


FIG. 11.4.

space is the half plane of Fig. 11.4. The subspace specified by $H_0$ is the vertical line $\mu = 0$. The likelihood of the sample is

$$P_s = \left(\frac{1}{\sigma\sqrt{2\pi}}\right)^n e^{-\frac{1}{2}\Sigma(X-\mu)^2/\sigma^2}.$$

The values of $\mu$ and $\sigma^2$ which maximize $P_s$ in $\Omega$ have already been found to be

$$\hat{\mu} = (1/n)\Sigma X = \bar{X},$$
$$\widehat{\sigma^2} = (1/n)\Sigma(X - \bar{X})^2.$$

Hence,

$$P_s(\hat{\Omega}) = \left[\frac{2\pi}{n}\Sigma(X - \bar{X})^2\right]^{-n/2} e^{-n/2}.$$

Also,

$$P_s(\hat{\omega}) = \left[\frac{2\pi}{n}\Sigma X^2\right]^{-n/2} e^{-n/2}.$$

Hence

$$\lambda = \left[\frac{\Sigma(X - \bar{X})^2}{\Sigma X^2}\right]^{n/2}$$

Now, we know that if $H_0$ is true

$$t^2 = \frac{n\bar{X}^2}{s^2} = \frac{n(n-1)\bar{X}^2}{\Sigma(X - \bar{X})^2}.$$

Then, since $\Sigma X^2 = \Sigma(X - \bar{X})^2 + n\bar{X}^2$,

$$\lambda^{2/n} = \frac{\Sigma(X - \bar{X})^2}{\Sigma(X - \bar{X})^2 + n\bar{X}^2} = \frac{1}{1 + \dfrac{n\bar{X}^2}{\Sigma(X - \bar{X})^2}} = \frac{1}{1 + t^2/(n-1)}.$$

In this case, then, the likelihood-ratio test becomes the $t$ test since $t$ is a monotonic function of $\lambda$. Then

$$\mathcal{P}(\lambda \leq \lambda_\alpha) = \mathcal{P}(|t| \geq t_\alpha) = \alpha.$$

The region for rejection for $t$ is $|t| > t_\alpha$, and we see that large values of $t$ correspond to small values of $\lambda$.

## EXERCISES

**11.1.** Construct the power curve for $H_a\colon \mu_a < \mu_0$. Consider values of $5(\mu_a - \mu_0) = \pm 4, \pm 3, \pm 2, \pm 1, 0$, given the conditions of the example of Sec. 11.4.

**11.2.** Discuss rejection regions for testing the hypothesis that the difference between the population means of two variates, each, respectively, from $N(\mu_i,\sigma^2)$, $i = 1, 2$, is zero. Take $\Omega\colon -\infty < \mu_1, \mu_2 < \infty, 0 < \sigma^2 < \infty$, and $H_0\colon \mu_1 = \mu_2$. HINT: Consider the example of Sec. 11.5.

**11.3.** Set up the admissible hypotheses $\Omega$ and the region of rejection, $R$, for testing the hypothesis that the population variance of $N(\mu,\sigma^2)$ is $\sigma_0^2$, based on a random sample of size $n$. What can be said regarding the power of the test for various alternatives?

**11.4.** Determine $\Omega$ and the region of rejection, $R$, for testing the hypothesis that the variances of two normal populations are equal ($\sigma_1^2 = \sigma_2^2$) against the alternative hypothesis that $\sigma_1^2 = a\sigma_2^2$ ($a > 1$). Since the test criterion is $F$, show that $F_a = F_0/a$ and that $\beta_a = \beta_X\left(\frac{n_2}{2}, \frac{n_1}{2}\right)$, where $X = \left(1 + \frac{n_1}{n_2}\right)F^{-1}$, $n_1 = (df)_1$, $n_2 = (df)_2$. Complete the following power table for $n_1 = 2$, $n_2 = 10$:

| $a$ | $F_a$ | $X$ | $\beta_a$ |
|---|---|---|---|
| | | .3466 | .005 |
| | | .3981 | .010 |
| | | .4782 | .025 |
| | | .5493 | .050 |
| | | .6310 | .100 |
| | | .7579 | .250 |
| | | .8706 | .500 |

**11.5.** Derive the $\lambda$ criterion for testing the null hypothesis $H_0: m = m_0$, given a random sample of size $n$ from the Poisson distribution

$$f(X) = e^{-m}(m^X/X!),$$

$0 \leq X < \infty$, $m \geq 0$. The parameter space $\Omega$ is the half line $m \geq 0$.

**11.6.** Given two random samples of sizes $n_1$ and $n_2$ from each of two populations $N(0,\sigma_1^2)$ and $N(0,\sigma_2^2)$. Derive the $\lambda$ criterion for testing the null hypothesis $H_0: \sigma_1^2 = \sigma_2^2 = \sigma^2$ (unspecified). The entire parameter space $\Omega$ is the quarter plane determined by $\sigma_1^2 > 0$, $\sigma_2^2 > 0$. The subspace $\omega$ is the line $\sigma_1^2 = \sigma_2^2 = \sigma^2$ (unspecified). HINT: First determine the joint distribution of $s_1^2$ and $s_2^2$, the sample estimates of $\sigma_1^2$ and $\sigma_2^2$, respectively. Show that the criterion reduces to Snedecor's $F$.

**11.7.** Repeat Exercise 11.6 when the samples are from the populations $N(\mu_1,\sigma_1^2)$ and $N(\mu_2,\sigma_2^2)$.

**11.8.** Given a random sample of size $n$ from $N(\mu,\sigma^2)$. Show that the $\lambda$ criterion for testing the null hypothesis $H_0: \sigma^2 = \sigma_0^2$, $\mu$ unspecified, reduces to $\chi^2$. The entire parameter space is determined so that both $\mu$ and $\sigma^2$ are unspecified.

**11.9.** Repeat Example 11.4 when the null hypothesis to be tested is $H_0: \mu = \mu_0$.

**11.10.** Repeat Example 11.3 when the random sample $n$ is from $N(\mu,\sigma^2)$ and $\sigma^2$ is unspecified by $H_0$.

**11.11.** Given two random samples of sizes $n_1$ and $n_2$ from the normal populations $N(\mu_1,\sigma^2)$ and $N(\mu_2,\sigma^2)$. Find the $\lambda$ criterion for testing the null hypothesis $H_0: \mu_1 = \mu_2 = \mu$, $\sigma^2$ unspecified. The entire parameter space is three-dimensional, with coordinates $(\mu_1,\mu_2,\sigma^2)$. The subspace $\omega$ is two-dimensional, with coordinates $(\mu,\sigma^2)$.

### References Cited

1. NEYMAN, J., and E. S. PEARSON, "On the Use and Interpretation of Certain Test Criteria for Purposes of Statistical Inference," *Biometrika*, **20A**:175–263 (1928).
2. NEYMAN, J., and E. S. PEARSON, "The Problem of the Most Efficient Tests of Statistical Hypotheses," *Phil. Trans. Roy. Soc.*, **A231**:289–337 (1938).
3. NEYMAN, J., "Statistical Estimation," *Phil. Trans. Roy. Soc.*, **A236**:333–380 (1937).
4. CRAMER, H., *Mathematical Methods of Statistics*, Princeton University Press, Princeton, N.J., 1946.
5. NEYMAN, J., and B. TOKARSKA, "Errors of the Second Kind in Testing Student's Hypothesis," *J. Am. Stat. Assoc.*, **31**:318–326 (1936).
6. TANG, P. C., "The Power Function of the Analysis of Variance Tests with Tables and Illustrations of Their Use," *Stat. Research Mem.*, **2**:126–157.

### Other Reading

DANTZIG, G. B., "On the Non-existence of Tests of Student's Hypothesis Having Power Functions Independent of $\sigma$," *Ann. Math. Stat.*, **11**:186–192 (1940).

FISHER, R. A., "Inverse Probability," *Proc. Cambridge Phil. Soc.*, **26**:528 (1930).

FISHER, R. A., "The Concepts of Inverse Probability and of Fiducial Probability Referring to Unknown Parameters," *Proc. Roy. Soc. (London)*, **A139**:343 (1933).

FISHER, R. A., "The Fiducial Argument in Statistical Inference," *Ann. Eugenics London*, **6**:391 (1935).

FISHER, R. A., "Logic of Inductive Inference," *J. Roy. Stat. Soc.*, **98**:39–54 (1935).

FISHER, R. A., "Uncertain Inference," *Proc. Roy. Soc. (London)*, **B122**:1 (1936).

LEHMER, E., "Inverse Tables of Probabilities of Errors of the Second Kind," *Ann. Math. Stat.*, **15**:388–398 (1944).

NEYMAN, J., "Basic Ideas and Some Recent Results of the Theory of Testing Statistical Hypotheses," *J. Roy. Stat. Soc.*, **105**:292–327 (1942).

WALD, A., *The Principles of Statistical Inference*, Notre Dame Mathematical Lectures, No. 1 (1942).

WALD, A., "Asymptotically Most Powerful Tests of Statistical Hypotheses," *Ann. Math. Stat.*, **12**:1–19 (1941).

WALD, A., "Some Examples of Asymptotically Most Powerful Tests," *Ann. Math. Stat.*, **12**:396–408 (1941).

# CHAPTER 12

## SPECIAL USES OF CHI-SQUARE

**12.1. Introduction.** Chi-square has found many uses in applied statistics in the testing of hypotheses. Some of these uses are exact, that is, the proposed test criterion follows the chi-square distribution exactly.

In Chap. 7 it was shown that $(n-1)s^2/\sigma^2$, where

$$s^2 = \Sigma(X - \bar{X})^2/(n-1)$$

is evaluated for a random sample $\{X_i\}$ of $n$ from $N(\mu,\sigma^2)$, is distributed as $\chi^2$ with $(n-1)$ degrees of freedom. Methods were described and examples given in Chaps. 10 and 11 for using the chi-square distribution to set confidence limits for $\sigma^2$ and to test a hypothesis concerning specified values of $\sigma^2$.

It is proposed to discuss in this chapter the theory behind other of the important exact and approximate uses of chi-square in making tests of hypotheses in applied statistics.

**12.2. Goodness of Fit.** Suppose that we have $k$ classes with $X_1$, $X_2, \ldots, X_k$ observations in the respective classes. The expected values in the corresponding classes are specified a priori to be $m_1$, $m_2$, $\ldots, m_k$ and $\sum_{i=1}^{k} X_i = \sum_{i=1}^{k} m_i = n$. Then $p_i = m_i/n$ is the probability of an observation falling in the $i$th class. We wish to test the hypothesis that the sample distribution in the classes might have come from a population with the particular set of $m$'s.

In Example 5.14 it was shown that if an event could take any one of $k$ values $y_1, y_2, \ldots, y_k$ with respective probabilities

$$p_1, p_2, \ldots, p_k, \left(\sum_{i=1}^{k} p_i = 1\right),$$

the probability that out of $n$ independent trials $y_1$ would appear $X_1$ times, $y_2$ would appear $X_2$ times, $\ldots$, $y_k$ would appear $X_k$ times $\left(\sum_{i=1}^{k} X_i = n\right)$

is

$$f\{X_i\} = \frac{n!}{\prod_{i=1}^{k} X_i\,!} \prod_{i=1}^{k} p_i^{X_i}.$$

Now, this may be written as

$$f\{X_i\} = \prod_{i=1}^{k} \left\{ \frac{(np_i)^{X_i} e^{-np_i}}{X_i!} \right\} \frac{n!}{n^{\sum_{i=1}^{k} X_i} e^{-\sum_{i=1}^{k} np_i}} = \frac{\prod_{i=1}^{k} \left\{ \frac{m_i^{X_i} e^{-m_i}}{X_i!} \right\}}{\frac{e^{-\sum_{i=1}^{k} m_i} n^{\sum_{i=1}^{k} X_i}}{n!}}.$$

If we identify this last expression with

$$\mathcal{P}(A|B) = \frac{\mathcal{P}(AB)}{\mathcal{P}(B)},$$

we see that $f\{X_i\}$ is the probability of obtaining a set of $k$ independent Poisson variates, subject to the condition or restriction that the sum of the $k$ Poisson variates is equal to $n$. Hence, our problem is to find such a distribution.

First, we shall show that the Poisson distribution with large $m$ approaches a normal distribution. Let

$$f(X;m) = \frac{e^{-m} m^X}{X!}.$$

Then

$$\log f(X;m) = -m + X \log m - \log X!.$$

But

$$\log X! = \log \sqrt{2\pi} + (X + \tfrac{1}{2}) \log X - X + \tfrac{1}{12}X + \ldots,$$

by Stirling's approximation. Let $X = m + \xi$; then

$$\log f(X;m) = -m + m \log m + \xi \log m - \log \sqrt{2\pi}$$
$$-\left(m + \xi + \frac{1}{2}\right) \log m - \left(m + \xi + \frac{1}{2}\right)\left[\frac{\xi}{m} - \frac{\xi^2}{2m^2} + \frac{\xi^3}{3m^3}\right]$$
$$+ (m + \xi) - \frac{1}{12m} = -\log \sqrt{2\pi m} - \frac{\xi^2}{2m} + O(m^{-\frac{1}{2}}),$$

where $O(m^{-\frac{1}{2}})$ means that the remaining terms are of order $m^{-\frac{1}{2}}$ or smaller. Hence,

$$f(X;m) = \frac{1}{\sqrt{2\pi m}} e^{-\frac{(X-m)^2}{2m}[1+O(m^{-1/2})]}$$

or, for large $m$, $f(X;m)$ is distributed approximately as $N(m,m)$.

We may now write the joint distribution of the $X$'s for large $m_i$ as

$$\prod_{i=1}^{k} \frac{1}{\sqrt{2\pi m_i}} e^{-(X_i - m_i)^2/2m_i}$$

subject to the linear restriction

$$\sum_{i=1}^{k} (X_i - m_i) = 0,$$

where $\sum_{i=1}^{k} X_i = n$. Consider the transformation

$$d_i = \frac{X_i - m_i}{\sqrt{m_i}}$$

where $m_i = np_i$. Using results of Example 5.14, it may be shown that

$$\sigma_{ij} = E(d_i d_j) = -\frac{\sqrt{m_i m_j}}{n},$$

$$\sigma_i^2 = \frac{n - m_i}{n}.$$

It has been shown that the $d_i$ approach normal variates as $n$ is increased. Hence, in the limit

$$\sum_{i=1}^{k} d_i^2 = \sum_{i=1}^{k} \frac{(X_i - m_i)^2}{m_i}$$

would be distributed as $\chi^2$ with $k$ degrees of freedom, except for the one linear restriction $\Sigma(X_i - m_i) \equiv 0$. This is equivalent to $\Sigma d_i \sqrt{m_i} \equiv 0$, which indicates explicitly that the $d_i$ are not independent.

By the use of completely orthogonal linear forms, it may be shown that in the limit, $\Sigma d_i^2$ is actually distributed as $\chi^2$ with $(k - 1)$ degrees of freedom. To this end consider the case $k = 2(n = m_1 + m_2)$. Let

$$z_1 = (d_1 \sqrt{m_1} + d_2 \sqrt{m_2})/\sqrt{n} \equiv 0,$$
$$z_2 = (b_1 d_1 + b_2 d_2),$$

where $b_1$ and $b_2$ are to be chosen so that $\sigma_{z_2}^2 = 1$ and $\sigma_{z_1 z_2} = 0$. It follows that

$$\sigma_{z_1 z_2} = \frac{b_1 m_2 \sqrt{m_1} + b_2 m_1 \sqrt{m_2} - (b_2 \sqrt{m_1} + b_1 \sqrt{m_2}) \sqrt{m_1 m_2}}{n \sqrt{n}} \equiv 0,$$

$$\sigma_{z_2}^2 = \frac{b_1^2 m_2 + b_2^2 m_1 - 2 b_1 b_2 \sqrt{m_1 m_2}}{n} = 1.$$

From the first equation, we see that the value of one of the $b_i$ can be chosen at random; then this value is inserted in the second equation to solve for the other $b_i$. Suppose we let $b_1 = \sqrt{m_2/n}$; then $b_2 = -\sqrt{m_1/n}$. Also, $d_1^2 + d_2^2 = z_1^2 + z_2^2 = z_2^2$. Since $z_2$ approaches a variate which is $N(0,1)$, $d_1^2 + d_2^2 = z_2^2$ approaches a $\chi^2$ variate with 1 degree of freedom.

For $k$ classes, we set up the following completely orthogonal linear forms

$$z_1 = \frac{d_1\sqrt{m_1} + d_2\sqrt{m_2} + \cdots + d_k\sqrt{m_k}}{\sqrt{\sum_{i=1}^{k} m_i}} \equiv 0,$$

$$z_2 = \frac{d_1\sqrt{m_1 m_2} - m_1 d_2}{\sqrt{m_1(m_1 + m_2)}},$$

$$z_3 = \frac{d_1\sqrt{m_1 m_3} + d_2\sqrt{m_2 m_3} - (m_1 + m_2)d_3}{\sqrt{(m_1 + m_2)(m_1 + m_2 + m_3)}},$$

$$\cdots\cdots\cdots\cdots\cdots\cdots\cdots\cdots\cdots$$

$$z_k = \frac{d_1\sqrt{m_1 m_k} + d_2\sqrt{m_2 m_k} + \cdots - \left(\sum_{i=1}^{k-1} m_i\right) d_k}{\sqrt{\sum_{i=1}^{k-1} m_i \cdot \sum_{i=1}^{k} m_i}}.$$

Since $\sigma_{ij} = -\sqrt{m_i m_j}/n$, $i \neq j$, and $\sigma_i^2 = (n - m_i)/n$ for the $d$'s, it follows that the $\{z_i\}$ are NID(0,1), and since $z_1 \equiv 0$,

$$\sum_{i=1}^{k} d_i^2 = \sum_{i=1}^{k} z_i^2 = \sum_{i=2}^{k} z_i^2.$$

But the last expression on the right is distributed as $\chi^2$ with $(k - 1)$ degrees of freedom, and hence so is $\sum_{i=1}^{k} d_i^2$.

A test of the hypothesis that the expected values in the several classes are given by the specified $m_i (i = 1,2, \ldots ,k)$ is approximated by obtaining the probability of getting a $\chi^2$ with $(k - 1)$ degrees of freedom greater than the computed

$$\chi_0^2 = \sum_{i=1}^{k} \frac{(X_i - m_i)^2}{m_i}.$$

If this probability is unusually small, say .05, we may choose to reject the hypothesis.

**Example 12.1.** Genetic data provide examples of the use of $\chi^2$ in "goodness of fit" tests. Some possible theoretical genetic ratios are 3:1, 1:1, 9:7, 15:1, and 63:1.

In a study of chlorophyll inheritance in corn, Lindstrom[1] found 98 green and 24 yellow seedlings in one progeny of 122 young corn plants. Presumably green is dominant to yellow and is segregated in a ratio 3:1, so that we should expect $m_1 = 91.5$ green seedlings and $m_2 = 30.5$ yellow seedlings if this ratio is correct. To test this hypothesis, we calculate

$$\chi_0^2 = \frac{(98 - 91.5)^2}{91.5} + \frac{(24 - 30.5)^2}{30.5} = 1.85.$$

By interpolation, the probability of obtaining a chi-square value of this size or larger on the assumption that the genetic ratio is 3:1 is .18. Hence, the 3:1 ratio is not rejected as a possible fit to the data.

**Example 12.2.** Federer[2] fitted a normal curve to the frequency distribution below of rubber content (percentage) in 378 guayule plants

| Class center | 1.5 | 2.5 | 3.5 | 4.5 | 5.5 | 6.5 | 7.5 | 8.5 |
|---|---|---|---|---|---|---|---|---|
| Frequency | 1 | 1 | 2 | 33 | 139 | 155 | 42 | 5 |

The mean and standard deviation of the 378 observations were found to be 6.07 and .892, respectively. Using the tables for the normal curve, Federer calculated the expected values for the respective classes set out below:

| Class | <4.0 | 4.0–5.0 | 5.0–6.0 | 6.0–7.0 | 7.0–8.0 | >8.0 | Total |
|---|---|---|---|---|---|---|---|
| Observed frequency | 4 | 33 | 139 | 155 | 42 | 5 | 378 |
| Expected frequency | 3.8 | 39.7 | 133.4 | 144.7 | 50.6 | 5.8 | 378.0 |

The frequencies of the first three classes in the first table have been pooled in the second table in order that the number in any class be not less than 5 approximately as suggested by Fisher.[3] Using the formula developed in this section Federer found $\chi_0^2 = 3.302$. The proof of the rule given by Fisher[3] for determining the degrees of freedom to be assigned $\chi_0^2$ for this example is beyond the scope of this text. This rule states that the correct number of degrees of freedom may be found by subtracting the total number of restrictions imposed on the data from the total number of classes. In the example this would be $6 - 3$, since the sum, mean, and standard deviation of the sample and hypothetical curve have been equated. The probability of obtaining a chi-square value as large as or larger than 3.30 with 3 degrees of freedom lies between .5 and .3. Hence, we have no evidence to reject the hypothesis that the rubber contents in the 378 guayule plants are normally distributed.

**12.3. Contingency Tables.** Consider the ordinary $2 \times 2$ contingency table used in applied statistics:

Expectations

| | $b_1$ | $b_2$ | $b$ |
|---|---|---|---|
| $a_1$ | $np_ap_b$ | $np_aq_b$ | $np_a$ |
| $a_2$ | $nq_ap_b$ | $nq_aq_b$ | $nq_a$ |
| $a$ | $np_b$ | $nq_b$ | $n$ |

Observations

| | $b_1$ | $b_2$ | $b$ |
|---|---|---|---|
| $a_1$ | $n_{11}$ | $n_{12}$ | $n_{1.}$ |
| $a_2$ | $n_{21}$ | $n_{22}$ | $n_{2.}$ |
| $a$ | $n_{.1}$ | $n_{.2}$ | $n_{..}$ |

In this case $k = 4$, but we have more than one linear restriction. If there is no a priori knowledge of the values of $p_a$ and $p_b$, we usually use their *maximum-likelihood* estimates, which are

$$np_a = n_{1.} \text{ or } nq_a = n_{2.}; \qquad np_b = n_{.1} \text{ or } nq_b = n_{.2}; \qquad n_{..} = n.$$

These relations constitute three distinct linear restrictions.

Using the methods of Sec. 12.2, it can be shown that, if the given number of restrictions $r$ can be reduced to $r$ orthogonal restrictions, then

$$\sum_{i=1}^{k} \frac{(X_i - m_i)^2}{m_i}$$

is distributed as $\chi^2$ with $(k - r)$ degrees of freedom. To this end we set up the following:

$$z_1 = d_{11}\sqrt{p_ap_b} + d_{12}\sqrt{p_aq_b} + d_{21}\sqrt{q_ap_b} + d_{22}\sqrt{q_aq_b} = 0,$$

$$z_2 = \frac{q_a\,d_{11}\sqrt{p_ap_b} + q_a\,d_{12}\sqrt{p_aq_b} - p_a\,d_{21}\sqrt{q_ap_b} - p_a\,d_{22}\sqrt{q_aq_b}}{\sqrt{p_aq_a}} = 0,$$

$$z_3 = \frac{q_b\,d_{11}\sqrt{p_ap_b} - p_b\,d_{12}\sqrt{p_aq_b} + q_b\,d_{21}\sqrt{q_ap_b} - p_b\,d_{22}\sqrt{q_aq_b}}{\sqrt{p_bq_b}} = 0,$$

where

$$d_{11} = \frac{n_{11} - np_ap_b}{\sqrt{np_ap_b}}, \text{ etc.}$$

By the methods similar to those of Sec. 12.2 it can be shown that $d_{11}$ approaches a $N(0,1)$ variate for large $m$.

Since

$$E(d_{11}z_1) = \sqrt{p_ap_b}\,(1 - p_ap_b) - \sqrt{p_aq_bp_ap_bp_aq_b} - \sqrt{q_ap_bp_ap_bq_ap_b} - \sqrt{q_aq_bp_ap_bq_aq_b}$$
$$= \sqrt{p_ap_b}\,[1 - (p_ap_b + p_aq_b + q_ap_b + q_aq_b)] = 0,$$

and similarly for the other $d$'s and $z$'s, then $E(z_iz_j) = 0$ for $i \neq j$.

A fourth orthogonal linear form is found to be

$$z_4 = d_{11}\sqrt{q_aq_b} - d_{12}\sqrt{q_ap_b} - d_{21}\sqrt{p_aq_b} + d_{22}\sqrt{p_ap_b} \neq 0.$$

It can be shown that $z_4$ is also $N(0,1)$ and is independent of the other three. It follows that $z_4^2 = \chi^2$ with 1 degree of freedom. It should be noted that the number of degrees of freedom is reduced by one for every parameter estimated from the data. If $r$ distinct parameters are estimated, the number of degrees of freedom for $\chi^2$ is $(k - r - 1)$ (1 degree of freedom was also lost in making $\sum_{i=1}^{k} n_i = \sum_{i=1}^{k} X_i = n$).

To make the test of the independence of the two classifications in the two-way table, we calculate

$$\chi_0^2 = \frac{(n_{11} - np_ap_b)^2}{np_ap_b} + \cdots + \frac{(n_{22} - nq_aq_b)^2}{nq_aq_b}$$

and compare this calculated $\chi^2$ with the tabular $\chi^2$ of 1 degree of freedom at the 5 per cent or 1 per cent points. If the calculated $\chi^2$ is greater than the tabular $\chi^2$ at either per cent point, we say that we have evidence from this sample that the two classifications are not independent. In other words, there would be evidence of an *interaction* between the two classifications.

More precisely we are evaluating the probability that an observed set of frequencies $X_1, X_2, \ldots, X_k$ could have resulted from a multinomial distribution with probabilities $p_1, p_2, \ldots, p_k$. The requirements that must be met in order that the $\chi^2$ approximation may be used to evaluate this probability are (i) the frequencies follow the multinomial distribution, (ii) the expectations are large enough so that the normal approximation is satisfactory, and (iii) any estimation of the $p$'s should be *efficient*. For discussions related to this problem consult Cochran.[4,5]

The second paper by Cochran referred to above discusses a "correction for continuity" which Yates[6] had proposed earlier and which was subsequently mentioned in texts by Fisher,[3] Snedecor,[7] and others. For the $2 \times 2$ contingency table, Yates suggested that .5 be subtracted from the absolute value of each deviation in computing $\chi^2$ in order to correct for a slight bias in determining the true probability levels. This slight bias arises from the fact that the $\chi^2$ distribution is continuous, whereas the frequencies are discrete. The correction for continuity is not very important for $\chi^2$ with more than a single degree of freedom and is never to be used when adding $\chi^2$ values.

**Example 12.3.** The $F_2$ progeny of a barley cross, Robertson[8] segregated in the following manner:

| | $F$ | $f$ | Total |
|---|---|---|---|
| $V$ | 1,178 | 273 | 1,451 |
| $v$ | 291 | 156 | 447 |
| Total | 1,469 | 429 | 1,898 |

We calculate

$$\chi^2 = \frac{(54.97)^2}{1{,}123.03} + \frac{(-54.97)^2}{327.97} + \frac{(-54.97)^2}{345.97} + \frac{(54.97)^2}{101.03} = 50.547.$$

The probability of obtaining a chi-square this large or larger on the assumption of independence of the classification is extremely small. Hence, there is considerable evidence in favor of association of these two attributes.

**12.4. Homogeneity of a Binomial Series.** Suppose that our data consist of $X_1, X_2, \ldots, X_k$ successes out of each of $n$ independent trials. In tabular form we have

| | | | | | Total |
|---|---|---|---|---|---|
| Successes | $X_1$ | $X_2$ | $\cdots$ | $X_k$ | $k\bar{X}$ |
| Failures | $n - X_1$ | $n - X_2$ | $\cdots$ | $n - X_k$ | $k(n - \bar{X})$ |
| Trials | $n$ | $n$ | $\cdots$ | $n$ | $nk$ |

We wish to test the hypothesis that the probability at every trial is $p$ (constant). The probability of obtaining the particular sample values on the assumption that the hypothesis is true is

$$P = \prod_{i=1}^{k} \frac{n!}{X_i!(n - X_i)!} p^{X_i} q^{n-X_i}.$$

The *maximum-likelihood* estimate of $p$ is $\bar{X}/n$. Then the expected values for each of the success cells is $n\hat{p} = \bar{X}$ and for each of the failure cells is $n\hat{q} = (n - \bar{X})$. Now, consider the expression

$$\sum_{i=1}^{k} \frac{(X_i - \bar{X})^2}{\bar{X}} + \sum_{i=1}^{k} \frac{(n - X_i - n + \bar{X})^2}{n - \bar{X}} = \frac{n \sum_{i=1}^{k} (X_i - \bar{X})^2}{\bar{X}(n - \bar{X})},$$

We may write this in the form

$$\left\{\sum_{i=1}^{k} \frac{(X_i - \bar{X})^2}{npq}\right\} \left\{\frac{npq}{n \cdot \frac{\bar{X}}{n}\left(1 - \frac{\bar{X}}{n}\right)}\right\}.$$

Now, as $n \to \infty$, $\sum_{i=1}^{k} (X_i - \bar{X})^2/npq$ approaches the tabular $\chi^2$ with $(k - 1)$ degrees of freedom and

$$\frac{npq}{n \cdot \frac{\bar{X}}{n}\left(1 - \frac{\bar{X}}{n}\right)}$$

approaches one with a negligible error. Hence an approximate test of homogeneity of a binomial series may be made by using

$$\chi^2 = \frac{n \sum_{i=1}^{k} (X_i - \bar{X})^2}{\bar{X}(n - \bar{X})}$$

with $(k - 1)$ degrees of freedom.

**Example 12.4.** Ten samples of 25 stalks of corn each examined for European corn-borer infestation gave the following counts: 11, 7, 3, 8, 15, 2, 10, 21, 18, 9. Is the infestation random?

We calculate

$$\chi^2 = \frac{(25)(336.4)}{(10.4)(25 - 10.4)} = 55.39,$$

with 9 degrees of freedom. Upon consulting the $\chi^2$ tables we find this $\chi^2$ value to be highly significant, and hence we have evidence that the infestation is not random.

**12.5. Homogeneity of a Poisson Series.** The data consist of $X_1$, $X_2$, . . . , $X_k$. We wish to test the hypothesis that each of the $X$'s comes from a Poisson distribution with the same $m$. The probability of obtaining the particular sample values on the assumption that the hypothesis is true is

$$\prod_{i=1}^{k} \frac{e^{-m} m^{X_i}}{X_i!}.$$

It can be shown that the maximum likelihood estimator for $m$ is $\bar{X}$. Consider the expression

$$\left\{\sum_{i=1}^{k} \frac{(X_i - \bar{X})^2}{m}\right\}\left\{\frac{m}{\bar{X}}\right\}.$$

Now, as $n \to \infty$, $\sum_{i=1}^{k} (X_i - \bar{X})^2/m$ approaches the tabular $\chi^2$ with $(k - 1)$ degrees of freedom and $\bar{X}/m$ approaches 1. Hence we may use

$$\chi^2 = \sum_{i=1}^{k} \frac{(X_i - \bar{X})^2}{\bar{X}}$$

with $(k - 1)$ degrees of freedom as an approximate test of homogeneity of a Poisson series.

**Example 12.5.** The number of wireworms in the check plots of a Latin square were 2, 6, 4, 9, 8. Is the infestation random?

Assuming that the counts are distributed in a Poisson fashion, we calculate $\chi^2 = 5.66$ with 4 degrees of freedom. Upon consulting the tables we find the probability of obtaining such a chi-square value on the assumption of homogeneity to be large; hence we have no evidence that the null hypothesis is false.

Further discussion relative to the material in Secs. 12.4 and 12.5 may be found in Fisher[9] and Cochran.[4]

**12.6. Combination of Probabilities.** Suppose that the following information has been obtained from two experiments:

*Experiment* 1. $\bar{A} - \bar{B} = 2.15$, estimated standard error is 1.28, degrees of freedom are 30, $t = 1.680$, and the single-tailed probability is $p_1 = .0544$.

*Experiment* 2. Out of 10 trials $\bar{A}$ was superior to $\bar{B}$ 8 times.

$$p_2 = (\tfrac{1}{2})^{10} + 10(\tfrac{1}{2})^9(\tfrac{1}{2}) + 45(\tfrac{1}{2})^8(\tfrac{1}{2})^2 = .0547.$$

Can we make a test of the hypothesis that $\bar{A} = \bar{B}$, with the alternate hypothesis that $\bar{A} > \bar{B}$, by combining the information from these two experiments?

Let $X$ be distributed as $f(X)\,dX$, $-\infty < X < \infty$; then it is possible to show that $-2 \log_e p_i$ follows the $\chi^2$ distribution with 2 degrees of freedom, where

$$p_i = \int_{-\infty}^{X} f(t)\,dt.$$

To this end we find the distribution of $p_i$ to be

$$f(X)\left(\frac{dX}{dp_i}\right) dp_i.$$

But

$$\frac{dp_i}{dX} = f(X);$$

hence the distribution of $p_i$ is $dp_i$. Also, when $X \to -\infty$, $p_i \to 0$, and when $X \to \infty$, $p_i \to 1$. Let

$$u = \log_e p_i;$$

then the distribution of $u$ is

$$\left(\frac{dp_i}{du}\right) du = e^u\, du, \qquad -\infty < u \leq 0.$$

Let

$$z = -2u, \qquad dz = -2\, du;$$

then the distribution of $z = -2 \log_e p_i$ is

$$(\tfrac{1}{2})e^{-z/2}\, dz, \qquad 0 \leq z < \infty.$$

But the distribution of $\chi^2$ with 2 degrees of freedom is

$$(\tfrac{1}{2})e^{-\chi^2/2}\, d(\chi^2).$$

Hence, $z = -2 \log_e p_i$ is distributed as $\chi^2$ with 2 degrees of freedom.

Since the $p_i$ are independent, the sum of $k$ such $\chi^2$ values is distributed as $\chi^2$ with $2k$ degrees of freedom.

Applying the method developed above to the two experiments, we find

$$\begin{aligned} \log_{10} p_1 &= \bar{2}.7356 \\ \log_{10} p_2 &= \bar{2}.7380 \\ &\overline{\bar{3}.4736} = -2.5264 \end{aligned}$$

and

$$\chi_0^2 = -2(-2.5264)(2.3026) = 11.634,$$

with 4 degrees of freedom. The probability of obtaining a $\chi^2$ as large as or larger than this value on the assumption that the hypothesis tested is true is .02.

**12.7. Bartlett's Test of Homogeneity of Variances.** Suppose we have $k$ independent sample variances $\{v_i\}$ with $n_i$ degrees of freedom each from populations which are $N(\mu_i,\sigma_i^2)$. It is desired to test

$$H_0: \sigma_1^2 = \sigma_2^2 = \cdots = \sigma_k^2,$$

in other words, that each $v_i$ is an estimate of the same population variance $\sigma^2$. Bartlett[10] has proposed the criterion $Q/l$, which can be shown to be approximately distributed as $\chi^2$ with $(k - 1)$ degrees of freedom, as a test of $H_0$. In this expression

$$Q = n \log \bar{v} - \sum_{i=1}^{k} n_i \log v_i,$$

and

$$l = 1 + \frac{1}{3(k-1)} \left[ \sum_{i=1}^{k} \frac{1}{n_i} - \frac{1}{n} \right],$$

where $n = \sum_{i=1}^{k} n_i$ and $\bar{v} = \sum_{i=1}^{k} n_i v_i / n$.

The proof that $Q/l$ is approximately distributed as $\chi^2$ with $(k-1)$ degrees of freedom will be outlined here. Using the distribution of $v_i$ (with $n_i$ degrees of freedom), we find that the moment generating function and cumulant generating function for $\log v_i$ are

$$m(t) = \frac{\Gamma\left(\frac{n_i}{2} + t\right)}{\Gamma\left(\frac{n_i}{2}\right)} \left(\frac{2\sigma^2}{n_i}\right)^t$$

and

$$K(t) = t \log \left(\frac{2\sigma^2}{n_i}\right) + \log \Gamma \left(\frac{n_i}{2} + t\right) - \log \Gamma \left(\frac{n_i}{2}\right).$$

From Stirling's formula for approximating factorials,

$$\Gamma(x) = e^{-(x-1)} (x-1)^{x-\frac{1}{2}} \left[1 + \frac{1}{12(x-1)}\right] \sqrt{2\pi}.$$

Hence, omitting the subscript $i$ for convenience,

$$\begin{aligned} K(t) \doteq t \left(\log \sigma^2 - \log \frac{n}{2}\right) - t + \left(t + \frac{n-1}{2}\right) \log \left(t + \frac{n-2}{2}\right) \\ - \left(\frac{n-1}{2}\right) \log \left(\frac{n-2}{2}\right) + \log \left[1 + \frac{1}{6(2t+n-2)}\right] \\ - \log \left[1 + \frac{1}{6(n-2)}\right]. \end{aligned}$$

Since

$$\log \left(t + \frac{n-2}{2}\right) = \log \left(1 + \frac{2t}{n-2}\right) + \log \left(\frac{n-2}{2}\right),$$

$$\log \left(\frac{n-2}{2}\right) - \log \frac{n}{2} = \log \left(1 - \frac{2}{n}\right),$$

and

$$\log(1+x) = x - \frac{x^2}{2} + \cdots,$$

$$K(t) \doteq t[\log \sigma^2 - 1] + \left(t + \frac{n-1}{2}\right)\left[\frac{2t}{n-2} - \frac{4t^2}{2(n-2)^2} + \frac{8t^3}{3(n-2)^3} - \cdots\right] - t\left[\frac{2}{n} + \frac{4}{2n^2} + \frac{8}{3n^3} + \cdots\right] + \left[\frac{1}{6(2t+n-2)} - \frac{1}{6(n-2)} - \cdots\right].$$

Upon simplifying the last bracket to

$$\frac{-t}{3(n-2)^2\left(1 + \frac{2t}{n-2}\right)},$$

we may write the cumulants as, upon replacing the subscript $i$,

$$\kappa_1 \doteq \log \sigma^2 - 1 + \frac{n_i - 1}{n_i - 2} - \frac{2}{n_i} - \frac{2}{n_i^2} - \frac{1}{3(n_i-2)^2}$$

$$\doteq \log \sigma^2 - \frac{1}{n_i} - \frac{1}{3n_i^2} \qquad \text{neglecting terms of order } n_i^{-3},$$

$$\kappa_2 \doteq 2\left[\frac{2}{n_i-2} - \frac{n_i-1}{(n_i-2)^2} - \frac{2}{3(n_i-2)^3}\right] \doteq \frac{2}{n_i^3}\left(n_i^2 + n_i + \frac{2}{3}\right),$$

and

$$\kappa_3 \doteq 6\left[\frac{4(n_i-1)}{3(n_i-2)^3} - \frac{2}{(n_i-2)^2} - \frac{4}{3(n_i-2)^4}\right] \doteq \frac{4}{n_i^4}(n_i^2 + 2n_i + 2).$$

The above results may be used to find the cumulants of $Q$, which can be shown to be

$$\kappa_r[Q] = -(-n)^r\kappa_r(\log \bar{v}) + \Sigma(-n_i)^r\kappa_r(\log v_i).$$

Bartlett obtains the above results by the following arguments: Now,

$$Q = \log \prod_{i=1}^{k} \left(\frac{\bar{v}}{v_i}\right)^{n_i}.$$

It can be shown that the distribution of $\bar{v}/v_i$ is independent of $\bar{v}$; hence

$$K[Q + (-n \log \bar{v})] \doteq K(Q) + K(-n \log \bar{v}),$$

or

$$K(Q) = K[Q + (-n \log \bar{v})] - K(-n \log \bar{v})$$

$$= K\left[\sum_{i=1}^{k} (-n_i) \log v_i\right] - K[-n \log \bar{v}].$$

Hence, the cumulants for $Q$ are

$$\kappa_1 = \mu = \left(n \log \sigma^2 - 1 - \frac{1}{3n}\right) - n \log \sigma^2 + k + \sum_{i=1}^{k} \frac{1}{(3n_i)}$$

$$= (k-1)\left[1 + \frac{1}{3(k-1)}\left(\sum_{i=1}^{k} \frac{1}{n_i} - \frac{1}{n}\right)\right] = (k-1)l,$$

$$\kappa_2 = \sigma^2 = -\frac{2}{n}\left(n^2 + n + \frac{2}{3}\right) + 2\sum_{i=1}^{k}\left(n_i + 1 + \frac{2}{3n_i}\right)$$

$$= 2(k-1)\left[1 + \frac{2}{3(k-1)}\left(\sum_{i=1}^{k} \frac{1}{n_i} - \frac{1}{n}\right)\right]$$

$$\doteq 2(k-1)\left[1 + \frac{1}{3(k-1)}\left(\sum_{i=1}^{k} \frac{1}{n_i} - \frac{1}{n}\right)\right]^2 = 2(k-1)l^2,$$

and

$$\kappa_3 = \mu_3 = -\frac{4}{n}(n^2 + 2n + 2) + 4\sum_{i=1}^{k}\left(n_i + 2 + \frac{2}{n_i}\right)$$

$$\doteq 8(k-1)\left[1 + \frac{1}{3(k-1)}\left(\sum_{i=1}^{k} \frac{1}{n_i} - \frac{1}{n}\right)\right]^3 = 8(k-1)l^3.$$

Since

$$\kappa_r\left(\frac{Q}{l}\right) = \frac{\kappa_r(Q)}{l^r},$$

we obtain the first three approximate cumulants of $Q/l$ as

$$\kappa_1 \doteq (k-1), \qquad \kappa_2 \doteq 2(k-1), \qquad \kappa_3 \doteq 8(k-1),$$

which are also the first three cumulants for the $\chi^2$ distribution with $(k-1)$ degrees of freedom. Hence, $Q/l$ will be approximately distributed as $\chi^2$ with $(k-1)$ degrees of freedom.

**12.8. Test of a Second-order Interaction in a 2 × 2 × 2 Contingency Table.** Suppose we extend the 2 × 2 contingency table of Sec. 12.3 to the 2 × 2 × 2 table below:

| $A_1$ | | | | $A_2$ | | | | |
|---|---|---|---|---|---|---|---|---|
| $B_1$ | | $B_2$ | | $B_1$ | | $B_2$ | | Totals |
| $C_1$ | $C_2$ | $C_1$ | $C_2$ | $C_1$ | $C_2$ | $C_1$ | $C_2$ | |
| $p_1$ | $p_2$ | $p_3$ | $p_4$ | $p_5$ | $p_6$ | $p_7$ | $p_8$ | 1 |
| $m_1$ | $m_2$ | $m_3$ | $m_4$ | $m_5$ | $m_6$ | $m_7$ | $m_8$ | $n$ |
| $x_1$ | $x_2$ | $x_3$ | $x_4$ | $x_5$ | $x_6$ | $x_7$ | $x_8$ | $n$ |

The three classifications are designated by $A$, $B$, and $C$, respectively, while $p_i$, $m_i$, and $x_i$ are the probabilities, expected values, and observed values, respectively, corresponding to the respective $C_i$ subclasses.

The first-order interactions such as $BC$ were discussed in Sec. 12.3. The $BC$ interaction for $A_1$ is defined as

$$\frac{p_1/p_2}{p_3/p_4}$$

and for $A_2$ as

$$\frac{p_5/p_6}{p_7/p_8}.$$

The null hypothesis tested for a $2 \times 2$ contingency table is

$$p_1/p_2 = p_3/p_4,$$

which is equivalent to

$$\frac{p_1/p_2}{p_3/p_4} = 1,$$

that is, the interaction is unity.

The null hypothesis for testing the existence of an $ABC$ interaction is that the $BC$ interaction is the same for both $A_1$ and $A_2$, or symbolically that

$$\frac{p_1/p_2}{p_3/p_4} = \frac{p_5/p_6}{p_7/p_8},$$

which reduces to

$$p_1p_4p_6p_7 = p_2p_3p_5p_8.$$

Estimates of the $p_i$'s or $m_i = p_in$ may be obtained by the method of maximum likelihood. The probability of obtaining a particular set of observed $x_i$'s is given by

$$P_s = \frac{n!}{x_1!x_2! \cdots x_8!} p_1^{x_1}p_2^{x_2} \cdots p_8^{x_8}.$$

It follows that

$$P_s \propto \prod_{i=1}^{8} m_i^{x_i}.$$

Hence, the logarithm of the likelihood function is

$$L = \sum_{i=1}^{8} x_i \log m_i,$$

which is subject to the restrictions

(i) $m_1m_4m_6m_7 = m_2m_3m_5m_8$,

(ii) $\sum_{i=1}^{8} m_i = n.$

In order to determine estimators of the $m_i$, we form the augmented function

$$L' = \sum_{i=1}^{8} x_i \log m_i + k(m_1m_4m_6m_7 - m_2m_3m_5m_8) - l\left(\sum_{i=1}^{8} m_i - n\right)$$

and obtain the partial derivatives

$$\frac{\partial L'}{\partial m_1} = \frac{x_1}{m_1} + \frac{k\lambda}{m_1} - l = 0,$$

$$\frac{\partial L'}{\partial m_2} = \frac{x_2}{m_2} - \frac{k\mu}{m_2} - l = 0,$$

$$\cdots\cdots\cdots\cdots\cdots$$

$$\frac{\partial L'}{\partial m_8} = \frac{x_8}{m_8} - \frac{k\mu}{m_8} - l = 0,$$

where we have set

$$\lambda = m_1m_4m_6m_7, \qquad \mu = m_2m_3m_5m_8.$$

The following equations may now be obtained:

$$\begin{aligned} x_1 &= m_1l - k\lambda, & x_2 &= m_2l + k\mu, \\ x_4 &= m_4l - k\lambda, & x_3 &= m_3l + k\mu, \\ x_6 &= m_6l - k\lambda, & x_5 &= m_5l + k\mu, \\ x_7 &= m_7l - k\lambda, & x_8 &= m_8l + k\mu. \end{aligned}$$

Upon adding the eight equations, we obtain

$$n = ln - 4k\lambda + 4k\mu,$$

or

$$n = ln,$$

since $\lambda = \mu$, and hence $l = 1$. Using this result, and setting $k\lambda = k\mu = \delta$, we obtain the estimators

$$\begin{aligned} \widehat{m_1} &= x_1 + \hat{\delta}, & \widehat{m_2} &= x_2 - \hat{\delta}, \\ \widehat{m_4} &= x_4 + \hat{\delta}, & \widehat{m} &= x_3 - \hat{\delta}, \\ \widehat{m_6} &= x_6 + \hat{\delta}, & \widehat{m_5} &= x_5 - \hat{\delta}, \\ \widehat{m_7} &= x_7 + \hat{\delta}, & \widehat{m_8} &= x_8 - \hat{\delta}. \end{aligned}$$

Multiplying both sides of the equality tested by the null hypothesis by $n$, we obtain

$$m_1 m_4 m_6 m_7 = m_2 m_3 m_5 m_8.$$

An equation for obtaining a value for $\hat{\delta}$ may be obtained by substitution, that is,

$$(x_1 + \hat{\delta})(x_4 + \hat{\delta})(x_6 + \hat{\delta})(x_7 + \hat{\delta}) = (x_2 - \hat{\delta})(x_3 - \hat{\delta})(x_5 - \hat{\delta})(x_8 - \hat{\delta}).$$

From $\hat{\delta}$ and the $x_i$'s, values for the $\widehat{m_i}$ may be obtained. A test of the null hypothesis may now be performed by using the criterion

$$\chi^2 = \sum_{i=1}^{8} \frac{(x_i - m_i)^2}{m_i},$$

where the associated degrees of freedom are determined by subtracting the number of independent parameters estimated from the total number of classes, that is, 8 − 1 − 6, or 1, in this case.

## EXERCISES

**12.1.** (Some of Beall's data given by Neyman.[11]) Fit a Poisson curve to the following distribution of European corn borers in 120 groups of 8 hills each. Use the method illustrated in Example 12.2 to calculate a "goodness of fit" chi-square.

| No. of borers | 0 | 1 | 2 | 3 | 4 | 5 | 6 | 7 | 8 | 9 | 10 | 11 | 12 |
|---|---|---|---|---|---|---|---|---|---|---|---|---|---|
| Observed frequency | 24 | 16 | 16 | 18 | 15 | 9 | 6 | 5 | 3 | 4 | 3 | 0 | 1 |

**12.2.** Use the method of Sec. 12.8 to develop a test for interaction in a $2 \times 2$ contingency table. Show that this is the same test as the test of independence of the two classifications developed in Sec. 12.3.

**12.3.** If the entries in the cells of a $2 \times 2$ contingency table are designated $a$, $b$, $c$, and $d$ and $a + b + c + d = n$, it can be shown that the exact probability of any observed set of entries is given by

$$\frac{(a+b)!(c+d)!(a+c)!(b+d)!}{n!a!b!c!d!},$$

where the marginal frequencies are assumed to be fixed in repeated sampling. Use the formula and Stirling's approximation for factorials for the data in Example 12.3.

**12.4.** Calculate chi-square corrected for continuity for Example 12.3.

**12.5.** A more rigorous derivation of the quantity distributed as chi-square to be used in testing homogeneity of a binomial series starts by showing that

$$\lim_{n \to \infty} C(n,x)p^x q^{n-x} \doteq \frac{1}{\sqrt{2\pi npq}} e^{-(x-np)^2/2npq}.$$

Assuming this relationship, complete the argument.

**12.6.** Using the approach suggested in Exercise 12.5, discuss an alternate method to that used in Sec. 12.5 of obtaining the quantity distributed as chi-square to be used in testing homogeneity of a Poisson series.

**12.7.** The method used in Sec. 12.6 to obtain the distribution of $p$ incidentally proves a general theorem which states that any continuous distribution may be transformed into a rectangular distribution. Using this result, complete the argument for showing that there exists at least one transformation which will transform any continuous frequency distribution into any other continuous frequency distribution.

**12.8.** Check the expression given for $m(t)$ for $\log V_i$ in Sec. 12.7 by suitable modification of the results of Exercise 7.15.

**12.9.** Apply Bartlett's test of homogeneity of variances to Federer's[2] data from seven nonselected strains of guayule which were in the 54± chromosome group.

| $s_i^2$ | 9.28 | 6.80 | 7.26 | 7.43 | 9.99 | 14.02 | 10.80 |
|---|---|---|---|---|---|---|---|
| $n_i$ | 117 | 119 | 117 | 115 | 119 | 116 | 116 |

**12.10.** Check the agreement between values of $Q$ in Sec. 12.7 and Snedecor's $F$ for $k = 2$ and $n_1 = n_2 = 1, 2, 3,$ and 6. Is one of these exact?

**12.11.** Bartlett,[12] using published data of Hoblyn and Palmer given below, obtained $\hat{\delta} = 5.1$, an uncorrected $\chi^2 = 2.274$, and a corrected $\chi^2 = 1.850$ in testing interaction in a $2 \times 2 \times 2$ contingency table. The experiment was planned to investigate the propagation of plum rootstocks from root cuttings, the number of cuttings for the variety represented being 240 for each of the four treatments (only one treatment is considered here).

| Length of cutting | Alive | | Total | Dead | | Total |
|---|---|---|---|---|---|---|
| | Time of planting | | | Time of planting | | |
| | At once | In spring | | At once | In spring | |
| Long | 156 | 84 | 240 | 84 | 156 | 240 |
| Short | 107 | 31 | 138 | 133 | 209 | 342 |
| Total | 263 | 115 | 378 | 217 | 365 | 582 |

Check Bartlett's results.

**References Cited**


1. LINDSTROM, E. W., *Cornell Univ., Agr. Expt. Sta. Mem.* 13 (1918).
2. FEDERER, W. T., "Variability of Certain Seed, Seedling, and Young Plant Characters of Guayule," *U.S. Dept. Agr. Tech. Bull.* 919 (1946).
3. FISHER, R. A., *Statistical Methods for Research Workers,* 10th ed., Oliver & Boyd, Ltd., Edinburgh and London, 1946.
4. COCHRAN, W. G., "The Chi-square Distribution for the Binomial and Poisson Series with Small Expectations," *Ann. Eugenics,* **7**:207–217 (1936).
5. COCHRAN, W. G., "The Chi-square Correction for Continuity," *Iowa State Coll. J. Sci.,* **16**:421–436 (1942).
6. YATES, F., "Contingency Tables Involving Small Numbers and $\chi^2$ Test," *J. Roy. Stat. Soc. Suppl.,* **1**:217–235 (1934).
7. SNEDECOR, G. W., *Statistical Methods,* 4th ed., Collegiate Press, Inc., of Iowa State College, Ames, Iowa, 1946.
8. ROBERTSON, D. W., "Material Inheritance in Barley," *Genetics,* **22**:104–113 (1937).
9. FISHER, R. A., "Conditions under Which $\chi^2$ Measures the Discrepancy between Observation and Hypothesis," *J. Roy. Stat. Soc.,* **87**:442–450(1924).
10. BARTLETT, M. S., *Proc. Roy. Soc. (London),* **A901, 160**:273–275 (1937).
11. NEYMAN, J., "On a New Class of Contagious Distributions, Applicable in Entomology and Bacteriology," *Ann. Math. Stat.,* **10**:35–57 (1939).
12. BARTLETT, M. S., "Contingency Table Interactions," *J. Roy. Stat. Soc. Suppl.,* **2**:248–252 (1935).

# Part II

# ANALYSIS OF EXPERIMENTAL MODELS BY LEAST SQUARES

# CHAPTER 13

## REGRESSION ANALYSIS

**13.1. Introduction.** In Part I, we have presented some of the basic statistical concepts of estimation and tests of significance. We presented as our basic estimation procedure the method of maximum likelihood, because it has certain optimum properties such as giving a minimum variance estimator and a sufficient estimator if the latter exists. Now we propose to consider the problem of estimating the value of some *dependent variate*, $Y$, on the basis of information on one or more other *fixed variates*, $X_1, X_2 \ldots$. A dependent variate will be understood to have a probability distribution, while a fixed variate does not have a probability distribution. Another way of saying this is that inferences are to be made regarding the variability of $Y$ for this particular set of $X$'s. The $Y$'s are expected to fluctuate from sample to sample, while the $X$'s remain fixed. For example, we might wish to estimate the yield of wheat, $Y$, for different amounts, $X$, of a standard fertilizer applied to the soil. Or, more exactly, we might estimate this same yield on the basis of the amount of nitrogen, $X_1$, phosphate, $X_2$, and potash, $X_3$, applied to the soil. There is a great demand for information on the effect of temperature and precipitation on yields. The economist tries to predict future employment and price relationships on the basis of past data on the same and other economic variables. The engineer has the problem of estimating the probable length of life of roads or other structures in terms of such things as probable use, type of construction, and weather conditions. The doctor must decide on the basis of certain measurements how much of a given drug can be safely administered to a patient.

As indicated in a previous chapter on bivariate distributions, the expected value of $Y$ for a single fixed $X$ gave the so-called *regression curve* of $Y$ on $X$. A first approximation to this curve was indicated to be a straight line of the form

$$E(Y|X) \approx \alpha + \beta X.$$

In fact, if $X$ and $Y$ were distributed as a bivariate normal,

$$E(Y|X) \equiv \alpha + \beta X.$$

$Y$ is called the dependent variate and $X$ the fixed variate. $X$ is often called the *independent variate*. However, it should be understood that in general the straight line is only an approximation to the true relationship between $Y$ and $X$. It is well known that we can approximate a short interval of most functions by a straight line; hence, if we collect data for a small range of $X$, it is possible that a straight line would fit the data quite well even though the true relationship were curvilinear.

Let us assume that the measured value of $Y$ can be written as

$$Y = E(Y|X) + \epsilon,$$

where $\epsilon$ represents some residual or error, the amount of $Y$ not accounted for by the regression curve of $Y$ on $X$. We postulate that the regression curve is selected so that the residuals are of a random nature, with the usual added assumption that the $\epsilon$ are NID$(0,\sigma^2)$. If $Y$ is a linear function of $r$ fixed variates, we might write

$$Y = \alpha + \beta_1 X_1 + \beta_2 X_2 + \cdots + \beta_r X_r + \epsilon,$$

where $E(Y) = \alpha + \beta_1 X_1 + \beta_2 X_2 + \cdots + \beta_r X_r$. This equation assumes that the only error involved is $\epsilon$; in other words, there is no error in the $X$'s. Hence we are considering only a one-variable normal distribution with the mean of $Y$ being approximated by a simple linear function of the $X$'s. If the $X$'s are not measured without error (in other words, the $X$'s have probability distributions of their own), we are led to consider the more complicated problem of multivariate analysis. Also, we are considering here only regression equations which are linear in the regression coefficients, $\alpha$ and the $\beta$'s. Methods of handling multivariate problems and problems of nonlinearity of the regression coefficients are beyond the scope of this book. It should be emphasized that nonlinearity of the $X$'s can be handled by the introduction of substitute terms in the regression equation. For example, $X_2$ might very well represent $X_1^2$.

In order to estimate the relationship between $Y$ and $X$ (or between $Y$ and $X_1, X_2, \ldots, X_r$, for $r$ fixed variates), $n$ simultaneous observations will be obtained on $Y$ and $X$. We can write each observed value $Y_j$ in terms of estimates of $E(Y_j)$ and $\epsilon_j$ as

$$Y_j = \hat{Y}_j + e_j, \qquad j = 1, 2, \ldots, n,$$

where $\hat{Y}_j$ is the estimate of $E(Y_j)$ and $e_j$ the estimate of $\epsilon_j$. Hence if $E(Y)$ is a linear relationship,

$$Y_j = \alpha + \beta X_j + \epsilon_j = a + bX_j + e_j,$$

where $\alpha \doteq a$ and $\beta \doteq b$. The symbol $\doteq$ will be used in this part to stand for "is estimated by." We can represent these two equations graphically, as in Fig. 13.1. $E(Y)$ is the true regression line and $\hat{Y}$ the observed regression line. For a given observation $(X_j,Y_j)$, the true error is given by $\epsilon_j(QP)$, the estimated residual by $e_j(RP)$, and the difference between $\hat{Y}$ and $E(Y)$ by $\delta_j( = \epsilon_j - e_j = QR)$.

In order to obtain the values of $a$ and $b$, at least two sets of observations $(X,Y)$ are required. Of course, if only two sets are obtained, $\hat{Y}$ will pass through the two points, both values of $e$ will be 0, and the values of $a$ and $b$ can be determined by a simultaneous solution of the two equations representing the two points. However, if more than two sets of observations are obtained, we shall have the situation pictured in Fig. 13.1 with a sample residual, $e$, corresponding to each set $(X,Y)$. When there are more than two sets of points, some new method of determining $a$ and $b$ must be found. In the chapter on bivariate distributions, we indicated that $a$ and $b$ could be determined by the method of moments. There are many

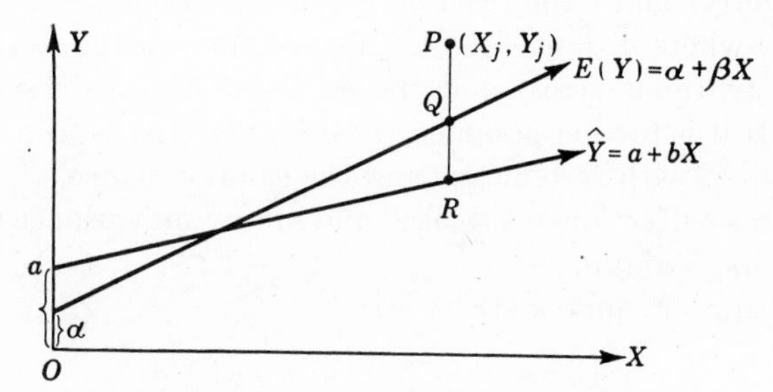


FIG. 13.1. True and estimated regression lines.

other methods of determining these estimates of the parameters, $\alpha$ and $\beta$, in order to obtain the "best" linear fit to the data.

In any case, it seems reasonable to make the $\{e\}$ as small as possible. But what do we do to make these $\{e\}$ small? Many courses are suggested, among which are:

(i) Minimize the sum of the absolute values of the $e$.

(ii) Minimize the greatest of the absolute residuals.

(iii) Minimize the sum of the squares of the residuals.

Method (iii), called the "method of least squares," is probably the easiest to apply and has certain optimum properties. It has been shown for fixed $X$'s that this method produces a linear unbiased estimate of $Y$ which has minimum variance.[1,2] Also if the errors, $\epsilon$, are NID, the method of least squares produces the same estimates as does the method of maximum likelihood. The method of moments will also give the same estimates for NID errors, provided the regression equation is linear in the parameters.

In the derivations which follow for estimating the parameters in the regression equation, for example, $\alpha$ and $\beta$, we need postulate only that the errors are noncorrelated and have the same variance. When the usual tests of significance (such as $t$ and F) and confidence limits are introduced, it is necessary to assume further that the errors are normally and independently distributed. Of course, noncorrelated normal errors are independent. In general we shall assume NID errors, with the understanding that the assumption of normality can be omitted if the investigator is interested only in point estimates and not in confidence limits or tests of significance.

**13.2. Regression of $Y$ on a Single Fixed Variate.** Let us first consider the problem of estimating the best linear relationship between $Y$ and a single fixed variate, $X$, so that

$$Y = \alpha + \beta X + \epsilon = a + bX + e,$$

where $\alpha$ and $\beta$ are the parameters and $a$ and $b$ their respective estimates. $\epsilon$ is the true error and $e$ the residual about the estimated regression line ($e = Y - \hat{Y}$, where $\hat{Y} = a + bX$). We assume that a sample of $n$ $X$'s are selected (without error) and the corresponding values of $Y$'s then measured. If it is further assumed that the true errors ($\epsilon$) are independently distributed with zero means and the same variance, $\sigma^2$, the method of least squares will produce unbiased and minimum variance estimates of the parameters, $\alpha$ and $\beta$.

The error sum of squares (SSE) is†

$$\text{SSE} = Se^2 = S(Y - a - bX)^2.$$

$a$ and $b$ are to be determined so as to minimize SSE. The estimating equation for $a$ is

$$\frac{\partial \text{SSE}}{\partial a} = 0, \qquad SY = na + bSX.$$

Hence

$$a = \frac{SY}{n} - b\frac{SX}{n} = \bar{Y} - b\bar{X}.$$

If we insert this value of $a$ in SSE, we find that

$$\text{SSE} = S[(Y - \bar{Y}) - b(X - \bar{X})]^2 \equiv S(y - bx)^2,$$

where $y = (Y - \bar{Y})$ and $x = (X - \bar{X})$. Hence we might as well have written

$$\hat{Y} = \bar{Y} + bx \qquad \text{instead of} \qquad \hat{Y} = a + bX,$$

and similarly

$$E(Y) = \mu + \beta x,$$

where $\bar{Y}$ is the least-squares estimate of $\mu$ and $\alpha = \mu - \beta\bar{X}$. The least-

† In Part II the letter $S$ will be used for summation over sample values, while $\Sigma$ will be reserved for a sum of fixed variates.

squares equation for $b$, using $x$ and $y$, is

$$\frac{\partial[S(y - bx)^2]}{\partial b} = 0, \qquad b = \frac{Sxy}{Sx^2},$$

where $Sxy = SXY - (SX)(SY)/n$ and $Sx^2 = SX^2 - (SX)^2/n$.

If we substitute this value of $b$ in the equation for SSE,

$$\text{SSE} = S(y - bx)^2 = Sy^2 - bSxy = SY^2 - n\bar{Y}^2 - b^2Sx^2.$$

Hence we can say that the regression has resulted in a reduction of

$$bSxy = b^2Sx^2 = (Sxy)^2/Sx^2 \equiv \text{SSR}$$

in the sum of squares for $Y$, since $n\bar{Y}^2$ is the reduction attributable to the mean (the sum of squares of deviations from the mean is $Sy^2 = SY^2 - n\bar{Y}^2$). The proportional reduction in the sum of squares attributable to the regression on $x$ is usually indicated as

$$\frac{b^2Sx^2}{Sy^2} = \frac{(Sxy)^2}{(Sx^2)(Sy^2)} \equiv r^2,$$

where $r$ is the correlation coefficient between $X$ and $Y$. That is,

$$\text{SSE} = (1 - r^2)Sy^2.$$

In terms of the parameters, $\mu$ and $\beta$, and the true errors $\{\epsilon\}$,

$$\bar{Y} = \frac{SY}{n} = \frac{S(\mu + \beta x + \epsilon)}{n} = \mu + \bar{\epsilon},$$

$$y = Y - \bar{Y} = \mu + \beta x + \epsilon - \mu - \bar{\epsilon} = \beta x + (\epsilon - \bar{\epsilon}),$$

$$b = \frac{Sxy}{Sx^2} = \frac{Sx(\beta x + \epsilon - \bar{\epsilon})}{Sx^2} = \beta + \frac{Sx\epsilon}{Sx^2},$$

$$a = \bar{Y} - b\bar{X} = \mu + \bar{\epsilon} - \left[\beta + \frac{Sx\epsilon}{Sx^2}\right]\bar{X}$$

$$= \alpha + \bar{\epsilon} - \frac{Sx\epsilon}{Sx^2}\bar{X},$$

since $Sx = 0$.

Since $E(\epsilon) = 0$, we see that $\bar{Y}$, $b$, and $a$ are, respectively, unbiased estimates of $\mu$, $\beta$, and $\alpha$. And since the $\epsilon$ are independently distributed with the same variance,

$$\sigma^2(\bar{Y}) = \frac{\sigma^2}{n}, \qquad \sigma^2(b) = \frac{\sigma^2}{Sx^2}, \dagger$$

and

$$\sigma^2(a) = \left[\frac{1}{n} + \frac{\bar{X}^2}{Sx^2}\right]\sigma^2 = \frac{SX^2}{nSx^2}\sigma^2.$$

† In Part II, we shall use the notation $\sigma^2(x)$ and $s^2(x)$ to stand for the variance of $x$.

The predicted value of $Y$ for a given $X$, say $X'$, is

$$\hat{Y}' = \bar{Y} + b(X' - \bar{X}) = \bar{Y} + bx'.$$

If the experimenter wants to put confidence limits on $Y'$, he must choose one of the following:

(i) The confidence limits for the average of all $Y'$, $E(Y')$, which might occur for the given value $X = X'$.

(ii) The confidence limits for any single predicted value, $Y'$.

For (i) we need to determine the variance of the difference between an ordinate on the computed regression line, $\hat{Y}'$, and the corresponding ordinate on the true regression line, $E(Y')$. This difference is

$$\delta' = \hat{Y}' - E(Y') = (\bar{Y} - \mu) + (b - \beta)x',$$

with variance

$$\left[\frac{1}{n} + \frac{x'^2}{Sx^2}\right]\sigma^2.$$

But for (ii) it is necessary to estimate the variance of the difference between the ordinate on the computed regression line, $\hat{Y}'$, and the corresponding true ordinate, $Y'$. This difference is

$$e' = Y' - \hat{Y}' = \epsilon' - \bar{\epsilon} - \frac{Sx\epsilon}{Sx^2}x',$$

with variance

$$\left[1 + \frac{1}{n} + \frac{x'^2}{Sx^2}\right]\sigma^2,$$

where $\epsilon'$ is not one of the $\epsilon$'s in the original sample of $n$.

If we now assume that the $\epsilon$ are NID$(0,\sigma^2)$, SSE is distributed as $\chi^2\sigma^2$ with $(n - 2)$ degrees of freedom, so that

$$s^2 = \text{SSE}/(n - 2)$$

is an unbiased estimate of $\sigma^2$. The proof is as follows:

$$\text{SSE} = Se^2 = S\left(\epsilon - \bar{\epsilon} - \frac{Sx\epsilon}{Sx^2}x\right)^2 = S\epsilon^2 - n\bar{\epsilon}^2 - \frac{(Sx\epsilon)^2}{Sx^2}.$$

Set $\sqrt{n}\,\bar{\epsilon} = \sqrt{n}\,(\bar{Y} - \mu) = z_0$ and $(Sx\epsilon)/\sqrt{Sx^2} = (b - \beta)\sqrt{Sx^2} = z_1$. Then

$$\text{SSE} = S\epsilon^2 - z_0^2 - z_1^2.$$

But $z_0$ and $z_1$ are orthogonal linear functions of NID$(0,\sigma^2)$ variables, each $z$ being itself NID$(0,\sigma^2)$. Hence each $z^2$ is independently distributed as $\chi^2\sigma^2$ with 1 degree of freedom, and SSE is then distributed as $\chi^2\sigma^2$ with

$(n - 2)$ degrees of freedom.† Therefore we can use $s^2$ as an estimate of $\sigma^2$ in the above variances and obtain the following confidence limits:

(i) $\hat{Y}' - t_\alpha s(\delta') < E(Y') < \hat{Y}' + t_\alpha s(\delta')$,

(ii) $\hat{Y}' - t_\alpha s(e') < Y' < \hat{Y}' + t_\alpha s(e')$,

where $s(\delta')$ and $s(e')$ are the same as the corresponding $\sigma$'s but with $\sigma$ replaced by $s$, and $\mathcal{P}(t > t_\alpha) = \alpha/2$.

In both cases, we estimate $\hat{Y}' = \bar{Y} + bx'$, where $\bar{Y}$ and $b$ were computed from the previous sample. The two sets of confidence limits reflect

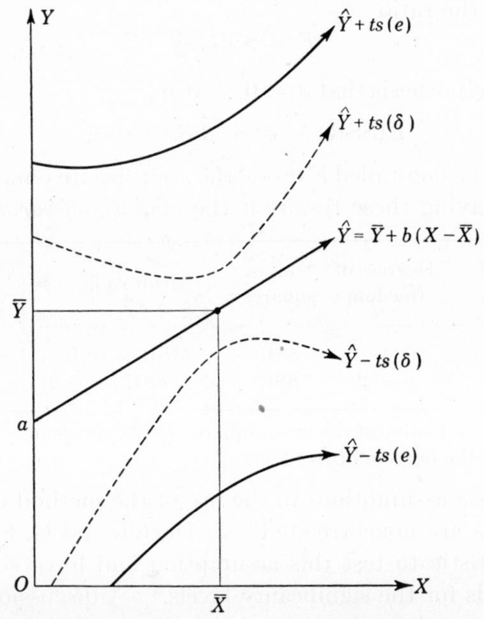


FIG. 13.2. Regression line and confidence bands.

two different uses of this estimate: those for (i) are concerned with estimating the average $Y$ for the given $X$, while those for (ii) are concerned with a single $Y$ on a given experiment. It should be reemphasized that we assume a distribution of $Y$'s for each $X$ and that the second confidence interval is necessarily much wider because the variability of separate $Y$'s is also considered. It should be noted that $s^2(e') = s^2(\delta') + s^2$.

These results are illustrated in Fig. 13.2. The reader will note that the confidence lines form a hyperbola, with the curvature being much greater for the average $Y[\hat{Y} \pm ts(\delta)]$ than for a single predicted $Y[\hat{Y} \pm ts(e)]$.

† See Sec. 14.3 for a formal proof of this. The essence of the proof is that SSE is the sum of $(n - 2)$ independent $\chi^2$ variables, each with 1 degree of freedom.

Finally we can use Student's $t$ as a test criterion to test the null hypothesis $\beta = \beta_0$:

$$t = (b - \beta_0)\sqrt{Sx^2}/s,$$

since the estimated variance of $b$ will be $s^2/Sx^2$.

We note that

$$\text{SSR} = b^2Sx^2 = (z_1 + \beta\sqrt{Sx^2})^2 = (z_1^2 + 2z_1\beta\sqrt{Sx^2} + \beta^2Sx^2).$$

Hence SSR is distributed as $\chi^2\sigma^2$ with 1 degree of freedom when $\beta = 0$, and we can use the ratio

$$F = \text{SSR}/s^2$$

to test the null hypothesis that $\beta = 0$. Also

$$E(\text{SSR}) = \sigma^2 + \beta^2Sx^2 \geq \sigma^2,$$

indicating that the one-tailed $F$ test is the appropriate one. A convenient method of displaying these results is the *analysis-of-variance table:*

| Source of variation | Degrees of freedom | Sum of squares | Mean square | $E$(MS)† |
|---|---|---|---|---|
| Regression | 1 | SSR | MSR = SSR | $\sigma^2 + \beta^2Sx^2$ |
| Error | $n - 2$ | SSE | $s^2 = \text{SSE}/(n - 2)$ | $\sigma^2$ |

† $E$(MS) = expected value of the mean square, where the mean square is the sum of squares divided by the degrees of freedom.

One of the basic assumptions in the use of the method of least squares is that the errors are noncorrelated. J. Durbin and G. S. Watson have developed a statistic to test this assumption and have computed upper and lower bounds for the significance levels.[3] A discussion of regression analysis when the variance is not assumed constant for all $X$'s is presented in Sec. 14.4.

The results of the regression analysis cannot be applied to the entire $(X,Y)$ population—only to the set of $X$'s used in the analysis. C. P. Winsor[4] has prepared an excellent discussion of the problem of fitting regressions when errors of measurement are present in one or both sets of variates and when a random bivariate sample is secured. Wald[5] and Bartlett[6] have presented methods of fitting a straight line when both variables are subject to error.

If a random bivariate sample has been secured, methods have been devised to obtain estimates of and confidence limits for the value of $X$ for a future $Y$, as well as for the value of $Y$ for a future $X$. The method of least squares, regarding $X$ as fixed, produces the same results as the bivariate solution when predicting $Y$ for a future $X$ but not for the inverse

TABLE 13.1
Data for Example 13.1†

| $X$ | $n$ | $SY$ | $n'$ | $S'Y$ | $X$ | $n$ | $SY$ | $n'$ | $S'Y$ |
|---|---|---|---|---|---|---|---|---|---|
| 39 | 3 | 1.9 | 3 | 1.9 | 65 | 11 | 17.4 | 11 | 17.4 |
| 41 | 3 | 3.4 | 3 | 3.4 | 66 | 19 | 36.3 | 17 | 23.9 |
| 42 | 18 | 13.1 | 18 | 13.1 | 67 | 8 | 15.3 | 7 | 10.0 |
| 43 | 1 | .7 | 1 | .7 | 68 | 7 | 14.9 | 6 | 10.5 |
| 44 | 11 | 7.1 | 11 | 7.1 | 69 | 11 | 23.8 | 10 | 19.8 |
| 45 | 51 | 49.9 | 51 | 49.9 | 70 | 12 | 22.7 | 10 | 14.0 |
| 46 | 3 | 2.6 | 3 | 2.6 | 71 | 13 | 23.4 | 13 | 23.4 |
| 47 | 34 | 31.9 | 33 | 27.6 | 72 | 8 | 17.2 | 8 | 17.2 |
| 48 | 86 | 78.3 | 86 | 78.3 | 73 | 9 | 12.2 | 9 | 12.2 |
| 49 | 17 | 10.7 | 17 | 10.7 | 74 | 12 | 43.1 | 9 | 20.7 |
| 50 | 51 | 44.3 | 51 | 44.3 | 75 | 14 | 34.0 | 13 | 28.5 |
| 51 | 39 | 40.0 | 39 | 40.0 | 76 | 11 | 22.9 | 11 | 22.9 |
| 52 | 31 | 36.2 | 31 | 36.2 | 77 | 9 | 33.0 | 6 | 9.0 |
| 53 | 63 | 65.2 | 63 | 65.2 | 78 | 4 | 7.5 | 4 | 7.5 |
| 54 | 45 | 64.5 | 45 | 64.5 | 79 | 14 | 29.6 | 13 | 23.8 |
| 55 | 52 | 55.1 | 52 | 55.1 | 80 | 6 | 11.8 | 6 | 11.8 |
| 56 | 39 | 58.0 | 39 | 58.0 | 81 | 6 | 17.5 | 5 | 13.2 |
| 57 | 23 | 34.2 | 22 | 28.3 | 82 | 3 | 13.6 | 2 | 5.2 |
| 58 | 30 | 37.7 | 30 | 37.7 | 83 | 4 | 32.0 | 2 | 3.8 |
| 59 | 25 | 41.4 | 25 | 41.4 | 84 | 7 | 24.7 | 5 | 12.2 |
| 60 | 17 | 26.0 | 16 | 22.0 | 85 | 2 | 5.5 | 2 | 5.5 |
| 61 | 26 | 41.0 | 25 | 31.9 | 88 | 2 | 9.9 | 0 | 0 |
| 62 | 11 | 15.6 | 10 | 11.4 | 89 | 1 | 16.3 | 0 | 0 |
| 63 | 24 | 32.8 | 24 | 32.8 | 91 | 1 | 10.3 | 0 | 0 |
| 64 | 12 | 29.5 | 9 | 16.4 | | | | | |
| | | | | | Total | 909 | 1,316.0 | 876 | 1,093.0 |

† $X$ = socioeconomic score; $Y$ = net farm income ($1,000); $n$ = number of farmers; $n'$ = number of farmers with income less than $4,000.

problem of predicting $X$ for a future $Y$. Eisenhart,[7] Bliss,[8] and Winsor[4] have discussed the latter problem when the method of least squares was used to estimate the regression line.

**Example 13.1.** A study was made of the relationship between the net income ($Y$) of 909 Southern farm families and a socioeconomic score ($X$), the latter based on the possession of certain items such as radio, telephone, automobile, and electricity and the education and church attendance of the heads of the families.[9] The possible range of $X$'s was 39 to 91. The number of sample families and the total income for each $X$ are presented in Table 13.1, for all families and for the families with incomes less than $4,000. A sample of these data is presented graphically in Fig. 13.3. The following sums and sums of squares and cross products were obtained:

$$SX = 51{,}852, \qquad SY = 1{,}316,$$
$$SX^2 = 3{,}053{,}808, \qquad SXY = 81{,}621, \qquad SY^2 = 3{,}898,$$

where $Y$ was in terms of thousands of dollars. The sums of squares and

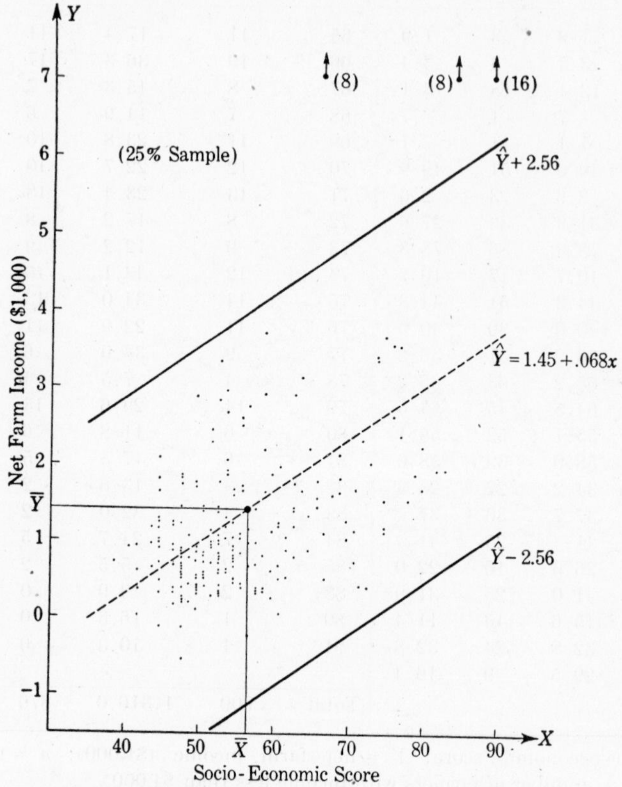


FIG. 13.3. Regression of net income on socioeconomic score.

products adjusted for the means were

$$Sx^2 = 3{,}053{,}808 - (51{,}852)^2/909 = 96{,}019,$$
$$Sxy = 81{,}621 - (51{,}852)(1{,}316)/909 = 6{,}552.5,$$
$$Sy^2 = 3{,}898 - (1{,}316)^2/909 = 1{,}993.$$

Hence

$$b = Sxy/Sx^2 = .06824, \qquad \bar{Y} = 1.448, \qquad \bar{X} = 57.04,$$
$$\text{SSR} = bSxy = (Sxy)^2/Sx^2 = 447, \qquad \text{SSE} = Sy^2 - \text{SSR} = 1{,}546,$$
$$s^2 = \text{SSE}/907 = 1.704, \qquad s = 1.305, \qquad s(b) = s/\sqrt{Sx^2} = .004211,$$
$$t = b/s(b) = 16.2.$$

The 95 per cent confidence limits for $\beta$ are $\beta = .06824 \pm (1.96)(.004211)$, or

$$.05999 < \beta < .07649,$$

since the 95 per cent value of $t$ is 1.96 for 907 degrees of freedom. Hence one could state that on the average an increase of one unit on the socioeconomic score would be associated with an increase of from \$59.99 to \$76.49 in net income. The analysis-of-variance table is:

| Source of variation | Degrees of freedom | Sum of squares | Mean square |
|---|---|---|---|
| Regression | 1 | 447 | 447 |
| Error | 907 | 1546 | 1.704 |

$$F = 447/1.704 = 262.3 = t^2.$$

There is an undoubted significant relationship between net income and socioeconomic score, but the percentage of variation accounted for by the regression is only (447)100/1,993 = 22 per cent. It was hoped that the relationship would be close enough so that in future surveys an adequate measure of income could be obtained from the socioeconomic score, since it is much easier to obtain socioeconomic information than income data (most of the socioeconomic items can be observed by the interviewer; hence interviewing biases can be eliminated). However, if only 22 per cent of the total income variability can be explained by the socioeconomic score, some other means of estimating net income must be devised. An attempt was made to obtain a possibly better fit to the data displayed in Fig. 13.3 by redefining the population to contain only incomes less than \$4,000. However, when a new fit was attempted, the proportional reduction in sum of squares due to regression was even less; hence this approach also was abandoned. Since the variation about the regression line seemed to increase with increasing $X$, it was thought that a logarithmic relationship might fit the data better; however, there was no real improvement in the percentage of variability accounted for by the regression.

The failure of the socioeconomic score to estimate net income is shown in the 95 per cent confidence limits for a predicted value of $Y$.

$$\text{(i)}\quad E(Y') = \hat{Y}' \pm 2.558\sqrt{.00111 + \frac{x'^2}{96{,}019}},$$

$$\text{(ii)}\quad Y' = \hat{Y}' \pm 2.558\sqrt{1.00111 + \frac{x'^2}{96{,}019}}.$$

As an example, consider the confidence limits if $X' = 80$. In this case $\hat{Y}' = \bar{Y} + bx' = 1.448 + (0.06824)(22.96) = 3.015$. Hence the 95 per cent confidence limits are

$$\text{(i)}\quad E(Y') = 3.015 \pm 2.558\sqrt{.006600} = 3.015 \pm .208,$$

$$\text{(ii)}\quad Y' = 3.015 \pm 2.558\sqrt{1.006600} = 3.015 \pm 2.567.$$

Since it was hoped to use this regression equation for an individual family, the appropriate set of confidence limits to consider is (ii):

$$.448 < Y' < 5.582.$$

Hence we could only estimate the income as falling between \$448 and \$5,582 with 95 per cent confidence. The regression line, $\hat{Y}$, and the 95 per cent confidence band for a single predicted $Y$ are shown in Fig. 13.3. Note that the confidence lines are practically parallel to $\hat{Y}$, because $s^2(e) = s^2(\delta) + s^2$, and $s^2$ is the dominant term.

## EXERCISES

**13.1.** Use the confidence limits for predicting $E(Y')$ for a future $X'$ to show that the confidence limits of $X'$ for a future $Y'$ are

$$X' = \bar{X} + \frac{b(Y' - \bar{Y})}{\lambda} \pm \frac{t_\alpha s}{\lambda} \sqrt{\frac{\lambda}{n} + \frac{(Y' - \bar{Y})^2}{Sx^2}},$$

where $\lambda = b^2 - (t_\alpha^2 s^2 / Sx^2)$ and $\bar{X}$, $\bar{Y}$, $b$, $s$, and $Sx^2$ are based on the original sample of $n$.

**13.2.** What changes would be made in the confidence limits in Exercise 13.1 if $Y'$ were the average of $k$ observations?

**13.3.** The analysis of socioeconomic scores is simplified for those items with only two alternatives, for example, with or without electricity. Suppose we want to correlate the scores on one such item with income. Let $w_0$ be the score for each of the $n_0$ families without this item and $w_1$ the score for each of the $n_1$ families with this item ($n_0 + n_1 = n$ total families). Show that $r^2$ is independent of $w_0$ and $w_1$.

**13.4.** Girshick and Haavelmo have made an analysis of the demand for food in the United States for the years 1922 to 1941.[10] One equation in their analysis involved the relationship between disposable income adjusted for the cost of living ($Y$) and investment per capita adjusted for the cost of living ($X_1$). The values of $Y$ and $X_1$ are shown in the accompanying table.

DATA FOR EXERCISE 13.4

| $Y$ | $X_1$ | $Y$ | $X_1$ | $Y$ | $X_1$ |
|---|---|---|---|---|---|
| 87.4 | 92.9 | 107.8 | 142.9 | 103.1 | 114.3 |
| 97.6 | 142.9 | 96.6 | 92.9 | 105.1 | 121.4 |
| 96.7 | 100.0 | 88.9 | 97.6 | 96.4 | 78.6 |
| 98.2 | 123.8 | 75.1 | 52.4 | 104.4 | 109.5 |
| 99.8 | 111.9 | 76.9 | 40.5 | 110.7 | 128.6 |
| 100.5 | 121.4 | 84.6 | 64.3 | 127.1 | 238.1 |
| 103.2 | 107.1 | 90.6 | 78.6 | 1,950.7 | 2,159.7 |

(*a*) Set up a simple linear regression of $Y$ on $X_1$, and determine the constants in the regression equation.

(*b*) Set up the analysis of variance.

(*c*) Make a test of significance of the usefulness of the regression equation. Are there any aspects of these data which might invalidate this test?

(*d*) Plot the data (rounded to nearest integer), and draw in the regression line and the 95 per cent confidence lines for $E(Y|X_1)$. From the nature of the residuals from the regression line, would you suggest any changes in the form of the regression equation?

**13.5.** R. A. Fisher has compared the body weights (in kilograms) with the heart weights (in grams) of 47 female and 97 male cats.[11] The sums of squares and products were as follows:

| | Degrees of freedom | (Body)² | (Body × heart) | (Heart)² |
|---|---|---|---|---|
| Females: | | | | |
| Total | 47 | 265.13 | 1029.62 | 4064.71 |
| Correction for mean | 1 | 261.677 | 1020.516 | 3979.92 |
| Difference | 46 | 3.453 | 9.104 | 84.79 |
| Males: | | | | |
| Total | 97 | 836.75 | 3275.55 | 13056.17 |
| Correction for mean | 1 | 815.77 | 3185.07 | 12435.70 |
| Difference | 96 | 20.98 | 90.48 | 620.47 |

(*a*) Determine the regression of heart weight on body weight for both males and females.

(*b*) Are these two regressions different from one another?

(*c*) Are the two error variances essentially the same?

**13.6.** In a study of lobster population, D. B. DeLury[12] presents the following data on the catch per unit of effort for the time interval $t$, $C(t)$, and the total catch up to $t$, $K(t)$, in thousands of pounds:

| $t$ | 1 | 2 | 3 | 4 | 5 | 6 | 7 | 8 | 9 | 10 | 11 | 12 | 13 | 14 | 15 | 16 | 17 |
|---|---|---|---|---|---|---|---|---|---|---|---|---|---|---|---|---|---|
| $C$ | .82 | .75 | .94 | .80 | .83 | .89 | .70 | .58 | .64 | .55 | .52 | .45 | .45 | .49 | .45 | .48 | .43 |
| $K$ | 0 | 7 | 13 | 16 | 22 | 25 | 32 | 37 | 40 | 45 | 50 | 53 | 54 | 55 | 57 | 60 | 62 |

(*a*) A linear equation of the form $C = a + bK + e$ was set up. Determine the values of $a$ and $b$ and their standard errors.

(*b*) The total population at time $t = 0$ is estimated by $N_0 = -a/b$. Determine $N_0$.

**13.7.** Read a brief note in the December, 1948, issue of the *American Statistician* (pages 16 to 17) on the use of regression methods for business statistics.

**13.8.** Suppose a sample of $n_1$ is used to estimate the parameters in the equation $Y_1 = \mu_1 + \beta_1 x_1 + \epsilon_1$ and a sample of $n_2$ for the equation $Y_2 = \mu_2 + \beta_2 x_2 + \epsilon_2$, where $\sigma_1^2$ is assumed to equal $\sigma_2^2$. How would you test the null hypothesis that $\beta_1 = \beta_2$? What would you do if $\sigma_1^2 \neq \sigma_2^2$?

**13.9.** (*a*) Show that $\bar{Y}$ and $b$ are the ML estimates of $\mu$ and $\beta$, respectively.

(*b*) What is the ML estimate of $\sigma^2$? Is this estimate unbiased?

**13.10.** Use the data in Table 13.1 for incomes less than \$4,000 to fit a new regression of net income on socioeconomic score ($Sy^2 = 623$ for these incomes under \$4,000).

**13.11.** As mentioned in Example 13.1, a logarithmic relationship was also used. Since there were some negative incomes, $Z = \log\ (Y + 1)$

Data for Exercise 13.11

| X | SZ | S'Z | X | SZ | S'Z |
|---|---|---|---|---|---|
| 39 | .5215 | .5215 | 65 | 4.4110 | 4.4110 |
| 41 | .9755 | .9755 | 66 | 7.7002 | 5.9932 |
| 42 | 3.8118 | 3.8118 | 67 | 3.3000 | 2.5018 |
| 43 | .2217 | .2217 | 68 | 3.1725 | 2.4361 |
| 44 | 2.2455 | 2.2455 | 69 | 5.1685 | 4.6628 |
| 45 | 13.8419 | 13.8419 | 70 | 5.1154 | 3.6538 |
| 46 | .7811 | .7811 | 71 | 5.3964 | 5.3964 |
| 47 | 9.0067 | 8.2792 | 72 | 3.6718 | 3.6718 |
| 48 | 22.2637 | 22.2637 | 73 | 3.0164 | 3.0164 |
| 49 | 3.3421 | 3.3421 | 74 | 7.2008 | 4.5188 |
| 50 | 12.7787 | 12.7787 | 75 | 7.0135 | 6.2004 |
| 51 | 11.1653 | 11.1653 | 76 | 5.2177 | 5.2177 |
| 52 | 9.6366 | 9.6366 | 77 | 4.9095 | 2.0622 |
| 53 | 18.1929 | 18.1929 | 78 | 1.7054 | 1.7054 |
| 54 | 16.1329 | 16.1329 | 79 | 6.3518 | 5.5146 |
| 55 | 15.4700 | 15.4700 | 80 | 2.8142 | 2.8142 |
| 56 | 14.7077 | 14.7077 | 81 | 3.4868 | 2.7624 |
| 57 | 7.9962 | 7.1611 | 82 | 2.0645 | 1.0923 |
| 58 | 9.8522 | 9.8522 | 83 | 3.2244 | .9187 |
| 59 | 9.8317 | 9.8317 | 84 | 4.3589 | 2.6452 |
| 60 | 6.3001 | 5.5959 | 85 | 1.1415 | 1.1415 |
| 61 | 9.3233 | 8.3207 | 88 | 1.5469 | 0 |
| 62 | 3.9073 | 3.1950 | 89 | 1.2370 | 0 |
| 63 | 8.2960 | 8.2960 | 91 | 1.0531 | 0 |
| 64 | 5.6077 | 3.4258 | | | |
| | | | Total | 310.4883 | 282.3832 |

was used as the dependent variate with $X$ still the fixed variate ($Y$ in terms of thousands of dollars). The data for this regression analysis are presented in the table (the values of $n$ and $n'$ are not reproduced here, as they are the same as in Table 13.1).

(*a*) Fit a new regression line using all incomes, but with $Z = \log (Y + 1)$ as the dependent variate. ($Sz^2 = 32.279$.)

(*b*) Do the same for the incomes under $4,000. ($Sz^2 = 22.470$.)

### References Cited

1. Markoff, A. A., *Wahrscheinlichkeitsrechnung*, B. G. Teubner, Leipzig, 1912.
2. David, F. N., and J. Neyman, "Extension of the Markoff Theorem on Least Squares," *Stat. Research Mem.*, **2**:105–116 (1938).
3. Durbin, J., and G. S. Watson, "Testing for Serial Correlation in Least Squares Regression," *Biometrika*, **37**:409–428 (1950), **38**:159–178 (1951).
4. Winsor, C. P., "Which Regression?" *Biom. Bull.*, **2**:101–109 (1946).
5. Wald, A., "The Fitting of Straight Lines If Both Variables Are Subject to Error," *Ann. Math. Stat.*, **11**:284*ff*. (1940).
6. Bartlett, M. S., "Fitting a Straight Line When Both Variables Are Subject to Error," *Biometrics*, **5**:207–212 (1949).
7. Eisenhart, C., "The Interpretation of Certain Regression Methods and Their Use in Biological and Industrial Research," *Ann. Math. Stat.*, **10**:162–186 (1939).
8. Bliss, C. I., "Confidence Limits for Biological Assay," *Biom. Bull.*, **1**:57–65 (1945).
9. Jordan, M. E., *The Relationship of Current Net Income to Socio-economic Status*, unpublished thesis, North Carolina State College, Raleigh, N.C., 1949.
10. Girshick, M. A., and T. Haavelmo, "Statistical Analysis of the Demand for Food," *Econometrica*, **15**:79–110 (1947).
11. Fisher, R. A., "The Analysis of Covariance Methods for the Relation between a Part and the Whole," *Biom. Bull.*, **3**:65–68 (1947).
12. DeLury, D. B., "On the Estimation of Biological Populations," *Biom. Bull.*, **3**:145–167 (1947).

# CHAPTER 14

## GENERAL REGRESSION MODEL WITH *r* FIXED VARIATES

**14.1. Introduction.** Let us suppose that we can approximate $Y$ by means of the general linear equation

$$Y = \mu + \sum_{i=1}^{r} \beta_i x_i + \epsilon = \bar{Y} + \sum_{i=1}^{r} b_i x_i + e, \qquad (1)$$

where the *regression coefficients* $\{b_i\}$ are to be determined from $n(\geq r+1)$ simultaneous observations on $Y$ and the $X_i$'s ($x_i = X_i - \bar{X}_i$). The first relationship represents the true experimental model in terms of the parameters ($\mu$ and the $\beta_i$) and the *true error*, $\epsilon$, while the second is in terms of the estimates of these parameters and the *residual*, $e$. The $b$'s are determined by minimizing the sum of the squared residuals.

The usual assumptions are:

(i) The $\{X_i\}$ are fixed variates and may be looked upon as population parameters. Often the $X$'s are chosen deliberately and the $Y$'s are produced or chosen at random.

(ii) For a fixed set of $X$'s, say $\{X_i'\}$, the $Y$'s associated with this set are NID with mean $E(Y') = \mu + \sum_{i=1}^{r} \beta_i x_i'$ and variance $\sigma^2$. The observed regression surface is $\hat{Y}' = \bar{Y} + \Sigma b_i x_i'$. As mentioned in Sec. 13.1, the assumption of normality is required only when confidence limits and tests of significance are used.

(iii) For any set of $X$'s, the variance of $Y$ shall be the same; this is the assumption of *homoscedasticity*.

Even though we are considering only one $Y$ for each set of $X$'s, it is understood that there is an underlying normal population of $Y$'s for each set of $X$'s and that the residuals from the true regression surface are NID$(0,\sigma^2)$. The assumption of fixed $X$'s indicates that the results cannot be applied to the entire multivariate $\{Y,X_i\}$ population—only to the sets of $X$'s used in the analysis.

The form of the general equation should be based on some theoretical framework, which a research man in the particular field of application should be asked to furnish. In many cases the particular set of fixed variates may not be the ideal ones from a theoretical point of view, but they may be the best substitutes for which data are available. Also, the form of the regression model might not be ideal, but often the ease of computing from a linear model will outweigh the advantage of using a more exact but cumbersome model. Of course, if the nonlinear model is simply a multiplicative one, it can be linearized by use of a logarithmic transformation, provided the error is also multiplicative.

In a graduate thesis, Monroe[1] has presented some of the uses of nonlinear models for nutritional experiments, plus an extensive bibliography on the subject. An article on this subject by Hartley[2] outlines a method of using least-squares estimation for nonlinear parameters.

The error sum of squares, which is to be minimized, is

$$\text{SSE} = Se^2 = S\left(y - \sum_{i=1}^{r} b_i x_i\right)^2, \tag{2}$$

where we shall use $S$ for summation over the sample values and $\Sigma$ for summation of variates. The following general equation is obtained when SSE is minimized with respect to $b_k$ ($k = 1,2, \ldots ,r$):

$$b_1 Sx_k x_1 + b_2 Sx_k x_2 + \cdots + b_k Sx_k^2 + \cdots + b_r Sx_k x_r = Sx_k y. \tag{3}$$

In order to simplify the presentation which follows, let $Sx_i x_j = a_{ij}$ and $Sx_i y = g_i$, where $a_{ij} = a_{ji}$. Then we can write the set of $r$ equations in the $r$ unknown $\{b_i\}$ as follows:

$$\begin{aligned}
a_{11}b_1 + a_{12}b_2 + \cdots + a_{1k}b_k + \cdots + a_{1r}b_r &= g_1, \\
a_{21}b_1 + a_{22}b_2 + \cdots + a_{2k}b_k + \cdots + a_{2r}b_r &= g_2, \\
\cdots\cdots\cdots\cdots\cdots\cdots\cdots\cdots\cdots \\
a_{k1}b_1 + a_{k2}b_2 + \cdots + a_{kk}b_k + \cdots + a_{kr}b_r &= g_k, \\
\cdots\cdots\cdots\cdots\cdots\cdots\cdots\cdots\cdots \\
a_{r1}b_1 + a_{r2}b_2 + \cdots + a_{rk}b_k + \cdots + a_{rr}b_r &= g_r.
\end{aligned} \tag{4}$$

These are called the *normal* equations.

This system of $r$ linear equations can be solved for the $\{b_i\}$ by the usual methods of simultaneous equations given in elementary algebra. Methods of solution have been presented by Snedecor[3] and in a special computing manual by Wallace and Snedecor.[4] However, we believe that, in general, it is better to solve for the $b$'s by use of a method called *matrix inversion*. Computing techniques have been devised so that they can be followed without a knowledge of matrix theory. A detailed discussion of these techniques and the necessary matrix theory are presented by Dwyer.[5] We shall present two computing techniques in Chap. 15.

In order to determine the $b$'s by a method of matrix inversion, an intermediate computing step is necessary. A new set of $r^2$ constants

$\{c_{ij}\}$ must be determined. Suppose we arrange the $a$'s and $c$'s in rows and columns as follows:

$$A = \begin{bmatrix} a_{11} & a_{12} & \cdots & a_{1r} \\ a_{21} & a_{22} & \cdots & a_{2r} \\ \cdot & \cdot & \cdot & \cdot \\ a_{r1} & a_{r2} & \cdots & a_{rr} \end{bmatrix}, \qquad C = \begin{bmatrix} c_{11} & c_{12} & \cdots & c_{1r} \\ c_{21} & c_{22} & \cdots & c_{2r} \\ \cdot & \cdot & \cdot & \cdot \\ c_{r1} & c_{r2} & \cdots & c_{rr} \end{bmatrix}.$$

These arrangements are called *matrices*, and the individual $a$'s and $c$'s are called *elements*. The $c$'s must satisfy the following conditions:

$$\sum_{j=1}^{r} a_{ij}c_{jk} = \begin{cases} 1 & i = k. \\ 0 & i \neq k. \end{cases} \tag{5}$$

In other words, the sum of the products of corresponding elements in a row of $A$ and a column of $C$ must be unity for the same row and column (for example, the first row of $A$ and the first column of $C$) and must be zero for an unlike row and column (for example, the first row of $A$ and the second column of $C$). The $C$ matrix is called the *inverse* of the $A$ matrix. The computing techniques mentioned above refer to the computations required to determine the $c$'s.

After the $c$'s have been determined, the solution for $b_k$ is as follows:

$$b_k = \sum_{j=1}^{r} c_{kj}g_j = \sum_{j=1}^{r} c_{kj}Sx_jy, \qquad k = 1, 2, \ldots, r. \tag{6}$$

In other words, any $b_k$ can be computed by adding up the products of the elements in the $k$th row of $C$ times the corresponding $g$'s. A brief discussion of this matrix theory is presented in Sec. 14.2 for those readers who desire a more theoretical presentation.

From the model equation (1), we see that

$$y = Y - \bar{Y} = \Sigma\beta_i x_i + \epsilon - \bar{\epsilon},$$

where $\bar{\epsilon} = S\epsilon/n$. Hence using the definition $Sx_jx_i = a_{ji}$ and equation (5),

$$b_k = \sum_j c_{kj}\left[Sx_j\left(\sum_i \beta_i x_i + \epsilon - \bar{\epsilon}\right)\right] = \sum_i\left(\sum_j c_{kj}a_{ji}\right)\beta_i + \sum_j c_{kj}(Sx_j\epsilon)$$
$$= \beta_k + \sum_j c_{kj}(Sx_j\epsilon).$$

Since the $\{\epsilon\}$ are NID$(0,\sigma^2)$,

$$E(b_k) = \beta_k \text{ (indicating } b_k \text{ is an unbiased estimate of } \beta_k\text{);}$$
$$\sigma^2(b_k) = E[(b_k - \beta_k)^2] = E[(\Sigma c_{kj}Sx_j\epsilon)^2] = c_{kk}\sigma^2;$$
$$\sigma(b_ib_k) = c_{ik}\sigma^2;$$
$$\sigma^2(b_i - b_k) = (c_{ii} - 2c_{ik} + c_{kk})\sigma^2.$$

In order to prove that $\sigma^2(b_k) = c_{kk}\sigma^2$, we make use of the linear-form techniques of Part I. $\sum_j c_{kj}Sx_j\epsilon \equiv l$ can be represented as a linear function of the $n$ $\epsilon$'s, that is,

$$l = \mathop{S}_{p=1}^{n} w_p\epsilon_p,$$

where $w_p = \sum_j c_{kj}x_{jp}$ and $x_{jp}$ is the $p$th observation on $x_j$. Since the $\epsilon$ are NID$(0,\sigma^2)$, $\sigma^2(l) = (Sw_p^2)\sigma^2$. But we can write

$$Sw_p^2 = \mathop{S}_{p}\left[\left(\sum_{j=1}^{r} c_{kj}x_{jp}\right)\left(\sum_{j'=1}^{r} c_{kj'}x_{j'p}\right)\right] = \sum_j\sum_{j'} c_{kj}c_{kj'}a_{j'j} = c_{kk},$$

since

$$\sum_{j'} c_{kj'}a_{j'j} = \begin{cases} 1 & \text{when } k = j. \\ 0 & \text{when } k \neq j. \end{cases}$$

A similar proof can be set up for $\sigma(b_ib_k)$.

It should be noted that since the $\epsilon$ are assumed NID$(0,\sigma^2)$, the $\{b_i\}$ are multivariate normally distributed with means $\{\beta_i\}$, variances $c_{ii}\sigma^2$, and covariances $c_{ij}\sigma^2$.

The error sum of squares, as given in equation (2), is

$$\begin{aligned} \text{SSE} &= S\left(y - \sum_{i=1}^{r} b_ix_i\right)^2 \\ &= Sy^2 - \left(\sum_{i=1}^{r} b_iSx_iy\right) + \sum_{i=1}^{r} b_i\left(\sum_{k=1}^{r} b_kSx_ix_k - Sx_iy\right) \\ &= Sy^2 - \left(\sum_{i=1}^{r} b_iSx_iy\right), \end{aligned}$$

because the values in parentheses of the second equation are simply the normal equations, where $\sum_{k=1}^{r} b_kSx_ix_k = Sx_iy$. Hence the reduction due to regression is

$$\text{SSR} = \sum_{i=1}^{r} b_iSx_iy \equiv R^2Sy^2,$$

where $R$ is called the *multiple correlation coefficient*.

In Sec. 14.3, we shall prove that†

$$E(\text{SSE}) = (n - r - 1)\sigma^2, \qquad s^2 = \text{SSE}/(n - r - 1),$$
$$E(\text{SSR}) = r\sigma^2 \qquad \text{when all } \beta_i = 0.$$

Hence $F = \text{SSR}/rs^2$ can be used to test the null hypothesis that all $\beta_i = 0$. $F$ has $(r, n - r - 1)$ degrees of freedom. Also, SSR $> r\sigma^2$ when some $\beta_i \neq 0$.

If it is desired to know if the last $(r - k)$ of the $r$ fixed variates made a significant contribution to SSR, we can obtain the reduction due to the first $k$ fixed variates by using

$$\hat{Y} = \bar{Y} + b_1'x_1 + \cdots + b_k'x_k.$$

This reduction will be called $\text{SSR}_k$. Then the added reduction due to the last $(r - k)$ fixed variates is $(\text{SSR} - \text{SSR}_k)$. The expected value of $(\text{SSR} - \text{SSR}_k)$ is a function of only the last $(r - k)$ $\beta$'s. Hence we can test the null hypothesis that each of these $(r - k)$ $\beta$'s vanishes without saying anything about the first $k$ fixed variates. The analysis of variance is:

| Source of variation | Degrees of freedom | Mean square | $E$(MS) |
|---|---|---|---|
| First $k$ fixed variates | $k$ | | |
| Added reduction by last $(r - k)$ fixed variates | $r - k$ | $(\text{SSR} - \text{SSR}_k)/(r - k)$ | $\sigma^2 + \theta\{\beta_{k+1}, \ldots, \beta_r\}$† |
| Error | $n - r - 1$ | $s^2$ | $\sigma^2$ |

† $\theta$ is a function of only $\{\beta_{k+1}, \beta_{k+2}, \ldots, \beta_r\}$.

Under the null hypothesis $H_0$: $\{\beta_{k+1} = \beta_{k+2} = \cdots = \beta_r = 0\}$, $\theta = 0$. Hence

$$\frac{\text{SSR} - \text{SSR}_k}{s^2(r - k)} = F,$$

with $(r - k)$ and $(n - r - 1)$ degrees of freedom.

Exercises 14.1 to 14.10 pertain to Sec. 14.1.

**14.2. Matrix Algebra.‡** We shall digress here in order that the reader who is unfamiliar with the methods of matrix algebra may become acquainted with the necessary concepts and techniques used in simplifying the theory and computations of regression.

† $s^2$ is denoted as $s^2_{y \cdot x}$ in most discussions of regression analysis.

‡ The reader may omit this section if he does not want a more theoretical discussion than Sec. 14.1.

A *matrix* is an array of quantities and may be represented as follows:

$$\begin{bmatrix} a_{11} & a_{12} & \cdots & a_{1n} \\ a_{21} & a_{22} & \cdots & a_{2n} \\ \cdots & \cdots & \cdots & \cdots \\ a_{m1} & a_{m2} & \cdots & a_{mn} \end{bmatrix}.$$

The quantities $a_{ij}$ are called the *elements* of the matrix. This is a matrix of $m$ rows and $n$ columns. If $m = n$, the matrix is called a *square matrix*. The number of rows or columns of the square matrix is called the order of the matrix. If $a_{ij} = a_{ji}$, the matrix is called a *symmetric matrix*. Two matrices are equal if and only if corresponding elements are identical. For the most part we shall be concerned in regression analyses with square symmetric matrices.

Two matrices are added in the following manner:

$$\begin{bmatrix} a_{11} & a_{12} \\ a_{21} & a_{22} \end{bmatrix} + \begin{bmatrix} b_{11} & b_{12} \\ b_{21} & b_{22} \end{bmatrix} = \begin{bmatrix} a_{11} + b_{11} & a_{12} + b_{12} \\ a_{21} + b_{21} & a_{22} + b_{22} \end{bmatrix}.$$

Subtraction is defined in a similar fashion.

In multiplying two matrices, the elements of the product matrix are obtained by multiplying the elements of a row of the first matrix by the corresponding elements of a column of the second matrix and adding these product terms. For example,

$$\begin{bmatrix} a_{11} & a_{12} \\ a_{21} & a_{22} \end{bmatrix} \cdot \begin{bmatrix} b_{11} & b_{12} \\ b_{21} & b_{22} \end{bmatrix} = \begin{bmatrix} a_{11}b_{11} + a_{12}b_{21} & a_{11}b_{12} + a_{12}b_{22} \\ a_{21}b_{11} + a_{22}b_{21} & a_{21}b_{12} + a_{22}b_{22} \end{bmatrix}.$$

If we let $A$ stand for the first matrix on the left above and $B$ the second, it is obvious that $A \cdot B$ may not necessarily be equal to $B \cdot A$.

Division of one matrix by another is defined as an inverse operation of multiplication. Let

$$A \cdot B = G.$$

Then, multiplying the equation on the left by $A^{-1}$ (the inverse of $A$), we find

$$A^{-1} \cdot A \cdot B = A^{-1}G. \tag{7}$$

Now, $A^{-1}$ is defined to be a matrix such that

$$A^{-1} \cdot A = A \cdot A^{-1} = I,$$

where $I$ is called the *identity matrix* and plays the same role in matrix algebra that 1 plays in ordinary algebra. The identity matrix $I$ in terms of its elements is

$$I = \begin{bmatrix} 1 & 0 & \cdots & 0 \\ 0 & 1 & \cdots & 0 \\ \cdots & \cdots & \cdots & \cdots \\ 0 & 0 & \cdots & 1 \end{bmatrix}.$$

Returning to equation (7), we see that

$$B = A^{-1}G.$$

We can now define the operation of dividing matrix $G$ by matrix $A$ as yielding the matrix $B$ obtained by multiplying matrix $G$ on the left by the inverse matrix of $A$.

In order to explain a general method of obtaining the inverse of a matrix, we need to recall the definition and basic properties of *determinants.* The elements of a square matrix determine the determinant of the matrix. A determinant is a function of the elements of a square array. It may be expressed as a polynomial by expanding the determinant by *minors* according to Cramer's rule.

The *order* of a determinant is its number of rows or columns. A minor of an element of a determinant is the determinant of one less order found by striking out the row and column containing the particular element. The cofactor $A_{ij}$ of the element $a_{ij}$ is obtained by multiplying $(-1)^{i+j}$ by the minor of $a_{ij}$. Cramer's rule permits us to evaluate a determinant by multiplying the elements of any row or column by the corresponding cofactors and summing these products.

The element $a^{ij}$ of the inverse $A^{-1}$ of the matrix $A$ is obtained by dividing the cofactor $A_{ji}$ by the determinant $|A|$ of the matrix, that is,

$$a^{ij} = \frac{A_{ji}}{|A|}.$$

**Example 14.1.** In order to find the inverse $A^{-1}$ of the matrix

$$A = \begin{bmatrix} 0 & 3 & 2 \\ 1 & 2 & 4 \\ 3 & 0 & 2 \end{bmatrix},$$

we evaluate the determinant of this matrix:

$$|A| = \begin{vmatrix} 0 & 3 & 2 \\ 1 & 2 & 4 \\ 3 & 0 & 2 \end{vmatrix} = 0\begin{vmatrix} 2 & 4 \\ 0 & 2 \end{vmatrix} - 3\begin{vmatrix} 1 & 4 \\ 3 & 2 \end{vmatrix} + 2\begin{vmatrix} 1 & 2 \\ 3 & 0 \end{vmatrix}$$
$$= 0 - 3(2 - 12) + 2(0 - 6) = 18.$$

The cofactors are

$$A_{11} = (-1)^{1+1}\begin{vmatrix} 2 & 4 \\ 0 & 2 \end{vmatrix} = 4,$$

$$A_{12} = (-1)^{1+2}\begin{vmatrix} 1 & 4 \\ 3 & 2 \end{vmatrix} = 10,$$

and so forth. We find the complete matrix of the cofactors to be

$$A_{ij} = \begin{bmatrix} 4 & 10 & -6 \\ -6 & -6 & 9 \\ 8 & 2 & -3 \end{bmatrix}.$$

Upon interchanging rows and columns and dividing each element by $|A|$, we obtain the inverse matrix

$$A^{-1} = \begin{bmatrix} \frac{4}{18} & -\frac{6}{18} & \frac{8}{18} \\ \frac{10}{18} & -\frac{6}{18} & \frac{2}{18} \\ -\frac{6}{18} & \frac{9}{18} & -\frac{3}{18} \end{bmatrix}.$$

We may verify numerically that

$$A \cdot A^{-1} = A^{-1} \cdot A = I = \begin{bmatrix} 1 & 0 & 0 \\ 0 & 1 & 0 \\ 0 & 0 & 1 \end{bmatrix}.$$

For example, the first element of the $I$ matrix is obtained as

$$0 \cdot (\tfrac{4}{18}) + 3 \cdot (\tfrac{10}{18}) + 2 \cdot (-\tfrac{6}{18}) = 1.$$

Some of the results of this section will now be used to simplify and develop the theory of Sec. 14.1. The normal equations of Sec. 14.1 may be written in matrix form as

$$A \cdot B = G, \tag{4'}$$

where

$$A = \begin{bmatrix} Sx_1^2 & Sx_1x_2 & \cdots & Sx_1x_r \\ Sx_1x_2 & Sx_2^2 & \cdots & Sx_2x_r \\ \cdot & \cdot & \cdot & \cdot \\ Sx_1x_r & Sx_2x_r & \cdots & Sx_r^2 \end{bmatrix},$$

$$B = \begin{bmatrix} b_1 \\ b_2 \\ \cdot \\ b_r \end{bmatrix},$$

and

$$G = \begin{bmatrix} Sx_1y \\ Sx_2y \\ \cdots \\ Sx_ry \end{bmatrix}.$$

The matrix $A$ is a square symmetric matrix, while the matrices $B$ and $G$ are single-column matrices.

Upon multiplying equation (4′) on the left by $A^{-1}$, we find

$$A^{-1} \cdot A \cdot B = A^{-1}G,$$
$$\therefore B = A^{-1}G.$$

Let

$$A^{-1} = C = \begin{bmatrix} c_{11} & c_{12} & \cdots & c_{1r} \\ c_{21} & c_{22} & \cdots & c_{2r} \\ \cdots & \cdots & \cdots & \cdots \\ c_{r1} & c_{r2} & \cdots & c_{rr} \end{bmatrix}.$$

Then,

$$\begin{bmatrix} b_1 \\ b_2 \\ \cdot \\ b_k \\ \cdot \\ b_r \end{bmatrix} = \begin{bmatrix} c_{11} & c_{12} & \cdots & c_{1r} \\ c_{21} & c_{22} & \cdots & c_{2r} \\ \cdots & \cdots & \cdots & \cdots \\ c_{k1} & c_{k2} & \cdots & c_{kr} \\ \cdots & \cdots & \cdots & \cdots \\ c_{r1} & c_{r2} & \cdots & c_{rr} \end{bmatrix} \cdot \begin{bmatrix} Sx_1y \\ Sx_2y \\ \cdots \\ Sx_ky \\ \cdots \\ Sx_ry \end{bmatrix}.$$

Hence, since two matrices are equal if and only if corresponding elements are equal, we see that

$$b_k = c_{k1}Sx_1y + c_{k2}Sx_2y + \cdots + c_{kr}Sx_ry$$

or

$$b_k = \sum_{j=1}^{r} c_{kj}Sx_jy,$$

which is the same as the results of equation (6).

Instead of inverting the matrix $A$ directly, as illustrated earlier, in order to obtain the elements $c_{ij}$ of $C = A^{-1}$, it is more convenient to proceed indirectly. We know that

$$A \cdot A^{-1} = I$$

or

$$A \cdot C = I.$$

Writing the elements in for each matrix, we have

$$\begin{bmatrix} Sx_1^2 & Sx_1x_2 & \cdots & Sx_1x_r \\ Sx_1x_2 & Sx_2^2 & \cdots & Sx_2x_r \\ \cdots & \cdots & \cdots & \cdots \\ Sx_1x_r & Sx_2x_r & \cdots & Sx_r^2 \end{bmatrix} \cdot \begin{bmatrix} c_{11} & c_{12} & \cdots & c_{1r} \\ c_{21} & c_{22} & \cdots & c_{2r} \\ \cdots & \cdots & \cdots & \cdots \\ c_{r1} & c_{r2} & \cdots & c_{rr} \end{bmatrix} = \begin{bmatrix} 1 & 0 & \cdots & 0 \\ 0 & 1 & \cdots & 0 \\ \cdots & \cdots & \cdots & \cdots \\ 0 & 0 & \cdots & 1 \end{bmatrix}$$

Again, since two matrices are equal if and only if the corresponding elements are equal, we can immediately write down $r$ sets of equations. For example, the first set may be obtained by multiplying all the rows of the $A$ matrix by the first column of the $C$ matrix and setting these sums of products in turn equal to the elements of the first column of the identity matrix. We obtain

$$\begin{aligned} c_{11}Sx_1^2 + c_{21}Sx_1x_2 + \cdots + c_{r1}Sx_1x_r &= 1, \\ c_{11}Sx_1x_2 + c_{21}Sx_2^2 + \cdots + c_{r1}Sx_2x_r &= 0, \\ \cdots\cdots\cdots\cdots\cdots\cdots\cdots\cdots\cdots \\ c_{11}Sx_1x_r + c_{21}Sx_2x_r + \cdots + c_{r1}Sx_r^2 &= 0. \end{aligned}$$

In a similar fashion the other $(r - 1)$ sets of equations may be obtained. The solution of these sets of equations enables us to find the elements $c_{ij}$ of the inverse matrix $C = A^{-1}$. Short methods for obtaining simultaneous solutions to all $r$ sets of equations will be presented in Chap. 15. It should be noted that $c_{ij} = c_{ji}$ because of the symmetry of matrix $A$.

**14.3. Theory of Tests of Significance.**† For references to the theory of tests of significance with regression problems see Bartlett,[6] Yates,[7] and R. A. Fisher.[8]

The equation $Y = \mu + \Sigma\beta_i x_i + \epsilon = \bar{Y} + \Sigma b_i x_i + e$ can be replaced by a new equation

$$Y = \mu + \Sigma\beta_i' z_i + \epsilon = \bar{Y} + \Sigma b_i' z_i + e,$$

where $\{z_i\}$ are functions of $\{x_i\}$ so constructed that $\{z_i\}$ are completely orthogonal variates. As before, the $\epsilon$ are NID$(0,\sigma^2)$. Hence the $Y$'s are NID$(\mu + \Sigma\beta_i' z_i, \sigma^2)$. We might write

$$\begin{aligned} z_1 &= w_{11}x_1, \\ z_2 &= w_{21}x_1 + w_{22}x_2, \\ \cdots&\cdots\cdots\cdots \\ z_r &= w_{r1}x_1 + w_{r2}x_2 + \cdots + w_{rr}x_r, \end{aligned}$$

where $Sz_i^2 = 1$ and $S(z_i z_j) = 0$ $(i \neq j)$. Hence

$$Y = \mu + \Sigma\beta_i x_i + \epsilon \equiv \mu + \Sigma\beta_i' z_i + \epsilon,$$

where $\{x_i\}$ are solved backward in terms of $\{z_i\}$. The least-squares estimate of $\beta_i'$ is $b_i' = Sz_i y = Sz_i Y$, because of the orthogonal relationships. Also,

$$\text{SSE} = S(y - \Sigma b_i' z_i)^2 = Sy^2 - \sum_{i=1}^{r} (b_i')^2.$$

Hence $\Sigma(b_i')^2$ is the reduction in sum of squares due to the regression.

† This section can be omitted if the reader is not interested in a more theoretical presentation than in Sec. 14.1.

Before continuing, we should show that our solution to the least-squares equations is unique. We know that

$$\hat{Y} = \bar{Y} + \sum_{i=1}^{r} b'_i z_i \equiv \bar{Y} + \sum_{i=1}^{r} b''_i x_i,$$

where $b''_i = \sum_{j=1}^{r} w_{ji} b'_j$. For example,

$$b''_1 = w_{11}b'_1 + w_{21}b'_2 + \cdots + w_{r1}b'_r.$$

But $b''_i \equiv b_i$, because both were derived by minimizing $Se^2$. There can be but one minimum because the $Se^2$ equation is quadratic in the $b$'s. Hence

$$\Sigma(b'_i)^2 = \Sigma b_i S x_i y.$$

We shall use the orthogonalized regression coefficients $\{b'_i\}$ in the theory which follows, always remembering that any $x_j$ is a function of only $z_1, z_2, \ldots, z_j$.

Because of the relationship

$$Sz_i z_j = \begin{cases} 0 & i \neq j, \\ 1 & i = j, \end{cases}$$

$$Sz_i\left(Y - \mu - \sum_{j=1}^{r} \beta'_j z_j\right) = Sz_i\epsilon = Sz_i Y - \sum_{j=1}^{r} \beta'_j Sz_i z_j = b'_i - \beta'_i.$$

Hence

$$(b'_i - \beta'_i) = Sz_i\epsilon,$$

a completely orthogonal form in the $\epsilon$, which are NID$(0,\sigma^2)$. From our theory on orthogonal forms, we know that

$$E(b'_i - \beta'_i) = Sz_i E(\epsilon) = 0 \qquad \text{or} \qquad E(b'_i) = \beta'_i,$$
$$\sigma^2(b'_i) = E[(b'_i - \beta'_i)^2] = Sz_i^2\sigma^2 = \sigma^2,$$
$$E[(b'_i - \beta'_i)(b'_j - \beta'_j)] = 0, \qquad i \neq j.$$

Since the $\epsilon$ are NID, so are $(b'_i - \beta'_i)$. Also, $t = (b'_i - \beta'_i)/s$, where $E(s^2) = \sigma^2$. Or in terms of the original variates $\{X_i\}$

$$t = (b_i - \beta_0)/s\sqrt{\sum_j w_{ji}^2}, \qquad i = 1, 2, \ldots, r.$$

Next we need to determine $s^2$.

$$\text{SSE} = S\left(y - \sum_i b'_i z_i\right)^2 = S\left[y - \sum_i \beta'_i z_i - \sum_i (b'_i - \beta'_i) z_i\right]^2$$
$$= S\left(y - \sum_i \beta'_i z_i\right)^2 - \sum_i (b'_i - \beta'_i)^2 = S(\epsilon - \bar{\epsilon})^2 - \sum_i (b'_i - \beta'_i)^2.$$
$$E(\text{SSE}) = (n - 1)\sigma^2 - r\sigma^2 = (n - r - 1)\sigma^2.$$

Hence if we let $s^2 = \text{SSE}/(n - r - 1)$, $E(s^2) = \sigma^2$.

If it is desired to make a test of the hypothesis $\{\beta_i' = 0\}$, it would be useful to be able to use the $F$ ratio as a test criterion. In order to use $F$, it is necessary to find two quantities distributed as $\chi^2\sigma^2$, such that the ratio of the two will test the hypothesis $\{\beta_i' = 0\}$ against the alternative $\{\beta_i' \neq 0\}$. It would appear from the above that SSE is distributed as $\chi^2\sigma^2$ with $(n - r - 1)$ degrees of freedom. A more rigorous method of proof is the following:

Augment the existing set of $r$ completely orthogonal variates $\{z_i\}$ by $(n - r - 1)$ others, which we shall designate as $\{p_j\}$ $(j = 1,2, \ldots, n - r - 1)$. The estimation equation will then be

$$Y = \mu + \sum_{i=1}^{r} \beta_i' z_i + \epsilon = \bar{Y} + \sum_i b_i' z_i + \sum_j c_j' p_j,$$

where $c_j'$ is the regression coefficient for $p_j[E(\Sigma c_j' p_j) = 0]$. Note that with these $n$ orthogonal variates, there is no residual sum of squares. Hence

$$S[y - \Sigma b_i' z_i - \Sigma c_j' p_j]^2 = 0.$$

$$\begin{aligned} 0 &= S[y - \Sigma \beta_i' z_i - \Sigma (b_i' - \beta_i') z_i - \Sigma c_j' p_j]^2 \\ &= S\left[y - \sum_i \beta_i' z_i\right]^2 - \sum_i (b_i' - \beta_i')^2 - \sum_j (c_j')^2, \end{aligned}$$

or

$$\sum_{j=1}^{n-r-1} (c_j')^2 = S(\epsilon - \bar{\epsilon})^2 - \sum_{i=1}^{r} (b_i' - \beta_i')^2 = \text{SSE}.$$

Hence we have broken SSE into $(n - r - 1)$ orthogonal squares. Furthermore,

$$c_j' = S(yp_j) = S(\epsilon p_j) + \sum_i \beta_i' S(z_i p_j),$$

$$E\left[c_j' - \sum_i \beta_i' S(z_i p_j)\right] = 0, \qquad E(c_j') = \sum_i \beta_i' S(z_i p_j) = 0.$$

$$\sigma^2(c_j') = E[(S\epsilon p_j)^2] = \sigma^2, \qquad \sigma(c_j' c_k') = 0, \qquad k \neq j.$$

$$\sigma(c_j' b_i') = E[c_j'(b_i' - \beta_i')] = E[S(\epsilon p_j) S(\epsilon z_i)] = 0.$$

Since the $\{c_j'\}$ are orthogonal linear forms in NID$(0,\sigma^2)$ variates, they are NID$(0,\sigma^2)$. Hence the $(c_j')^2$ are independently distributed as $\chi^2\sigma^2$ with 1 degree of freedom each, or SSE is so distributed with $(n - r - 1)$ degrees of freedom.†

We have already shown that the $(b_i' - \beta_i')$ are NID$(0,\sigma^2)$; hence, $(b_i' - \beta_i')^2$ is distributed as $\chi^2\sigma^2$ with 1 degree of freedom, and $\Sigma(b_i')^2$ will be distributed as $\chi^2\sigma^2$ with $r$ degrees of freedom, under the null hypothesis $\{\beta_i' = 0\}$.† Hence

† Since $\{c_j'\}$ and $\{b_i'\}$ are independent of one another, SSE and SSR are independent of one another. This is a necessary condition for the statements concerning $F$.

$$F = \frac{\Sigma(b_i')^2}{r} \bigg/ \frac{\text{SSE}}{n - r - 1}$$

can be used to test the null hypothesis. Also, we see that the single-tailed $F$ test should be used if the alternative hypothesis is $\{\beta_i' \neq 0\}$, because the expected value of the denominator is still $\sigma^2$ while the expected value of the numerator is

$$\sum_i E[(b_i')^2]/r = \sum_i \{E[(b_i' - \beta_i')^2] + 2E[\beta_i'(b_i' - \beta_i')] + E[(\beta_i')^2]\}/r$$
$$= \sum_i [\sigma^2 + (\beta_i')^2]/r = \sigma^2 + \sum_i (\beta_i')^2/r > \sigma^2.$$

There are many conditions under which it would be desirable to assume several of the $\beta_i' \neq 0$. For a general test, we shall assume $\{\beta_1', \beta_2', \ldots, \beta_k' \neq 0\}$ and test the null hypothesis that $\{\beta_{k+1}', \ldots, \beta_r' = 0\}$.

We have shown that SSE, found by fitting $\{b_i'\}$ for $i = 1, 2, \ldots, r$, is independent of the hypotheses for $\{\beta_i'\}$ and that the $(b_i' - \beta_i')^2$ are independently distributed as $\chi^2\sigma^2$ with 1 degree of freedom each. Hence under the null hypothesis that $\{\beta_{k+1}', \ldots, \beta_r' = 0\}$,

$$\sum_{i=k+1}^{r} (b_i')^2$$

is distributed as $\chi^2\sigma^2$ with $(r - k)$ degrees of freedom. We know that the reduction in the residual sum of squares due to fitting $r$ $\{b_i'\}$ is given by

$$\sum_{i=1}^{r} (b_i')^2,$$

and that due to fitting the first $k$ $\{b_i'\}$ is

$$\sum_{i=1}^{k} (b_i')^2.$$

Hence

$$\sum_{i=k+1}^{r} (b_i')^2$$

is the additional reduction in sum of squares gained by using $\{b_{k+1}', \ldots, b_r'\}$ in the regression equation after first using $\{b_1', \ldots, b_k'\}$. It should be emphasized that, by use of the orthogonal transformation, every $b_i'$ can be computed independently of all the others. Hence the reduction due to any one of the regression coefficients is independent of whether any others have been used and is independent of any assumptions made about the expected values of these others.

The major difficulty facing us at this stage is to transfer these results on the additional reduction due to the last $(r - k)$ fixed variates back to the original $\{b_i,\beta_i\}$ setup, where the value of any regression coefficient depends upon all the others included in the analysis. For example, the values of $\{b_1,b_2, \ldots ,b_k\}$ as estimated from all the $r$ $\{x_i\}$ will not be the same as the $\{b_1'',b_2'', \ldots ,b_k''\}$ as estimated from the first $k$ $\{x_i\}$. In order to use our orthogonal results, the following conditions must hold:

(1) If we let $R_r$ be the reduction in the residual sum of squares due to the first $r$ $\{x_i\}$ and $R_k$ that due to the first $k$ $\{x_i\}$, then $(R_r - R_k)$ must be distributed as $\chi^2\sigma^2$ with $(r - k)$ degrees of freedom under the null hypothesis $\{\beta_{k+1}, \beta_{k+2}, \ldots , \beta_r = 0\}$.

(2) The residual sum of squares $Sy^2 - R_r$ is independently distributed as $\chi^2\sigma^2$ with $(n - r - 1)$ degrees of freedom.

We have shown that

$$\sum_{i=1}^{k} (b_i' - \beta_i')^2$$

is distributed as $\chi^2\sigma^2$ with $k$ degrees of freedom,

$$\sum_{i=k+1}^{r} (b_i' - \beta_i')^2$$

as $\chi^2\sigma^2$ with $(r - k)$ degrees of freedom, and

$$\text{SSE} = S(\epsilon - \bar{\epsilon})^2 - \sum_{i=1}^{r} (b_i' - \beta_i')^2 = Sy^2 - \sum_{i=1}^{r} (b_i')^2$$

as $\chi^2\sigma^2$ with $(n - r - 1)$ degrees of freedom—all independent of one another.

But we have also shown that both methods of deriving the regression coefficients minimize $Se^2$ and hence produce the same SSE. Hence

$$Sy^2 - R_r = \text{SSE}$$

is distributed as $\chi^2\sigma^2$ with $(n - r - 1)$ degrees of freedom. Also

$$R_r = \sum_{i=1}^{r} (b_i')^2.$$

If we solve backward for the $\{x_i\}$ in terms of the $\{z_i\}$, we find that

$$x_i = w_{i1}'z_1 + w_{i2}'z_2 + \cdots + w_{ii}'z_i,$$

where $w'_{ij}$ are functions of the $w_{ij}$. For example,

$$w'_{11} = 1/w_{11}, \qquad w'_{21} = -(w_{21}/w_{11}w_{22}), \qquad w'_{22} = 1/w_{22}.$$

Since $\Sigma\beta_j x_j \equiv \Sigma\beta'_j z_j$, and by equating the coefficients of $\{z_i\}$, we find that

$$\beta'_j = \sum_{i=j}^{r} w'_{ij}\beta_i.$$

This shows that the null hypothesis $\{\beta_{k+1}, \ldots, \beta_r = 0\}$ means that $\{\beta'_{k+1}, \ldots, \beta'_r = 0\}$ because the $\beta'_j$ are functions of only $\{\beta_j, \beta_{j+1}, \ldots, \beta_r\}$. Hence $\sum_{i=k+1}^{r} (b'_i)^2$ is distributed as $\chi^2\sigma^2$ with $(r - k)$ degrees of freedom under the null hypothesis for the $\{\beta_i\}$.

Now $R_k$ is the reduction due to the first $k$ $\{x_i\}$. But the first $k$ $\{z_i\}$ are functions of only the first $k$ $\{x_i\}$. For example,

$$z_k = \sum_{j=1}^{k} w_{kj}x_j.$$

Again the reduction due to using the $\{x_i\}$ or $\{z_i\}$ must be the same, so that $R_k = \sum_{i=1}^{k} (b'_i)^2$. But since $R_r = \sum_{i=1}^{r} (b'_i)^2$, the added reduction after the first $k$ $\{x_i\}$ is given by

$$R_r - R_k = \sum_{i=k+1}^{r} (b'_i)^2.$$

It might be added that the $\{z_i\}$ behave just like orthogonal polynomials, which will be discussed in Chap. 16.

**14.4. The Regression Problem When Certain Assumptions Are Relaxed.** Suppose we relax the assumptions of normality and homoscedasticity in the previous sections of this chapter. For this case, David and Neyman[9] give a proof of the following theorem on least squares. Given

(i) $Y_1, Y_2, \ldots, Y_n$ are independent.

(ii) $E(Y_j) = \sum_{i=1}^{r} \beta_i X_{ij}$ and the $X$'s are fixed variates.†

(iii) Out of the $n$ equations in (ii), it is possible to select at least one system of $r$ equations soluble with respect to the $\beta$'s.

(iv) The variances of the $Y_j$ satisfy the relationship

$$\sigma_j^2 = \sigma^2/w_j, \qquad j = 1, 2, \ldots, n,$$

† If it is desired to use the intercept $\alpha$ in the equation, set $X_{1j} \equiv 1$.

where $\sigma^2$ may be unknown but the $\{w_j\}$ are known positive constants $> 0$. Then

(*a*) The best linear estimate of $Y$ is

$$\hat{Y} = \Sigma b_i X_i,$$

where the $b$'s are obtained by minimizing the weighted sum of squares

$$\text{SSE}_w = \underset{j}{S} w_j \left( Y_j - \sum_{i=1}^{r} b_i X_{ij} \right)^2$$

with respect to the $b_i$. The typical least-squares equation is

$$\frac{\partial \text{SSE}_w}{\partial b_k} = 0\colon b_1 SwX_1X_k + \cdots + b_k SwX_k^2 + \cdots + b_r SwX_rX_k = SwX_kY.$$

(*b*) The estimate of $\sigma^2(\hat{Y})$ is given by

$$s^2(\hat{Y}) = \frac{-\Delta_0\Delta_1}{(n-r)\Delta^2},$$

where

$$\Delta_0 = \begin{vmatrix} H_0 & H_1 & \cdots & H_r \\ H_1 & G_{11} & \cdots & G_{1r} \\ \cdot & \cdot & \cdots & \cdot \\ H_r & G_{r1} & \cdots & G_{rr} \end{vmatrix}, \qquad \Delta_1 = \begin{vmatrix} 0 & X_1 & \cdots & X_r \\ X_1 & G_{11} & \cdots & G_{1r} \\ \cdot & \cdot & \cdots & \cdot \\ X_r & G_{r1} & \cdots & G_{rr} \end{vmatrix},$$

$$\Delta = \begin{vmatrix} G_{11} & \cdots & G_{1r} \\ \cdot & \cdots & \cdot \\ G_{r1} & \cdots & G_{rr} \end{vmatrix}, \qquad \begin{aligned} H_0 &= SwY^2, \\ H_i &= SwX_iY, \\ G_{ii'} &= SwX_iX_{i'}. \end{aligned}$$

If $r = 2$, with $\beta_1 = \alpha$ and $\beta_2 = \beta$, we have

$$\hat{Y} = a + bX = \bar{Y}_w + b(X - \bar{X}_w),$$

where $X_1 \equiv 1$, $X_2 \equiv X$, $\bar{Y}_w = SwY/Sw$, and $\bar{X}_w = SwX/Sw$. Also, $b = Swxy/Swx^2$, where $x = X - \bar{X}_w$ and $y = Y - \bar{Y}_w$, and $\bar{X}_w$ and $\bar{Y}_w$ are called weighted means and $b$ a weighted regression coefficient. Often the weights are adjusted so that $Sw = 1$.

**Example 14.2.** The following data are taken from an experiment on soybeans with three nitrogen treatments plus a check treatment (no nitrogen) to find out the relation between the mean yield of soybeans per acre ($Y$) and amount of nitrogen in pounds per acre ($X$):

| | | | | |
|---|---|---|---|---|
| Lb N per acre ($X$) | 0 | 47 | 94 | 157 |
| Bu beans per acre ($Y$) | 14.7 | 14.6 | 17.8 | 22.1 |
| No. of plots | 14 | 7 | 7 | 7 |
| $w$ | 2 | 1 | 1 | 1 |

Since 14 plots were used for the 0 level of nitrogen and 7 plots for the three treatments, the variance of the mean yield for the 0 nitrogen plots was one-half that of the mean yields for the three treatments; so weights of (2,1,1,1) were used in estimating the regression of mean yield on amount of nitrogen per acre.

The calculations needed were

$$\bar{X}_w = 59.60, \qquad \bar{Y}_w = 16.78,$$

$$Swx^2 = 17{,}933.20, \qquad Swxy = 828.66, \qquad Swy^2 = 42.75,$$

$$b = 0.0462,$$

$$\hat{Y} = 16.78 + 0.0462(X - 59.60).$$

In this case the estimate of variance was taken from the $13 + 3(6) = 31$ degrees of freedom within treatments: $s^2 = 7.56$. Hence the estimated variance of each of the $Y$'s, which were means of $7w$ plots, was

$$\frac{7.56}{7w} = \frac{1.08}{w}.$$

See Exercise 14.12 for another estimate of the variance, using these 31 degrees of freedom plus the 2 degrees of freedom for deviations from regression.

TABLE 14.1

Estimates of $\sigma^2(Y)$ for Example 13.1†

| Range of $X$ | | All incomes | | | | Income < $4,000 | | | |
|---|---|---|---|---|---|---|---|---|---|
| | | $\bar{X}$ | $Sn$ | $s^2(Y)$ | $w$ | $\bar{X}$ | $Sn$ | $s^2(Y)$ | $w$ |
| 1 | 39–44 | 42.3 | 36 | .366 | 2.732 | 42.3 | 36 | .366 | 2.732 |
| 2 | 45–46 | 45.1 | 54 | .457 | 2.188 | 45.1 | 54 | .457 | 2.188 |
| 3 | 47–48 | 47.7 | 120 | .431 | 2.320 | 47.7 | 119 | .332 | 3.012 |
| 4 | 49–50 | 49.9 | 68 | .314 | 3.185 | 49.9 | 68 | .314 | 3.185 |
| 5 | 51–52 | 51.4 | 70 | .545 | 1.835 | 51.4 | 70 | .545 | 1.835 |
| 6 | 53–54 | 53.4 | 108 | .587 | 1.704 | 53.4 | 108 | .587 | 1.704 |
| 7 | 55–56 | 55.4 | 91 | .435 | 2.299 | 55.4 | 91 | .435 | 2.299 |
| 8 | 57–60 | 58.4 | 95 | 1.111 | 0.900 | 58.4 | 93 | .837 | 1.195 |
| 9 | 61–64 | 62.3 | 73 | 1.807 | 0.553 | 62.3 | 68 | .678 | 1.475 |
| 10 | 65–70 | 67.4 | 68 | 1.845 | 0.542 | 67.3 | 61 | .623 | 1.605 |
| 11 | 71–76 | 73.6 | 67 | 2.727 | 0.367 | 73.5 | 63 | 1.063 | 0.941 |
| 12 | 77–91 | 80.8 | 59 | 8.254 | 0.121 | 80.1 | 45 | .894 | 1.119 |
| Total | | | 909 | | | | 876 | | |

† $\sigma^2(Y)$ measures the variation of net farm incomes about their means. $Sn$ is the number of farmers for each class (summing the values of $n$ in Table 13.1). The number of degrees of freedom for each $s^2(Y)$ is $Sn$ less the number of $X$'s for the class (total of 860 and 830, respectively). $w = 1/s^2(Y)$.

**Example 14.3.** It appeared from the graph of the data of Example 13.1 (Fig. 13.3) that the variability about the regression line tended to increase with increasing $X$. In order to investigate this matter, the data were grouped into 12 classes, and a separate estimate of variance was computed for each group. This was done both for all the income data and for that portion of the data after eliminating all incomes of over $4,000. These estimates of variance are presented in Table 14.1.

In Table 14.1, $s^2(Y)$ was computed by adding together

$$Sy^2 = S(Y - \bar{Y})^2$$

for each $X$ in a class and dividing this sum by the total degrees of freedom for the group. For example, with the first group ($X$ from 39 to 44), we had the following distribution:

| $X$ | $n$ | $d.f.$ | $Sy^2$ | $s^2$ |
|---|---|---|---|---|
| 39 | 3 | 2 | 1.213 | .607 |
| 41 | 3 | 2 | .341 | .170 |
| 42 | 18 | 17 | 8.325 | .490 |
| 43 | 1 | 0 | 0 | |
| 44 | 11 | 10 | 1.475 | .148 |
| Total | 36 | 31 | 11.354 | .366 |

The data were grouped like this in order to smooth out the estimates of $\sigma^2(Y)$ by increasing the number of degrees of freedom for each estimate.

A weighted regression of $Y$ on $X$ can then be computed using as weights the values of $w$ given in Table 14.1; for example, any observation with $X$ to 39 to 44 will receive a weight of 2.73. These weights are applied to the data presented in Table 13.1. Since the same weights are used for many observations, a short-cut computing procedure can be used as follows:

(i) Compute for each class: $S(nX)$, $S(SY)$, $S(nX^2)$, $S[X(SY)]$, and $S[(SY)^2/n]$. It might be easier to compute $\bar{Y}$ for each class and make the last computation as $S[\bar{Y}(SY)]$.

(ii) Multiply each sum in (i) by the corresponding weight, $w$, in Table 14.1, and sum these weighted values over the 12 classes, for example, $S(w) = S[w(Sn)]$, $S(wX) = S[w(SnX)]$, $S(wX^2) = S[w(SnX^2)]$.

(iii) Adjust the sums in (ii) for the means, for example,

$$S(wx^2) = S(wX^2) - \frac{(SwX)^2}{S(w)}.$$

(iv) $b = S(wxy)/S(wx^2)$; $\text{SSR} = (Swxy)^2/S(wx^2)$.

There is some question as to the proper error term to use in this case, because the weights were derived from the data. The simplest procedure is to use

$$\text{SSE} = S(wy^2) - \text{SSR},$$

with $N - 2$ degrees of freedom ($N = 909$ or $876$). In this case

$$S(wy^2) = (n - m) + S[wS(\hat{Y}SY)] - \frac{(SwY)^2}{S(w)},$$

where $m$ is the number of $X$'s in Table 13.1 ($m = 49$ or $46$) and the sums are taken from step (ii) above. In this case $s^2 = \text{SSE}/(N - 2)$, and $F = \text{SSR}/s^2$ can be used to test for the significance of the regression of $Y$ on $X$. In Sec. 25.2, we shall consider another estimate of the error variance.

The sums in (i) for each class and the weighted sums (ii) over all classes are presented in Table 14.2.

TABLE 14.2

| Class | $S(nX)$ | $S(SY)$ | $S(nX^2)$ | $S(XSY)$ | $S(\hat{Y}SY)$ | $w$ |
|---|---|---|---|---|---|---|
| 1 | 1,523 | 26.2 | 64,503 | 1,106 | 19.7 | 2.732 |
| 2 | 2,433 | 52.5 | 109,623 | 2,365 | 51.1 | 2.188 |
| 3 | 5,726 | 110.2 | 273,250 | 5,258 | 101.2 | 2.320 |
| 4 | 3,383 | 55.0 | 168,317 | 2,739 | 45.2 | 3.185 |
| 5 | 3,601 | 76.2 | 185,263 | 3,922 | 83.3 | 1.835 |
| 6 | 5,769 | 129.7 | 308,187 | 6,939 | 159.9 | 1.704 |
| 7 | 5,044 | 113.1 | 279,604 | 6,278 | 144.6 | 2.299 |
| 8 | 5,546 | 139.3 | 323,872 | 8,139 | 206.6 | .900 |
| 9 | 4,548 | 118.9 | 283,438 | 7,423 | 204.1 | .553 |
| 10 | 4,580 | 130.4 | 308,690 | 8,796 | 252.3 | .542 |
| 11 | 4,930 | 152.8 | 362,964 | 11,270 | 380.7 | .367 |
| 12 | 4,769 | 211.7 | 386,097 | 17,399 | 1,112.6 | .121 |
| Sum† | 73,953 | 1,581.6 | 3,889,486 | 85,013 | 2,012.0 | |

† Weighted by weights, $w$. $S(wSn) = 1{,}427.63$.

The sums adjusted for the mean are

$$S(wx^2) = 3{,}889{,}486 - 3{,}830{,}857 = 58{,}629,$$
$$S(wxy) = 85{,}013 - 81{,}929 = 3{,}084,$$
$$S(wy^2) = 860 + 2{,}012 - 1{,}752 = 1{,}120.$$

Hence

$$b = S(wxy)/S(wx^2) = 0.05260,$$
$$\text{SSR} = (Swxy)^2/S(wx^2) = 162,$$
$$\text{SSE} = S(wy^2) - \text{SSR} = 958,$$
$$s^2 = \text{SSE}/907 = 1.056,$$
$$\hat{Y} = 1.108 + 0.0526(X - 51.80).$$

## EXERCISES†

**14.1.** Show that the variance of $\bar{Y}$ is $\sigma^2/n$ and that $\bar{Y}$ is independent of each of the $b_i$.

**14.2.** (*a*) If we use the model, $\hat{Y} = a + \Sigma b_i X_i$, show that

$$a = \bar{Y} - \Sigma b_i \bar{X}_i.$$

(*b*) What is the variance of $a$?

**14.3.** What changes should be made in the regression analysis if

$$E(Y) = \sum_{i=1}^{r} \beta_i X_i?$$

**14.4.** Given the regression model $Y = \mu + \sum_{i=1}^{r} \beta_i x_i + \epsilon = \hat{Y} + e$. Show that

(*a*) $e$ is uncorrelated with any of the $x_i$, that is, $Sx_i e = 0$ (for any $i$).

(*b*) $S\hat{Y}e = 0$.

(*c*) $Se^2 = \text{SSE} = SY^2 - S\hat{Y}^2$.

**14.5.** How could you test the hypothesis that $\beta_i = \beta_j$?

**14.6.** Set up the model and normal equations for $r = 2$.

(*a*) Show that

$$c_{11} = Sx_2^2/DSx_1^2, \qquad c_{12} = c_{21} = -Sx_1x_2/DSx_1^2, \qquad c_{22} = 1/D,$$

where $D = Sx_2^2 - (Sx_1x_2)^2/Sx_1^2$.

(*b*) Show that

$$b_1 = \beta_1 + c_{11}Sx_1\epsilon + c_{12}Sx_2\epsilon.$$

Set up the same equation for $b_2$. Using these results, prove algebraically that

$$\sigma^2(b_1) = c_{11}\sigma^2, \qquad \sigma^2(b_2) = c_{22}\sigma^2, \qquad \sigma(b_1b_2) = c_{12}\sigma^2.$$

(*c*) Prove that $b_1$ and $b_2$ can be estimated in a two-stage estimation procedure:

(i) $y = b_1'x_1 + e_1$; $x_2 = b_x x_1 + e_x$,

(ii) $e_1 = b_2 e_x + e_2 = b_2(x_2 - b_x x_1) + e_2$.

Determine $b_1'$, $b_x$, and $b_2$ by least squares, and show that

$$y = b_1'x_1 + b_2\left(x_2 - \frac{Sx_1x_2}{Sx_1^2}x_1\right) + e_2$$

and

$$b_1 = b_1' - b_2\frac{Sx_1x_2}{Sx_1^2}.$$

† Exercise 14.6 should be worked by everyone.

Hence the regression of $y$ on $x_1$ and $x_2$ can be regarded as the regression on $x_1$ (with regression coefficient $b_1'$) and on $x_2$ adjusted for $x_1$ (with regression coefficient $b_2$), where $x_2 - (Sx_1x_2/Sx_1^2)x_1$ is the value of $x_2$ adjusted for $x_1$.

(*d*) Using the results in (*c*), show that

$$\text{SSR} = \frac{(Sx_1y)^2}{Sx_1^2} + \frac{(Se_xy)^2}{Se_x^2} = z_1^2 + z_2^2.$$

(*e*) Finally show that

$$E(z_1^2) = \left[\beta_1 + \beta_2 \frac{Sx_1x_2}{Sx_1^2}\right]^2 Sx_1^2 + \sigma^2, \qquad E(z_2^2) = D\beta_2^2 + \sigma^2,$$

$$E(\text{SSR}) = \beta_1^2 Sx_1^2 + 2\beta_1\beta_2 Sx_1x_2 + \beta_2^2 Sx_2^2 + 2\sigma^2, \qquad E(\text{SSE}) = (n-3)\sigma^2.$$

Set up the analysis-of-variance table to summarize these results.

(*f*) How would you test the null hypothesis that $\beta_2 = 0$? $\beta_1 = \beta_2 = 0$?

(*g*) Can you set up a two stage estimating procedure to test the null hypothesis that $\beta_1 = 0$? How would you fit these results into the analysis-of-variance table?

(*h*) What are the variances of $\delta'$ and $e'$ for predicting $Y$ from $X_1 = X_1'$, $X_2 = X_2'$?

**14.7.** Given $Y = \mu + \beta_1x_1 + \beta_2x_2 + \epsilon$, but we estimate only

$$\hat{Y} = \bar{Y} + b_1'x_1.$$

Show that $b_1'$ is a biased estimate of $\beta_1$ and that $s^2$ is also a biased estimate of $\sigma^2$.

**14.8.** Given $Y = \mu + \beta_1'x_1 + \epsilon$, but we estimate with

$$\hat{Y} = \bar{Y} + b_1x_1 + b_2x_2.$$

Determine whether or not $b_1$ and $s^2$ are unbiased estimates of $\beta_1'$ and $\sigma^2$, respectively.

**14.9.** In the analysis of the data given in Exercise 13.4, it was thought advisable to use as a second fixed variate ($X_2$) the value of $Y$ for the previous year: 77.4, 87.4, 97.6, . . . , 110.7. Use the results in Exercise 14.6 to:

(*a*) Estimate the two regression coefficients and their standard errors.

(*b*) Set up the complete analysis of variance, as in (*e*) and (*g*).

(*c*) Estimate the average $Y$ for $X_1' = 100$ and $X_2' = 100$ and the standard error of this estimate.

**14.10.** Show that the normal equations are also the maximum-likelihood equations for estimating the $\beta$'s.

**14.11.** Use the orthogonal transformations of Sec. 14.3 for $r = 5$. Note that $\sigma^2(b_i') = \sigma^2$ and $\sigma(b_i'b_j') = 0$. Show that (*a*) $b_5 = w_{5,5}b'_5$ and $b_4 = w_{4,4}b'_4 + w_{5,4}b'_5$.

(*b*) The added reduction in residual sum of squares due to the last two fixed variates ($X_4$ and $X_5$) over the reduction due to the first three fixed variates ($X_1$, $X_2$, and $X_3$) alone is given by

$$\frac{w_{5,5}^2 b_4^2 - 2w_{5,4}w_{5,5}b_4b_5 + (w_{4,4}^2 + w_{5,4}^2)b_5^2}{w_{4,4}^2 w_{5,5}^2} = \frac{c_{5,5}b_4^2 - 2c_{4,5}b_4b_5 + c_{4,4}b_5^2}{c_{4,4}c_{5,5} - c_{4,5}^2}.$$

**14.12.** (*a*) Show that, for $r \doteq 2$,

$$\text{SSE}_w = Swy^2 - \frac{(Swy)^2}{Swx^2}; \quad \widehat{\sigma^2} = \text{SSE}_w/(n-2).$$

What would be the value of $\text{SSE}_w$ for Example 14.2?

(*b*) Also show that $\sigma^2(\bar{Y}_w) = \sigma^2/Sw$, $\sigma^2(b) = \sigma^2/Swx^2$, $\sigma^2(\delta') = \sigma^2\left[\frac{1}{Sw} + \frac{x'^2}{Swx^2}\right]$, and $\sigma^2(e') = \sigma^2\left[\frac{1}{w'} + \frac{1}{Sw} + \frac{x'^2}{Swx^2}\right]$, where $x' = (X' - \bar{X}_w)$.

(*c*) In Example 14.3, determine 95 per cent confidence limits for $\beta$ and for $E(Y')$ and $Y'$ when $X' = 80$. What weight do you use for $X' = 80$?

**14.13.** Use the data given in Tables 13.1 and 14.1 for incomes less than $4,000 to compute a weighted regression of $Y$ on $X$.

**14.14.** G. A. Baker[10] furnishes an example on ovarian weights (in milligrams) of rats receiving five dosages of Serum VII, 16 rats for each dosage.

| Dosage in rat units ($X$) | 4 | 6 | 8 | 12 | 16 |
|---|---|---|---|---|---|
| Mean weight ($Y$) | 27.00 | 38.31 | 43.44 | 65.25 | 72.88 |
| $s^2(Y)$ | 1.59 | 3.96 | 3.64 | 18.96 | 45.95 |
| Smoothed weights ($w$) | 7.72 | 2.16 | 1.00 | .37 | .19 |

The "smoothed weights" were found by smoothing the values of $s(Y)$.

(*a*) Show that, if we use the "smoothed weights,"

$$\hat{Y} = -15.13 + 69.43 \log_{10} X,$$

where $\log_{10} X$ is used as the independent variate.

(*b*) Use as weights reciprocals of $s^2(Y)$ to derive another estimate of $\hat{Y}$.

**14.15.** It is evident from Table 14.1 that the variances increase systematically with $X$. If there is a perfect correlation between $X$ and $\sigma(Y)$, it can be shown that we should use a logarithmic relationship as was done in Exercise 13.11 (see reference 11). For all incomes, $s(Y)$ actually increases faster than $X$ but not for incomes less than $4,000. The individual values of $s^2(Z)$ and $s'^2(Z)$ are given below for the 12 groups in

Table 14.1, where $Z = \log(Y + 1)$ and $s'^2(Z)$ is used for the incomes under \$4,000. The variances have been multiplied by 10.

| Group | 1 | 2 | 3 | 4 | 5 | 6 | 7 | 8 | 9 | 10 | 11 | 12 |
|---|---|---|---|---|---|---|---|---|---|---|---|---|
| $s^2(Z)$ | .196 | .220 | .199 | .174 | .188 | .196 | .152 | .296 | .434 | .329 | .354 | .548 |
| $s'^2(Z)$ | .196 | .220 | .182 | .174 | .188 | .196 | .152 | .296 | .336 | .200 | .285 | .232 |

(*a*) Use Bartlett's test (Chap. 12) to test for unequal variances for $s'^2(Z)$. Is there a significant upward trend for these variances?

(*b*) What do you conclude about $s^2(Z)$?

(*c*) How would you determine whether or not a log transformation would be a useful one?

## References Cited

1. MONROE, R. J., *On the Use of Non-linear Systems in the Estimation of Nutritional Requirements of Animals*, unpublished thesis, North Carolina State College, Raleigh, N.C., 1949.
2. HARTLEY, H. O., "The Estimation of Non-linear Parameters by Internal Least Squares," *Biometrika*, **35**:32–45 (1948).
3. SNEDECOR, G. W., *Statistical Methods*, 4th ed., Collegiate Press, Inc., of Iowa State College, Ames, Iowa, 1946. Chaps. 13, 14.
4. WALLACE, H. A., and G. W. SNEDECOR, "*Correlation and Machine Calculation*," *Iowa State Coll., Official Pub.* 30, No. 4 (1931).
5. DWYER, P. S., *Linear Computations*, John Wiley & Sons, Inc., New York, 1951.
6. BARTLETT, M. S., "On the Theory of Statistical Regression," *Proc. Roy. Soc. Edinburgh*, **53**:260*ff*. (1933).
7. YATES, F., "Orthogonal Functions and Tests of Significance in the Analysis of Variance." *J. Roy. Stat. Soc. Suppl.*, **5**:177–180 (1938).
8. FISHER, R. A., "Applications of Student's Distribution," *Metron*, **5**:90–104 (1926).
9. DAVID, F. N., and J. NEYMAN, "Extension of the Markoff Theorem on Least Squares," *Stat. Research Mem.*, **2**:105–116 (1938).
10. BAKER, G. A., "Linear Regression When the Standard Deviations of Arrays Are Not All Equal," *J. Am. Stat. Assoc.*, **36**:500–506 (1941).
11. BARTLETT, M. S., "The Use of Transformations," *Biometrics*, **3**:39–52 (1947).

## Other Reading

DEMING, W. E., *Statistical Adjustment of Data*, John Wiley & Sons, Inc., New York, 1943.

GAUSS, C. F., *Werke*, Göttingen, 1880. Vol. 4.

KENDALL, M. G., *The Advanced Theory of Statistics*, Chas. Griffin & Co., Ltd., London, 1946. Vol. II, Chap. 22.

WILKS, S. S., *Mathematical Statistics*, Princeton University Press, Princeton, N.J., 1943. Chap. 8.

## CHAPTER 15

# COMPUTATIONAL METHODS AND METHODS OF ANALYSIS FOR A GENERAL REGRESSION MODEL

**15.1. Introduction.** In general, if $r$ is large, some short-cut procedure is needed to solve for the $c_{ij}$ values. Snedecor[1] and R. A. Fisher[2] discuss the use of the $C$ matrix and the Doolittle method of obtaining it. Waugh and Dwyer[3] and Dwyer[4] present a variety of computational methods. Dwyer[4] outlines the theoretical background for matrix inversion and presents numerous examples.

We shall present an example for $r = 4$, using some data collected by the Southern Cooperative Group[5] to estimate the quantity of vitamin $B_2$ in milligrams per gram for turnip greens ($Y$) from a knowledge of the radiation in relative gram calories per square centimeter per minute during the preceding half day of sunlight ($X_1$), average soil moisture tension ($X_2$), air temperature in degrees Fahrenheit ($X_3$), and the product ($X_1 \cdot X_2$) or ($X_4$). In all, 27 sets of observations were taken on these variates. In order to simplify the computations, these variates were coded as follows: $X_1$ and $X_2$ were divided by 100, $X_3$ was divided by 10, and $X_4$ was divided by 10,000. In general it is advisable to code the original data so that the $a_{ij}$ ($Sx_ix_j$) are reduced to values between 1 and 10, if possible. The coded data are presented in Table 15.1.

The matrices of the sums of squares and cross products are

$$A = \begin{bmatrix} 10.25767 & .03798 & 6.87167 & 1.17904 \\ & 1.11550 & -.06320 & 1.99828 \\ & & 15.94667 & .166956 \\ & & & 3.94418 \end{bmatrix},$$

$$G = \begin{bmatrix} 31.6650 \\ -86.8374 \\ 46.7156 \\ -152.8797 \end{bmatrix}, \qquad B = \begin{bmatrix} b_1 \\ b_2 \\ b_3 \\ b_4 \end{bmatrix}.$$

The elements of the $A$ matrix are represented as $a_{ij}$ and the $G$ matrix as $g_i$ ($Sx_iy$), while the elements of the $B$ matrix are the estimates of the population regression coefficients.

Two methods of obtaining the inverse matrix will be presented, the *Doolittle method* and the *abbreviated Doolittle method*. The latter is often called the *Gauss-Doolittle method*.

TABLE 15.1

| | $Y$ | $X_1$ | $X_2$ | $X_3$ | $X_4$ |
|---|---|---|---|---|---|
| | 110.4 | 1.76 | .070 | 7.8 | .123 |
| | 102.8 | 1.55 | .070 | 8.9 | .108 |
| | 101.0 | 2.73 | .070 | 8.9 | .191 |
| | 108.4 | 2.73 | .070 | 7.2 | .191 |
| | 100.7 | 2.56 | .070 | 8.4 | .179 |
| | 100.3 | 2.80 | .070 | 8.7 | .196 |
| | 102.0 | 2.80 | .070 | 7.4 | .196 |
| | 93.7 | 1.84 | .070 | 8.7 | .128 |
| | 98.9 | 2.16 | .070 | 8.8 | .151 |
| | 96.6 | 1.98 | .020 | 7.6 | .039 |
| | 99.4 | .59 | .020 | 6.5 | .011 |
| | 96.2 | .80 | .020 | 6.7 | .016 |
| | 99.0 | .80 | .020 | 6.2 | .016 |
| | 88.4 | 1.05 | .020 | 7.0 | .021 |
| | 75.3 | 1.80 | .020 | 7.3 | .036 |
| | 92.0 | 1.80 | .020 | 6.5 | .036 |
| | 82.4 | 1.77 | .020 | 7.6 | .035 |
| | 77.1 | 2.30 | .020 | 8.2 | .046 |
| | 74.0 | 2.03 | .474 | 7.6 | .962 |
| | 65.7 | 1.91 | .474 | 8.3 | .905 |
| | 56.8 | 1.91 | .474 | 8.2 | .905 |
| | 62.1 | 1.91 | .474 | 6.9 | .905 |
| | 61.0 | .76 | .474 | 7.4 | .360 |
| | 53.2 | 2.13 | .474 | 7.6 | 1.009 |
| | 59.4 | 2.13 | .474 | 6.9 | 1.009 |
| | 58.7 | 1.51 | .474 | 7.5 | .715 |
| | 58.0 | 2.05 | .474 | 7.6 | .971 |
| Total | 2,273.5 | 50.16 | 5.076 | 206.4 | 9.460 |

**15.2. The Doolittle Method of Inverting a Matrix.** This method is used by Fisher[2] and Snedecor.[1] The computations are presented in Table 15.2 with accompanying explanations.

The procedures followed in the computations in Table 15.2 were:

I. The original $A$ matrix on the left and an *identity matrix* on the right (zeros everywhere except 1's on the main diagonal) and a *check column* (sum of all elements in each row). In all of the computations which follow, the same procedure is followed with the check column. Then if the computing was done correctly, the sum of each row will equal the value in the check column.

II. Divide each row by the element in the $x_4$ column of the $A$ matrix. Be sure to carry at least five significant digits, and preferably six, in all quotients. Remember that the important point is the number of significant digits and not the number of decimal places.

Table 15.2

| | A matrix | | | | Identity matrix | | | | Check |
|---|---|---|---|---|---|---|---|---|---|
| | $x_1$ | $x_2$ | $x_3$ | $x_4$ | (1) | (2) | (3) | (4) | |
| I | 10.25767 | .03798 | 6.87167 | 1.17904 | 1 | 0 | 0 | 0 | 19.34636 |
| | .03798 | 1.11550 | −.06320 | 1.99828 | 0 | 1 | 0 | 0 | 4.08856 |
| | 6.87167 | −.06320 | 15.94667 | .166956 | 0 | 0 | 1 | 0 | 23.92210 |
| | 1.17904 | 1.99828 | .166956 | 3.94418 | 0 | 0 | 0 | 1 | 8.28846 |
| II | 8.70002 | .032213 | 5.82819 | 1 | .848148 | 0 | 0 | 0 | 16.40857 |
| | .019006 | .558230 | −.031627 | 1 | 0 | .500430 | 0 | 0 | 2.04604 |
| | 41.15857 | −.378543 | 95.51421 | 1 | 0 | 0 | 5.98960 | 0 | 143.28384 |
| | .298932 | .506640 | .042331 | 1 | 0 | 0 | 0 | .253538 | 2.10144 |
| III | 8.40109 | −.474427 | 5.78586 | | .848148 | 0 | 0 | −.253538 | 14.30713 |
| | −.279926 | .051590 | −.073958 | | 0 | .500430 | 0 | −.253538 | −.055402 |
| | 40.85964 | −.885183 | 95.47188 | | 0 | 0 | 5.98960 | −.253538 | 141.18240 |
| IV | 1.45200 | −.081998 | 1 | | .146590 | 0 | 0 | −.043820 | 2.47277 |
| | 3.78493 | −.697558 | 1 | | 0 | −6.76641 | 0 | 3.428135 | .74910 |
| | .42798 | −.009272 | 1 | | 0 | 0 | .062737 | −.002656 | 1.47879 |
| V | 1.02402 | −.072726 | | | .146590 | 0 | −.062737 | −.041164 | .99398 |
| | 3.35695 | −.688286 | | | 0 | −6.76641 | −.062737 | 3.430791 | −.72969 |
| VI | −14.08052 | 1 | | | −2.01565 | 0 | .862649 | .566015 | −13.6675 |
| | −4.87726 | 1 | | | 0 | 9.83081 | .091150 | −4.98454 | 1.06016 |
| VII | −9.20326 | | | | −2.01565 | −9.83081 | .77150 | 5.55056 | −14.7276 |
| VIII | $(1)c_{11}$ | $c_{12}$ | $c_{13}$ | $c_{14}$ | .219015 | 1.06819 | −.083829 | −.603108 | 1.60027 |
| IX | $c_{21}$ | $(1)c_{22}$ | $c_{23}$ | $c_{24}$ | 1.06819 | 15.04066 | −.317707 | −7.92605 | 8.86519 |
| X | $c_{31}$ | $c_{32}$ | $(1)c_{33}$ | $c_{34}$ | −.083829 | −.317707 | .095668 | .181973 | .87610 |
| XI | $c_{41}$ | $c_{42}$ | $c_{43}$ | $(1)c_{44}$ | −.603108 | −7.92605 | .181973 | 4.44178 | −2.90543 |
| XII | $g_i$ | | | | 31.6650 | −86.8374 | 46.7156 | −152.8797 | |
| XIII | $b_i$ | | | | 2.4631 | −75.3773 | 1.5836 | −1.3769 | |
| XIV | $s(b_i) = \sqrt{c_{ii}s^2}$ | | | | 4.7251 | 39.1567 | 3.1229 | 21.2790 | |
| XV | $t$ | | | | $< 1$ | 1.93 | $< 1$ | $< 1$ | |
| XVI | SSR = 6,908.04; SSE = 2,242.49; $s^2$ = 101.93 | | | | | | | | |

III. Subtract the last line from all the others, dropping the $x_4$ column in the left-hand matrix.

IV. Divide by the elements of the right column in this new left-hand matrix.

V. Again subtract the last line from the others and now drop the $x_3$ column.

VI, VII. Same as above.

VIII. The first line gives the $c_{1j}$ values, which are computed by dividing the elements in (VII) by the left-hand number, $-9.20326$.

IX. Substitute in turn the $c_{1j}$ values in either line of the left-hand matrix of (VI) as follows to determine $c_{2j}$. For example,

$$c_{21} = \left\{\begin{array}{c} -2.01565 - (-14.08052)(.219015) \\ \text{or} \\ 0 \quad - (-4.87726)(.219015) \end{array}\right\} = 1.06819.$$

Note that $c_{21}$ should equal $c_{12}$, except for rounding errors.

$$c_{22} = \left\{\begin{array}{c} 0 \quad - (-14.08052)(1.06819) \\ \text{or} \\ 9.83081 - (-4.87726)(1.06819) \end{array}\right\} = 15.04066.$$

X. Next substitute the values of $c_{1j}$ and $c_{2j}$ in any of the equations in (IV) and solve for $c_{3j}$ as in (IX) for $c_{2j}$. For example

$$c_{31} = \left\{\begin{array}{l} .146590 - (1.45200)(.219015) - (-.081998)(1.06819) \\ \qquad = -.083830. \\ 0 \quad - (3.78493)(.219015) - (-.697558)(1.06819) \\ \qquad = -.083832. \\ 0 \quad - (.42798)(.219015) - (-.009272)(1.06819) \\ \qquad = -.083830. \end{array}\right.$$

We note that two of these equations give the same result to five significant digits (six decimal places), while the middle one deviates very slightly from these two. We have used the value given in (VIII) for $c_{13}$. Rounding errors are quite a problem in matrix-inversion calculations. Hence it is advisable to carry several unnecessary digits at first in order to be able to drop digits as the computing proceeds and end up with as many as was thought necessary.

XI. Next substitute the values of $c_{1j}$, $c_{2j}$, and $c_{3j}$ in any of the equations in (II), and solve for $c_{4j}$. For example,

$$c_{41} = \begin{cases} .848148 - 8.70002c_{11} - .032213c_{21} - 5.82819c_{31} \\ \qquad = -.603125. \\ 0 - .019006c_{11} - .558230c_{21} + .031627c_{31} \\ \qquad = -.603110. \\ 0 - 41.15857c_{11} + .378543c_{21} - 95.51421c_{31} \\ \qquad = -.603128. \\ 0 - .298932c_{11} - .506640c_{21} - .042331c_{31} \\ \qquad = -.603111. \end{cases}$$

In this case two equations are out of line, and two almost agree with $c_{14}$. In general it is a good practice to omit equations like the first and third, because several of the elements are so large. These large coefficients (such as 41 and 95) are subject to a much greater rounding error, because extra digits are needed to give six-decimal accuracy. That is, we are trying to calculate $c_{41}$ to six decimal places; hence, the individual multipliers should be accurate to six decimal places. But for numbers like 41 and 95 to have six decimal places, eight significant digits are required, and we cannot obtain eight significant digits in our computing unless we use several more in the original $A$ matrix.

The $C$ matrix has now been completed, but the computer should have some more checking besides the check column. The final check is to find whether or not the product of the $A$ and $C$ matrices is the identity matrix. That is

$$AC = D = I$$

where $I$ contains only 1's in the main diagonal. To compute an element in the $i$th row and $j$th column of $AC$, we find the sums of the products of corresponding elements in the $i$th row of $A$ and the $j$th column of $C$. Let $a_{ik}$ be the elements in $A$ and $c_{kj}$ those in $C$. Then the $(i,j)$ element in $D$ is

$$d_{ij} = \sum_{k=1}^{4} a_{ik}c_{kj}.$$

We generally compute the diagonal elements $d_{ii}$ to see whether or not they are nearly 1 (to the desired degree of accuracy). In the vitamin $B_2$ example

$$\begin{aligned} d_{11} &= (10.25767)(.219015) + \cdots + (1.17904)(-.603108) = 1.0000198, \\ d_{22} &= (.03798)(1.06819) + \cdots + (1.99828)(-7.92605) = 1.0000380, \\ d_{33} &= 1.0000014, \\ d_{44} &= 1.0000057. \end{aligned}$$

The last two diagonal elements are within the desired five-decimal-place accuracy, but $d_{11}$ and $d_{22}$ only to four places. Hence if we use the present

$C$ matrix, we cannot hope for more than four-place accuracy in the $b$'s, and possibly only three-place accuracy.

XII. The sums of the cross products of the $x_i$ with $y$ are given here ($g_i = Sx_iy$).

XIII. $b_i = \sum_{j=1}^{4} c_{ij}g_j$. For example,

$$b_1 = (.219015)(31.6650) + \cdots + (-.603108)(-152.8797) = 2.4631.$$

At this stage it is advisable either to recompute the $b_i$ or to substitute these values in the original normal equations. For example,

$$10.25767b_1 + \cdots + 1.17904b_4 = 31.6650.$$

Substituting the above values of the $b_i$, this sum is 31.6614, indicating slight inaccuracies. More nearly exact values are given by use of $C''$ below.

XVI. $\text{SSR} = \Sigma b_i g_i = (2.4631)(31.6650) + \cdots + (-1.3769)(-152.8797) = 6{,}908.04.$

$$\text{SSE} = Sy^2 - \text{SSR} = 9{,}150.53 - 6{,}908.04 = 2{,}242.49.$$
$$s^2 = \text{SSE}/22 = 101.93.$$

XIV. The standard error of $b_i = \sqrt{c_{ii}s^2}$.

XV. $t = |b_i|/s(b_i)$.

If it is desired to improve the results to more significant figures, we can use an iterative device advanced by Hotelling.[6] The procedure is as follows:

(1) Compute the matrix $(2 - AC)$, which is the same as $AC$, except the diagonal elements are subtracted from 2 and the signs of all other elements are reversed.

$$(2 - AC) = \begin{bmatrix} .9999802 & -.0000771 & .0000044 & .0000195 \\ -.0000035 & .9999620 & -.0000008 & -.0000046 \\ -.0000033 & -.0000092 & .9999986 & -.0000124 \\ -.0000079 & -.0000778 & -.0000013 & .9999943 \end{bmatrix}.$$

(2) Now compute $C(2 - AC) = C''$, the new $C$ matrix.

$$C'' = \begin{bmatrix} .219012 & 1.068180 & -.083828 & -.603104 \\ 1.068180 & 15.040626 & -.317704 & -7.926049 \\ -.083828 & -0.317704 & .095668 & .181971 \\ -.603104 & -7.926049 & .181971 & 4.441777 \end{bmatrix}.$$

(3) $$b_i'' = [2.46332 \quad -75.3747 \quad 1.58369 \quad -1.37645].$$

(4) Substituting in the normal equations, we obtain as estimates of the $g_i$

$$[31.6649 \quad -86.8375 \quad 46.7156 \quad -152.8800],$$

as compared with the exact values

$$[31.6650 \quad -86.8374 \quad 46.7156 \quad -152.8797].$$

(5) If we use these values of $b_i''$, we find that SSR $= \Sigma b_i'' g_i = 6{,}907.76$ as compared with 6,908.04 above. Hence there is no real difference in the results by using the $b_i$.

**15.3. The Abbreviated Doolittle Method.** Now we shall present a short-cut method of inverting a symmetric matrix ($a_{ij} = a_{ji}$), the *abbreviated Doolittle method*, described by Dwyer.[4,7]

TABLE 15.3
Forward Solution

| | | $x_1$ | $x_2$ | $x_3$ | $x_4$ | $y$ | Check |
|---|---|---|---|---|---|---|---|
| I | | 10.25767 | .037980 | 6.87167 | 1.17904 | 31.6650 | 50.0114 |
| | | | 1.11550 | −.063200 | 1.99828 | −86.8374 | −83.7488 |
| | | | | 15.94667 | .166956 | 46.7156 | 69.6377 |
| | | | | | 3.94418 | −152.8797 | −145.5912 |
| II | $A_1$ | 10.25767 | .037980 | 6.87167 | 1.17904 | 31.6650 | 50.0114 |
| | $B_1$ | 1 | .00370260 | .669906 | .114942 | 3.08696 | 4.87551 |
| III | $A_2$ | | 1.11536 | −.088643 | 1.99391 | −86.9546 | −83.9340 |
| | $B_2$ | | 1 | −.079475 | 1.78768 | −77.9610 | −75.2528 |
| IV | $A_3$ | | | 11.33625 | −.464424 | 18.5923 | 29.4641 |
| | $B_3$ | | | 1 | −.040968 | 1.64007 | 2.59910 |
| V | $A_4$ | | | | .22516 | −.3104 | −.0852 |
| | $B_4$ | | | | 1 | −1.3786 | −.3784 |

Backward Solution (for $c_{ij}$)

$$\begin{matrix} c_{1j} \\ c_{2j} \\ c_{3j} \\ c_{4j} \end{matrix} \begin{bmatrix} .219003 & 1.06806 & -.0838254 & -.603037 \\ & 15.03894 & -.317667 & -7.92514 \\ & & .0956668 & .181951 \\ & & & 4.44129 \end{bmatrix}$$

The procedures followed in the abbreviated Doolittle method computations were:

I. The original $A$ matrix with only the upper right corner is reproduced plus the $G$ column ($Sx_iy$) and a check column. For the check column, we assume the entire $A$ matrix is present. Since the $A$ matrix is symmetrical, the lower corner is an image of the upper corner. We shall call these elements $a_{ij}$.

II. $A_{1j} = a_{1j}$, the first row of (I) is reproduced.

$$B_{1j} = A_{1j}/A_{11} = A_{1j}/10.25767.$$

III. $A_{2j} = a_{2j} - [A_{12}B_{1j} \text{ or } A_{1j}B_{12}]$, where $a_{2j}$ is the element in the second row of (I) and $A_{12}B_{1j} = A_{1j}B_{12}$ except for rounding errors. As we noted in commenting on rounding errors for the Doolittle method, it is advisable to choose from these two ($A_{12}B_{1j}$ or $A_{1j}B_{12}$) the one for which the two members are more nearly equal.

$$A_{22} = 1.11550 - (.037980)(.0037026) = 1.11536.$$

$$A_{23} = -.063200 - \begin{cases} (.037980)(.669906) = -0.088643. \\ (.0037026)(6.87167) = -0.088643. \end{cases}$$

$$B_{2j} = A_{2j}/A_{22}.$$

IV. $A_{3j} = a_{3j} - (A_{13}B_{1j} + A_{23}B_{2j}) = a_{3j} - (A_{1j}B_{13} + A_{2j}B_{23}).$

$$A_{33} = 15.94667 - [(6.87167)(.669906) + (-.088643)(-.079475)] = 11.33625.$$

$$A_{34} = .166956 - \begin{cases} (6.87167)(.114942) + (-.088643)(1.78768) = -0.464422. \\ (1.17904)(.669906) + (-.079475)(1.99391) = -0.464424. \end{cases}$$

$$B_{3j} = A_{3j}/A_{33}.$$

V. $A_{4j} = a_{4j} - (A_{14}B_{1j} + A_{24}B_{2j} + A_{34}B_{3j}) = a_{4j} - (A_{1j}B_{14} + A_{2j}B_{24} + A_{3j}B_{34}).$

$$A_{44} = 3.94418 - [(1.17904)(.114942) + (1.99391)(1.78768) + (.464424)(.040968)] = 0.22516.$$

$$B_{4j} = A_{4j}/A_{44}.$$

This completes the forward solution. If the experimenter desires to compute only the $\{b_i\}$ and the over-all reduction in sum of squares due to regression (SSR) without the individual $s^2(b_i)$ and $s(b_ib_j)$, he can make these computations without determining the inverse matrix, as follows:

VI. $b_4 = B_{4y} = -1.3786.$

$$b_3 = B_{3y} - B_{34}b_4 = 1.64007 + (.040968)(-1.3786) = 1.5836.$$

$$b_2 = B_{2y} - B_{23}b_3 - B_{24}b_4 = -77.9610 - (-.079475)(1.5836) - (1.78768)(-1.3786) = -75.3706.$$

$$b_1 = B_{1y} - B_{12}b_2 - B_{13}b_3 - B_{14}b_4 = 3.08696 - (.0037026)(-75.3706) - (.669906)(1.5836) - (.114942)(-1.3786) = 2.4636.$$

$$\text{SSR} = \Sigma b_i Sx_iy = (2.4636)(31.6650) + \cdots + (-1.3786)(-152.8797) = 6{,}907.74.$$

If we let $b_i'$ be the estimate of the last $b$ in the Doolittle procedure when $i$ fixed variates are used, we note that $B_{iy} = b_i'$; in other words, we note that $B_{iy}$ will give the value of $b_i$ if this is the last $b$ to be computed. This is called a completely adjusted $b$, since $x_i$ has been adjusted for all the other $x$'s. In our case with $r = 4$, $b_4' = B_{4y}$.† But if only the first three $x$'s were used, we would omit the $x_4$ column and the $A_4$ and $B_4$ rows, so that the regression coefficient for $x_3$ would then equal $B_{3y}$. This would be $b_3'$. We also note that $A_{1y} = Sx_1y$ and, proceeding as in Exercise 14.6, $A_{2y} = S(x_2 \text{ adjusted for } x_1)y$, $A_{3y} = S(x_3 \text{ adjusted for } x_1 \text{ and } x_2)y$, and $A_{4y} = S(x_4 \text{ adjusted for } x_1, x_2, \text{ and } x_3)y$. Hence, using the same method as in Exercise 14.6, we can consider the regression equation as†

$$y = b_1'x_1 + b_2'(x_2 \text{ adjusted for } x_1) + b_3'(x_3 \text{ adjusted for } x_1 \text{ and } x_2) + b_4'(x_4 \text{ adjusted for } x_1, x_2, \text{ and } x_3) + e.$$

Hence we can write

$$\text{SSR} = \sum_{i=1}^{4} A_{iy}b_i' = \sum_{i=1}^{4} A_{iy}B_{iy}$$
$$= (31.6650)(3.08696) + \cdots + (-.3104)(-1.3786) = 6{,}907.74.$$

The above results indicate that a decided saving in computation can be made by use of the abbreviated Doolittle method if the experimenter decides to omit the last $k$ fixed variates from the regression model; in this case, the computations for the first $(r - k)$ variates need not be changed. Of course the experimenter seldom knows which fixed variates might be omitted before he starts the computations; hence, he does not know which should be put last in the computing scheme. However, in many cases, there are some fixed variates which he would like to omit because they are costly or difficult to measure. In such a case he might put these $k$ fixed variates last and omit them if they contributed little extra to SSR. For example, the added contribution of $x_3$ and $x_4$ above to SSR is only $(A_{3y}B_{3y} + A_{4y}B_{4y}) = 30.91$, with 2 degrees of freedom.

Despite the obvious errors of rounding in computing the $b_i$ by the abbreviated Doolittle procedure, SSR is only .02 less than the value computed after the use of the Hotelling iterative procedure on the Doolittle solutions.

If the computer needs the inverse ($C$) matrix, the computations proceed as given for the so-called "backward" solution.

VII. *First compute $c_{i4}$ values.*

$c_{44} = 1/A_{44} = 1/.22516 = 4.44129,$

$c_{34} = -c_{44}B_{34} = -(4.44129)(-.040968) = .181951,$

† $b_4'$ is often written as $b_{4.123}$, which reads the regression coefficient for $x_4$ adjusted for $x_1$, $x_2$, and $x_3$. $b_3'$ would be $b_{3.12}$, and $b_2' = b_{2.1}$, while $b_1'$ is an unadjusted $b_1$.

$c_{24} = -c_{34}B_{23} - c_{44}B_{24} = (.181951)(.079475) - (4.44129)(1.78768)$
$= -7.92514,$
$c_{14} = -c_{24}B_{12} - c_{34}B_{13} - c_{44}B_{14} = -.603037.$

Check by use of $a_{14}c_{14} + \cdots + a_{44}c_{44} = .99997.$

VIII. $c_{i3}$ *values.*

$c_{43} = c_{34} = .181951,$
$c_{33} = 1/A_{33} - c_{34}B_{34} = .0882136 - (.181951)(-.040968) = .0956668,$
$c_{23} = -c_{33}B_{23} - c_{34}B_{24} = (.0956668)(.079475) - (.181951)(1.78768)$
$= -.317667,$
$c_{13} = -c_{23}B_{12} - c_{33}B_{13} - c_{34}B_{14} = -.0838254.$

Again check by use of $a_{13}c_{13} + \cdots + a_{43}c_{43} = 1.0000008.$

IX. $c_{i2}$ *values.*

$c_{42} = c_{24} = -7.92514, \qquad c_{32} = c_{23} = -.317667,$
$c_{22} = 1/A_{22} - c_{23}B_{23} - c_{24}B_{24}$
$= .8965715 - (-.317667)(-.079475) + (7.92514)(1.78768)$
$= 15.03894,$
$c_{12} = -c_{22}B_{12} - c_{23}B_{13} - c_{24}B_{14} = 1.06806,$ and
$c_{12}a_{12} + \cdots + c_{42}a_{42} = .99993.$

X. $c_{11} = 1/A_{11} - c_{12}B_{12} - c_{13}B_{13} - c_{14}B_{14}$
$= .0974880 - (1.06806)(.0037026) + (.0838254)(.669906)$
$+ (.603037)(.114942) = .219003,$ and
$c_{11}a_{11} + \cdots + c_{41}a_{41} = 1.0000002.$

XI. The solutions for the $b_i$, SSR, and $s^2(b_i)$ proceed as with the Doolittle method,

$b_i = [2.46334 \quad -75.3693 \quad 1.58356 \quad -1.37975], \qquad \text{SSR} = 6{,}907.79.$

These $b$'s can be checked against those computed in (VI) above. Again we note that some of the $b_i$ are not very accurate but that SSR is off only slightly in the last decimal place. The Hotelling iterative procedure can be used to improve this $C$ matrix also. Rounding errors seem to be of more importance with the abbreviated method; hence, it is especially advisable to carry extra places at first in order to secure the desired accuracy at the end without having to use the Hotelling iterative device to improve the accuracy. If it is known in advance that the $C$ matrix will be needed, an identity matrix can be carried on the right of the abbreviated Doolittle matrix as with the Doolittle matrix and the same computations used there as in steps I to VI; the computing procedure is described on page 191 of reference 4.

**15.4. Analysis of the Results.** The experimenter will generally look at the simple regressions of $Y$ on each of the fixed variates first, in order to obtain some idea of the usefulness of each of these fixed variates. This does not mean that a fixed variate will be omitted if its simple regression coefficient was not significantly different from zero; there may be good theoretical reasons for adjusting all other fixed variates for one which, of itself, was not too important as a predictor. But if the experimenter had first run the simple regression of $Y$ on $X_2$, he would have discovered a highly significant relationship; yet the $t$ value was not significant when all four $X$'s were used. And he would be even more perplexed when he studied the following analysis of variance for all four fixed variates (based on the Doolittle solution):

| Source of variation | Degrees of freedom | Sum of squares | Mean square |
|---|---|---|---|
| Regression (4 variates) | 4 | 6,907.76 | 1,726.94 |
| Regression ($X_2$ only) | 1 | 6,759.98 | 6,759.98 |
| Added reduction due to $X_1$, $X_3$, $X_4$ | 3 | 147.78 | 49.26 |
| Error | 22 | 2,242.77 | 101.94 |

From this analysis of variance, we conclude that the over-all reduction due to the use of the regression equation is highly significant

$$\left(F = \frac{1{,}726.94}{101.94} = 16.94\right)$$

and that the added reduction due to the three fixed variates other than $X_2$ is decidedly nonsignificant. Hence we are led to conclude that $X_2$ is a very important predictor and that the other predictors add nothing to the reliability of the estimate of vitamin $B_2$ content.

Why then is $b_2$ not highly significant when all four $X$'s are used in the model? The answer lies in the peculiar nature of $X_4$, which is the product of $X_1$ and $X_2$, causing $X_4$ and $X_2$ to be highly correlated. Hence $b_2$ and $b_4$ are also highly correlated, so that the actual influence of $X_2$ on $Y$ is split into a part contributed by $b_2$ and another part contributed by $b_4$. It is impossible to interpret $b_2$ as the change in $Y$ when $X_2$ varies while holding the other $X_i$ constant, because $X_4$ will vary when $X_2$ varies. The change in $\hat{Y}$ when $X_2$ varies is given by

$$z = \frac{\partial \hat{Y}}{\partial X_2} = b_2 + b_4 X_1.$$

The average value of this change is

$$\bar{z} = b_2 + b_4 \bar{X}_1 = -75.3747 - 1.3765(1.8578) = -77.9320.$$

This average change is almost the same as $b_2'$, the average change in $\hat{Y}$ for a unit change in $X_2$, neglecting all other fixed variates. The estimated variance of this average change, $\bar{z}$, is

$$\begin{aligned} s^2(\bar{z}) &= s^2(b_2) + (\bar{X}_1)^2 s^2(b_4) + 2\bar{X}_1 s(b_2 b_4) \\ &= [15.04063 + 4.44178(1.8578)^2 - 2(1.8578)(7.92605)](101.94) \\ &= (.92105)(101.94) = 93.893, \end{aligned}$$

and the standard error is 9.6899, so that

$$t = \frac{77.93}{9.69} = 8.04,$$

a highly significant value. We have used (2) and (3) (page 196), in this computing.

This example was selected because it illustrates some of the difficulties of interpreting regression analyses when some of the fixed variates are closely related to one another. If two fixed variates are highly correlated, it is unrealistic to assume that one can be held constant while the other varies. A multiple regression coefficient can be interpreted only as the average change in $Y$ for a unit change in $X_i$ when the other $X$'s are not changed. Hence to interpret two highly correlated regression coefficients, we should like to know the relationship between the $X$'s in order to study the real change in $Y$ when one of the $X$'s changes. This is not to say that the use of a fixed variate like $X_4 (= X_1 X_2)$ is undesirable. On the contrary, it is often quite desirable to be able to say how $z$ differs for various values of $X_1$. For example, if $X_1$ were temperature and $X_2$ were rainfall, then it would be highly desirable to know how the effect of 1 inch of rainfall varied for different temperatures, $X_1$. We know that for most crops high rainfall may be detrimental at low temperatures but quite valuable at high temperatures. Hence a knowledge of the regression of yield on temperature and rainfall alone would be rather useless unless the cross-product term were also included (see reference 8 for an example of such a study). In some analyses, it may be impractical to consider that any of the fixed variates can be held constant while some other one varies. In this case the regression equation should be considered as a whole. One example of this is given in Exercise 15.4.

The estimated variance of the average value of $Y$ for a fixed set of $X$'s, $\{X_i'\}$, can be computed directly from the $\{c_{ij}\}$ and the value of $s^2$.

Given $\hat{Y}' = \bar{Y} + \sum_{i=1}^{r} b_i (X_i' - \bar{X}_i)$.

$$s^2(\hat{Y}') = s^2 \left[ \frac{1}{n} + \sum_{i=1}^{r} c_{ii} x_i'^2 + 2 \sum\sum_{i<j} c_{ij} x_i' x_j' \right] = s^2 \left[ \frac{1}{n} + \sum\sum_{i,j=1}^{r} c_{ij} x_i' x_j' \right],$$

where $x_i' = X_i' - \bar{X}_i$. Using the values of the $c_{ij}$, found by the use of the Hotelling iterative procedure (page 196), we have for our vitamin $B_2$ example

$$\begin{aligned} s^2(\hat{Y}') = 101.94[\tfrac{1}{27} &+ x_1'(.219012x_1' + 1.068180x_2' - .083828x_3' \\ &- .603104x_4') + x_2'(1.068180x_1' + 15.040626x_2' - .317704x_3' \\ &-7.926049x_4') + x_3'(-.083828x_1' - .317704x_2' + .095668x_3' \\ &+ .181971x_4') + x_4'(-.603104x_1' - 7.926049x_2' + .181971x_3' \\ &+ 4.441777x_4')] \end{aligned}$$

Similarly the estimated variance of a single predicted value of $Y$ is given by

$$s^2(\hat{Y}') + s^2.$$

Confidence limits can be assigned to the various estimates as follows:

$$b_i - t_\alpha s(b_i) < \beta_i < b_i + t_\alpha s(b_i),$$
$$\hat{Y}' - t_\alpha s(\hat{Y}') < E[Y|\{X_i'\}] < \hat{Y}' + t_\alpha s(\hat{Y}'),$$
$$\hat{Y}' - t_\alpha \sqrt{s^2(\hat{Y}') + s^2} < Y|\{X_i'\} < \hat{Y}' + t_\alpha \sqrt{s^2(\hat{Y}') + s^2},$$

where

$$\mathcal{P}(|t| > t_\alpha) = \alpha.$$

## EXERCISES

**15.1.** Show how the sum of squares for the regression of $Y$ on $X_1$ and $X_2$ alone could be obtained in Sec. 15.4.

**15.2.** Select some data in a familiar field of application with one dependent and at least three fixed variates, and carry out the calculations leading to the estimates of the regression coefficients and their standard errors. Investigate the usefulness of the various fixed variates, and indicate whether or not any should be discarded.

**15.3.** (*a*) Show that if $X_3$ is omitted from the regression equation for the vitamin $B_2$ example, the new regression coefficients ($b_i''$) and $c$ values ($c''$) are

$$b_i'' = b_i - \frac{b_3}{c_{33}} c_{3i}, \qquad c_{ij}'' = c_{ij} - \frac{c_{3i}c_{3j}}{c_{33}}.$$

(See reference 2.)

(*b*) See reference 9 for the adjustments needed if one extra fixed variate is used.

**15.4.** A cost study was made of 89 dairy farms in 1941.[10] The dependent variate was the amount of milk sold ($Y$) with the following fixed variates: amount of concentrates ($X_1$), amount of silage ($X_2$), pasture cost ($X_3$), and amount of roughage ($X_4$). The means and sums of squares and cross products adjusted for the means are given below, with the amounts in thousand pounds per cow and the pasture cost in \$10 per cow.

| | $x_1$ | $x_2$ | $x_3$ | $x_4$ | $y$ |
|---|---|---|---|---|---|
| $x_1$ | 50.5154 | −66.1617 | −4.84289 | −.937732 | 36.7974 |
| $x_2$ | | 967.1077 | 13.5895 | 32.4425 | 39.0556 |
| $x_3$ | | | 12.5457 | −12.5195 | 7.02815 |
| $x_4$ | | | | 192.3053 | 9.99432 |
| $y$ | | | | | 113.5872 |
| Mean | 2.94310 | 3.90647 | 1.16426 | 3.60326 | 5.73994 |

(*a*) Compute the regression coefficients and their standard errors. Use the abbreviated Doolittle method, and complete the backward solution also.

(*b*) Show that all regression coefficients except $b_4$ are significant at the 1 per cent probability level.

(*c*) Use the $y$ column in the forward solution to determine the error variance when $x_4$ is removed from the prediction equation.

(*d*) In 1941 the cost per thousand pounds was $18 for concentrates, $2.70 for silage, and $8.50 for roughage and milk sold for 3.2 cents per pound. Estimate the profit or loss and its standard error if 3,200 pounds of concentrates, 4,000 pounds of silage, 3,000 pounds of roughage, and $15 worth of pasture were used per cow.

**15.5.** J. T. Wakeley[11] has compiled some soils weather data and data on the vitamin content of turnip greens, contributed by the Georgia Agricultural Experiment Station for the Southern Cooperative Group. The dependent variates are milligrams of ascorbic acid [$Y_1$] and micrograms of riboflavin [$Y_2$], each per 100 milligrams of dry weight. The fixed variates are soil moisture tension (atmospheres ÷ 10) [$X_1$] and mean temperature (degrees Fahrenheit ÷ 100) [$X_2$], each at 8 inches depth; total radiation in gram calories per square centimeter per minute ÷ 1,000 [$X_3$] and evaporation in centimeters [$X_4$], each for the previous 48 hours; and number of days since planting ÷ 100 [$X_5$].

The means and sums of squares and cross products are:

| | $x_1$ | $x_2$ | $x_3$ | $x_4$ | $x_5$ | Mean |
|---|---|---|---|---|---|---|
| $x_1$ | 6.6510 | 2.6722 | 4.4957 | 2.6338 | .14360 | .5475 |
| $x_2$ | | 4.8750 | 8.3609 | 4.3597 | −3.2533 | 2.7156 |
| $x_3$ | | | 19.8174 | 9.5315 | −6.6767 | 1.4353 |
| $x_4$ | | | | 5.2394 | −3.1452 | .5810 |
| $x_5$ | | | | | 3.7799 | 1.0881 |
| $y_1$ | −.60160 | −1.5771 | −1.6953 | −.81984 | .94173 | 2.8497 |
| $y_2$ | −3.2590 | 7.1768 | 10.9862 | 5.9285 | −7.1415 | 6.1834 |

$$Sy_1^2 = 1.5025, \qquad Sy_2^2 = 28.6900, \qquad n = 32.$$

Since the problem of computing a regression with five fixed variates is quite a long one, the student may wish to select particular variates as an exercise.

**15.6.** Woltz *et. al.*[12] and Foster[13] analyzed 25 samples of tobacco leaf for organic and inorganic chemical constituents, and multiple regression was used to discover the nature and extent of the relationship of certain of these constituents. The dependent variates considered were rate of cigarette burn in inches per 1,000 seconds ($Y_1$), per cent sugar in the leaf ($Y_2$), and per cent nicotine ($Y_3$). The fixed variates were percentages of total nitrogen ($X_1$), of chlorine ($X_2$), of potassium ($X_3$), of phosphorus ($X_4$), of calcium ($X_5$), and of magnesium ($X_6$). The original data (25 observations) and corrected sums of squares and products are given in the accompanying tables.

DATA OF EXERCISE 15.6

| | $Y_1$ | $Y_2$ | $Y_3$ | $X_1$ | $X_2$ | $X_3$ | $X_4$ | $X_5$ | $X_6$ |
|---|---|---|---|---|---|---|---|---|---|
| | 1.55 | 20.05 | 1.38 | 2.02 | 2.90 | 2.17 | .51 | 3.47 | .91 |
| | 1.63 | 12.58 | 2.64 | 2.62 | 2.78 | 1.72 | .50 | 4.57 | 1.25 |
| | 1.66 | 18.56 | 1.56 | 2.08 | 2.68 | 2.40 | .43 | 3.52 | .82 |
| | 1.52 | 18.56 | 2.22 | 2.20 | 3.17 | 2.06 | .52 | 3.69 | .97 |
| | 1.70 | 14.02 | 2.85 | 2.38 | 2.52 | 2.18 | .42 | 4.01 | 1.12 |
| | 1.68 | 15.64 | 1.24 | 2.03 | 2.56 | 2.57 | .44 | 2.79 | .82 |
| | 1.78 | 14.52 | 2.86 | 2.87 | 2.67 | 2.64 | .50 | 3.92 | 1.06 |
| | 1.57 | 18.52 | 2.18 | 1.88 | 2.58 | 2.22 | .49 | 3.58 | 1.01 |
| | 1.60 | 17.84 | 1.65 | 1.93 | 2.26 | 2.15 | .56 | 3.57 | .92 |
| | 1.52 | 13.38 | 3.28 | 2.57 | 1.74 | 1.64 | .51 | 4.38 | 1.22 |
| | 1.68 | 17.55 | 1.56 | 1.95 | 2.15 | 2.48 | .48 | 3.28 | .81 |
| | 1.74 | 17.97 | 2.00 | 2.03 | 2.00 | 2.38 | .50 | 3.31 | .98 |
| | 1.93 | 14.66 | 2.88 | 2.50 | 2.07 | 2.32 | .48 | 3.72 | 1.04 |
| | 1.77 | 17.31 | 1.36 | 1.72 | 2.24 | 2.25 | .52 | 3.10 | .78 |
| | 1.94 | 14.32 | 2.66 | 2.53 | 1.74 | 2.64 | .50 | 3.48 | .93 |
| | 1.83 | 15.05 | 2.43 | 1.90 | 1.46 | 1.97 | .46 | 3.48 | .90 |
| | 2.09 | 15.47 | 2.42 | 2.18 | .74 | 2.46 | .48 | 3.16 | .86 |
| | 1.72 | 16.85 | 2.16 | 2.16 | 2.84 | 2.36 | .49 | 3.68 | .95 |
| | 1.49 | 17.42 | 2.12 | 2.14 | 3.30 | 2.04 | .48 | 3.28 | 1.06 |
| | 1.52 | 18.55 | 1.87 | 1.98 | 2.90 | 2.16 | .48 | 3.56 | .84 |
| | 1.64 | 18.74 | 2.10 | 1.89 | 2.82 | 2.04 | .53 | 3.56 | 1.02 |
| | 1.40 | 14.79 | 2.21 | 2.07 | 2.79 | 2.15 | .52 | 3.49 | 1.04 |
| | 1.78 | 18.86 | 2.00 | 2.08 | 3.14 | 2.60 | .50 | 3.30 | .80 |
| | 1.93 | 15.62 | 2.26 | 2.21 | 2.81 | 2.18 | .44 | 4.16 | .92 |
| | 1.53 | 18.56 | 2.14 | 2.00 | 3.16 | 2.22 | .51 | 3.73 | 1.07 |
| Sum | 42.20 | 415.39 | 54.03 | 53.92 | 62.02 | 56.00 | 12.25 | 89.79 | 24.10 |
| $Sx^2$ or $Sy^2$ | .6690 | 101.4644 | 6.5921 | 1.8311 | 8.8102 | 1.5818 | .0258 | 3.7248 | .3828 |

Sums of Cross Products

| | $x_2$ | $x_3$ | $x_4$ | $x_5$ | $x_6$ | $y_1$ | $y_2$ | $y_3$ |
|---|---|---|---|---|---|---|---|---|
| $x_1$ | −.3589 | −.0125 | −.0244 | 1.6379 | .5057 | .2501 | −9.6105 | 2.6691 |
| $x_2$ | | −.3469 | .0352 | .7920 | .2173 | −1.5136 | 12.8511 | −2.0617 |
| $x_3$ | | | −.0415 | −1.4278 | −.4753 | .5007 | 2.4054 | −.9503 |
| $x_4$ | | | | .0043 | .0154 | −.0421 | .3945 | −.0187 |
| $x_5$ | | | | | 9120 | −.1914 | −9.3692 | 3.4020 |
| $x_6$ | | | | | | −.1586 | −3.2733 | 1.1663 |

(*a*) Analyze the regression of per cent nicotine ($Y_3$) on the percentages of total nitrogen ($X_1$) and potassium ($X_3$).

(*b*) Analyze the regression of cigarette burn ($Y_1$) on $X_2$, $X_3$, and $X_4$. What would be the effect of omitting $X_3$?

(*c*) Analyze the regression of per cent sugar ($Y_2$) on $X_1$, $X_2$, $X_5$, and $X_6$. What would be the effect of omitting $X_5$ and $X_6$?

## References Cited


1. SNEDECOR, G. W., *Statistical Methods*, 4th ed., Collegiate Press, Inc., of Iowa State College, Ames, Iowa, 1946. Chaps. 13, 14.
2. FISHER, R. A., *Statistical Methods for Research Workers*, 10th ed. Oliver & Boyd, Ltd., London and Edinburgh, 1946. Chap. 5.
3. WAUGH, F. V., and P. S. DWYER, "Compact Computation of the Inverse of a Matrix," *Ann. Math. Stat.*, **16**:259–271 (1945).
4. DWYER, P. S., *Linear Computations*, John Wiley & Sons, Inc., New York, 1951.
5. WAKELEY, J. T., "Annual Progress Report on the Soils-weather Project—1948," *Inst. Stat. Mim. Ser.* 19 (1949).
6. HOTELLING, HAROLD, "Some New Methods in Matrix Calculation," *Ann. Math. Stat.*, **14**:1–54 (1943).
7. DWYER, P. S., "The Solution of Simultaneous Equations," *Psychometrica*, **6**:101–129 (1941).
8. HENDRICKS, W. A., and J. C. SCHOLL, "The Joint Effect of Temperature and Precipitation on Corn Yields," *N. Carolina Agr. Expt. Sta. Tech. Bull.* 74 (1943).
9. COCHRAN, W. G., "The Omission or Addition of an Independent Variate in Multiple Linear Regression," *J. Roy. Stat. Soc. Suppl.*, **5**:171–176 (1938).
10. GREENE, R. E. L., "The Dairy Farm—Its Organization and Cost," *N. Carolina Agr. Expt. Sta. Bull.* 345 (1944).
11. WAKELEY, J. T., "Annual Progress Report on the Soils-weather Project—1949," *Inst. Stat. Mim. Ser.* 24 (1950).
12. WOLTZ, W. G., W. A. REID, and W. E. COLWELL, "Sugar and Nicotine in Cured Bright Tobacco as Related to Mineral Element Composition," *Proc. Soil Sci. Soc. Am.*, **13**:385–387 (1948).
13. FOSTER, W. D., *On the Selection of Predictors: Two Approaches*, unpublished thesis, North Carolina State College, Raleigh, N.C., 1950.

## CHAPTER 16

## CURVILINEAR REGRESSION: ORTHOGONAL POLYNOMIALS

**16.1. Introduction.** If it is desired to fit a regression equation using successive powers of one or more fixed variates, the methods given in Chap. 15 can be applied. For example, suppose we had a series of annual rainfall data ($Y$) for the years 1900 to 1949 and wished to determine a regression line such as the following polynomial:

$$Y = \alpha + \beta_1 X + \beta_2 X^2 + \beta_3 X^3 + \beta_4 X^4 + \epsilon,$$

where $X = 1, 2, \ldots, 50$. In order to use the methods of Chap. 15, merely set $X^i = X_i$. Snedecor[1] presents some examples using this technique of determining a polynomial regression line.

If the fixed variate is equally spaced, such as in time or space, a convenient method of curve fitting by orthogonal polynomials can be used.† This method was first developed by Tchebysheff[2] and has since been extended by many writers. Some of the books and articles on this subject are references 3 to 8. The advantage of orthogonal polynomials over the usual regression variates arises from the fact that the former are so constructed that any term of the polynomial is independent of any other term. This property of independence permits one to compute each regression coefficient independently of the others and also facilitates testing the significance of each coefficient. A summation method is illustrated by Fisher[9] and Snedecor,[1] but the $\xi'$ polynomial method presented by Fisher and Yates[10] with tables for $X$ through 75 is generally more expeditious if tests of significance of the succeeding terms of the polynomial are desired. Another method described by Aitken[5] is also recommended if tables are available.

We shall consider the use of the $\xi'$ polynomials, for which a computer's bulletin was prepared by Anderson and Houseman, who also included an extension of the $\xi'$ tables through $X = 104$.[11] An example is given in this bulletin for 62 annual United States sugar prices, 1875 to 1936.

**16.2. Determination of the Polynomial.** Suppose we wanted to fit a polynomial of high enough degree to $n$ equally spaced points so that

† The method of orthogonal polynomials can be used for unequally spaced $X$'s, but it is not so advantageous for such data.

succeeding terms would not reduce the residual sum of squares by a significant amount, for example,

$$Y_j = \beta_0 + \beta_1 x_j + \beta_2 x_j^2 + \beta_3 x_j^3 + \cdots + \beta_r x_j^r + \epsilon_j,$$

where $x_j = X_j - \bar{X} = j - \bar{j}$. Since $\bar{j} = (n+1)/2$, we see that $x_j$ takes on the values

$$-(n-1)/2, -(n-3)/2, \ldots, (n-3)/2, (n-1)/2.$$

Let us attempt to replace the above equation by one of the form

$$Y_j = \alpha_0 + \alpha_1 P_{1j} + \alpha_2 P_{2j} + \cdots + \alpha_r P_{rj} + \epsilon_j,\dagger$$

where the $\alpha$'s are functions of the $\beta$'s and the $P$'s are functions of the powers of $x$ chosen so that each $P_{ij}$ is a function of all powers of $x_j$ $(=j - \bar{j})$ equal to or less than $i$:

$$P_{ij} = C_{i0} + C_{i1} x_j + C_{i2} x_j^2 + \cdots + C_{ii} x_j^i.$$

Let us construct a set of $r$ polynomials, that is, determine the coefficients, $C$'s, so that each polynomial is orthogonal to all others including $P_0' \equiv 1$. That is,

$$\underset{j}{S} P_{ij} P_{kj} = 0, \qquad i = 0, 1, \ldots, r; k \neq i.$$

In the future, $S$ will refer to summation over $j$. For a given $P_{ij}$, we want the $i$ sums for $k = 0, 1, \ldots, i-1$ to be zero. Since each polynomial is a function of the powers of $x$ equal to or less than $k$, we can replace the above summations by

$$\underset{j}{S} P_{ij} x_j^k = 0, \qquad k = 0, 1, 2, \ldots, i-1.$$

That is, we have $i$ equations to determine the values of the $(i+1)$ coefficients: $C_{i0}, C_{i1}, \ldots, C_{ii}$. Hence it is necessary to fix the value of one constant; we shall set $C_{ii} \equiv 1$.

Using the definition of $P_{ij}$ in terms of the $x$'s, we have for a given $k$

$$\underset{j}{S}(C_{i0} + C_{i1} x_j + \cdots + C_{i,i-1} x_j^{i-1} + x_j^i) x_j^k = \sum_{l=0}^{i-1} C_{il} \underset{j}{S} x_j^{k+l} + \underset{j}{S} x_j^{i+k} = 0.$$

We know that $Sx^m = 0$ when $m$ is odd. Hence we have the following equations for $i$ odd:

† We shall use the letter $P$ instead of $\xi$ in the theory which follows.

| $k$ | Equation |
|---|---|
| 0 | $C_{i,0}n + C_{i,2}Sx^2 + \cdots + C_{i,i-1}Sx^{i-1} = 0$ |
| 2 | $C_{i,0}Sx^2 + C_{i,2}Sx^4 + \cdots + C_{i,i-1}Sx^{i+1} = 0$ |
| . | . . . . . . . . . . . . . . . . . . . . . . . . |
| $i-1$ | $C_{i,0}Sx^{i-1} + C_{i,2}Sx^{i+1} + \cdots + C_{i,i-1}Sx^{2(i-1)} = 0$ |
| 1 | $C_{i,1}Sx^2 + C_{i,3}Sx^4 + \cdots + C_{i,i-2}Sx^{i-1} + Sx^{i+1} = 0$ |
| 3 | $C_{i,1}Sx^4 + C_{i,3}Sx^6 + \cdots + C_{i,i-2}Sx^{i+1} + Sx^{i+3} = 0$ |
| . | . . . . . . . . . . . . . . . . . . . . . . . . |
| $i-2$ | $C_{i,1}Sx^{i-1} + C_{i,3}Sx^{i+1} + \cdots + C_{i,i-2}Sx^{2i-4} + Sx^{2i-2} = 0$ |

The $\frac{1}{2}(i+1)$ equations for $k$ even involve only the coefficients $\{C_{i,0},C_{i,2}, \ldots ,C_{i,i-1}\}$, and since these equations have no constant term, all the coefficients are zero. But the $\frac{1}{2}(i-1)$ equations for $k$ odd do have nonzero constant terms, and we can solve for the coefficients

$$\{C_{i,1},C_{i,3}, \ . \ . \ . \ ,C_{i,i-2}\}.$$

Hence we conclude that when $i$ is odd ($i = 1,3, \ldots$),

$$\begin{aligned} P_1 &= x, \\ P_3 &= x^3 + C_{3,1}x, \\ &\cdots \\ P_i &= x^i + C_{i,i-2}x^{i-2} + \cdots + C_{i,3}x^3 + C_{i,1}x. \end{aligned}$$

Similarly it can be shown that when $i$ is even ($i = 0,2,4, \ldots$),

$$\begin{aligned} P_0 &= 1, \\ P_2 &= x^2 + C_{2,0}, \\ P_4 &= x^4 + C_{4,2}x^2 + C_{4,0}, \\ &\cdots \\ P_i &= x^i + C_{i,i-2}x^{i-2} + \cdots + C_{i,2}x^2 + C_{i,0}. \end{aligned}$$

Note that we have omitted the $j$ subscript for convenience.

From these results we see that

$$xP_i = P_{i+1} + D_{i,1}P_{i-1} + D_{i,2}P_{i-3} + \cdots ,$$

where the $D$'s are functions of the $C$'s. For example

$$\begin{aligned} xP_1 &= x^2 = P_2 - C_{2,0}, \\ xP_2 &= x^3 + C_{2,0}x = P_3 + (C_{2,0} - C_{3,1})x, \\ D_{11} &= -C_{2,0}, \qquad D_{21} = C_{2,0} - C_{3,1}, \qquad D_{i,l} = 0 \text{ for } l > 1. \end{aligned}$$

Since $(xP_i)$ is a function of powers of $x$ equal to or less than $(i+1)$, the orthogonality requirement, $SP_lx^k = 0$ for $l > k$, guarantees that

$$SxP_iP_l = 0$$

for $l > (i+1)$ and because of the symmetry of $i$ and $l$ for $i > (l+1)$.

Also since $P_i^2$ is a function of even powers of $x$, $SxP_i^2 = 0$. Hence the only cases for which $SxP_iP_l \neq 0$ are $l = i \pm 1$. And when $l = i \pm 1$, all of the terms except those for $P_{i+1}$ and $P_{i-1}$ vanish. That is

$$SxP_iP_{i+1} = SP_{i+1}^2 \qquad \text{or} \qquad SxP_{i-1}P_i = SP_i^2,$$
$$SxP_iP_{i-1} = D_{i,1}SP_{i-1}^2.$$

Hence

$$D_{i,1} = \frac{SP_i^2}{SP_{i-1}^2}$$

and all other $D$'s $= 0$.

Therefore we now have a recursion formula to determine higher-order polynomials in terms of lower-order ones:

$$P_{i+1} = xP_i - \frac{SP_i^2}{SP_{i-1}^2} P_{i-1}.$$

Since $P_1 = x$, $P_0 = 1$, $SP_1^2 = Sx^2 = n(n^2 - 1)/12$, and $SP_0^2 = n$,

$$P_2 = x^2 - \frac{n^2 - 1}{12}.$$

Similarly

$$SP_2^2 = Sx^4 - n\left(\frac{n^2 - 1}{12}\right) = \frac{n(n^2 - 1)(n^2 - 4)}{180}$$

and

$$P_3 = x^3 - \left(\frac{n^2 - 1}{12} + \frac{n^2 - 4}{15}\right)x = x^3 - \frac{3n^2 - 7}{20}x.$$

A general formula for $SP_i^2$ is

$$SP_i^2 = \frac{n(n^2 - 1)(n^2 - 4) \cdots (n^2 - i^2)(i!)^2[(i - 1)!]^2}{4(2i + 1)[(2i - 1)!]^2}.$$

Hence

$$D_{i,1} = \frac{SP_i^2}{SP_{i-1}^2} = \frac{(n^2 - i^2)i^2}{4(4i^2 - 1)}.$$

A proof of these results is beyond the scope of this book but can be found in most of the sources cited in Sec. 16.1. Hence

$$P_4 = x^4 - \left[\frac{3n^2 - 7}{20} + \frac{(n^2 - 9)9}{140}\right]x^2 + \frac{9(n^2 - 1)(n^2 - 9)}{(12)(140)}$$
$$= x^4 - \frac{3n^2 - 13}{14}x^2 + \frac{3(n^2 - 1)(n^2 - 9)}{560}.$$

The reader will note that these polynomial values, $P_{ij}$, will be fractions. For convenience of computing and of presentation of tables of the polynomial values, it is desirable to use only integral values for the $P_{ij}$. The regular polynomial values have been multiplied by a constant, $\lambda_i$, in references 10 and 11, so chosen that the values of $P'_{ij} = \lambda_i P_{ij}$ are integers reduced to lowest terms. Hence

$$Y_j = \alpha'_0 + \alpha'_1 P'_{1j} + \alpha'_2 P'_{2j} + \cdots + \alpha'_r P'_{rj} + \epsilon_j,$$

where $\alpha_i = \alpha'_i \lambda_i$ and $\alpha_0 = \alpha'_0$.

**Example 16.1.** As an example, consider the construction of the $P_{ij}$ values for $n = 5$ (refer to Example 6.4 on page 62). Obviously, for five points, a fourth-degree polynomial will fit the data exactly; hence, only $P_0(\equiv 1)$, $P_1$, $P_2$, $P_3$, and $P_4$ exist. Using the formulas already indicated, we have $x_j = j - \dfrac{n+1}{2} = j - 3$, and

$$P_{1j} = x_j, \qquad P_{2j} = x_j^2 - 2, \qquad P_{3j} = x_j^3 - \tfrac{17}{5}x_j, \qquad P_{4j} = x_j^4 - \tfrac{31}{7}x_j^2 + \tfrac{72}{35}.$$

The polynomial values are given in the table below. We note that

| $j$ | $P_{1j}$ | $P_{2j}$ | $P_{3j}$ | $P_{4j}$ | $P'_{3j}$ | $P'_{4j}$ |
|---|---|---|---|---|---|---|
| 1 | $-2$ | 2 | $-\frac{6}{5}$ | $\frac{12}{35}$ | $-1$ | 1 |
| 2 | $-1$ | $-1$ | $\frac{12}{5}$ | $-\frac{48}{35}$ | 2 | $-4$ |
| 3 | 0 | $-2$ | 0 | $\frac{72}{35}$ | 0 | 6 |
| 4 | 1 | $-1$ | $-\frac{12}{5}$ | $-\frac{48}{35}$ | $-2$ | $-4$ |
| 5 | 2 | 2 | $\frac{6}{5}$ | $\frac{12}{35}$ | 1 | 1 |
| $S(P'_i)^2$ | 10 | 14 | | | 10 | 70 |

$P_{1j} = P'_{1j}$ and $P_{2j} = P'_{2j}$; that is, $\lambda_1 = \lambda_2 = 1$. $\lambda_3 = \frac{5}{6}$ and $\lambda_4 = \frac{35}{12}$, so that $P'_{3j} = (5P_{3j})/6$ and $P'_{4j} = (35P_{4j})/12$.

**16.3. Estimating the Parameters, $\alpha'_i$ and $\sigma^2$.** We are given the regression equation to fit to $n$ equally spaced points:

$$Y_j = \sum_{i=0}^{r} \alpha'_i P'_{ij} + \epsilon_j = \hat{Y}_j + e_j, \qquad r + 1 \le n,$$

where the $\{\epsilon\}$ are assumed NID$(0,\sigma^2)$ and

$$\hat{Y}_j = A'_0 + A'_1 P'_{1j} + \cdots + A'_r P'_{rj},$$

with $\alpha'_i \doteq A'_i$. The least-squares equations to determine the $A'_i$ are quite simple, because of the orthogonal property of the $P'$'s. In fact $A'_0 = \bar{Y}$, and

$$A'_i = \frac{S(YP'_i)}{S(P'_i)^2}.$$

The polynomial tables in reference 11 present values of the $P'_i$, $\lambda_i$, and $S(P'_i)^2$ for values of $n$ through 104. In these tables, $P'_i \equiv \xi'_i$.

The sum of squares of deviations from the regression is given by

$$\text{SSR} = n\bar{Y}^2 + A'_1S(YP'_1) + A'_2S(YP'_2) + \cdots + A'_rS(YP'_r),$$

where each term is the independent reduction due to the successive polynomials: mean, $P'_1, P'_2, \cdots, P'_r$. Also

$$\text{SSE} = SY^2 - \text{SSR} = Sy^2 - \sum_{i=1}^{r} \text{SSR}_i,$$

where

$$\text{SSR}_i = A'_iS(YP'_i) = (SYP'_i)^2/S(P'_i)^2.$$

$s^2 = \text{SSE}/(n - r - 1)$ is an unbiased estimate of $\sigma^2$. Hence we can set up the following analysis of variance:

| Source of variation | Degrees of freedom | Mean square |
|---|---|---|
| Linear regression ($P'_1$) | 1 | $\text{SSR}_1 = (SYP'_1)^2/S(P'_1)^2$ |
| Quadratic regression ($P'_2$) | 1 | $\text{SSR}_2 = (SYP'_2)^2/S(P'_2)^2$ |
| . | . | . |
| . | . | . |
| . | . | . |
| $r^{\text{th}}$ degree regression ($P'_r$) | 1 | $\text{SSR}_r = (SYP'_r)^2/S(P'_r)^2$ |
| Error | $n - r - 1$ | $s^2 = \text{SSE}/(n - r - 1)$ |

In general we do not know what degree ($r$) should be used; so tests of successive terms are made until there is no material reduction in $s^2$ by the use of additional terms.†

It should be pointed out that the equation

$$\hat{Y} = A'_0 + A'_1P'_1 + \cdots + A'_rP'_r$$

can be used for prediction purposes. However, if the original polynomial form of the equation is needed, the $P'_i$ will have to be replaced by their equivalent polynomial function,

$$P'_i = \lambda_i(C_{i0} + C_{i1}x + C_{i2}x^2 + \cdots + x^i).$$

This is adequately explained in reference 11.

**Example 16.2.** In order to compare the number of spears per asparagus plant for male and female plants, the California Agricultural Experiment Station at Davis obtained the following data on the differences ($Y$)

† This procedure introduces a slight bias into the estimate of $\sigma^2$, because the procedure is unbiased only if the model is postulated in advance ($r$ is known in advance). We doubt that this bias is very serious, but some theoretical or empirical studies of this point should be made.

| Year ($j$) | 1 | 2 | 3 | 4 | 5 | 6 | 7 | 8 | 9 | 10 | 11 | 12 | Sum of squares |
|---|---|---|---|---|---|---|---|---|---|---|---|---|---|
| $Y$ | 1.1 | 7.1 | 11.0 | 12.6 | 14.7 | 19.9 | 25.1 | 23.9 | 23.1 | 23.6 | 26.0 | 24.6 | 4,516.43 |
| $P_1'$ | −11 | −9 | −7 | −5 | −3 | −1 | 1 | 3 | 5 | 7 | 9 | 11 | 572 |
| $P_2'$ | 55 | 25 | 1 | −17 | −29 | −35 | −35 | −29 | −17 | 1 | 25 | 55 | 12,012 |
| $P_3'$ | −33 | 3 | 21 | 25 | 19 | 7 | −7 | −19 | −25 | −21 | −3 | 33 | 5,148 |
| $P_4'$ | 33 | −27 | −33 | −13 | 12 | 28 | 28 | 12 | −13 | −33 | −27 | 33 | 8,008 |

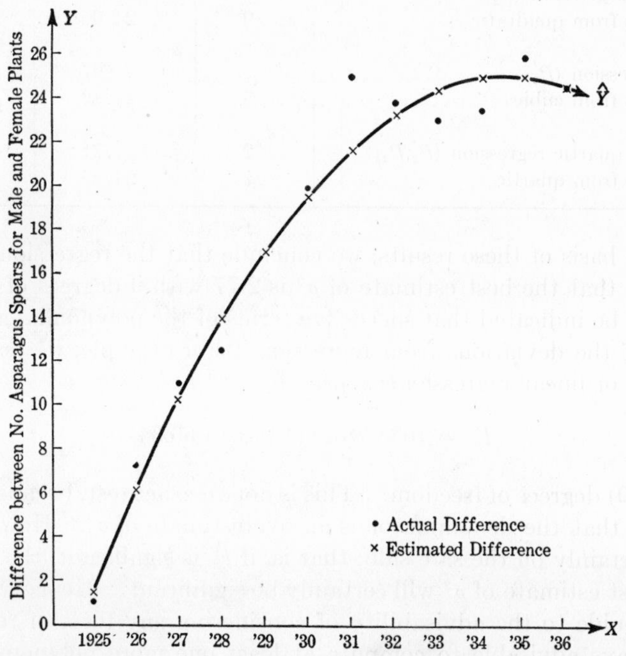


FIG. 16.1. Changes in differences between mean number of male and female asparagus spears, 1925 to 1936.

between the mean number of spears per plant for each of the years 1925 to 1936, here indicated as years 1 to 12 (see Fig. 16.1). The first four sets of polynomial values are given below the yields. The λ's are $\lambda_1 = 2$, $\lambda_2 = 3$, $\lambda_3 = \frac{2}{3}$, $\lambda_4 = \frac{7}{24}$. The computed results are given below.

$$SY = 212.7, \qquad A_0' = 17.725, \qquad n\bar{Y}^2 = 3{,}770.11,$$
$$SP_1'Y = 602.1, \qquad A_1' = 1.05262, \qquad \text{SSR}_1 = 633.78,$$
$$SP_2'Y = -1{,}025.7, \qquad A_2' = -.0853896, \qquad \text{SSR}_2 = 87.58,$$
$$SP_3'Y = -19.5, \qquad A_3' = -.00378788, \qquad \text{SSR}_3 = .07,$$
$$SP_4'Y = 71.7. \qquad A_4' = .00895355. \qquad \text{SSR}_4 = .64.$$

The analysis of variance is as follows:

| Source of variation | Degrees of freedom | Sum of squares | Mean square |
|---|---|---|---|
| $Sy^2$ | 11 | 746.32 | |
| Linear regression ($P'_1$) | 1 | 633.78 | 633.78 |
| Deviations from linear | 10 | 112.54 | 11.25 |
| Quadratic regression ($P'_2$) | 1 | 87.58 | 87.58 |
| Deviations from quadratic | 9 | 24.96 | 2.77 |
| Cubic regression ($P'_3$) | 1 | .07 | .07 |
| Deviations from cubic | 8 | 24.89 | 3.11 |
| Cubic and quartic regression ($P'_3,P'_4$) | 2 | .71 | .36 |
| Deviations from quartic | 7 | 24.25 | 3.46 |

On the basis of these results, we conclude that the regression is quadratic and that the best estimate of $\sigma^2$ is 2.77 with 9 degrees of freedom. It should be indicated that successive terms of the polynomial are tested by use of the deviations from regression. For example, we test for the existence of linear regression by use of

$$F' = (633.78)/(11.25) = 56.34$$

with (1,10) degrees of freedom. This is not an exact test, because we find out later that the denominator is an overestimate of $\sigma^2$. However, the test is certainly on the safe side; that is, if $F'$ is significant, the $F$ by use of the best estimate of $\sigma^2$ will certainly be significant. Hence we can use $F'$ as a guide to the advisability of considering any form of regression. It is always advisable to compute at least one more polynomial value after the first nonsignificant one. That is, we might have stopped with $P'_3$, but it is advisable to try out $P'_4$ to make sure it is not significant.

Using the quadratic regression equation,

$$\begin{aligned}\hat{Y} &= 17.725 + 1.053P'_1 - .0854P'_2 \\ &= 17.725 + 2.106(j - 6.5) - .0854[3(j - 6.5)^2 - 35.75] \\ &= 17.725 + 2.106(j - 6.5) - .0854(3j^2 - 39j + 91) \\ &= -3.735 + 5.437j - .2562j^2 \\ &= (1.45,\ 6.11,\ 10.27,\ 13.91,\ 17.04,\ 19.66,\ 21.77,\ 23.36,\ 24.45,\ 25.02, \\ &\qquad 25.07,\ 24.61).\end{aligned}$$

These results are displayed graphically in Fig. 16.1.

## EXERCISES

**16.1.** (*a*) Prove that $A'_i$ is an unbiased estimate of $\alpha'_i$, $\sigma^2(A'_i) = \sigma^2/S(P'_i)^2$, and $\sigma(A'_iA'_l) = 0$ for $i \neq l$.

(*b*) Prove that $s^2$ is an unbiased estimate of $\sigma^2$.

(*c*) Prove that SSR is independent of SSE.

**16.2.** Derive the formula for $P_5$.

**16.3.** Compute the polynomial values, $P'_i$, $i = 0, 1, \cdots, 5$, for $n = 6$.

**16.4.** (*a*) Determine the standard errors of $A'_1$ and $A'_2$ in Example 16.2, and then set up 95 per cent confidence limits for the true regression coefficients $\alpha'_1$ and $\alpha'_2$.

(*b*) Do the same for $A_1$ and $A_2$ as estimates of $\alpha_1$ and $\alpha_2$.

(*c*) What is the standard error of $\hat{Y}_j$?

**16.5.** Given the following data on the output ($Y_1$) in pounds per man-hour for General Motors employees and the aggregate weight of all General Motors automobile products in millions of pounds ($Y_2$) for the years 1929 to 1941.

| Year | 1929 | 1930 | 1931 | 1932 | 1933 | 1934 | 1935 | 1936 | 1937 | 1938 | 1939 | 1940 | 1941 |
|---|---|---|---|---|---|---|---|---|---|---|---|---|---|
| $Y_1$ | 12.55 | 13.41 | 14.79 | 14.56 | 15.05 | 15.67 | 17.60 | 18.30 | 18.61 | 19.69 | 19.87 | 20.81 | 21.83 |
| $Y_2$ | 5,632 | 3,537 | 3,175 | 1,692 | 2,477 | 3,812 | 5,338 | 6,617 | 6,868 | 4,020 | 5,618 | 7,492 | 8,631 |

(*a*) Use a set of orthogonal polynomial tables (reference 10 or 11), or construct such a set for $n = 13$ to determine the best fitting polynomial to fit to each set of data.

(*b*) If the same degree equation is to be used for both sets of data, what degree would you advise?

(*c*) How would you determine the regression of $Y_2$ on $Y_1$, both adjusted for time trends? What theoretical difficulties do you see in the determination of the regression of $Y_2$ on $Y_1$?

**16.6.** Snedecor[1] presents the following problem on the average weights of sunflowers:

| Week | 1 | 2 | 3 | 4 | 5 | 6 | 7 | 8 | 9 | 10 | 11 | 12 |
|---|---|---|---|---|---|---|---|---|---|---|---|---|
| Height | 18 | 36 | 68 | 98 | 131 | 170 | 206 | 228 | 247 | 250 | 254 | 254 |

(*a*) What degree of polynomial should be used to estimate the height after $j$ weeks?

(*b*) Plot the actual and estimated heights.

(*c*) Determine the standard errors of the regression coefficients.

**16.7.** We know that the graph of the equation

$$Y = 10 - 2X + 3X^2 - X^3$$

passes through the points

$$(1,10),\ (2,10),\ (3,4),\ (4,-14),\ (5,-50),\ (6,-110).$$

Use these points to derive the prediction equation

$$\hat{Y} = A'_0 + A'_1P'_1 + A'_2P'_2 + A'_3P'_3,$$

and show that $\hat{Y} \equiv Y$ in this case.

**16.8.** The student is advised to select some data from his own field of research for which a polynomial prediction equation is useful and to carry out the necessary computations to determine $\hat{Y}$.

**16.9.** (*a*) Use the general definition of orthogonal polynomials,

$$\underset{j}{S} P_{ij}x_j^k = 0, \quad i \neq k,$$

to derive a complete set of orthogonal polynomial values for the following $X$'s: 2, 3, 6, 9.

(*b*) When would it be useful to derive a set of orthogonal polynomial values for unequally spaced $X$'s?

### References Cited

1. Snedecor, G. W., *Statistical Methods*, 4th ed., Collegiate Press, Inc., of Iowa State College, Ames, Iowa, 1946. Chaps. 13, 14.
2. Tchebysheff, P. L., *Oeuvres*, 1854–1875.
3. Fisher, R. A., "An Examination of Yields of Dressed Grain from Broadbalk," *J. Agr. Sci.*, **11**:107–135 (1921).
4. Jordan, Charles, "Approximation and Graduation According to the Principles of Least Squares by Orthogonal Polynomials," *Ann. Math. Stat.*, **3**:257*ff*. (1932).
5. Aitken, A. C., "On the Graduation of Data by the Orthogonal Polynomials of Least Squares," *Proc. Roy. Soc. Edinburgh*, **53**:54–78 (1933).
6. Sasuly, Max, *Trend Analysis of Statistics*, Brookings Institution, Washington, D.C., 1934.
7. Allen, F. E., "The General Form of the Orthogonal Polynomials for Simple Series with Proofs of Their Simple Properties," *Proc. Roy. Soc. Edinburgh*, 50:310–320 (1936).
8. Birge, R. T., and J. W. Weinberg, "Least Squares Fitting of Data by Means of Polynomials," *Revs. Modern Phys.*, **19**:298–360 (1947).
9. Fisher, R. A., *Statistical Methods for Research Workers*, 10th ed. Oliver & Boyd, Ltd., Edinburgh & London, 1946. Chap. 5.
10. Fisher, R. A., and F. Yates, *Statistical Tables for Biological, Agricultural and Medical Research*, 3d ed., Oliver & Boyd, Ltd., Edinburgh & London, 1948.
11. Anderson, R. L., and E. E. Houseman, "Tables of Orthogonal Polynomial Values Extended to $N = 104$," *Iowa State Coll., Agr. Expt. Sta. Research Bull.* 297 (1942).

# CHAPTER 17

# LEAST SQUARES FOR EXPERIMENTAL DESIGN MODELS

**17.1. Introduction.** The least-squares methods outlined in the preceding chapters can be used to analyze the effects of different treatments in a planned experiment. We shall consider a variety of experimental results in succeeding chapters, among these being the following:

(i) The yields of a crop for different varieties and different fertilizers.

(ii) The gains of weight of animals for different rations.

(iii) The effects of different temperatures on the plating of steel wire.

(iv) The effects of varying periods of cold storage on the tenderness and flavor of beef.

(v) The toxicity of various chemicals on insects.

In the discussion which follows, the word *treatments* will be used to apply to the varieties, fertilizers, rations, or chemicals used in the experiment. And the word *yield* will be used to describe the result of the experiment, whether it be bushels of oats, pounds of grain, or per cent of insects killed by a spray. It is further assumed that the yields were obtained by applying the treatments to a variety of *experimental units*, such as plots of ground, animals, or pieces of wire.

When the experiment is set up, some restrictions may be placed on the assignment of the treatments to the experimental units. These restrictions are included in the general topic of *experimental design* and are extensively discussed in references 1 to 4. Four important types of designs will be discussed in the next two chapters.

(i) *Completely randomized designs.* No restrictions are placed on the assignment of the treatments to the experimental units, except that each treatment shall be used a specified number of times.

(ii) *Randomized complete-blocks designs.* The experimental units are divided into relatively homogeneous sets, called *blocks,* the number of experimental units per block being equal to the number of treatments and each treatment assigned to one experimental unit in each block.

(iii) *Latin-square designs.* The experimental units are arranged in homogeneous blocks in two directions, called *rows* and *columns,* each treatment appearing in each row and column once and only once.

(iv) *Incomplete-blocks designs.* The number of treatments is greater than the number of experimental units which can be grouped in each block.

The first three designs, which can be classified as *complete-blocks designs*, will be discussed in Chap. 18 and the incomplete-blocks designs in Chap. 19.

Then in Chap. 20 different combinations of treatments will be discussed as *factorial designs*. These factorial designs can be used with any of the above field designs and are discussed in detail in references 1, 2, and 5.

Some attention will also be paid to the analysis of data collected in *sample surveys*. The basic data are collected from *sampling units*, such as people or plots of ground; after the sampling units have been contacted, they may be subdivided into subclasses according to some of the information secured in the survey. Or the population may be divided into classes before the survey is started and a fixed number of sampling units contacted in each class. Since most surveys are set up with several sources of random variation, they will be discussed in detail in Chap. 22. A few examples are included in Sec. 18.2, where the sampling design corresponds to a completely randomized experimental design. In the discussion which follows we shall refer only to the analysis of experimental results, but the reader should understand that survey results can be analyzed by similar methods if the assumptions apply.

When an experimenter sets up an experiment to examine the yielding ability of different treatments, he usually desires the following information:

(i) A test of whether there are any real treatment effects.

(ii) Average yield or effect of each treatment or the difference in yields between two different treatments.

(iii) Confidence limits for these average yields or differences.

(iv) A measure of the precision of the experiment.

(v) An estimate of the efficiency of the particular experimental design as compared with some alternative design.

The experimenter should have some ideas concerning the pattern of response of the experimental material to the treatments. In order to use the method of least squares to analyze the data, we must assume that the yield for a given experimental unit can be represented as a linear function of the *treatment effect*, *block effect*, and *error* for that particular experimental unit, that is,

$$\text{Yield} = (\text{general mean}) + (\text{treatment effect}) + (\text{block effect}) + (\text{error}),$$

where the mean measures the average yield for this experimental setup, the treatment and block effects add or subtract from the mean depending on how they affect the yield, and the error measures the failure of these effects to predict the exact yield. The error is a measure of the uncontrolled sources of variation in the experiment, such as differences in the yielding abilities of experimental units in the same block, and errors in applying the treatments to the experimental units and in collecting the data.

If the errors in the above *experimental model* can be assumed to be noncorrelated and to have the same amount of variability for every treatment and block, the method of least squares will give unbiased minimum variance estimates of the effects. In addition, if the errors are normally distributed, the $F$ and $t$ tests can be used to test for the significance of treatment differences, and the usual confidence limits for means can be used. A more detailed discussion of these assumptions is presented in the next section.

As indicated in previous chapters, a computational device which furnishes the requisite data for estimating variances and making tests of significance for the method of least squares is the *analysis of variance.* The analysis of variance is a simple arithmetic device for dividing the total sum of squares into separate orthogonal parts, and if the least-squares assumptions are met, these sums of squares can be used to make tests and to set up confidence limits.

In Chap. 14 it was shown that if we had $r$ fixed variates split into two groups of $k$ and $(r - k)$ variates each, the prediction equation was

$$Y = \mu + \sum_{i=1}^{k} \beta_i x_i + \sum_{i=k+1}^{r} \beta_i x_i + \epsilon.$$

The analysis of variance was:

| Source of variation | Degrees of freedom | Sum of squares | Mean square |
|---|---|---|---|
| First $k$ fixed variates | $k$ | $R_k$ | $R_k/k$ |
| Added reduction by last $(r - k)$ fixed variates | $r - k$ | $R_r - R_k$ | $(R_r - R_k)/(r - k)$ |
| Error | $n - r - 1$ | SSE | $s^2 = \text{SSE}/(n - r - 1)$ |

We can test the null hypothesis that the last $(r - k)$ $\beta$'s are 0, without assuming anything about the first $k$ $\beta$'s, by use of $F = (R_r - R_k)/(r - k)s^2$, with $(r - k)$ and $(n - r - 1)$ degrees of freedom. We generally wish to eliminate the effect of the mean from the regression first and do not want to test if the mean is 0. Hence everything has been indicated as deviations from the mean with $\mu$ estimated by $\bar{Y}$. When it is desired to test the null hypothesis that any subset of $(r - k)$ of the $\beta_i$'s are all zero, we would determine the reduction, $R_r$, due to all $r$ fixed variates and then the reduction $R_k$ due to the other $k$ fixed variates alone. The difference between the two reductions furnishes the necessary data to test the desired hypothesis by use of $F$, as indicated above. If the two sets of fixed variates happen to be orthogonal, then the first $k$ fixed variates can be tested by use of $F = R_k/ks^2$. This merely means that the added reduction for these $k$ fixed variates after fitting the last $(r - k)$ fixed variates alone is the same as $R_k$ or, conversely, that the reduction due to fitting the last $(r - k)$ fixed variates alone is the same as $R_r - R_k$.

In a planned experiment, the first set of fixed variates could represent block effects and the second set treatment effects. As will be explained in more detail in later sections, the $X$'s are either 1 or 0 for experimental data and the regression coefficients are the effects. Many experiments are designed so that the block and treatment effects are orthogonal; in other words, each part of the analysis of variance can be used to test a particular set of effects. When the treatment and block effects are orthogonal, the computations are simplified and the estimates of the effects are generally more efficient. However, there are circumstances for which orthogonality is not possible or advisable. Some of these are discussed in Chap. 19.

The reader is advised to read reference 6 for a discussion of the general theory of tests of significance for analysis-of-variance problems and reference 7 for the power of these significance tests. In the chapters which follow, it will be shown that the expected value of the reduction in the total sum of squares attributable to certain treatments used in the experiments can be written as

$$(p - 1)\sigma^2 + r \sum_{i=1}^{p} \tau_i^2,$$

where the $p$ $\{\tau_i\}$ are the true treatment effects, each treatment being used $r$ times in the experiment, and $\sigma^2$ is the population variance. Tang[7] has prepared tables of the Type II error (1 − power) in terms of the treatment and error degrees of freedom and a constant $\phi$, where

$$\phi = \sqrt{r\Sigma\tau_i^2/p\sigma^2}.$$

**17.2. Assumptions Made in the Experimental Model.** Before using the analysis of variance to summarize the results of an experiment, it is advisable to check the reasonableness of the assumptions which are set up. A discussion of these assumptions, the consequences of their not being true, and some methods of handling aberrant data are presented in the March, 1947, issue of *Biometrics*.[8] A brief summary of these assumptions is presented here, but the reader might prefer to reread this section after going over the next two chapters.

(i) *In order to connect the analysis of variance with the theory of linear regression, we must assume that the various fixed effects and the error are additive.* If the physical make-up of the data or of the operations producing the data are of such nature that the effects are really not additive, then the sum of squares attributable to such effects by the analysis of variance do not represent the true effects. If nonadditive effects are actually multiplicative, then we could use the logarithms of the original data and have additive effects. Some other type of transformation might be useful for other kinds of nonadditivity. Except for the multiplicative case, it is usually assumed that the additive assumption is a good first approximation to the true relationship and that refinements here would produce only minor improvements in the analysis. In general, if the treatment and block effects are small, for example, the largest mean is not more than 50 per cent greater than the smallest, it is doubtful that one needs to worry about nonadditivity. But if there are large treatment or block effects, caution should be exercised in the use of an additive linear model. With large treatment differences, these differences may not be the same from one block to another. This is called an *interaction* between treatments and blocks; if this interaction is also additive, a design may be set up to measure it (see Chap. 23). For some recent ideas on this subject, see reference 9.

(ii) *In addition, the errors must be noncorrelated.* In field experiments, it is known that the errors in adjacent plots are usually positively correlated. A device, called *randomization*, is used to circumvent much of this difficulty. By this device, the treatments are allocated at random to the experimental units, subject to the design restrictions mentioned in the previous section, so that there is an equal chance of any two treatments appearing in adjacent and in nonadjacent plots. Hence the expected value of the total error for any one treatment is independent of that for any other treatment. It should be emphasized that randomization does not remove the correlation between the inherent characteristics of adjacent plots; rather it provides a mechanism by which this expected correlation between two treatments tends to cancel as the number of experimental units per treatment is increased. A more complete treatment of this subject is given by R. A. Fisher,[2] Cochran,[8] and Yates.[10] Cochran and Cox[1] (page 8) make the following remark concerning randomization: "Randomization is somewhat analogous to insurance, in that it is a precaution against disturbances that may or may not occur and that may or may not be serious if they do occur. It is generally advisable to take the trouble to randomize even when it is not expected that there will be any serious bias from failure to randomize."

Such data as daily price and production figures cannot fulfill the randomization requirement. Hence it is generally stated that the analysis of variance is not a valid method of testing for yearly or monthly price differences. To date, the mathematical difficulties of testing for the existence of correlations between errors have prevented any definite statements on the validity of the analysis of variance for such data. Research in the field of *serial correlation* may lead to an approximate solution of this problem. The serial correlation coefficient measures the correlation between successive members of a series. See reference 11 for some recent articles on this subject.

(iii) *In order to have a simple analysis of variance, it is desirable that the errors be the same from one experimental unit to another, regardless of the treatment used.* Also, if the errors are not equal, it is necessary to know the relative sizes of the variances before the experiment is conducted, a knowledge which is generally not available. Sometimes the data can be split into parts, each part with homogeneous errors, but with unequal errors from one part to another. An example of this is presented in Chap. 3 of reference 1 and by Cochran.[8] For example, it often happens that some experimental units are subjected to a control treatment, which often is no treatment at all. If the experimental units are quite variable and the treatment is effective in raising the yield, there may be much more variability between control yields than between yields from treated plots, because the treatments will tend to increase the yields of the poor plots more than the good plots (hence decreasing the variability).

Bartlett[8] discusses various transformations of the original data to stabilize the variance when there is a fixed relationship between the mean and the variance. For example, we have shown that if a sample is drawn from a Poisson population, the mean and the variance will tend to be the same. In this case, it can be shown that if the dependent variable $Z = \sqrt{Y}$ is used in the analysis, the variance of $Z$ will be approximately the same for all levels of $Z$; if there are many small values of $Y$, use $Z = \sqrt{Y + \frac{1}{2}}$. Many social, economic, and production data tend to have the standard deviation increase with the mean; the variance of the transformed variate $Z = \log Y$ will tend to be approximately stable. However, it should be apparent in all of these cases that if the treatment and block differences are small, there is seldom any need for a transformation.

(iv) *If it is desired to use the analysis of variance to make the usual tests of significance or set up confidence limits, the errors must be normally distributed.* The principal nonnormal feature to be concerned about is skewness. But even this probably does not affect two-tailed tests too much. However, there may be serious biases for single-tailed tests or confidence limits. Some investigations have been made on the effects of nonnormality on the significance levels and power of tests (see Cochran[8]), but few general results have been obtained. Perhaps more empirical sampling studies should be made.

**17.3. Principles of Setting Up an Experiment.** While the statistician and experimenter are deciding on a realistic model which can be analyzed by available techniques (including transformations, if necessary), the details of how the experiment is to be conducted and analyzed should also be outlined.

(i) *The experimenter should clearly set forth his objectives before proceeding with the experiment.* Is this a preliminary experiment to determine the future course of experimentation, or is it intended to furnish answers to immediate questions? Are the results to be carried into practical use at once, or are they to be used to explain aspects of theory not adequately understood before? Are you mainly interested in estimates or in tests of significance? Over what range of experimental conditions do you wish to extend your results?

(ii) *The experiment should be described in detail.* The treatments should be clearly defined. Is it necessary to use a control treatment in order to make comparisons with past results? The size of the experiment should be determined. If insufficient funds are available to conduct an experiment from which useful results can be obtained, the experiment should not be started. And above all, the necessary material to conduct the experiment should be available.

(iii) *An outline of the analysis should be drawn up before the experiment is started.*

**17.4. Methods of Increasing the Accuracy of the Experiment.** *Accuracy* refers to the success of estimating the true value of a quantity; it is often confused with *precision*, which refers to the clustering of sample values about their own average, which will not be the true value if this average is biased. Precision can be thought of as the inverse of variance. Hence accuracy is a more inclusive term, since it involves both biasedness and precision. Often the experimenter has to choose between an unbiased estimate with rather low precision (high variance) and a slightly biased one with high precision. The choice of the proper estimate is often dictated by circumstances beyond his control, but certain methods of increasing the accuracy of the experiment should be kept in mind. If there is no bias in the experimental and estimation procedures, accuracy and precision are for all practical purposes synonymous.

(i) *Accuracy can generally be increased by increasing the size of the experiment.* There are certain limitations to this statement, such as the fact that increasing size may bring in more heterogeneous material and also may result in a poorer supervision of the experiment with a possible biased result. The latter point is often true in industrial and psychological experiments and in sample surveys. But in general the accuracy of an estimate increases with increasing size of the experiment. Increasing the number of blocks or treatments also furnishes more degrees of freedom for the estimate of the experimental error.

(ii) *The experimental techniques should be refined as much as possible.*

(*a*) There should be a uniform method of applying the treatments to the experimental units.

(*b*) Sufficient control over external influences should be exercised so that every treatment operates under as nearly the same conditions as possible.

(*c*) Unbiased measures of the treatment effects should be devised so that they are fully understood by those running the experiment and by other research workers. As yet we do not have good enough measures of such things as socioeconomic status, educational progress, and economic conditions to enable us to compare adequately the results of one experiment or sample with another.

(*d*) As far as possible, checks should be set up to avoid gross errors in recording and analyzing the data.

(iii) *The experimental material should be selected to suit the experiment.*

(*a*) The size and shape of the experimental unit should be prepared to achieve maximum accuracy and unbiasedness.

(*b*) Often additional measurements can be taken to help explain the final results (see Chap. 21 on covariance techniques).

(*c*) Finally the treatments should be grouped together in the best manner. In other words, the proper selection of the experimental design is of the utmost importance. If there are too many treatments or the experimental units are quite heterogeneous, an incomplete-blocks design might be used. If interactions are important, some type of factorial design is needed; if higher-order interactions are not important, some system of *confounding* might be used (see Sec. 20.6). The problem of whether to balance the treatments or not must be decided on the basis of the importance of various comparisons and the amount of experimental material available.

Anyone who has attended lectures on experimental designs by Prof. Gertrude Cox will recognize the origin of many of the above remarks, which also have been included in reference 1.

**References Cited**

1. Cochran, W. G., and G. M. Cox, *Experimental Designs*, John Wiley & Sons, Inc., New York, 1950.
2. Fisher, R. A., *Design of Experiments*, 4th ed., Oliver & Boyd, Ltd., Edinburgh and London, 1947.
3. Snedecor, G. W., *Statistical Methods*, 4th ed., Collegiate Press, Inc., of Iowa State College, Ames, Iowa, 1946.
4. Goulden, C. H., *Methods of Statistical Analysis*, John Wiley & Sons, Inc., New York, 1939.
5. Yates, F., "The Design and Analysis of Factorial Experiments," *Imp. Bur. Soil Sci., Tech. Commun.* 35 (1937).
6. Kolodziejczyk, S., "On an Important Test of Statistical Hypotheses," *Biometrika*, **27**:161–190 (1935).
7. Tang, P. C., "The Power Function of the Analysis of Variance Tests with Tables and Illustrations of Their Use," *Stat. Research Mem.*, **2**:126–149 (1938).
8. Eisenhart, C., "The Assumptions Underlying the Analysis of Variance," *Biometrics*, **3**:1–21 (1947).
   Cochran, W. G., "Some Consequences When the Assumptions for the Analysis of Variance Are Not Satisfied," *Biometrics*, **3**:22–38 (1947).
   Bartlett, M. S., "The Use of Transformations," *Biometrics*, **3**:39–52 (1947).
9. Tukey, J. W., "One Degree of Freedom for Non-additivity," *Biometrics*, **5**:232–242 (1949).
10. Yates, F., "The Formation of Latin Squares for Use in Field Experiments," *Empire J. Exptl. Agr.*, **1**:235–244 (1933).
11. Durbin, J., and G. S. Watson, "Testing for Serial Correlation in Least Squares Regression," *Biometrika*, **37**:409–428 (1950), **38**:159–178 (1951).

**Other Reading**

Bliss, C. I., and M. K. Cattell, "Biological Assay," *Ann. Rev. Physiol.*, **5**:479–539 (1943).

Cochran, W. G., "Some Difficulties in the Statistical Analysis of Replicated Experiments," *Empire J. Exptl. Agr.*, **6**:157–175 (1938).

Davies, O. L., *Statistical Methods in Research and Production*, 2d ed. (Imperial Chemical Industries, Ltd.), Oliver & Boyd, Ltd., Edinburgh and London, 1949.

Fisher, R. A., *Statistical Methods for Research Workers*, 10th ed., Oliver & Boyd, Ltd., Edinburgh and London, 1948.

Immer, F. R., *Manual of Applied Statistics*, University of Minnesota, 1936.

Irwin, J. O., "Mathematical Theorems Involved in the Analysis of Variance," *J. Roy. Stat. Soc.*, **94**:284–300 (1931).

Irwin, J. O., "Independence of the Constituent Items in the Analysis of Variance," *J. Roy. Stat. Soc. Suppl.*, **1**:236–251 (1934).

Irwin, J. O., "Statistical Method Applied to Biological Assays," *J. Roy. Stat. Soc. Suppl.*, **4**:1–60 (1937).

Johnson, P. O., *Statistical Methods in Research*, Prentice-Hall, Inc., New York, 1949.

Lindquist, E. F., *Statistical Analysis in Educational Research*, Houghton Mifflin Company, Boston, 1940.

Love, H. H., *Application of Statistical Methods to Agricultural Research*, The Commercial Press, Ltd., Shanghai, 1936.

LOVE, H. H., *Experimental Methods in Agricultural Research*, University of Puerto Rico Agricultural Experiment Station, 1943.

MANN, H. B., *Analysis and Design of Experiments*, Dover Pub., Inc., New York, 1949.

MATHER, K., *Statistical Analysis of Biology*, 2d ed., Interscience Pub., Inc., New York, 1937.

PATERSON, D. D., *Statistical Technique in Agricultural Research*, McGraw-Hill Book Company, Inc., New York, 1939.

Statistical Research Group, Columbia University, *Techniques of Statistical Analysis*, McGraw-Hill Book Company, Inc., New York, 1947.

"Student" (W. S. Gosset), "The Probable Error of a Mean," *Biometrika*, **6**:1–25 (1908).

TIPPETT, L. H. C., *Technological Applications of Statistics*, John Wiley & Sons, Inc., New York, 1950.

WISHART, J., *Field Trials: Their Lay-out and Statistical Analysis*, Imperial Bureau of Plant Breeding and Genetics, Cambridge, 1940.

WISHART, J., "Statistics in Agricultural Research," *J. Roy. Stat. Soc. Suppl.* **1**:26–61 (1934).

YATES, F., "Complex Experiments." *J. Roy. Stat. Soc. Suppl.*, **2**:181–223 (1935).

YOUDEN, W. J., *Statistical Methods for Chemists*, John Wiley & Sons, Inc., New York, 1951.

## CHAPTER 18

## THE ANALYSIS OF DESIGNS IN COMPLETE BLOCKS

**18.1. Steps in the Analysis.** In the analysis of experimental data, we shall generally consider the following steps:

(i) Construct a regression model which expresses symbolically the nature of the variables used in the experiment and the method of conducting the experiment.

(ii) Determine estimates of the parameters in the regression model by least squares.

(iii) Indicate the reduction in the total variation due to the regression in an analysis of variance table.

(iv) Compute $s^2$ and the necessary $F$ values.

(v) Compute variances of the estimates in (ii) and confidence limits.

(vi) If possible, compare the error variance using this design with the expected variance if some other design had been used—this is called the *efficiency* of the design.

(vii) Present actual examples with a discussion of the results.

**18.2. Completely Randomized Design.** (i) Suppose we have $p$ different treatments which are to be tested for yield-producing ability. Let us assume that each treatment is planted on $r$ different experimental units which we shall call plots. $r$ is often called the number of *replications* for each treatment. Then we might estimate the yield for the $i$th treatment on the $j$th plot of its $r$ plots as

$$Y_{ij} = \mu + \sum_{k=1}^{p} \tau_k X_{ki} + \epsilon_{ij},$$

where

$$X_{ki} = \begin{cases} 0 & \text{for } k \neq i \\ 1 & \text{for } k = i \end{cases} \quad i = 1, 2, \ldots, p; j = 1, 2, \ldots, r;$$

$\tau_i$ is the differential effect of the $i$th treatment (over the mean, $\mu$) and $\sum_i \sum_k \tau_k X_{ki} = 0$. Some restriction such as the last one is necessary, since there will be only $p$ treatment totals to estimate $(p + 1)$ constants ($\mu$ and the $p$ $\tau$'s). If the restriction mentioned above ($\Sigma\Sigma\tau_k X_{ki} = 0$) is used, $\mu$ will be the over-all mean effect.

Since the $X$'s are 0 or 1, the regression model can be simplified to

$$Y_{ij} = \mu + \tau_i + \epsilon_{ij},$$

where $\sum_i \tau_i = 0$. As mentioned in Chap. 17, it is assumed that the $\epsilon_{ij}$ are NID$(0,\sigma^2)$ and independent of the $\tau_i$. Hence the expected mean yield for the $i$th treatment is $\mu + \tau_i$. This assumes that there is no interaction between the treatment and the error, that the treatment and error are truly additive; otherwise, the difference between $Y$ and $\mu + \tau_i$ on a particular plot would not be the same for all treatments. The assumption that all $\epsilon$ have the same variance, $\sigma^2$, enables us to estimate $\sigma^2$ even though we have but one observation per plot. Actually it is assumed that the possible errors in repeated sampling at one plot are $N(0,\sigma^2)$, and we would like to estimate $\sigma^2$ by repeated sampling at this plot. But it is impossible in most experiments to do this (and still maintain the same other conditions); hence, we estimate $\sigma^2$ from the plot-to-plot variation of a single experiment. In order to do this, we must assume all $\epsilon$'s have the same $\sigma^2$.

One method of distinguishing between the $\tau$'s and the $\epsilon$'s has been to call the $\tau$'s *fixed effects* and $\epsilon$'s *random effects*. By fixed effects, we imply that all of the treatments about which inferences are to be made are included in the experiment. A random effect is assumed to be one of a large number of possible effects; in general, we shall regard the number of possible effects to be infinite. However, it is not too difficult to set up the theory corresponding to the assumption that the number of possible random effects is a known finite number (greater than the number in the sample). In the model used here, the $\epsilon$'s represent the differences in the yielding abilities of the various plots, plus errors made in applying the treatments to the plots, in measuring the size of the plots, and even in measuring the actual yields produced. If the $\epsilon$'s represented only the differences in the yielding ability of the plots, one might believe that the number of $\epsilon$'s would be fixed; however, the other components of the $\epsilon$'s are certainly unlimited in number. But we do not feel that even the yielding ability of a given plot is fixed, because this will change with time and will be influenced at a given time by particular environmental conditions which affect that plot and not the others, such as weather for crops and social and psychological factors with people. Hence, on all counts, it seems reasonable to regard the plot errors ($\epsilon$) as random variables or variates.

(ii) We wish to estimate the values of $\mu$, $\{\tau_i\}$, and $\sigma^2$ from an experiment which has produced $r$ yields for each of the $p$ treatments.† The method of experimentation is to select $rp$ plots in the field and then to

† Or we may consider a survey with $p$ classes and $r$ samples from each class.

allocate $p$ treatments at random on these plots, with the restriction that each treatment should appear on $r$ plots.† Let us designate the estimates of $\mu$ and $\tau_i$ as $m$ and $t_i$. Hence the regression equation can be set up in the form

$$Y_{ij} = m + t_i + e_{ij},$$

where the residual $e_{ij}$ is the estimate of $\epsilon_{ij}$. $m$ and the $\{t_i\}$ are to be chosen so as to minimize $Se^2$.

The normal equations are

$$\begin{aligned} m&: rpm + r\Sigma t_i = SY = G \\ t_i&: rm + rt_i = \underset{j}{S} Y_{ij} = T_i, \qquad i = 1, 2, \ldots, p, \end{aligned}$$

where $T_i$ is the total yield for the $i$th treatment and $G$ the grand total for the experiment and where the $m$ equation is found by differentiating $Se^2$ with respect to $m$, and similarly for $t_i$. If the $t_i$ equations are added together, this sum is exactly the $m$ equation. This shows that the $p$-treatment equations are not independent of the equation for $m$. In order to solve these equations, an auxiliary relationship must be used. Since $\Sigma\tau_i = 0$, a reasonable relationship is

$$\Sigma t_i = 0,$$

so that each $t_i$ measures a differential effect from the mean. Also, this makes $m = G/rp = \bar{Y}$, the sample mean. And

$$t_i = (T_i/r) - m = (T_i - \bar{T})/r,$$

where $\bar{T} = G/p$. If the average yield for the $i$th treatment is desired, we calculate

$$t_i' = t_i + m = T_i/r.$$

A simple method of setting up the normal equations is to write down the estimated value for each observation and then obtain the estimating equation for each effect by adding together all observation equations which contain this effect. If the experiment is designed so that the various sets of effects are orthogonal, the resultant equation will be a

† The randomization feature is needed to assure that each treatment has the same chance of appearing on a given plot. As pointed out in Sec. 17.2, randomization also helps to validate the assumption of noncorrelated errors. The errors for adjacent plots are often positively correlated. However, when we consider all possible randomizations, any two $\epsilon$'s will apply equally often to adjacent and to distant plots. Hence, if the errors tend to be as negatively correlated for distant plots as they are positively correlated for adjacent plots (a rather reasonable assumption in many experiments), the average correlation between these two $\epsilon$'s should be approximately zero. And regardless of the plot-to-plot correlation pattern, randomization should tend to minimize the effect of this correlation on the errors in the model.

function of only the effect under consideration (plus the mean); otherwise there will be a mixture of effects, necessitating the simultaneous solution of several equations to estimate the effects (as was done in Chap. 15). For our completely randomized design, the observation equations involving $t_1$ are:

| Yield | Effects |
|---|---|
| $Y_{11}$ | $m + t_1 = t'_1$ |
| $Y_{12}$ | $m + t_1 = t'_1$ |
| . . . | . . . |
| $Y_{1r}$ | $m + t_1 = t'_1$ |
| $T_1 = \underset{j}{S} Y_{1j}$ | $r(m + t_1) = rt'_1$ |

Hence $t'_1$ is simply $T_1/r$.

Since $m$ appears in all of the observation equations, we must add all of them together to compute $m$, giving us

$$SY = rpm + r(\Sigma t_i) = rpm.$$

Hence $m = SY/rp = \bar{Y}$, assuming $\sum_i t_i = 0$.

(iii) The error sum of squares is

$$\text{SSE} = \underset{ij}{S}(Y_{ij} - m - t_i)^2 = \underset{ij}{S}\left(Y_{ij} - \frac{T_i}{r}\right)^2$$

$$= \underset{ij}{S}Y_{ij}^2 - \frac{\sum_{i=1}^{p} T_i^2}{r} = \underset{ij}{S}y_{ij}^2 - \left(\frac{\Sigma T_i^2}{r} - C\right),$$

where $C = G^2/rp$. Hence the reduction in sum of squares due to treatments, called the *treatment sum of squares* (and indicated by SST), is

$$\text{SST} = \frac{\Sigma T_i^2}{r} - C.$$

Another method of deriving this result is to use the abbreviated Doolittle results. If we eliminate $m$ from the $t_i$ equation, we have

$$rt_i = T_i - G/p = T_i - \bar{T}.$$

Hence the $A_{iy}$ value is $T_i - \bar{T}$, and the $B_{iy}$ value is $(T_i - \bar{T})/r$. Therefore $\text{SST} = \sum_{i=1}^{p} A_{iy}B_{iy} = \sum_{i=1}^{p} (T_i - \bar{T})^2/r = (\Sigma T_i^2/r) - C$. This simple result is obtained because the $i$th equation contains $t_i$ and no other $t$.

Expressed in terms of the original model,

$$T_i - \bar{T} = \left(r\mu + r\tau_i + \sum_j \epsilon_{ij}\right) - \frac{\left(rp\mu + r\sum_i \tau_i + \sum_i \sum_j \epsilon_{ij}\right)}{p}$$

$$= r(\tau_i - \bar{\tau}) + \left(\frac{p-1}{p}\right)\sum_{j=1}^{r} \epsilon_{ij} - \frac{1}{p}\sum_{l \neq i}\sum_j \epsilon_{lj},$$

and

$$E(T_i - \bar{T}) = r(\tau_i - \bar{\tau}).$$

But it has been shown that $\sum_i \tau_i = p\bar{\tau} = 0$ is a necessary part of the original model. Therefore

$$E[(T_i - \bar{T})^2] = r^2\tau_i^2 + \left[\left(\frac{p-1}{p}\right)^2 r + \left(\frac{1}{p}\right)^2 r(p-1)\right]\sigma^2$$

$$= r^2\tau_i^2 + \frac{r(p-1)}{p}\sigma^2,$$

and

$$E(\text{SST}) = r\sum_{i=1}^{p} \tau_i^2 + (p-1)\sigma^2.$$

The analysis-of-variance table is:

| Source of variation | Degrees of freedom | Sum of squares | Mean square | $E(MS)$† |
|---|---|---|---|---|
| Treatments | $p - 1$ | SST | MST = SST/$(p - 1)$ | $\sigma^2 + r\sum_i \tau_i^2/(p-1)$ |
| Error | $p(r - 1)$ | SSE | $s^2$ = SSE/$p(r-1)$ | $\sigma^2$ |

† $E$(MS) = expected value of the mean square.

(iv) From Chap. 14, we know that SSE is distributed as $\chi^2\sigma^2$ with $n - p = rp - p = p(r - 1)$ degrees of freedom. If we set

$$s^2 = \text{SSE}/p(r-1),$$

$E(s^2) = \sigma^2$. Hence we can use $F = \text{MST}/s^2$ to test $H_0$: $\{\tau_i = 0\}$ against the alternative that some $\tau_i \neq 0$. The one-tailed $F$ test is used since the numerator of $F$ is expected to be greater than the denominator when any $\tau_i \neq 0$.

(v) Since $t_i' = T_i/r = \left(r\mu + r\tau_i + \sum_j \epsilon_{ij}\right)/r$ and $m = G/rp = \mu + \bar{\epsilon}$, it is seen that

$$E(t_i') = \mu + \tau_i, \qquad E(m) = \mu,$$
$$\sigma^2(t_i') = \sigma^2/r, \qquad \sigma^2(m) = \sigma^2/rp.$$

Also for any other treatment $t'_l = T_l/r$, and

$$\sigma(t'_i t'_l) = 0.$$

The estimated difference between the mean effects of these two treatments is

$$d = t_i - t_l = t'_i - t'_l,$$
$$E(d) \equiv \delta = \tau_i - \tau_l.$$

Since $t'_i$ and $t'_l$ are noncorrelated, $\sigma^2(d) = 2\sigma^2/r$ and the confidence limits for $\delta$ are

$$d - t_\alpha s \sqrt{2/r} < \delta < d + t_\alpha s \sqrt{2/r}.$$

**Example 18.1.** As a first example, we might consider an experiment which was run to investigate the number of warp skein breaks on tent twill in 5 consecutive days of testing with 4 breaks per test.[1] The results are:

| | Day | | | | | Total |
|---|---|---|---|---|---|---|
| | 1 | 2 | 3 | 4 | 5 | |
| | 30 | 30 | 40 | 45 | 55 | |
| | 35 | 40 | 45 | 40 | 45 | |
| | 25 | 45 | 55 | 35 | 60 | |
| | 40 | 45 | 35 | 40 | 50 | |
| Total | 130 | 160 | 175 | 160 | 210 | 835 |
| Mean | 32.5 | 40.0 | 43.75 | 40.0 | 52.5 | 41.75 |

Analysis of Variance

| Source of variation | Degrees of freedom | Sum of squares | Mean square |
|---|---|---|---|
| Days | 4 | 845.00 | 211.25 |
| Error | 15 | 668.75 | 44.58 |

The error variance is estimated to be 44.58. There are significant differences among the day means, since $F = 211.25/44.58 = 4.74$ with 4 and 15 degrees of freedom. Also, the standard error of the difference between any two day means is given by $s(d) = \sqrt{2(44.58)/4} = 4.72$. Hence the 95 per cent confidence limits for the difference between the mean number of breaks for the first two days are

$$7.5 - 10.1 < \delta < 7.5 + 10.1 \quad \text{or} \quad -2.6 < \delta < 17.6,$$

where $10.1 = ts(d) = (2.13)(4.72)$, $t$ with 15 degrees of freedom. This example will be discussed further in Exercise 18.2. (See Fig. 18.1 for a graphical presentation.)

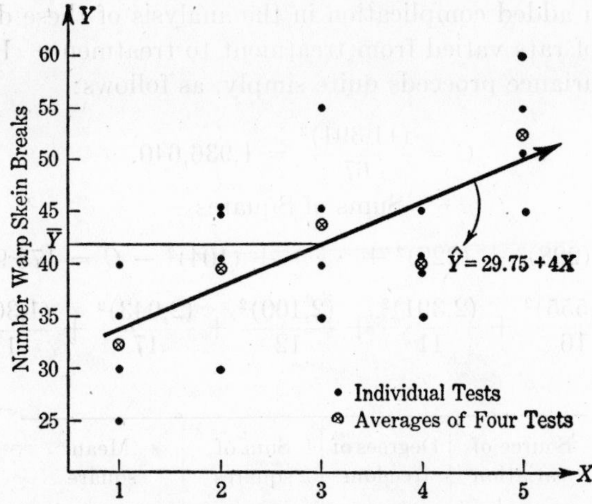


FIG. 18.1. Number of warp skein breaks in 5 consecutive days of testing.

**Example 18.2.** A second example presents an analysis of the gains in weight (grams per 100 days) of rats on a stock ration with various amounts of gossypol added (Halverson and Sherwood, North Carolina State College, 1932), as shown in Table 18.1.

TABLE 18.1

| | Amounts of gossypol added | | | | | Total |
|---|---|---|---|---|---|---|
| | None | .04% | .07% | .10% | .13% | |
| | 228 | 186 | 179 | 130 | 154 | |
| | 229 | 229 | 193 | 87 | 130 | |
| | 218 | 220 | 183 | 135 | 130 | |
| | 216 | 208 | 180 | 116 | 118 | |
| | 224 | 228 | 143 | 118 | 118 | |
| | 208 | 198 | 204 | 165 | 104 | |
| | 235 | 222 | 114 | 151 | 112 | |
| | 229 | 273 | 188 | 59 | 134 | |
| | 233 | 216 | 178 | 126 | 98 | |
| | 219 | 198 | 134 | 64 | 100 | |
| | 224 | 213 | 208 | 78 | 104 | |
| | 220 | | 196 | 94 | | |
| | 232 | | | 150 | | |
| | 200 | | | 160 | | |
| | 208 | | | 122 | | |
| | 232 | | | 110 | | |
| | | | | 178 | | |
| No. of rats | 16 | 11 | 12 | 17 | 11 | 67 |
| Sum | 3,555 | 2,391 | 2,100 | 2,043 | 1,302 | 11,391 |
| Mean | 222.2 | 217.4 | 175.0 | 120.2 | 118.4 | 170.0 |

There is an added complication in the analysis of these data, because the number of rats varied from treatment to treatment. However, the analysis of variance proceeds quite simply, as follows:

$$C = \frac{(11{,}391)^2}{67} = 1{,}936{,}640.$$

Sums of Squares

Total: $(228)^2 + (229)^2 + \cdot \cdot \cdot + (104)^2 - C = 178{,}985.$

Rations: $$\frac{(3{,}555)^2}{16} + \frac{(2{,}391)^2}{11} + \frac{(2{,}100)^2}{12} + \frac{(2{,}043)^2}{17} + \frac{(1{,}302)^2}{11} - C = 140{,}083.$$

| Source of variation | Degrees of freedom | Sum of squares | Mean square |
|---|---|---|---|
| Rations | 4 | 140,083 | 35,020.75 |
| Error | 62 | 38,902 | 627.45 |

In this experiment, $s^2 = 627.45$, $F = 55.8$, a highly significant value ($\alpha < .01$). See Exercise 18.3 for more details.

**18.3. Randomized Complete Blocks.** (i) Suppose that the $rp$ plots are divided into $r$ blocks of $p$ plots each and that each treatment is assigned at random to one of these plots in each block. Then the estimation equation is

$$Y_{ij} = \mu + \tau_i + \beta_j + \epsilon_{ij} = m + t_i + b_j + e_{ij},$$

where $\beta_j$ is the differential effect of the $j$th block ($j = 1,2, \ldots ,r$) being estimated by $b_j$, and $\sum_j \beta_j = 0$. In this case we assume that the block effects are also fixed—that inferences are to be made for these particular $p$ treatments applied only to these $r$ blocks. Since most experimentation is set up to make inferences over a wider variety of experimental conditions than we have in the particular blocks used in a given experiment, the blocks usually are regarded as representative of a population which is larger than the sample. The analysis of data under these assumptions is not too different from that presented in this section; this problem will be discussed in Chap. 23. It is further assumed that there is no real treatment by block *interaction*. A discussion of the problem when there is interaction (that is, treatment effects are not constant from block to block) also will be presented in Chap. 23. (See the footnote on page 229 for a discussion of the need for randomization.) The equations for a randomized complete-blocks experiment with 3 treatments and 4 blocks are indicated in Fig. 18.2. The treatments (1,2,3) were assigned to the plots at random, the random arrangement being (1,3,2), (3,2,1), (2,1,3), and (3,1,2).

Block 1

| | | |
|---|---|---|
| $Y = m + b_1 + t_1 + e_{11}$ | $Y = m + b_1 + t_3 + e_{31}$ | $Y = m + b_1 + t_2 + e_{21}$ |

Block 2

| | | |
|---|---|---|
| $Y = m + b_2 + t_3 + e_{32}$ | $Y = m + b_2 + t_2 + e_{22}$ | $Y = m + b_2 + t_1 + e_{12}$ |

Block 3

| | | |
|---|---|---|
| $Y = m + b_3 + t_2 + e_{23}$ | $Y = m + b_3 + t_1 + e_{13}$ | $Y = m + b_3 + t_3 + e_{33}$ |

Block 4

| | | |
|---|---|---|
| $Y = m + b_4 + t_3 + e_{34}$ | $Y = m + b_4 + t_1 + e_{14}$ | $Y = m + b_4 + t_2 + e_{24}$ |

$$m + t_i + b_j + e_{ij} = \mu + \tau_i + \beta_j + \varepsilon_{ij}$$

FIG. 18.2. An example of the model equations for a randomized complete-blocks design ($r = 4$, $p = 3$).

(ii) The least-squares equations are

$$\begin{aligned} m&: rpm + r\Sigma t_i + p\Sigma b_j = G, \\ t_i&: \quad r(m + t_i) + \Sigma b_j = T_i, \\ b_j&: \quad p(m + b_j) + \Sigma t_i = B_j, \end{aligned}$$

where $B_j$ is the total yield for the $j$th block and the $b_j$ equation is found by minimizing $Se^2$ with respect to $b_j$. In this case, two auxiliary equations are required; in order to make $m = \bar{Y} = G/rp$, an unbiased estimate of $\mu$, we set $\Sigma t_i = \Sigma b_j = 0$. Hence $t_i = (T_i - \bar{T})/r$, and $b_j = (B_j - \bar{B})/p$, where $\bar{T} = G/p$ and $\bar{B} = G/r$. We let

$$t_i' = t_i + m = T_i/r; \qquad b_j' = b_j + m = B_j/p.$$

(iii) Using the abbreviated Doolittle approach, we see that the $t$ equations are the same as in Sec. 18.2 (iii) and that

$$pb_j = B_j - \bar{B}.$$

Hence the reduction in sum of squares due to blocks and treatments is

$$\frac{\sum_i (T_i - \bar{T})^2}{r} + \frac{\sum_j (B_j - \bar{B})^2}{p}.$$

Therefore the added reduction due to blocks alone (indicated by SSB) must be

$$\text{SSB} = \frac{\sum_j (B_j - \bar{B})^2}{p}.$$

We note that

$$rt_i = T_i - \bar{T} = r\tau_i + \sum_j \epsilon_{ij} - \sum_i \sum_j \epsilon_{ij}/p,$$

$$pb_j = B_j - \bar{B} = p\beta_j + \sum_i \epsilon_{ij} - \sum_i \sum_j \epsilon_{ij}/r.$$

Hence $E(t_i) = \tau_i$ and $E(b_j) = \beta_j$. Furthermore, it can be shown that $\sigma[(T_i - \bar{T})(B_j - \bar{B})] = 0$. This also proves that the treatment and block effects are noncorrelated; hence, SST and SSB are orthogonal parts of the total reduction (the total reduction equals SST plus SSB).

The analysis of variance table is:

| Source of variation | Degrees of freedom | Sum of squares | Mean square | $E$(MS) |
|---|---|---|---|---|
| Blocks | $r - 1$ | SSB | MSB | $\sigma^2 + p\Sigma\beta_j^2/(r - 1)$ |
| Treatments | $p - 1$ | SST | MST | $\sigma^2 + r\Sigma\tau_i^2/(p - 1)$ |
| Error | $(r - 1)(p - 1)$ | SSE | $s^2$ | $\sigma^2$ |

(iv) $s^2 = \text{SSE}/(r - 1)(p - 1)$, and $F = \text{MST}/s^2$ to test for over-all treatment differences. Note that $\text{SSE} = Sy^2 - \text{SST} - \text{SSB}$. There is usually no reason to test for block differences, since the blocks are generally chosen to be different.

(v) As in 18.2, $\sigma^2(t') = \sigma^2/r$, and $\sigma^2(d) = 2\sigma^2/r$.

(vi) The experimenter often is interested in estimating how much he reduced his estimated error variance by the imposition of the block restrictions on the design. In other words, how much would he have increased his estimate of the error variance if the treatments had been randomly distributed over all $rp$ plots, instead of being randomly distributed over the $p$ plots of each of $r$ blocks? Let us call $s_w^2$ the error variance for the completely randomized design and $s_{rb}^2$ that for the randomized complete-blocks design. Then the estimated *efficiency* of the latter design relative to the former is given by

$$I = s_w^2/s_{rb}^2.$$

Since the estimated variance of the difference between two treatment means is

$$s^2(d) = 2s^2/r,$$

$rI$ measures the number of replications needed for a completely randomized design to give the same value of $s^2(d)$ as $r$ replications in a randomized complete-blocks design.

Since we have only the analysis of variance for the randomized complete-blocks design, it is necessary to use these data to estimate $s_w^2$. This estimate is as follows:

$$s_w^2 \doteq \frac{s_{rb}^2 \text{ (error d.f. + treatment d.f.)} + \text{SSB}}{\text{error d.f.} + \text{treatment d.f.} + \text{block d.f.}} = \frac{r(p-1)s_{rb}^2 + \text{SSB}}{rp-1},$$

where d.f. stands for "degrees of freedom." We shall derive this formula by considering a uniformity trial, in which all the treatments are alike. In this case $s_w^2$ is the total sum of squares for a completely randomized design divided by $(rp - 1)$. But since we are concerned with the same field as with our randomized complete-blocks design, SSB and SSE will remain unchanged (on the average for all possible randomizations). Since we are considering a uniformity trial, the treatment sum of squares will be an estimate of $(p - 1)\sigma^2$; hence, the best estimate of this treatment sum of squares will be $(p - 1)s_{rb}^2$. Adding these together and dividing by $(rp - 1)$, we find that

$$s_w^2 \doteq \frac{\text{SSE} + (p-1)s_{rb}^2 + \text{SSB}}{(rp-1)} = \frac{r(p-1)s_{rb}^2 + \text{SSB}}{(rp-1)}.$$

We note that if there are no block effects, $E(s_w^2) = \sigma^2$; however, if there are block effects, $E(s_w^2) > \sigma^2$.

At first glance one might think that, since the only difference between the two designs is that the block effects are included in $s_w^2$ and not in $s_{rb}^2$, the best estimate of $s_w^2$ would be $(\text{SSB} + \text{SSE})/p(r - 1)$. However, since the total sum of squares is assumed the same for both designs, this would assume (falsely) that SST is the same for both designs. Cochran and Cox[4] present a more rigorous proof, which avoids the use of the uniformity device by estimating the average value of SST for both designs.

Actually the efficiency is slightly less than $I$, because there is a loss in the number of error degrees of freedom when the block sum of squares is removed from the error. Fisher[6] calculates the *amount of information* which $d$ furnishes concerning $\delta$, the true difference between two means. If $\sigma^2$ were known, the amount of information would be proportional to $1/\sigma^2$; with $\sigma^2$ estimated by $s^2$, the amount of information is $(n + 1)/(n + 3)s^2$, where there are $n$ degrees of freedom for the error mean square. Hence if there are $n_1$ degrees of freedom for one design with error variance $s_1^2$ and $n_2$ degrees of freedom for a second design with error variance $s_2^2$, the efficiency of the first design relative to the second is

$$\frac{(n_1 + 1)(n_2 + 3)s_2^2}{(n_1 + 3)(n_2 + 1)s_1^2}.$$

Since we have set $s_2^2/s_1^2 = I$, $I$ would be multiplied by

$$h = \frac{(n_1 + 1)(n_2 + 3)}{(n_1 + 3)(n_2 + 1)}$$

to adjust for the loss in degrees of freedom.

Cochran and Cox[4] (pages 27 to 28) discuss several other methods of adjusting for the loss of degrees of freedom. One might consider yet another adjusting constant

$$h' = \frac{F_\alpha[(p - 1), n_2]}{F_\alpha[(p - 1), n_1]},$$

where there are $(p - 1)$ degrees of freedom for treatments and $n_2$ and $n_1$ respective degrees of freedom for error. If testing is done at the $\alpha = .05$ significance level, $F_{.05}$ should be used.

**Example 18.3.** This example presents the analysis of the differences between fat absorption by doughnuts in 8 different fats, all being tested on each of 6 days.

Grams of Fat Absorbed by Mixes of 24 Doughnuts during Cooking Period

| Day (Block) | Fat (treatment) number | | | | | | | | Total |
|---|---|---|---|---|---|---|---|---|---|
| | 1 | 2 | 3 | 4 | 5 | 6 | 7 | 8 | |
| 1 | 164 | 172 | 177 | 178 | 163 | 163 | 150 | 164 | 1,331 |
| 2 | 177 | 197 | 184 | 196 | 177 | 193 | 179 | 169 | 1,472 |
| 3 | 168 | 167 | 187 | 177 | 144 | 176 | 146 | 155 | 1,320 |
| 4 | 156 | 161 | 169 | 181 | 165 | 172 | 141 | 149 | 1,294 |
| 5 | 172 | 180 | 179 | 184 | 166 | 176 | 169 | 170 | 1,396 |
| 6 | 195 | 190 | 197 | 191 | 178 | 178 | 183 | 167 | 1,479 |
| Total | 1,032 | 1,067 | 1,093 | 1,107 | 993 | 1,058 | 968 | 974 | 8,292 |
| Mean | 172.0 | 177.8 | 182.2 | 184.5 | 165.5 | 176.3 | 161.3 | 162.3 | 172.8 |

Computations

$$C = \frac{(8{,}292)^2}{48} = 1{,}432{,}443,$$

$$Sy^2 = (164)^2 + (172)^2 + \cdots + (167)^2 - 1{,}432{,}443 = 9{,}143.00,$$

$$\text{SST} = \frac{(1{,}032)^2 + (1{,}067)^2 + \cdots + (974)^2}{6} - 1{,}432{,}443 = 3{,}344.33,$$

$$\text{SSB} = \frac{(1{,}331)^2 + (1{,}472)^2 + \cdots + (1{,}479)^2}{8} - 1{,}432{,}443 = 3{,}986.75,$$

$$\text{SSE} = Sy^2 - \text{SST} - \text{SSB} = 1{,}811.92.$$

Analysis of Variance

| Source of variation | Degrees of freedom | Sum of squares | Mean square |
|---|---|---|---|
| Between day means | 5 | 3,986.75 | 797.35 |
| Between fat means | 7 | 3,344.33 | 477.76** |
| Error | 35 | 1,811.92 | 51.77 = $s^2$ |

** Significant at 1 per cent probability level.

We note that the efficiency of this design as compared with the completely randomized design is

$$I = \frac{42(51.77) + 3{,}986.75}{47(51.77)} = \frac{6{,}161.09}{2{,}433.19} = 2.53.$$

In this case $h = (36)(43)/(38)(41) = .994$, which is almost unity. $h'$ is slightly less. This indicates that if the fats had been distributed randomly over the 6 days, the error variance would have been expected to be about 2.5 times as large as that with the randomized blocks design, where each fat was used each day. In other words, we have made our estimates of fat differences about $2\frac{1}{2}$ times as precise by planning the experiment so that every fat was used on each day of the experiment.

The 95 per cent confidence limits for the difference between any two fat means are $(d - 8.43 < \delta < d + 8.43)$. A word of caution about the use of these confidence limits should be given. These are average confidence limits, assuming that you select the treatments to be compared in advance of the experiment. If you wait until the experiment is over and then select, for example, the highest and lowest treatment means to compare, the confidence limits are much wider than $[d \pm t_\alpha s(d)]$. One excellent article on this point is presented by J. W. Tukey.[5] R. A. Fisher[6] (page 58) advocates the following approximate procedure for testing the largest against the smallest in a set of $p$ means: Compute the significance probability by the ordinary $t$ test, and multiply this by $p(p-1)/2$. $p(p-1)/2$ is the number of ways of drawing 2 from $p$ means, and we are selecting the most extreme of these combinations; since the probability of drawing this extreme set is $2/p(p-1)$, it seems reasonable to divide the probability of obtaining such a difference (by use of the $t$ test) on the average by the probability of drawing the extreme set.

**18.4. Latin-square Designs.** A design slightly more complicated than the randomized complete-blocks design is the *Latin-square* design. In this design, each treatment is assigned at random within a row and a column so that all treatments appear in each row and column. Hence it is possible to adjust the error for plot heterogeneity in two directions. Of course the rows may be fields and the columns similar locations in these fields. The basic design looks as follows for 3 treatments (there then must be 3 rows and 3 columns):

| | $C_1$ | $C_2$ | $C_3$ | Total |
|---|---|---|---|---|
| $R_1$ | $T_1(23)$ | $T_2(17)$ | $T_3(29)$ | 69 |
| $R_2$ | $T_2(16)$ | $T_3(25)$ | $T_1(16)$ | 57 |
| $R_3$ | $T_3(24)$ | $T_1(18)$ | $T_2(12)$ | 54 |
| Total | 63 | 60 | 57 | 180 |

The figures represent yields in an experiment. In the field the rows and columns of the basic design would have been randomized. One such field arrangement would be:

| | $C_1$ | $C_2$ | $C_3$ |
|---|---|---|---|
| $R_1$ | $T_3$ | $T_1$ | $T_2$ |
| $R_2$ | $T_2$ | $T_3$ | $T_1$ |
| $R_3$ | $T_1$ | $T_2$ | $T_3$ |

In general it is also advisable to assign the treatment numbers at random to the treatments.

The regression model for this design is:

$$Y_{ijk} = \mu + \alpha_i + \gamma_j + \tau_{k(i,j)} + \epsilon_{i,k},$$

where $\alpha_i$ and $\gamma_j$ are fixed row and column effects and $\tau_k$ the fixed treatment effect. We note that, once $i$ and $j$ are specified in a particular field arrangement, we know $k$. Hence $k$ is a function of $i$ and $j$. For example, in the field arrangement mentioned above, if $i = 2$ and $j = 3$, $k = 1$.

The analysis-of-variance table is similar to that of the randomized complete-blocks design except that there are two sets of blocks—rows and columns. The analysis of the $3 \times 3$ example is as follows:

| Source of variation | Degrees of freedom | Sum of squares | Mean square |
|---|---|---|---|
| Rows | 2 | 42 | 21 |
| Columns | 2 | 6 | 3 |
| Treatments | 2 | 186 | 93 |
| Error | 2 | 6 | 3 |

The $F$ value to test for treatment differences is $\frac{93}{3} = 31$ with (2,2) degrees of freedom, which is significant at the $\alpha = .05$ significance level.

**18.5. Summary.** In order to help the experimenter decide what design to use, we are including a summary (Table 18.2) of some of the advantages and disadvantages of the three designs discussed in this chapter.

TABLE 18.2

| Feature of the experiment | Completely randomized | Randomized complete blocks | Latin square |
|---|---|---|---|
| Replications per treatment | Need not be the same | Same for all treatments | Same for all treatments |
| Number of treatments ($p$) | Unlimited, except for plot variability | If too many, may lose advantage of blocks | Usually between 5 and 10, because $r = p$ |
| Ease of setting up experiment | Easy | Fairly easy, but must set up blocks of required size | More difficult than other two |
| Error degrees of freedom | Maximum number | Lose blocks | Lose both rows and columns |
| High plot variability | Quite bad | Takes care of variability in one direction | Very good if variability in two directions |
| Test of unequal error variance | Easy | Difficult, but often can pull out sets of error d.f. | Very difficult |
| Missing data | No difficulty | Not too bad, but some loss of efficiency | Quite bad if several missing plots |
| Effect on analysis of error in assignment of treatments to plots | Minor | May require more complicated analysis | May be badly upset |

## EXERCISES

**18.1.** Assume you have $r_i$ samples for the $i$th treatment. (*a*) Show that you can obtain an estimate of $\sigma^2$ from each treatment with $(r_i - 1)$ degrees of freedom. (*b*) How can you use this result to test the assumption of equal variances?

**18.2.** (*a*) In Example 18.1, use the method of orthogonal polynomials, outlined in Chap. 16, to divide the sum of squares for days (SSD) into four orthogonal parts, each with 1 degree of freedom (linear, quadratic, cubic, and quartic). For example, the polynomial values ($P'_1$) for the linear effect are $(-2,-1,0,1,2)$. Consider the totals as the $Y$ values, and show that $SP'_1Y = 160$. It has been proved that $\text{SSR}_1 = (SP'_1Y)^2/S(P'_1)^2 = 25{,}600/10 = 2{,}560$, but this is larger than SSD. Under the null hypothesis of no day differences, show that $E(\text{SSR}_1) = 4\sigma^2$. Hence to put $\text{SSR}_1$ on the same basis as $s^2$ (whose expected value is $\sigma^2$), we must divide $\text{SSR}_1$ by $r = 4$, so that the linear effect is $2{,}560/4 = 640$. (See Fig. 18.1.)

(*b*) Complete the analysis of the quadratic, cubic, and quartic effects. Is there a significant departure from linearity? Hence what do you conclude regarding the day-to-day fluctuations in the quality of the product?

(*c*) Suppose we had used the means as the $Y$ values. What changes must be made in the above analyses?

(*d*) Can you make any general statement of how to analyze by orthogonal polynomials $p$ equally spaced sets of observations with $r$ observations at each point?

**18.3.** (*a*) Set up the mathematical model for Example 18.2. Solve the normal equations, and show that the analysis presented there is correct. Show how the observation equations can be used to estimate the effect of the .04 per cent treatment.

(*b*) Prove that the standard error of the difference between the effects of any two treatments is $s\sqrt{\left(\frac{1}{r_1}+\frac{1}{r_2}\right)}$, where $r_1$ and $r_2$ are the numbers of rats on the two rations. Hence show that the standard error of the difference between the gains for rations no Gossypol and .04 per cent is 9.81.

(*c*) What is the standard error of the average of the first two against the third ration? The third against the last two?

(*d*) How would you test for departure from linearity in this case? Graph these results.

(*e*) Is there any evidence that the error variance is not the same for all treatments?

**18.4.** An investigation of North Carolina farmers' retail produce markets was made in 1948.[2] Data were collected on the dollar value of livestock owned by a sample of sellers on these markets, shown in the accompanying table.

Data of Exercise 18.4

| | Market | | | | | | | | | | | | | Total |
|---|---|---|---|---|---|---|---|---|---|---|---|---|---|---|
| | 1 | 2 | 3 | 4 | 5 | 6 | 7 | 8 | 9 | 10 | 11 | 12 | 13 | |
| | 721 | 750 | 3,480 | 627 | 469 | 812 | 393 | 369 | 332 | 249 | 1,106 | 1,703 | 1,462 | |
| | 64 | 756 | 293 | 169 | 604 | 271 | 841 | 785 | 842 | 371 | 1,702 | 563 | 1,088 | |
| | 664 | 1,315 | 370 | 976 | 165 | 1,100 | 426 | 655 | | 361 | 1,154 | 714 | 273 | |
| | 134 | 293 | 284 | 109 | | 305 | | 1,947 | | 1,061 | 962 | 908 | 1,080 | |
| | 610 | 865 | 119 | 704 | | | | | | 359 | | 97 | 2,195 | |
| | 546 | 3,274 | 1,980 | 1,557 | | | | | | 1,026 | | 442 | 428 | |
| | 278 | | | 697 | | | | | | 477 | | | 310 | |
| | 29 | | | | | | | | | | | | 295 | |
| | | | | | | | | | | | | | 178 | |
| Total | 3,046 | 7,253 | 6,526 | 4,839 | 1,238 | 2,488 | 1,660 | 3,756 | 1,174 | 3,904 | 4,924 | 4,427 | 7,309 | 52,544 |
| No. sellers | 8 | 6 | 6 | 7 | 3 | 4 | 3 | 4 | 2 | 7 | 4 | 6 | 9 | 69 |
| Mean | 381 | 1,209 | 1,088 | 691 | 413 | 622 | 553 | 939 | 587 | 558 | 1,231 | 738 | 812 | 761.5 |

(*a*) Analyze these data to see whether or not there are any real differences among markets.

(*b*) Compare the mean value per seller for the first nine markets with the mean value for markets 10 and 11.

(*c*) Is there any evidence of unequal variation for these data?

**18.5.** Snedecor and Cox[3] analyzed some data on the gain in weight (grams) of 149 Wistar rats over a 6 weeks' period for 4 successive generations. The gains for the males and females in each of these generations were:

| | Male | | | | Female | | | | Total |
|---|---|---|---|---|---|---|---|---|---|
| Generation | 1 | 2 | 3 | 4 | 1 | 2 | 3 | 4 | |
| No. of rats | 21 | 15 | 12 | 7 | 27 | 25 | 23 | 19 | 149 |
| Total gain | 3,716 | 2,422 | 1,868 | 1,197 | 2,957 | 2,852 | 2,496 | 2,029 | 19,537 |
| Mean gain | 176.95 | 161.47 | 155.67 | 171.00 | 109.52 | 114.08 | 108.52 | 106.79 | 131.12 |

The total sum of squares adjusted for the mean was $Sy^2 = 176{,}836$.

(*a*) Set up the analysis of variance among and within the 8 classes and determine whether or not there are significant differences among the 8 mean gains.

(*b*) What is the standard error to test for the difference between the mean gain for the males of a given generation and the mean gain for the females of the same generation? What would you say regarding the differences between the population means for each of the 4 generations?

(*c*) Can you make a statement regarding the difference between males and females over all 4 generations?

**18.6.** The relationship between the vitamin $B_2$ content of turnip greens and the average soil moisture tension (Chap. 15) can be analyzed as a completely randomized design with $p = 3$ and $r = 9$.

(*a*) Set up the analysis of variance of the vitamin $B_2$ content with the three soil moistures as treatments.

(*b*) Test whether or not there was a significant departure from linearity in this case.

(*c*) Is there any evidence that the error variance is not the same for the three treatments?

**18.7.** Derive the observation equations for $t_1$ and $b_1$, and show how they can be used to obtain the normal equations (Sec. 18.3).

**18.8.** (*a*) Set up another randomization plan for Fig. 18.2, and write down the model equations. How many different randomizations can be devised for 4 blocks and 3 treatments?

(*b*) Draw up a randomization plan for Example 18.3.

**18.9.** In the investigation of farmers' markets (Exercise 18.4), the incomes of a sample of regular, former, and potential patrons were studied at 10 markets with the results given in the accompanying table.

DATA OF EXERCISE 18.9
Average Monthly Incomes ($10)

| City | Regular | Former | Potential | Total |
|---|---|---|---|---|
| Asheville † | 30 | 30 | 28 | 88 |
| Asheboro | 39 | 36 | 27 | 102 |
| Charlotte † | 41 | 37 | 28 | 106 |
| Durham † | 29 | 29 | 24 | 82 |
| Greensboro † | 32 | 27 | 22 | 81 |
| Raleigh † | 29 | 27 | 29 | 85 |
| Goldsboro | 25 | 24 | 20 | 69 |
| Rocky Mount | 27 | 28 | 27 | 82 |
| Franklin | 30 | 29 | 24 | 83 |
| Jacksonville | 29 | 28 | 27 | 84 |
| Total | 311 | 295 | 256 | 862 |

† Cities of over 50,000 population.

(*a*) Would you conclude that there are any real income differences among the three groups of people?

(*b*) What are the confidence limits for the difference between the average income of the regular and potential patrons?

(*c*) Is there any feature of this analysis which might be open to question?

**18.10.** An analysis was made of the fiber diameters in microns at 6 different regions on the seed coat of the Mexican 128 variety of cotton.[7] The analysis was made on a sample of 10 seeds as shown in the accompanying table.

DATA OF EXERCISE 18.10

| Plant | Region 1 | 2 | 3 | 4 | 5 | 6 | Total |
|---|---|---|---|---|---|---|---|
| *A* | 16.49 | 17.80 | 17.54 | 16.75 | 17.54 | 17.54 | 103.66 |
| *B* | 15.45 | 15.96 | 15.71 | 14.13 | 14.40 | 14.40 | 90.05 |
| *C* | 16.23 | 15.96 | 16.49 | 14.92 | 14.66 | 14.92 | 93.18 |
| *D* | 18.33 | 17.28 | 16.49 | 16.49 | 17.28 | 17.80 | 103.67 |
| *E* | 16.49 | 18.33 | 17.54 | 17.02 | 17.28 | 18.06 | 104.72 |
| *F* | 16.49 | 17.54 | 17.05 | 15.71 | 15.45 | 14.66 | 96.90 |
| *G* | 15.96 | 15.71 | 16.23 | 16.49 | 15.18 | 16.49 | 96.06 |
| *H* | 16.75 | 16.23 | 14.66 | 15.96 | 13.35 | 16.75 | 93.70 |
| *I* | 14.40 | 18.33 | 17.02 | 14.66 | 15.71 | 17.02 | 97.14 |
| *J* | 16.49 | 17.02 | 16.75 | 17.54 | 15.71 | 16.49 | 100.00 |
| Total | 163.08 | 170.16 | 165.48 | 159.67 | 156.56 | 164.13 | 979.08 |

(*a*) Show that the analysis of variance is correct, and fill in the degrees of freedom.

| Source of variation | Degrees of freedom | Mean square |
|---|---|---|
| Plants | | 4.15 |
| Regions | | 2.22 |
| Error | | .692 |

(*b*) What statement would you make regarding region differences?
(*c*) What is the standard error of a region mean?
(*d*) What are the confidence limits for the difference between regions 1 and 6?

**18.11.** Middleton and Chapman conducted an experiment to determine the best variety out of eight varieties of oats at Laurinburg, N.C., in 1940. The yields of grain in grams for a 16-foot row were as shown in the accompanying table.

DATA OF EXERCISE 18.11

| Variety | Blocks | | | | | Sum | Mean |
|---|---|---|---|---|---|---|---|
| | I | II | III | IV | V | | |
| 1 | 296 | 357 | 340 | 331 | 348 | 1,672 | 334.4 |
| 2 | 402 | 390 | 431 | 340 | 320 | 1,883 | 376.6 |
| 3 | 437 | 334 | 426 | 320 | 296 | 1,813 | 362.6 |
| 4 | 303 | 319 | 310 | 260 | 242 | 1,434 | 286.8 |
| 5 | 469 | 405 | 442 | 487 | 394 | 2,197 | 439.4 |
| 6 | 345 | 342 | 358 | 300 | 308 | 1,653 | 330.6 |
| 7 | 324 | 339 | 357 | 352 | 220 | 1,592 | 318.4 |
| 8 | 488 | 374 | 401 | 338 | 320 | 1,921 | 384.2 |
| Sum | 3,064 | 2,860 | 3,065 | 2,728 | 2,448 | 14,165 | 354.1 |

(*a*) Determine whether or not there are significant differences among the varieties. Which variety would you recommend?
(*b*) What is the efficiency of this design compared with a completely randomized design?
(*c*) What is the standard error for the difference between two varietal means?
(*d*) Set up a field plan for conducting this experiment.

**18.12.** Frequently one or more plots in a randomized blocks experiment will be missing because of some adverse condition such as a washout or insect infestation. As a result the orthogonal properties of the analysis are upset, and the statistician must either use an approximate analysis or run a complete least-squares analysis. Let us assume in the oats experiment of Exercise 18.11 that the plot for variety 1 in block I had been washed out. An approximate method of analysis is to set this yield equal to $y$, run up the analysis of variance in terms of $y$ and the other yields, and estimate $y$ by minimizing SSE. Then substitute $y$ for the missing plot yield, and complete the analysis, decreasing the error degrees of freedom by one.

(*a*) Show that $y = (pT + rB - G)/(r - 1)(p - 1)$, where $T$ and $B$ are the yields for the treatment and block with the missing plot.

(*b*) Estimate $y$ for the oats experiment, and compute the analysis of variance.

(*c*) Make a complete least-squares analysis of the data, regarding the missing plot as nonexistent; in other words, we have only 4 plots for variety 1 and 7 plots in block I. Show that you obtain the same value of SSE as in (*b*) but that SST in (*b*) is too large by $(2{,}768 - 7y)^2/56$.

**18.13.** Prove that $\sigma[(T_i - \bar{T})(B_j - \bar{B})] = 0$ in Sec. 18.3.

**18.14.** (*a*) The student should set up the least-squares equations and the analysis-of-variance table for an $r \times r$ Latin-square design and indicate the expected values of the mean squares in the analysis of variance.

(*b*) What is the standard error of the difference between any two treatment means?

(*c*) Show that the efficiency (neglecting the loss of degrees of freedom) of the rows in reducing the error variance in an $(r \times r)$ Latin-square design as compared with a randomized complete-blocks design with the $r$ columns as blocks is given by

$$I = \frac{\text{SSR} + (r - 1)^2 s_L^2}{r(r - 1)s_L^2},$$

where SSR is the sum of squares for rows and $s_L^2$ is the error mean square for the Latin-square design. Similarly the efficiency of the columns is found by replacing SSR by SSC (sum of squares for columns). HINT: Use the same method as given in Sec. 18.3 (vi) for the efficiency of the randomized complete-blocks design as compared with a completely randomized design.

(*d*) What is $h$ in this case? What is $h'$?

**18.15.** Given a Latin-square design with $r$ rows, columns, and treatments. Assume that the data for one plot were lost. Show that the estimate of the missing value found by minimizing SSE is

$$y = \frac{r(R + C + T) - 2G}{(r - 1)(r - 2)},$$

where $R$, $C$, and $T$ are, respectively, the totals of the row, column, and treatment which contain the missing value.

**18.16.** A Latin-square design was used at the University of Hawaii to compare 6 different legume intercycle crops for pineapples.[8] The yields in 10-gram units are given in the accompanying table.

DATA OF EXERCISE 18.16

| | | | | | | | Row totals |
|---|---|---|---|---|---|---|---|
| | *B* 220 | *F* 98 | *D* 149 | *A* 92 | *E* 282 | *C* 169 | 1,010 |
| | *A* 74 | *E* 238 | *B* 158 | *C* 228 | *F* 48 | *D* 188 | 934 |
| | *D* 118 | *C* 279 | *F* 118 | *E* 278 | *B* 176 | *A* 65 | 1,034 |
| | *E* 295 | *B* 222 | *A* 54 | *D* 104 | *C* 213 | *F* 163 | 1,051 |
| | *C* 187 | *D* 90 | *E* 242 | *F* 96 | *A* 66 | *B* 122 | 803 |
| | *F* 90 | *A* 124 | *C* 195 | *B* 109 | *D* 79 | *E* 211 | 808 |
| Col. totals | 984 | 1,051 | 916 | 907 | 864 | 918 | 5,640 |

(*a*) Make a complete analysis of this experiment, and state which legume you would recommend for planting.

(*b*) Use the Tukey method[5] to determine whether or not there are significant differences among the three top treatments.

(*c*) Was the Latin-square design useful in this case (see Exercise 18.14)?

(*d*) Set up another field plan for this experiment.

**18.17.** Professor John Wishart furnishes us this exercise:[9]

"An experiment on the use of nitrogenous fertilizers on wheat was arranged as a 5 × 5 Latin square, each plot being $\frac{1}{40}$ acre in size. The control plot (having no fertilizer) is denoted by *O*; *S* marks the plots which received a single dressing of sulphate of ammonia in March, while *SS* marks the plots which received the same total dressing, but in 6 monthly dressings from November to April. Plots which received cyanamide in October to an equivalent amount (in nitrogen) as the others are marked *C*, while *D* marks plots which received half their dressing as cyanamide and half as dicyanodiamide. The plan is given below, the numbers denoting the yields of the plots in pounds. Conduct the statistical analysis of the data, measuring the significance of the effect of applying a nitrogenous dressing, of whatever kind; also see if you can determine, by a statistical test, whether some forms of dressing are more effective than others. Set out a full summary table with your conclusions.

| | | | | |
|---|---|---|---|---|
| *D* 72.2 | *SS* 55.4 | *O* 36.6 | *C* 67.9 | *S* 73.0 |
| *O* 36.4 | *C* 46.9 | *SS* 46.8 | *S* 54.9 | *D* 68.5 |
| *SS* 71.5 | *S* 55.6 | *D* 71.6 | *O* 67.5 | *C* 78.4 |
| *S* 68.9 | *O* 53.2 | *C* 69.8 | *D* 79.6 | *SS* 77.2 |
| *C* 82.0 | *D* 81.0 | *S* 76.0 | *SS* 87.9 | *O* 70.9 |

The sum of squares of the 25 numbers in the table is 113,574.73."

### References Cited

1. PEACH, PAUL, *Industrial Statistics and Quality Control*, 2d ed., Edwards and Broughton Co., Raleigh, N.C., 1947.
2. CURTIS, J. M., *A Study of the Business Organization and Operating Methods of Farmer Retail Produce Markets in North Carolina*, unpublished thesis, North Carolina State College, Raleigh, N.C., 1949.
3. SNEDECOR, G. W., and G. M. COX, "Disproportionate Subclass Numbers in Tables of Multiple Classification," *Iowa State Coll., Agr. Expt. Sta., Bull.* 180 (1935).
4. COCHRAN, W. G., and G. M. COX, *Experimental Designs*, John Wiley & Sons, Inc., New York, 1950.
5. TUKEY, J. W., "Comparing Individual Means in the Analysis of Variance," *Biometrics*, **5**:99–114 (1949).
6. FISHER, R. A., *Design of Experiments*, 4th ed., Oliver & Boyd, Ltd., Edinburgh and London, 1947.
7. MOORE, J. H., "The Distribution and Relation of Fiber Population, Length, Breaking Load, Weight, Diameter and Percentage of Thin-walled Fibers on the Cottonseed in Five Varieties of American Upland Cotton," *J. Agr. Research*, **62**:255–302 (1941).
8. MAGISTAD, O. C., N. KING, and O. N. ALLEN, "A Comparison of Legume Intercycle Crops for Pineapples," *J. Agron.*, **26**: 372–380 (1934).
9. WISHART, J., "Design of Experiments," *Inst. Stat. Mim. Ser.* 15 (1949).

### Other Reading

WELCH, B. L., "On the *z*-test in Randomized Blocks and Latin Squares," *Biometrika*, **29**:21–52 (1937).

# CHAPTER 19

# THE ANALYSIS OF INCOMPLETE-BLOCKS DESIGNS

**19.1. Introduction.** In this chapter, we shall discuss the use of designs in which the number of plots per block is less than the number of treatments. As before, we assume $p$ treatments, but with only $k$ plots per block ($k < p$). Assume further that each treatment is applied to $r$ plots (each treatment is replicated $r$ times) and that there are a total of $q$ blocks ($q > r$). Hence there are a total of $N = kq = rp$ plots in the experiment. The $i$th treatment appears in the $j$th block $n_{ij}$ times ($n_{ij} = 0$ or 1). Hence $\sum_j n_{ij} = r$, and $\sum_i n_{ij} = k$. This design is called an *incomplete-blocks design.*

It might be noted that there are two important situations for which these incomplete-blocks designs are used:

(*a*) *The number of possible plots per block is less than p.* Examples of this are:

(i) Nutrition studies on animals where the block is a litter, the individual animal is the plot, and the smallest litter size is smaller than the number of rations to be studied.
(ii) Chemical experiments where the block is a day, an individual analysis is the plot, and the number of possible analyses in a day is less than the number of treatments.
(iii) Tasting experiments where the block is a single trial by an individual taster, the score on a given product is the plot yield, and the number of different products which a taster can differentiate on a single trial is less than the number of products being tasted.
(iv) Education or psychology tests in which the block is the trials by a single child on a given day, the plot is a single test on this day, and the number of tests being considered is greater than the number the child can take on a given day without tiring.
(v) An engineering experiment in which the block is an oven and the number of treatments is greater than the number of items which can be heated at a time.

(b) *The number of treatments is so large that enough homogeneous plots cannot be found for a complete block.*

(i) If we have 81 varieties of corn to test, it is often impossible to find 81 more or less homogeneous plots to form a complete block.

(ii) For greenhouse experiments, temperature and light conditions vary so much that it is desirable to form blocks of rather small size, the size often being smaller than needed to include all of the pots for a complete block.

We shall not include many examples of these designs in this book, because of a limitation of space. Students interested in more examples should consult references 1 to 3.

**19.2. General Least-squares Equations.** The experimental model for this design is

$$Y_{ij} = n_{ij}(\mu + \tau_i + \beta_j + \epsilon_{ij}), \qquad i = 1, 2, \ldots, p; j = 1, 2, \ldots, q,$$

where $n_{ij} = 0$ or 1 and $\sum_i \tau_i = \sum_j \beta_j = 0$.

The least-squares equations for this model are

$$m\colon Nm = G,$$

$$b_j\colon km + \sum_{l=1}^{p} n_{lj}t_l + kb_j = B_j,$$

$$t_i\colon rm + rt_i + \sum_{j=1}^{q} n_{ij}b_j = T_i.$$

The reader will note that the block and treatment effects are mixed up in these equations; this is called *confounding* of the treatment and block effects.

The first step in solving for the treatment effects is to adjust the treatment effects for the block effects by removing the block constants from the treatment equations. This is accomplished by multiplying the $b_j$ equation by $n_{ij}/k$ and subtracting the sum of all of these altered $b_j$ equations from the $t_i$ equation. The resultant equation is

$$rt_i - \frac{1}{k}\sum_{j=1}^{q}\sum_{l=1}^{p} n_{ij}n_{lj}t_l = T_i - \frac{1}{k}\sum_j n_{ij}B_j \equiv A_i,$$

where $A_i$ is called an *adjusted treatment total* (adjusted for block effects) and $\sum_i A_i = 0$. The adjusting factor $\sum_j n_{ij}B_j$ is often written as $T_{bi}$, the total yield of all blocks containing treatment $i$. Suppose the $i$th treatment appears $\lambda_{il}$ times in the same block with the $l$th treatment. Then

$$\sum_j n_{ij}n_{lj} = \begin{cases} \lambda_{il} & l \neq i. \\ r & l = i. \end{cases}$$

Hence we obtain

$$[r(k-1)t_i - \sum_{l \neq i} \lambda_{il}t_l]/k = A_i, \qquad i, l = 1, 2, \ldots, p.$$

The values of the $t_i$ can be solved only by the simultaneous solution of the $p$ equations in $A_i$, with the linear restraint, $\sum_i t_i = 0$. One method of solving these $p$ equations is to set $t_i = t_i'' + t_p$, so that $t_p'' = 0$ and $t_p = -\Sigma t_i''/p$. Hence

$$A_i = [r(k-1)t_i'' - \sum_{l \neq i} \lambda_{il}t_l'']/k, \qquad i = 1, 2, \ldots, p-1,$$

since $\sum_{l \neq i} \lambda_{il} = r(k-1)$. We see that

$$t_i'' = \sum_{l=1}^{p-1} c_{il}''A_l,$$

where the $c_{il}''$ are the elements of the inverse matrix of the coefficients of $t_i''$ in the $(p-1)$ equations in $A_i$.

In this case

$$\text{SST(adj)} = \sum_{i=1}^{p-1} t_i''A_i = \sum_{i=1}^{p} (t_i - t_p)A_i = \sum_{i=1}^{p} t_iA_i,$$

since $\sum_i A_i = 0$. It can be shown that

$$E[\text{MST(adj)}] = \sigma^2 + \theta\{\tau_i\}/(p-1),$$

where $\theta$ is 0 when $\{\tau_i = 0\}$. Also,

$$\sigma^2(t_i'') = c_{ii}''\sigma^2 \qquad \text{and} \qquad \sigma^2(t_i'' - t_l'') = (c_{ii}'' - 2c_{il}'' + c_{ll}'')\sigma^2,$$

where $\sigma^2 \doteq s^2 = \text{SSE}/(n - p - q + 1)$.

If only a test of the null hypothesis $\{\tau_i = 0\}$ is desired, the forward solution of the abbreviated Doolittle method is sufficient, where the $A$ values replace the $G$ values in the computations of Sec. 15.3 and the coefficients of $t_i''$ and $t_l''$ are the elements of the original matrix. An example of this computing procedure will be given in Chap. 20 (Example 20.4). No detailed computing techniques are given in the present chapter, because almost all incomplete-blocks designs which are used have certain restrictions to make the analysis simpler. Some of these designs will be discussed in succeeding sections of this chapter.

**19.3. Balanced Incomplete-blocks Designs.** If every treatment appears with every other treatment in the same block an equal number of times, say $\lambda$, the incomplete-blocks design is said to be *balanced* (all $\lambda_{il} \equiv \lambda$). In this case the adjusted treatment equation becomes

$$\frac{r(k-1)t_i - \lambda \sum_{l \neq i} t_l}{k} = \frac{r(k-1)+\lambda}{k} t_i = A_i,$$

because $\sum_{l=1}^{p} t_l = 0$, so that $\sum_{l \neq i} t_l = -t_i$.

If we set $\dfrac{r(k-1)+\lambda}{k} = rE_f$,

$$t_i = A_i/rE_f.$$

$E_f$ is called the *efficiency factor* for the incomplete-blocks design, since the number of effective replications is $rE_f$, instead of $r$, where $E_f < 1$. We see that the number of blocks in this case is

$$q = \lambda C(p,2)/C(k,2) = \lambda p(p-1)/k(k-1),$$

where $C(a,b)$ is the number of combinations of $a$ things taken $b$ at a time. Hence $\lambda p(p-1) = qk(k-1) = rp(k-1)$, and

$$E_f = \frac{r(k-1)+\lambda}{rk} = \frac{\lambda p}{rk} = \frac{p(k-1)}{k(p-1)}.$$

We might say that a necessary condition for "balance" is that

$$\lambda p(p-1) = qk(k-1) = rp(k-1).$$

However, it may not be possible to construct a balanced design even though this condition is met.

The adjusted mean yield for the $i$th treatment is

$$t_i' = t_i + m = A_i/rE_f + G/rp = [k(p-1)A_i + (k-1)G]/rp(k-1).$$

In Sec. 15.3 (page 199), it was indicated that the reduction due to any fixed variate, $X_i$, adjusted for all previous fixed variates is given by $A_{iy}B_{iy}$, where $A_{iy} = Sy(x_i$ adjusted for all previous fixed variates in the matrix) and $B_{iy}$ was the regression coefficient for $X_i$. In the balanced incomplete-blocks design, the regression coefficient $t_i = A_i/rE_f$, where $A_i$ is the sum of cross products, adjusted for block effects. Hence the treatment sum of squares adjusted for block effects is

$$\text{SST(adj)} = \sum_i A_i^2/rE_f.$$

A more formal proof would be the following:

The total reduction in sum of squares due to blocks and treatments is

$$\text{SSR} = \sum_j b_j B_j + \sum_i t_i T_i.$$

If the treatment effects are omitted from the model,

$$\text{SSR}' \text{ (omitting treatments)} = \sum_j (B_j - \bar{B})^2/k = \sum_j B_j(B_j - \bar{B})/k.$$

Hence the sum of squares due to treatments is

$$\begin{aligned}\text{SST(adj)} &= \text{SSR} - \text{SSR}' \\ &= \sum_j \left(b_j - \frac{B_j}{k} + \frac{\bar{B}}{k}\right) B_j + \sum_i A_i \left(A_i + \frac{1}{k}\sum_j n_{ij}B_j\right) \Big/ rE_f \\ &= \sum_i A_i^2/rE_f + \sum_j B_j \left[b_j + \frac{1}{k}\sum_i n_{ij}t_i - \frac{B_j - \bar{B}}{k}\right],\end{aligned}$$

where $\bar{B} = G/q$. From the $G$ and $B_j$ least-squares equations (Sec. 19.2), we see that $b_j + (1/k)\sum_i n_{ij}t_i = (B_j - \bar{B})/k$. Hence $\text{SST(adj)} = \sum_i A_i^2/rE_f$.

Also, $\text{SSE} = Sy^2 - \text{SSR}$ with $(N - p - q + 1)$ degrees of freedom.

It might be noted that

$$B_j - \bar{B} = k\beta_j + \sum_i n_{ij}\tau_i + \left[\sum_i n_{ij}\epsilon_{ij} - \frac{1}{q}\sum_i\sum_j n_{ij}\epsilon_{ij}\right],$$

$$A_i = rE_f\tau_i + \left[\sum_j n_{ij}\epsilon_{ij} - \frac{1}{k}\sum_{i'}\sum_j n_{ij}n_{i'j}\epsilon_{i'j}\right],$$

$$G = rp\mu + \sum_i\sum_j n_{ij}\epsilon_{ij}.$$

It can be shown that†

$$\begin{aligned} E[(B_j - \bar{B})^2] &= (k\beta_j + \sum_i n_{ij}\tau_i)^2 + k(q-1)\sigma^2/q, \\ E(A_i^2) &= (rE_f)^2\tau_i^2 + r(k-1)\sigma^2/k, \\ E(G^2) &= (rp\mu)^2 + rp\sigma^2, \\ \sigma(A_iA_l) &= -\lambda\sigma^2/k, \qquad i \neq l, \\ \sigma[(B_j - \bar{B})A_i] &= 0 = \sigma[(B_j - \bar{B})G] = \sigma(A_iG). \end{aligned}$$

† These expectations are based on the assumption that the blocks are fixed. If the block effects are assumed to be random, more efficient estimates of the treatment means can be obtained by utilizing the so-called *recovery of interblock information*. This estimation procedure was first introduced by Yates[4] and will be discussed in Sec. 24.1.

The analysis of variance is:

| Source of variation | Degrees of freedom | Mean square | $E$(MS) |
|---|---|---|---|
| Blocks | $q - 1$ | $\sum_j (B_j - \bar{B})^2/k(q-1)$ | |
| Treatments (adj) | $p - 1$ | $\sum_i A_i^2/rE_f(p-1)$ | $\sigma^2 + rE_f\theta(\tau)$† |
| Error | $N - p - q + 1$ | $s^2$ | $\sigma^2$ |

† $\theta(\tau) = \sum_i \tau_i^2/(p-1)$.

It is easy to see that the one-tailed $F$ test is appropriate to test

$$H_0\colon \{\tau_i = 0\}$$

with $s^2$ estimated by the error sum of squares divided by $(N - p - q + 1)$.

$$\sigma^2(t_i) = (k-1)\sigma^2/rkE_f^2.$$
$$\sigma^2(t_i') = \sigma^2(t_i) + \sigma^2/rp.$$
$$\sigma^2(t_i - t_l) = \sigma^2(t_i' - t_l') = [2r(k-1) + 2\lambda]\sigma^2/k(rE_f)^2 = 2\sigma^2/rE_f.$$

The problem of estimating the efficiency of a balanced incomplete-blocks design as compared with other designs will be discussed in Chap. 24, except for a special type of balanced design which is discussed below.

**Example 19.1.** A special type of a balanced incomplete-blocks design is one with $p = k^2$ treatments, called a *balanced lattice design.*‡ This design can be set up in $r$ complete replications of $k$ blocks each (with $k$ treatments per block); hence, $q = rk$, $\lambda = r(k-1)/(p-1) = r/(k+1)$, and $E_f = k/(k+1)$. A balanced lattice design with $p = 9 (k = 3)$ and $r = 4$ was used to test 9 rations fed to rats. Hence $\lambda = 1$, and $E_f = \frac{3}{4}$. The gains for this experiment were (the ration numbers are in parentheses):

| Replication I | | | | | | | | Replication II | | | | | | | |
|---|---|---|---|---|---|---|---|---|---|---|---|---|---|---|---|
| $j$ | | | | | | | $B_j$ | $j$ | | | | | | | $B_j$ |
| 1 | (1) | 20 | (4) | 15 | (7) | 11 | 46 | 4 | (7) | 8 | (8) | 12 | (9) | 16 | 36 |
| 2 | (3) | 8 | (6) | 18 | (9) | 26 | 52 | 5 | (1) | 20 | (2) | 2 | (3) | 2 | 24 |
| 3 | (2) | 18 | (5) | 16 | (8) | 2 | 36 | 6 | (4) | 20 | (5) | 6 | (6) | 2 | 28 |
| Total | | | | | | | 134 | Total | | | | | | | 88 |

| Replication III | | | | | | | | Replication IV | | | | | | | |
|---|---|---|---|---|---|---|---|---|---|---|---|---|---|---|---|
| $j$ | | | | | | | $B_j$ | $j$ | | | | | | | $B_j$ |
| 7 | (1) | 13 | (9) | 19 | (5) | 14 | 46 | 10 | (5) | 19 | (7) | 23 | (3) | 6 | 48 |
| 8 | (8) | 14 | (4) | 34 | (3) | 2 | 50 | 11 | (1) | 22 | (6) | 12 | (8) | 2 | 36 |
| 9 | (6) | 14 | (2) | 20 | (7) | 14 | 48 | 12 | (9) | 27 | (2) | 7 | (4) | 20 | 54 |
| Total | | | | | | | 144 | Total | | | | | | | 138 |

‡ A more complicated lattice with $p = k^3$ treatments is called a *cubic lattice.*

The computations are as shown in Table 19.1.

TABLE 19.1

| Ration | Total gain $= T_i$ | $\sum_{j=1}^{12} n_{ij}B_j = T_{bi}$ | $3A_i = 3T_i - T_{bi}$ | $t_i' = (12A_i + G)/36$ |
|---|---|---|---|---|
| 1 | 75 | 152 | 73 | 22.11 |
| 2 | 47 | 162 | −21 | 11.67 |
| 3 | 18 | 174 | −120 | .67 |
| 4 | 89 | 178 | 89 | 23.89 |
| 5 | 55 | 158 | 7 | 14.78 |
| 6 | 46 | 164 | −26 | 11.11 |
| 7 | 56 | 178 | −10 | 12.89 |
| 8 | 30 | 158 | −68 | 6.44 |
| 9 | 88 | 188 | 76 | 22.44 |
| Total | $504 = G$ | $1,512 = 3G$ | 0 | 126.00 |

In this experiment, a constant for replications can be inserted in the model and a sum of squares for replications removed from the block sum of squares. The total sum of squares for blocks is

$$\text{SSB} = \frac{(46)^2 + (52)^2 + \cdots + (36)^2 + (54)^2}{3} - \frac{(504)^2}{36}$$
$$= 7{,}402.67 - 7{,}056 = 346.67.$$

The sum of squares for replications is

$$\frac{(134)^2 + \cdots + (138)^2}{9} - 7{,}056 = 219.56.$$

Hence the sum of squares for blocks in replications is

$$346.67 - 219.56 = 127.11.$$

The sum of squares for treatments (adjusted for blocks) is

$$\text{SST(adj)} = \frac{(73)^2 + (-21)^2 + \cdots + (76)^2}{(9)(3)} = 1{,}456.15.$$

The error sum of squares is

$$Sy^2 - \text{SSB} - \text{SST(adj)} = 9{,}316 - 7{,}056 - 346.67 - 1{,}456.15 = 457.18.$$

Hence the analysis-of-variance table is:

| Source of variation | Degrees of freedom | Sum of squares | Mean square | $E$(MS) |
|---|---|---|---|---|
| Replications | 3 | 219.56 | 73.19 | |
| Blocks (in replications) | 8 | 127.11 | 15.89 | |
| Treatments (adj) | 8 | 1,456.15 | 182.02 | $\sigma^2 + 3\theta(\tau)$ |
| Error | 16 | 457.18 | 28.57 | $\sigma^2$ |
| Total | 35 | 2,260 | | |

To test for treatment differences, $F = 182.02/28.52 = 6.37$ with 8 and 16 degrees of freedom, for which $\alpha < .001$. The standard error of the difference between any two adjusted treatment means $(t_i' - t_l')$ is

$$\sqrt{\frac{2(28.57)}{3}} = 4.36.$$

In this case we can compute the efficiency of this design relative to a randomized complete-blocks design with 4 replications (complete blocks). First we compute SST (unadjusted) and then the estimated randomized-blocks error as the difference $Sy^2$ − SST − SS (replications). The

| Source of variation | Degrees of freedom | Sum of squares | Mean square |
|---|---|---|---|
| Replications | 3 | 219.56 | |
| Treatments | 8 | 1,194.00 | |
| Randomized blocks error | 24 | 846.44 | 35.27 |
| Total | 35 | 2,260.00 | |

effective incomplete-blocks error is $28.57/E_f = 38.09$. Hence the efficiency of the incomplete-blocks design is only $35.27/38.09 = .93$. In addition there is another loss due to fewer error degrees of freedom (see reference 1, page 28).

**19.4. The Simple Lattice Designs.** One special type of a nonbalanced incomplete-blocks design is a lattice design with fewer replications than are needed for balance. A lattice design with two replications is called a *simple lattice*, one with three replications a *triple lattice*, etc. It was shown in Example 19.1 that a lattice is balanced if the number of replications $r = k + 1$. Hence, if $r < k + 1$, the lattice is not balanced. The analysis of a nonbalanced lattice is much simpler than the general analysis presented in Sec. 19.2, because of a special method of allocating the treatments to the blocks. The $k^2$ treatments are assigned at random one of the following treatment numbers:

$$\begin{array}{cccc} 11 & 12 & \cdots & 1k \\ 21 & 22 & \cdots & 2k \\ \cdot & \cdot & \cdots & \cdot \\ k1 & k2 & \cdots & kk \end{array}$$

If a simple lattice is used ($r = 2$), the row combinations (11,12, . . . ,1$k$; 21,22, . . . ,2$k$; etc.) are assigned to separate blocks in one replication, $X$, and the column combinations (11,21, . . . ,$k$1;12,22, . . . ,$k$2; etc.) assigned to separate blocks in the second replication, $Y$. If a triple lattice is used, an additional replication, $Z$, is taken from the diagonals (11,22, . . . ,$kk$; 21,32, . . . ,1$k$; etc.). For a complete discussion of this design, see references 2 and 7.

Let us consider the analysis of a simple lattice experiment ($r = 2$). We shall designate the treatment effects as $t_{ij}(i, j = 1,2, \ldots ,k)$ and similarly for treatment totals ($T_{ij}$) and adjusted treatment totals ($A_{ij}$). Let

$$a_i = \sum_j t_{ij} \qquad \text{and} \qquad d_j = \sum_i t_{ij}.$$

The yield of the ($i,j$) treatment in the $X$ replication is designated as $X_{ij}$ and in the $Y$ replication as $Y_{ij}$. Therefore $T_{ij} = X_{ij} + Y_{ij}$. And finally we shall use the notation

$$\sum_i X_{ij} = X_{.j}, \qquad \sum_j X_{ij} = X_{i.}, \qquad \sum_i \sum_j X_{ij} = X_{..}$$

and similarly for $Y$. Hence

$$A_{ij} = T_{ij} - \frac{1}{k}(X_{i.} + Y_{.j}).$$

Also we note that $\lambda$ will be 1 for those treatments with the same row or column subscript and 0 elsewhere. Hence

$$\begin{aligned} A_{ij} &= \left[ 2(k-1)t_{ij} - \sum_{j' \neq j} t_{ij'} - \sum_{i' \neq i} t_{i'j} \right] \Big/ k \\ &= 2t_{ij} - (a_i + d_j)/k. \end{aligned}$$

$$\sum_j A_{ij} = Y_{i.} - Y_{..}/k = a_i, \qquad \sum_i A_{ij} = X_{.j} - X_{..}/k = d_j,$$

since $\sum_i a_i = \sum_j d_j = \sum_i \sum_j t_{ij} = 0.$

We have shown that the sum of squares for treatments (adjusted for blocks) is

$$\text{SST(adj)} = \sum_i \sum_j A_{ij} t_{ij} = \tfrac{1}{2} \sum_i \sum_j A_{ij}[A_{ij} + (a_i + d_j)/k]$$

$$= \tfrac{1}{2} \sum_i \sum_j \{[T_{ij} - (X_{i.} + Y_{.j})/k] \cdot [T_{ij} - (X_{i.} + Y_{.j} - Y_{i.} - X_{.j})/k]\}.$$

By expanding these products term by term, we have

$$\text{SST(adj)} = \tfrac{1}{2} \Big\{ \sum_i \sum_j T_{ij}^2 - (X_{..} - Y_{..})^2/k^2 - \Big[ \sum_i T_{i.}^2 + \sum_j T_{.j}^2 \Big] \Big/ k + 2 \Big[ \sum_i Y_{i.}^2 + \sum_j X_{.j}^2 \Big] \Big/ k \Big\},$$

where $T_{i.} = X_{i.} + Y_{i.}$ and $T_{.j} = X_{.j} + Y_{.j}$.

The error sum of squares is obtained by computing the unadjusted block sum of squares, SSB, and then subtracting to obtain

$$\text{SSE} = Sy^2 - \text{SSB} - \text{SST(adj)}.$$

The analysis of variance is:

| Source of variation | Degrees of freedom | Sum of squares | Mean square |
|---|---|---|---|
| Blocks | $2k - 1$ | SSB | |
| Treatments(adj) | $k^2 - 1$ | SST(adj) | MST(adj) |
| Error | $(k - 1)^2$ | SSE | $s^2$ |

The blocks sum of squares can be divided into two parts, for replications (1 degree of freedom) and blocks in replications [$2(k - 1)$ degrees of freedom]. The replication part is independent of treatment effects and equals $(X_{..} - Y_{..})^2/2k^2$. The blocks-in-replication part is a mixture of block and treatment effects as well as error and is simply SSB $-$ $(X_{..} - Y_{..})^2/2k^2$.†

In this case it is not possible to give a single figure for the variance of the difference between two adjusted means, since some treatments will appear together in the same block and others never appear together in the same block. It seems reasonable that the variance of the difference will be lower for those treatments appearing together in the same block. Let us first consider two adjusted treatment means $t'_{1j}$ and $t'_{2j}$, which appear in the same block.

† Most analyses of lattice designs now make use of the recovery of interblock information, mentioned in the footnote on page 253. See references 1 and 8 for some examples of the theory and computational procedures.

$$t'_{ij} = \tfrac{1}{2}[X_{ij} + Y_{ij} - (X_{i\cdot} - Y_{i\cdot} - X_{\cdot j} + Y_{\cdot j})/k],$$

$$\begin{aligned} t'_{1j} - t'_{2j} &= \tfrac{1}{2}[X_{1j} + Y_{1j} - X_{2j} - Y_{2j} - (X_{1\cdot} - X_{2\cdot} - Y_{1\cdot} + Y_{2\cdot})/k] \\ &= \frac{1}{2}\left[\left(\frac{k-1}{k}\right)(X_{1j} - X_{2j}) - \left(\frac{1}{k}\right)\sum_{j' \neq j}(X_{1j'} - X_{2j'}) \right. \\ &\qquad \left. + \left(\frac{k+1}{k}\right)(Y_{1j} - Y_{2j}) + \left(\frac{1}{k}\right)\sum_{j' \neq j}(Y_{1j'} - Y_{2j'})\right], \end{aligned}$$

$$\begin{aligned} \sigma^2(t'_{1j} - t'_{2j}) &= (2/4k^2)[(k-1)^2 + (k-1) + (k+1)^2 + (k-1)]\sigma^2 \\ &= (k+1)\sigma^2/k. \end{aligned}$$

Now consider two treatments which do not appear together in the same block, such as $t_{11}$ and $t_{22}$. In this case the $X_{\cdot j}$ and $Y_{\cdot j}$ do not cancel out, as above, and we have

$$\sigma^2(t'_{11} - t'_{22}) = (k+2)\sigma^2/k.$$

We note that there are $k^2(k^2 - 1)/2$ possible treatment comparisons, of which $k^2(k-1)$ are between treatments in the same block and $\frac{1}{2}k^2(k-1)^2$ between treatments not in the same block. Hence we might use as an average variance of the difference between adjusted treatment effects,

$$\frac{[k^2(k-1)(k+1)/k + k^2(k-1)^2(k+2)/2k]\sigma^2}{k^2(k^2-1)/2} = \frac{(k+3)\sigma^2}{k+1}.$$

The factor $(k+1)/(k+3)$ is the efficiency factor, $E_f$, for this design.

**Example 19.2.** To illustrate the computing techniques for the simple lattice, we shall use the first two replications of the $(3 \times 3)$ experiment considered in Example 19.1. We shall designate the treatments as 11, 12, 13, . . . , 33 instead of 1, 2, . . . , 9, with $X$ for Replication II and $Y$ for Replication I. The treatment and $X$ and $Y$ totals are (treatment numbers in parentheses):

| | | | | | | $T_{i\cdot}$ |
|---|---|---|---|---|---|---|
| (11) | 40 | (12) | 20 | (13) | 10 | 70 |
| (21) | 35 | (22) | 22 | (23) | 20 | 77 |
| (31) | 19 | (32) | 14 | (33) | 42 | 75 |
| $T_{\cdot j}$ | 94 | | 56 | | 72 | 222 |

| $i,j$ | $X_{\cdot j}$ | $Y_{i\cdot}$ | $X_{i\cdot}$ | $Y_{\cdot j}$ |
|---|---|---|---|---|
| 1 | 48 | 46 | 24 | 46 |
| 2 | 20 | 49 | 28 | 36 |
| 3 | 20 | 39 | 36 | 52 |
| Total | 88 | 134 | 88 | 134 |

$$Sy^2 = 3{,}706 - \frac{(222)^2}{18} = 968,$$

$$\begin{aligned} \text{SST(adj)} &= \frac{1}{2}\left\{(40)^2 + \cdots + (42)^2 - \frac{(88-134)^2}{9} \right. \\ &\quad \left. - \frac{(70)^2 + (77)^2 + \cdots + (72)^2}{3} + \frac{2[(48)^2 + (20)^2 + \cdots + (39)^2]}{3}\right\} \\ &= \tfrac{1}{2}[6{,}530 - 235.11 - 11{,}203.33 + 6{,}094.67] = 593.11, \end{aligned}$$

$$\text{SSB} = \frac{(24)^2 + (28)^2 + \cdots + (52)^2}{3} - \frac{(222)^2}{18} = 186.$$

The analysis of variance is:

| Source of variation | Degrees of freedom | Sum of squares | Mean square |
|---|---|---|---|
| Replications | 1 | 118 | |
| Blocks (in replications) | 4 | 68 | |
| Treatments(adj) | 8 | 593 | 74 |
| Error | 4 | 189 | 47.2 |
| Total | 17 | 968 | |
| Treatments (unadjusted) | 8 | 527 | |
| Randomized blocks error | 8 | 323 | 40.4 |

The estimated average standard error of the difference between two adjusted treatment effects is $\sqrt{6s^2/4} = 8.4$. $t'_{ij} = [kT_{ij} - \delta_{ij}]/2k$, where $\delta_{ij} = (X_{i.} - Y_{i.} - X_{.j} + Y_{.j})$. The $\delta_{ij}$ and $t'_{ij}$ are presented below.

| $\delta_{ij}$ | 1 | 2 | 3 | |
|---|---|---|---|---|
| 1 | −24 | −6 | 10 | −20 |
| 2 | −23 | −5 | 11 | −17 |
| 3 | −5 | 13 | 29 | 37 |
| | −52 | 2 | 50 | 0 |

| $t'_{ij}$ | 1 | 2 | 3 | |
|---|---|---|---|---|
| 1 | 16.0 | 9.0 | 6.7 | 31.7 |
| 2 | 13.7 | 10.2 | 11.8 | 35.7 |
| 3 | 8.7 | 9.2 | 25.8 | 43.7 |
| | 38.4 | 28.4 | 44.3 | 111.1 |

The efficiency of this design as compared with randomized complete blocks is only $40.4 \div 3(47.2)/2 = 0.57$, plus the fact that we have only 4 instead of 8 error degrees of freedom. This result has no practical use because no experiment should be planned if it has only 4 degrees of freedom for the estimate of the error variance.

If the simple lattice is duplicated several times so that $2d$ replications ($2kd$ blocks) are used, the analysis is changed in the following respects:

(i) There are now $(2d - 1)$ degrees of freedom for replications and $2d(k - 1)$ degrees of freedom for blocks in replications. The differences between block totals with the same treatments in the blocks are free of treatment effects and hence indicate real block differences. The block totals can be analyzed as follows for the $X$ group (and similarly for the $Y$ group):

| | Degrees of freedom |
|---|---|
| Replications | $d - 1$ |
| $X$ groups | $k - 1$ |
| Block effect | $(d - 1)(k - 1)$ |

Hence there are $2(d - 1)(k - 1)$ degrees of freedom for real block differences and $2(k - 1)$ degrees of freedom with block and treatment effects mixed up.

(ii) Each $X_{ij}$ and $Y_{ij}$ is now a total of $d$ yields and $T_{ij}$ a total of $2d$ yields. Hence all sums of squares must be divided by $2d$ instead of 2 (similarly for means). Also, $\lambda$ will now be $d$ instead of 1.

(iii) The above variances of the differences between two adjusted treatment effects are divided by $d$.

(iv) There are now $(k - 1)(2dk - k - 1)$ degrees of freedom for error.

**19.5. Other Lattice Designs.** Yates[2] presents the theory for triple lattices. We shall not include the details in this book. The essential change is that each treatment is given a third subscript as was done for the Latin-square design, and a $Z$ replication is introduced. This design is also presented in references 1 and 8. If more than three replications are used, in almost all cases either the simple or triple lattice is duplicated or a balanced design is used.

It should be indicated that it is also possible to set up a lattice experiment in a Latin-square design, called a *lattice-square* design. The computing details are much more complicated than for the randomized blocks designs, but the reduction in error variance is often quite large especially for very heterogeneous experimental material. Details of these designs are also presented in reference 1.

Harshbarger[9,10] introduced a new type of lattice design, called the *rectangular lattice*, in which the number of treatments is $k(k + 1)$. This design enables the experimenter to utilize the simplicity of the lattice without restricting his experiments to exactly $k^2$ treatments. Cochran and Cox[1] present simplified computing techniques for this type of design also. A computing manual has been prepared by Robinson and Watson.[11]

Kempthorne and Federer[12] present the general theory of prime-power lattices.

**19.6. Methods of Constructing Incomplete-blocks Designs.** References 3 and 13 present methods of constructing balanced incomplete-blocks designs. The construction of the lattice designs is quite simple, since the experimenter needs only to randomize the treatment numbers, then the blocks within a replication and the treatments in each block. We shall present one example of a balanced design which is not a lattice.

**Example 19.3.** Consider the design for the 7 treatments in blocks of 3 in Exercise 19.3. There are $C(7,3) = 35$ combinations of these 7 treatments in groups of 3, but if we restrict ourselves to enough combinations so that each treatment appears once and only once with every other treatment ($\lambda = 1$), we can manage with 7 blocks. The method of construction is one of gradual elimination. Obviously there are many ways of selecting the set of 7 from the set of 35 combinations. One such set of 7 is

$$ABC, ADE, AFG, BDF, BEG, CDG, CEF.$$

Another was used in Exercise 19.3. Probably the best procedure to use is to select some basic rule, such as the one given in reference 1. The following set

$$ABD, BCE, CDF, DEG, EFA, FGB, GAC$$

was obtained by cyclic substitution (the first letter is one removed from the second and the third two removed from the second, where $F + 2 = A$, for example). Then randomly assign the 7 treatments to the 7 letters.

**19.7. Summary.** In Sec. 19.1, we indicated certain experimental conditions which might make the use of an incomplete-blocks design desirable. For illustrative purposes, some data from an experiment with nine treatments have been analyzed. Unless the blocks are so small that nine experimental units cannot be placed in each block, it is seldom advisable to use the incomplete-blocks design for so few treatments, unless enough replications can be used to give at least 20 degrees of freedom for the error mean square. Even then there is seldom enough gain in efficiency to warrant the extra computing time. The experimenter needs to know something about the block-to-block variability of his experimental material before he can decide whether or not he should use an incomplete blocks design. We believe that it is advisable to build up a body of evidence from continuing experiments in order to help with this decision. Many engineering experiments and experiments in the physical and social sciences may make use of the incomplete-blocks designs, because the size of the blocks is often limited. However, little information is available on this point to date (see reference 14 for one example in the field of chemistry).

Since the analyses of most incomplete-blocks data use the recovery of interblock information, more will be said on these points in Chap. 24. However, it should be warned here that it seems inadvisable to use this method of analysis unless there are at least 15 degrees of freedom for the block mean square (and preferably at least 25 degrees of freedom).

## EXERCISES

**19.1.** A simple example of a balanced incomplete-blocks experiment is the following balanced lattice with four treatments, six blocks, and two treatments per block:

| Treatments | Blocks | | | | | | Total |
|---|---|---|---|---|---|---|---|
| | I*a* | I*b* | II*a* | II*b* | III*a* | III*b* | |
| 1 | 30 | | 30 | | 25 | | 85 |
| 2 | 15 | | | 10 | | 20 | 45 |
| 3 | | 30 | 25 | | | 40 | 95 |
| 4 | | 10 | | 10 | 15 | | 35 |
| Total | 45 | 40 | 55 | 20 | 40 | 60 | 260 |
| | 85 | | 75 | | 100 | | |

(*a*) Set up the analysis of variance and adjusted treatment means for this experiment, and test for treatment differences.

(*b*) Estimate the standard error of the difference between any two adjusted treatment means.

(*c*) Show how the replication constants fit into the model, and determine the expected value of the replication mean square in the analysis of variance.

(*d*) Compute an estimate of the efficiency of this design relative to a randomized complete-blocks design.

**19.2.** Dr. Pauline Paul[5] conducted an experiment to compare the effects of cold storage on the tenderness and flavor of beef roasts. Six periods of storage (0, 1, 2, 4, 9, and 18 days) were tested ($p = 6$). Since the same cut of meat on each side of an animal was expected to be similar but different cuts on the same side dissimilar, it was decided to use a balanced incomplete-blocks design with $k = 2$, $\lambda = 1$, $q = 15$, and $r = 5$. In this case it was also possible to arrange the cuts in complete replications of 3 cuts from each side. The scores for tenderness of beef were (periods of storage in parentheses):

Replication I

| | | | | $B_i$ |
|---|---|---|---|---|
| (0) | 7 | (1) | 17 | 24 |
| (2) | 26 | (4) | 25 | 51 |
| (9) | 33 | (18) | 29 | 62 |
| | | | | 137 |

Replication II

| | | | | $B_i$ |
|---|---|---|---|---|
| (0) | 17 | (2) | 27 | 44 |
| (1) | 23 | (9) | 27 | 50 |
| (4) | 29 | (18) | 30 | 59 |
| | | | | 153 |

Replication III

| | | | | $B_i$ |
|---|---|---|---|---|
| (0) | 10 | (4) | 25 | 35 |
| (1) | 26 | (18) | 37 | 63 |
| (2) | 24 | (9) | 26 | 50 |
| | | | | 148 |

Replication IV

| | | | | $B_i$ |
|---|---|---|---|---|
| (0) | 25 | (9) | 40 | 65 |
| (1) | 25 | (4) | 34 | 59 |
| (2) | 34 | (18) | 32 | 66 |
| | | | | 190 |

Replication V

| | | | | $B_i$ |
|---|---|---|---|---|
| (0) | 11 | (18) | 27 | 38 |
| (1) | 24 | (2) | 21 | 45 |
| (4) | 26 | (9) | 32 | 58 |
| | | | | 141 |

The blocks run across the page.

(*a*) Make a complete analysis of these data, showing the adjusted treatment means, the analysis of variance, the standard error of treatment differences, and general conclusions.

(*b*) Show how to determine the number of paired cuts of beef (blocks) needed for a balanced experiment in this case.

(*c*) Suppose it had been possible to pair the cuts into groups of four like ones, instead of two. What design would you then set up?

(*d*) Is there any method of determining the trend of tenderness in terms of storage time?

(*e*) Was there any appreciable gain in using the incomplete-blocks design for this problem?

**19.3.** Moore and Bliss[6] set up a balanced incomplete-blocks design to compare the toxicity of each of 7 chemicals on *Aphis rumicis*. The measure of the toxicity was the logarithm of the dose (+3.806) required for a 95 per cent kill. Since only 3 chemicals could be tested on a given day, $k = 3$. Seven days were required to make a balanced design. The toxicities were as follows:

| Chemical | Day | | | | | | | $T_i$ |
|---|---|---|---|---|---|---|---|---|
| | 1 | 2 | 3 | 4 | 5 | 6 | 7 | |
| $A$ | .465 | .602 | | .443 | | | | 1.510 |
| $B$ | .343 | | | | .652 | .536 | | 1.531 |
| $C$ | | .873 | .875 | | 1.142 | | | 2.890 |
| $D$ | .396 | | .325 | | | | .609 | 1.330 |
| $E$ | | .634 | | | | .409 | .417 | 1.460 |
| $F$ | | | | .987 | .989 | | .931 | 2.907 |
| $G$ | | | .330 | .426 | | .309 | | 1.065 |
| $B_i$ | 1.204 | 2.109 | 1.530 | 1.856 | 2.783 | 1.254 | 1.957 | 12.693 |

(*a*) Can you separate out replications in the analysis of these data?

(*b*) Show how to determine the number of days required for a balanced experiment.

(*c*) Make a complete analysis of these data.

(*d*) $C$ and $F$ were basically the same chemical compound. Were they different from one another? How did they compare with the standard treatment, $A$?

(*e*) How did $A$ compare with all the others, excepting $C$ and $F$?

**19.4.** The data in the accompanying table represent the yields (in bushels per acre, minus 30 bushels) of a $5 \times 5$ simple lattice experiment on soybean varieties with 4 replications.[1] The variety numbers are given in parentheses.

(*a*) First analyze only the first two replications of this experiment, indicating whether or not there are significant varietal effects, the average standard error of adjusted varietal differences, and the efficiency of using the lattice design.

(*b*) Second analyze the entire experiment, making the necessary adjustments with $d = 2$.

(*c*) Show how this experiment might have been set out in the field.

DATA OF EXERCISE 19.4

Replication I

| | | | | | | | | | | Block Totals |
|---|---|---|---|---|---|---|---|---|---|---|
| (1) | 6 | (2) | 7 | (3) | 5 | (4) | 8 | (5) | 6 | 32 |
| (6) | 16 | (7) | 12 | (8) | 12 | (9) | 13 | (10) | 8 | 61 |
| (11) | 17 | (12) | 7 | (13) | 7 | (14) | 9 | (15) | 14 | 54 |
| (16) | 18 | (17) | 16 | (18) | 13 | (19) | 13 | (20) | 14 | 74 |
| (21) | 14 | (22) | 15 | (23) | 11 | (24) | 14 | (25) | 14 | 68 |
| | | | | | | | | | | 289 |

Replication II

| | | | | | | | | | | Block Totals |
|---|---|---|---|---|---|---|---|---|---|---|
| (1) | 24 | (6) | 13 | (11) | 24 | (16) | 11 | (21) | 8 | 80 |
| (2) | 21 | (7) | 11 | (12) | 14 | (17) | 11 | (22) | 23 | 80 |
| (3) | 16 | (8) | 4 | (13) | 12 | (18) | 12 | (23) | 12 | 56 |
| (4) | 17 | (9) | 10 | (14) | 30 | (19) | 9 | (24) | 23 | 89 |
| (5) | 15 | (10) | 15 | (15) | 22 | (20) | 16 | (25) | 19 | 87 |
| | | | | | | | | | | 392 |

Replication III

| | | | | | | | | | | Block Totals |
|---|---|---|---|---|---|---|---|---|---|---|
| (1) | 13 | (2) | 26 | (3) | 9 | (4) | 13 | (5) | 11 | 72 |
| (6) | 15 | (7) | 18 | (8) | 22 | (9) | 11 | (10) | 15 | 81 |
| (11) | 19 | (12) | 10 | (13) | 10 | (14) | 10 | (15) | 16 | 65 |
| (16) | 21 | (17) | 16 | (18) | 17 | (19) | 4 | (20) | 17 | 75 |
| (21) | 15 | (22) | 12 | (23) | 13 | (24) | 20 | (25) | 8 | 68 |
| | | | | | | | | | | 361 |

Replication IV

| | | | | | | | | | | Block Totals |
|---|---|---|---|---|---|---|---|---|---|---|
| (1) | 16 | (6) | 7 | (11) | 20 | (16) | 13 | (21) | 21 | 77 |
| (2) | 15 | (7) | 10 | (12) | 11 | (17) | 7 | (22) | 14 | 57 |
| (3) | 7 | (8) | 11 | (13) | 15 | (18) | 15 | (23) | 16 | 64 |
| (4) | 19 | (9) | 14 | (14) | 20 | (19) | 6 | (24) | 16 | 75 |
| (5) | 17 | (10) | 18 | (15) | 20 | (20) | 15 | (25) | 14 | 84 |
| | | | | | | | | | | 357 |

## References Cited


1. COCHRAN, W. G., and G. M. COX, *Experimental Designs*, John Wiley & Sons, Inc. New York, 1950.
2. YATES, F., "A New Method of Arranging Variety Trials Involving a Large Number of Varieties," *J. Agr. Sci.*, **26**:424–455 (1936).
3. BOSE, R. C., "On the Construction of Balanced Incomplete Block Designs," *Ann. Eugenics*, **9**:353–400 (1939).
4. YATES, F., "The Recovery of Inter-block Information in Balanced Incomplete Block Designs," *Ann. Eugenics*, **10**:317–325 (1940).
5. PAUL, PAULINE, *Changes in Palatability, Microscopic Appearance and Electrical Resistance in Beef during the Onset and Passing of Rigor and during Subsequent Storage*, unpublished thesis, Iowa State College, Ames, Iowa, 1943.
6. MOORE, W., and C. I. BLISS, "A Method for Determining Insecticidal Effectiveness Using *Aphid rumicis* and Certain Organic Compounds," *J. Econ. Entomol.*, **35**:544–553 (1942).
7. GOULDEN, C. H., "Modern Methods for Testing a Large Number of Varieties," *Dominion Canada, Dept. Agr., Tech. Bull.* 9 (1937).

8. Cox, G. M., R. C. Eckhardt, and W. G. Cochran, "The Analyses of Lattice and Triple Lattice Experiments in Corn Varietal Tests," *Iowa State Coll., Agri. Expt. Sta., Research Bull.*, **281**:1–66 (1940).
9. Harshbarger, B., "Rectangular Lattices," *Virginia Agr. Expt. Sta. Mem.* 1, (1947).
10. Harshbarger, B., "Triple Rectangular Lattices," *Biometrics*, **5**:1–13 (1949).
11. Robinson, H. F., and G. S. Watson, "An Analysis of Simple and Triple Rectangular Lattice Designs," *N. Carolina Agr. Expt. Sta. Tech. Bull.* 88 (1949).
12. Kempthorne, O., and W. T. Federer, "The General Theory of Prime-power Lattice Designs," I. $p^n$ Varieties in Blocks of $p$ Plots, *Biometrics*, **4**:54–79 (1948); II. $p^n$ Varieties in Blocks of $p^s$ Plots and in Squares, *Biometrics*, **4**:109–121 (1948).
Federer, W. T., "The General Theory of Prime-power Lattice Designs," III. $p^3$ Varieties in $p$ Plots with More Than 3 Replicates, *Biometrics*, **5**:144–161 (1949); IV. Analysis of $p^4$ Treatments in Blocks of $p$ Plots with Four or More Replicates, *Cornell Univ., Agr. Expt. Sta., Mem.* 299 (1950); V. The Analysis for a 6 × 6 Incomplete Lattice Square, *Biometrics*, **6**:34–58 (1950).
13. Cox, G. M., "Enumeration and Construction of Balanced Incomplete Block Configurations," *Ann. Math. Stat.*, **11**:72–85 (1940).
14. Youden, W. J., *Statistical Methods for Chemists*, John Wiley & Sons, Inc., New York, 1951.

**Other Reading**

Rao, C. R., "General Methods of Analysis for Incomplete Block Designs," *J. Am. Stat. Assoc.*, **42**:541–561 (1947).
Weiss, M. G., and G. M. Cox, "Balanced Incomplete Block and Lattice Square Designs for Testing Yield Differences among Large Numbers of Soybean Varieties," *Iowa State Coll., Agr. Expt. Sta., Research Bull.* 257 (1939).
Yates, F., "Complex Experiments," *J. Roy. Stat. Soc. Suppl.*, **2**:181–223 (1935).

# CHAPTER 20

# FACTORIAL EXPERIMENTS

**20.1. Introduction.** The experimenter often wishes to test various types of treatments, each with several different representatives. For example, he might wish to compare two varieties of corn ($v_1$ and $v_2$) and two different fertilizers ($f_1$ and $f_2$) in a single experiment, giving a total of four treatment combinations ($v_1f_1, v_1f_2, v_2f_1, v_2f_2$); this is called a $2 \times 2$, or $2^2$, *factorial experiment*. These treatments could be tested in any of the field designs presented in Chaps. 18 and 19. The methods of analysis presented in those chapters would apply to this problem if all four treatment combinations were considered to be four unrelated treatments; however, if there are treatment differences, the factorial design can be used to explain these differences in a more definite manner. Using the factorial model, the effect of any treatment combination is considered to be the sum of three effects, varietal effect, fertilizer effect, and *interaction* of the variety and fertilizer. The *interaction* measures the failure of the various fertilizer effects to be the same for each variety or, conversely, the failure of the various varietal effects to be the same with each fertilizer.

The interaction is the important effect about which the factorial design can give information. Many experimenters still examine the performance of one set of treatments, such as different fertilizers, for one standard variety and then different varieties for a standard fertilizer. Such an experiment tells little about the optimum fertilizer-variety combination which should be used, if the fertilizers do not respond in a similar manner for all varieties. Or if an engineer wants to know something about the relationship between the temperature of a process and the length of time the process is carried on, he needs to try out various combinations of the two variables—temperature and time. Similarly an animal feeder may want to know the optimum level of supplemental feeding and type of pasture or the optimum combination of concentrates and roughage in the ration. And the human nutritionist needs to know the best combination of various parts of the diet for healthy living. All of these experiments require some knowledge of how different amounts or kinds of one treatment interact with different amounts or kinds of another treatment. If the results are purely additive, that is, one treatment acts independently of the other treatment, the experiment can be divided into two simple experiments on the two treatments. However, the experimenter seldom is sure that there is no interaction and often is afraid that there will be some interaction, especially if the individual representatives of each treatment are widely different.

It should be pointed out that the factorial design can never lose any information even when there is no interaction (and if there is interaction, this design is indispensable). To illustrate this, suppose we consider the two varieties and two fertilizers, each of the four treatment combinations being used $r$ times in an experiment. However, if there is no interaction, the average difference between the two varieties is obtained from $2r$ individual differences, and similarly for the difference between the two fertilizers. Hence in the absence of interaction, we have obtained $2r$ replications for each variety and for each fertilizer. This feature of the factorial design, called *hidden replication*, should not be overemphasized, because it is built upon the thesis of no interaction. But it can be used as an argument against those who refuse to use this design, because they think they lose information when they have no interaction. The authors are firm believers in a wider use of the factorial type of experiment, because one cannot lose any information on the main effects and one can obtain information on something which may be equally important, the interactions. The reader is encouraged to read references 1 to 3 for more extensive discussions of the analysis and usefulness of various types of factorial designs.

**20.2. The Analysis of a $p \times q$ Factorial Experiment.** Let us assume we have two sets of treatments ($A$ and $C$), with $p$ $A$ treatments and $q$ $C$ treatments, with a randomized complete-blocks experimental plan. The experimental model can be written as follows (assuming $r$ blocks of $pq$ treatments per block):

$$\begin{aligned} Y_{ijk} &= \mu + \alpha_i + \gamma_j + (\alpha\gamma)_{ij} + \beta_k + \epsilon_{ijk} \\ &= m + a_i + c_j + (ac)_{ij} + b_k + e_{ijk}, \end{aligned}$$

where $\alpha_i$ is the added effect of the $i$th $A$ treatment ($i = 1,2, \ldots ,p$); $\gamma_j$ is the added effect of the $j$th $C$ treatment ($j = 1,2, \ldots ,q$); $(\alpha\gamma)_{ij}$ is the added effect of the interaction of the $i$th $A$ treatment and $j$th $C$ treatment; and $\beta_k$ is the added effect of the $k$th block ($k = 1,2, \ldots ,r$).† The estimates are $a_i$, $c_j$, $(ac)_{ij}$, and $b_k$, respectively. $\alpha_i$ and $\gamma_j$ are called the *main effects*. The following restrictions are imposed: $\sum_i \alpha_i = 0$; $\sum_j \gamma_j = 0$; $\sum_i (\alpha\gamma)_{ij} = \sum_j (\alpha\gamma)_{ij} = 0$.

† If a completely randomized design is used, $\beta_k$ is omitted from the model; and for a Latin-square design, row and column constants replace $\beta_k$. The use of the incomplete-blocks design will be discussed later.

It should be emphasized that the effect of a given $A$ treatment is assumed to be the same for all $C$ treatments; this assumption is justified only if there is no interaction. If there is an interaction, one should logically be studying different $A$ effects for each $C$ treatment and, conversely, different $C$ effects for each $A$ treatment. Hence, if there is a real interaction, the experimenter will want to compare the $pq$ treatment combinations. The analysis of most factorial experiments is usually a two-stage process:

(i) Test the null hypotheses that all main effects and interactions vanish.

(ii) If there is a significant interaction, then determine whether there are real $A$ effects for each $C$ treatment and real $C$ effects for each $A$ treatment.

The least-squares equations for this model are

$$A_i = qrm + qra_i = qr\mu + qr\alpha_i + \sum_j \sum_k \epsilon_{ijk},$$

$$C_j = prm + prc_j = pr\mu + pr\gamma_j + \sum_i \sum_k \epsilon_{ijk},$$

$$(AC)_{ij} = r[m + a_i + c_j + (ac)_{ij}] = r[\mu + \alpha_i + \gamma_j + (\alpha\gamma)_{ij}] + \sum_k \epsilon_{ijk},$$

$$B_k = pqm + pqb_k = pq(\mu + \beta_k) + \sum_i \sum_j \epsilon_{ijk},$$

$$G = pqrm = pqr\mu + \sum_i \sum_j \sum_k \epsilon_{ijk},$$

where $A_i$ is the total yield for the $qr$ plots using the $i$th $A$ treatment, $C_j$ for the $pr$ plots using the $j$th $C$ treatment, $(AC)_{ij}$ for the $r$ plots using the $i$th $A$ treatment and the $j$th $C$ treatment, $B_k$ for the $pq$ plots of the $k$th block, and $G$ for the total $pqr$ plots. Hence the solutions are

$$a_i = \frac{A_i}{qr} - m, \qquad c_j = \frac{C_j}{pr} - m,$$

$$(ac)_{ij} = \frac{(AC)_{ij}}{r} - \frac{A_i}{qr} - \frac{C_j}{pr} + m.$$

It can be shown that the reductions in sum of squares due to the various treatment effects are:

$$A\text{:}\quad \text{SSA} = \frac{\sum_i (A_i - \bar{A})^2}{qr} = \frac{\sum_i A_i^2}{qr} - \frac{G^2}{pqr},$$

$$C\text{:}\quad \text{SSC} = \frac{\sum_j (C_j - \bar{C})^2}{pr} = \frac{\sum_j C_j^2}{pr} - \frac{G^2}{pqr},$$

$$(AC):\quad \text{SS}(AC) = \frac{\sum_i \sum_j \left[ (AC)_{ij} - \frac{A_i}{q} - \frac{C_j}{p} + \frac{G}{pq} \right]^2}{r}$$

$$= \frac{\sum_i \sum_j (AC)_{ij}^2}{r} - \frac{G^2}{pqr} - \text{SSA} - \text{SSC},$$

where $\bar{A} = G/p$ and $\bar{C} = G/q$.

The analysis-of-variance table is

| Source of variation | Degrees of freedom | Sum of squares | Mean square | $E$(MS) |
|---|---|---|---|---|
| Blocks | $r - 1$ | SSB | MSB | $\sigma^2 + pq \sum_k \beta_k^2/(r-1)$ |
| $A$ treatments | $p - 1$ | SSA | MSA | $\sigma^2 + qr \sum_i \alpha_i^2/(p-1)$ |
| $C$ treatments | $q - 1$ | SSC | MSC | $\sigma^2 + pr \sum_j \gamma_j^2/(q-1)$ |
| $(AC)$ | $(p-1)(q-1)$ | SS$(AC)$ | MS$(AC)$ | $\sigma^2 + r \sum_i \sum_j (\alpha\gamma)_{ij}^2/(p-1)(q-1)$ |
| Error | $(pq-1)(r-1)$ | SSE | $s^2$ | $\sigma^2$ |

The $F$ ratios, MSA$/s^2$, MSC$/s^2$, and MS$(AC)/s^2$ can be used to test for the existence of real main effects and interactions.

If the $AC$ interaction were significantly greater than zero, the experimenter probably would want to test the $A$ treatments for each $C$ treatment and the $C$ treatments for each $A$ treatment. For each $C$ treatment there would be $(p - 1)$ degrees of freedom to test the $A$ treatments; and for each $A$ treatment, there would be $(q - 1)$ degrees of freedom to test the $C$ treatments. These two analyses are not orthogonal; hence, the significance levels may be somewhat upset, but the experimenter should make them, perhaps using $\alpha = .01$ or lower significance levels. When $p$ and $q$ are rather large, one would expect several significant $F$'s by chance, because of the large number of comparisons.

The extension of these results to more than two sets of treatments is simple, the only complication being the greater variety of interactions. For example if there are three sets of treatments ($A$, $C$, and $D$), we have the following interactions:

Two-factor: $AC$, $AD$, $CD$.
Three-factor: $ACD$.

The two-factor interactions are handled as above, while the three-factor interaction is handled as the remainder after accounting for the main effects and two-factor interactions. A significant three-factor interaction is more difficult to interpret. Many experiments are planned with $r = 1$, but with the three-factor and higher-factor interactions used to estimate the error mean square. We do not have the space to discuss these wider uses of the factorial design in this book, but they are discussed in detail in references 1 and 3.

**Example 20.1.** An experiment using 3 varieties of sugar cane ($V$) and 3 levels of nitrogen ($N$) was conducted in Hawaii in 1942, with 4 replications. The nitrogen levels were, respectively, 150, 210, and 270 pounds per acre. The yields in tons of cane per acre were:

| Blocks | $V_1N_1$ | $V_1N_2$ | $V_1N_3$ | $V_2N_1$ | $V_2N_2$ | $V_2N_3$ | $V_3N_1$ | $V_3N_2$ | $V_3N_3$ | Total |
|---|---|---|---|---|---|---|---|---|---|---|
| 1 | 70.5 | 67.3 | 79.9 | 58.6 | 64.3 | 64.4 | 65.8 | 64.1 | 56.3 | 591.2 |
| 2 | 67.5 | 75.9 | 72.8 | 65.2 | 48.3 | 67.3 | 68.3 | 64.8 | 54.7 | 584.8 |
| 3 | 63.9 | 72.2 | 64.8 | 70.2 | 74.0 | 78.0 | 72.7 | 70.9 | 66.2 | 632.9 |
| 4 | 64.2 | 60.5 | 86.3 | 51.8 | 63.6 | 72.0 | 67.6 | 58.3 | 54.4 | 578.7 |
| Total | 266.1 | 275.9 | 303.8 | 245.8 | 250.2 | 281.7 | 274.4 | 258.1 | 231.6 | 2,387.6 |

It is usually best to arrange these results in a 3 × 3 table of means as follows:

| | $V_1$ | $V_2$ | $V_3$ | Mean |
|---|---|---|---|---|
| $N_1$ | 66.52 | 61.45 | 68.60 | 65.52 |
| $N_2$ | 68.98 | 62.55 | 64.52 | 65.35 |
| $N_3$ | 75.95 | 70.42 | 57.90 | 68.09 |
| Mean | 70.48 | 64.81 | 63.67 | 66.32 |

$$C = (2{,}387.6)^2/36 = 158{,}350.94.$$

The analysis of variance is:

| Source of variation | Degrees of freedom | Sum of squares | Mean square |
|---|---|---|---|
| Blocks | 3 | 200.68 | 66.89 |
| Varieties | 2 | 319.37 | 159.69* |
| Nitrogen | 2 | 56.54 | 28.27 |
| $V \times N$ | 4 | 559.79 | 139.95* |
| Error | 24 | 1,053.78 | 43.91 |

* Significant at the $\alpha = .05$ level.

There were significant differences among the average varietal effects, but not among the average nitrogen effects. However, a significant interaction indicates that the nitrogens have different effects for each variety, possibly in opposite directions. In this case, $N_3$ is best for $V_1$ and $V_2$, while $N_1$ is best for $V_3$. The standard error for the difference between any two of the nine treatment means is $\sqrt{2(43.91)/4} = 4.68$. For $V_1$, $\bar{N}_3 - \bar{N}_1$ $(=9.43)$ is almost significant and for $V_3$, $\bar{N}_1 - \bar{N}_3$ $(= 10.70)$ is significant, at the 5 per cent probability level. These results are displayed in Fig. 20.1. These lines show that $V_1$ is better than $V_2$ and that nitrogen affects both in the same way, with a decided jump in yield for the third level. However, nitrogen had an adverse effect on the third variety. A closer examination of the experiment disclosed that $V_3$ with a large amount of nitrogen matured before the other two varieties, but all varieties were harvested at the same time. Hence some of the cane for $V_3$ with $N_2$ and $N_3$ had rotted, resulting in decreased yields for the high nitrogen treatments.

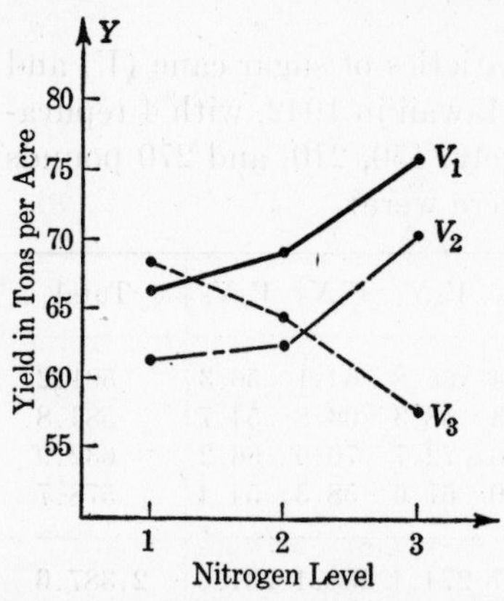


FIG. 20.1. Effects of different nitrogen treatments on the yield of three varieties of sugar cane.

**20.3. An Alternative Analysis for a 2 × 2 Factorial Experiment.** An alternative computing process for the treatment sums of squares makes use of the orthogonal linear forms introduced in Chap. 6. Since there are three treatment degrees of freedom, we can set up three orthogonal forms. These three orthogonal comparisons plus $G$ are:

| | Original treatment totals | | | | $E(L^2)$ |
|---|---|---|---|---|---|
| | $(AC)_{11}$ | $(AC)_{12}$ | $(AC)_{21}$ | $(AC)_{22}$ | |
| $L_1 = G$ | + | + | + | + | $16r^2\mu^2 + 4r\sigma^2$ |
| $L_2 = A$ | − | − | + | + | $4r^2(\alpha_2 - \alpha_1)^2 + 4r\sigma^2$ |
| $L_3 = C$ | − | + | − | + | $4r^2(\gamma_2 - \gamma_1)^2 + 4r\sigma^2$ |
| $L_4 = (AC)$ | + | − | − | + | $r^2I^2 + 4r\sigma^2$ |

where $I = [(\alpha\gamma)_{11} - (\alpha\gamma)_{12} - (\alpha\gamma)_{21} + (\alpha\gamma)_{22}]$. The computing procedure for $L_2$ is simply to subtract the total yield of the first $A$ treatment from that of the second $A$ treatment, and similarly for the other $L$'s. From $E(L_2^2)$ we see that if we set up the null hypothesis $H_0$: $\alpha_1 = \alpha_2$, $E(L_2^2) = 4r\sigma^2$, and if we divide $E(L_2^2)$ by $4r$, we have an unbiased estimate of $\sigma^2$. Hence, to test $H_0$, we need only compute the ratio

$$F = \frac{L_2^2}{4rs^2},$$

with 1 and $3(r - 1)$ degrees of freedom. And we see that if $\alpha_1 \neq \alpha_2$, the expected value of the numerator of $F$ is greater than that of the denominator; hence, the one-tailed $F$ should be used. To test $H_0$: $\gamma_1 = \gamma_2$, we use $F = L_3^2/4rs^2$. It is easily seen that if we use $F = L_4^2/4rs^2$, we are testing whether $[(\alpha\gamma)_{11} - (\alpha\gamma)_{12}]$ is different from $[(\alpha\gamma)_{21} - (\alpha\gamma)_{22}]$. In other words, is the difference between the two $C$ treatments the same using the first $A$ treatment as using the second? Or, conversely, we can use $[(\alpha\gamma)_{11} - (\alpha\gamma)_{21}]$ versus $[(\alpha\gamma)_{12} - (\alpha\gamma)_{22}]$. Since this is exactly what we wanted to test by our interaction effect, it seems reasonable to use $L_4$.

**Example 20.2.** An experiment was run to determine the effectiveness of four different fertilizers on the total yield of oranges over a 12-year period (1928 to 1939), at the Citrus Experiment Station, Riverside, Calif. The four fertilizers were nitrogen ($N$), nitrogen + phosphate ($NP$), nitrogen + potash ($NK$), and nitrogen + phosphate + potash ($NPK$). Four blocks were used, giving a total of 16 plots. The yields in pounds of oranges per tree per plot were as follows:

| Treatment | Block | | | | Total | Average |
|---|---|---|---|---|---|---|
| | 1 | 2 | 3 | 4 | | |
| $N$ | 1,290 | 1,531 | 1,469 | 1,631 | 5,921 | 1,480 |
| $NP$ | 1,085 | 1,348 | 1,555 | 1,328 | 5,316 | 1,329 |
| $NK$ | 1,479 | 1,484 | 1,556 | 1,759 | 6,278 | 1,570 |
| $NPK$ | 1,293 | 1,538 | 1,561 | 1,639 | 6,031 | 1,508 |
| Total | 5,147 | 5,901 | 6,141 | 6,357 | 23,546 | 1,472 |

The following orthogonal comparisons can be made:

| Total yield | Treatment | | | | $L$ | $L^2/16$ |
|---|---|---|---|---|---|---|
| | $N$ | $NP$ | $NK$ | $NPK$ | | |
| | 5,921 | 5,316 | 6,278 | 6,031 | | |
| $L_1 = G$ | + | + | + | + | 23,546 | 34,650,882 |
| $L_2 = P$ | − | + | − | + | −852 | 45,369 |
| $L_3 = K$ | − | − | + | + | 1,072 | 71,824 |
| $L_4 = PK$ | + | − | − | + | 358 | 8,010 |
| | | | Treatments | | | 125,203 |

The total sum of squares is

$$Sy^2 = SY^2 - G^2/16 = 35{,}067{,}370 - 34{,}650{,}882 = 416{,}488.$$

The block sum of squares is

$$\text{SSB} = 34{,}859{,}185 - 34{,}650{,}882 = 208{,}303.$$

Hence the error sum of squares is

$$\text{SSE} = Sy^2 - \text{SST} - \text{SSB} = 82{,}982.$$

The analysis-of-variance table is as follows:

| Source of variation | Degrees of freedom | Sum of squares | Mean square |
|---|---|---|---|
| Blocks | 3 | 208,303 | 69,434 |
| $P$ | 1 | 45,369 | 45,369 |
| $K$ | 1 | 71,824 | 71,824* |
| $PK$ | 1 | 8,010 | 8,010 |
| Error | 9 | 82,982 | 9,220 |

* Significant at the 5 per cent probability level.

Since the 5 per cent $F$ value for 1 and 9 degrees of freedom is 5.12, we see that $P$ is not quite significant, while $K$ is significant. There is no indication of a real $PK$ interaction. It would appear that added potash definitely increased the yield and that added phosphate possibly decreased the yield of oranges. In order to determine if there was a significant profit from the use of the added fertilizer, the cost of the fertilizer should be compared with the added returns from the oranges. These results are displayed graphically in Fig. 20.2. There is some evidence of a downward slope, indicating the detrimental effect of phosphate. Since the two lines are nearly parallel, there is no indication of an interaction between phosphate and potash.

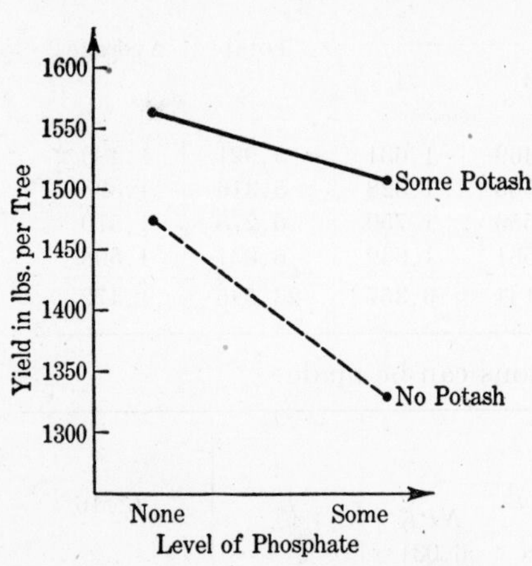


FIG. 20.2. Effects of different amounts of potash and phosphate on the yield of oranges.

**20.4. The Alternative Analysis of a $p \times q$ Factorial.** The general $p \times q$ factorial experiment can also be analyzed by the single-degree-of-freedom approach of Sec. 20.3. Often the representatives of one or both sets of treatments are simply levels of that treatment. For example, the treatments might be three levels of a nitrogen fertilizer ($A$) and three levels of a phosphate fertilizer ($C$), as in Exercise 20.4. An example of three fertilizer levels and two varieties is presented in Example 20.3. The experimenter should decide before the experiment is performed what comparisons should be made. It is not necessary to restrict oneself to orthogonal comparisons, except that most pertinent comparisons can be set up as one of a set of orthogonal comparisons. The significance probabilities presumably are less disturbed if each comparison is orthogonal to the others. Snedecor[4] (Chap. 15) discusses these single comparisons.

A factorial experiment with more than two sets of treatments can also be analyzed by the single-degree-of-freedom approach.

Matrix algebra techniques can be used to prove that the total treatment sum of squares obtained by the single-degree-of-freedom approach is the same as the treatment sum of squares of Chap. 18.

If there are $t$ treatment combinations and we set up $t$ orthogonal comparisons (such as the 4 $L$'s in Sec. 20.3),

$$\sum_{h=1}^{t} L_h'^2 = \sum_{i=1}^{t} T_i^2,$$

where $L_h'^2 = L_h^2/[\text{coefficient of } r\sigma^2 \text{ in } E(L^2)]$ and $T_i$ is the total yield for the $i$th treatment combination (based on $r$ plots). We consider that there are $t$ orthogonal forms

$$L_h' = \sum_{i=1}^{t} a_{hi}T_i, \qquad h = 1, 2, \ldots, t,$$

where $\sum_{i=1}^{t} a_{h'i}a_{hi} = \begin{cases} 0 \text{ for } h \neq h' \\ 1 \text{ for } h = h' \end{cases}$. If we solve for the $T_i$ in terms of the $L_h'$, we find that

$$T_i = \sum_{h=1}^{t} a_{hi}L_h'.$$

Hence

$$\sum_i T_i^2 = \sum_i \Big(\sum_h a_{hi}L_h'\Big)^2 = \sum_h \sum_i a_{hi}^2 L_h'^2 + \sum_{h' \neq h} \sum \sum_i a_{h'i}a_{hi}L_{h'}'L_h' = \sum_{h=1}^{p} L_h'^2.$$

Now if we let $L'_1 = G/\sqrt{t}$, as in Sec. 20.3,

$$\sum_i T_i^2 - G^2/t = \sum_{h=2}^{t} L_h'^2.$$

The variance of $L'_h$ is

$$\sigma^2(L'_h) = \sum_i \sum_{i'} a_{hi} a_{hi'} \sigma(T_i T_{i'}) = r\sigma^2,$$

since $\sigma(T_i T_{i'}) = \begin{cases} 0 \text{ for } i \neq i' \\ r\sigma^2 \text{ for } i = i' \end{cases}$ and $\sum_i a_{hi}^2 = 1$.

**Example 20.3.** An experiment on a small grain was conducted with two varieties ($v_1$ and $v_2$), three fertilizer levels ($f_1$, $f_2$, and $f_3$), and six blocks. The yields in pounds per plot were:

| F | V | Block 1 | 2 | 3 | 4 | 5 | 6 | Total | Linear forms $F_l$ | $F_q$ | $V$ | $F_lV$ | $F_qV$ |
|---|---|---|---|---|---|---|---|---|---|---|---|---|---|
| 1 | 1 | 161 | 166 | 113 | 103 | 132 | 180 | 855 | − | + | − | + | − |
| 1 | 2 | 192 | 253 | 208 | 171 | 196 | 198 | 1,218 | − | + | + | − | + |
| 2 | 1 | 145 | 231 | 131 | 158 | 176 | 216 | 1,057 | 0 | −2 | − | 0 | 2 |
| 2 | 2 | 232 | 231 | 190 | 171 | 242 | 238 | 1,304 | 0 | −2 | + | 0 | −2 |
| 3 | 1 | 172 | 204 | 104 | 135 | 178 | 175 | 968 | + | + | − | − | − |
| 3 | 2 | 227 | 214 | 144 | 146 | 186 | 230 | 1,147 | + | + | + | + | + |
| Total | | 1,129 | 1,299 | 890 | 884 | 1,110 | 1,237 | 6,549 | 42 | −534 | 789 | −184 | 48 |

In this case we need two linear forms to represent the fertilizer effects. In general the experimenter wants to know whether there is a consistent linear trend, as indicated by $F_l$, and whether there is a significant departure from linearity—in this case indicated by the quadratic component, $F_q$. $F_l$ measures the change from the lowest to the highest level of fertilizer, while $F_q$ compares the sum of the yields at these two extreme levels against twice the middle yield. If the response of yield to fertilizer is linear, $F_q$ will not be significantly different from zero. The two interaction forms are simply the respective products of $F_l$ and $F_q$ with $V$. ($F_lV$) represents the failure of the linear trend to be the same for the two varieties. That is, $(F_lV) = [(FV)_{32} - (FV)_{12}] - [(FV)_{31} - (FV)_{11}]$. A similar statement can be made for $(F_qV)$.

The expected values of the squares of the linear forms are:

| Linear form | | $E(L^2)$ | $L^2/(\text{coeff. } \sigma^2)$ |
|---|---|---|---|
| $F_l =$ | 42 | $144(f_3 - f_1)^2 + 24\sigma^2$ | 73.50 |
| $F_q =$ | −534 | $144(f_1 - 2f_2 + f_3)^2 + 72\sigma^2$ | 3,960.50 |
| $V =$ | 789 | $324(v_2 - v_1)^2 + 36\sigma^2$ | 17,292.25 |
| $(F_lV) =$ | −184 | $144I_l^2 + 24\sigma^2$ | 1,410.67 |
| $(F_qV) =$ | 48 | $144I_q^2 + 72\sigma^2$ | 32.00 |
| | | | SST = 22,768.92 |

$I_l = (fv_{32} - fv_{12} - fv_{31} + fv_{11})$, and $I_q = (fv_{32} - 2fv_{22} + fv_{12} - fv_{31} + 2fv_{21} - fv_{11})$. We have used $f$ and $v$ for the true fertilizer and variety effects to avoid the difficulty of identification with Greek letters.

The analysis of variance is:

| Source of variation | Degrees of freedom | Sum of squares | Mean square |
|---|---|---|---|
| Blocks | 5 | 24,938.92 | 4,987.78 |
| $F_l$ | 1 | 73.50 | 73.50 |
| $F_q$ | 1 | 3,960.50 | 3,960.50** |
| $V$ | 1 | 17,292.25 | 17,292.25** |
| $(F_lV)$ | 1 | 1,410.67 | 1,410.67 |
| $(F_qV)$ | 1 | 32.00 | 32.00 |
| Error | 25 | 9,896.91 | 395.88 |

** Significant at the 1 per cent probability level.

Apparently the effect of fertilizer was definitely nonlinear, with the maximum yield near the middle rate of application and the yield at the highest rate little more than the yield at the lowest rate. There was a real difference between the two varieties, but the fertilizer effects were about the same for the two varieties as shown by the nonsignificant interaction. These statements are confirmed graphically in Fig. 20.3, where we see that both lines are almost parallel and that each shows a decline for the third level of fertilizer. The estimated efficiency of the randomized complete-blocks design

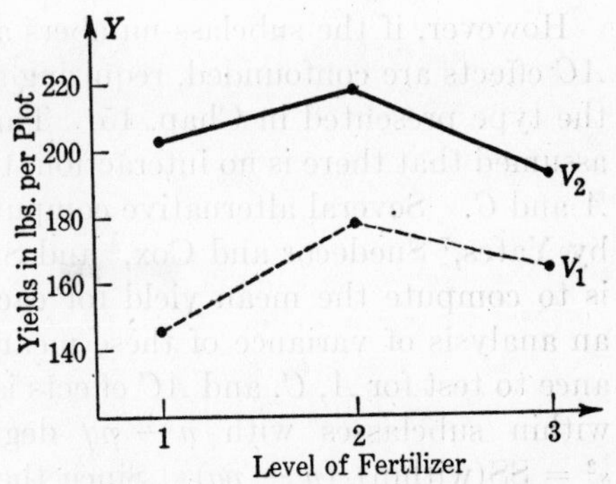


FIG. 20.3. Effects of different levels of fertilizer on the yields of two varieties of small grain.

as compared with a completely randomized design (neglecting the loss of error degrees of freedom) is

$$I = \frac{30(395.88) + 24{,}938.92}{35(395.88)} = 2.65,$$

indicating an expected increase of about 165 per cent in the error variance if the completely randomized design had been used.

If the experimenter were interested only in the over-all fertilizer effects, he would compute

$$\text{SSF} = \frac{F_1^2 + F_2^2 + F_3^2}{12} - \frac{G^2}{36} = 4{,}034.$$

$$\text{SS}(FV) = \frac{(FV)_{11}^2 + \cdots + (FV)_{32}^2}{6} - \frac{G^2}{36} - \text{SSV} - \text{SSF} = 1{,}442.67.$$

**20.5. The Analysis of a $p \times q$ Factorial Experiment with Unequal Numbers in the Subclasses.** The factorial experiments in the previous sections of this chapter have had a fixed number of replications ($r$) per treatment combination. If the number of replications is not the same from one subclass to another, the analysis is much more complicated. Snedecor[4] shows that if the numbers are proportional to the main effect totals, the usual analysis can be carried out. That is, assume there are $n_{ij}$ entries for the subclass with the $i$th $A$ treatment and the $j$th $C$ treatment and $n_{i.} = \sum_j n_{ij}$, $n_{.j} = \sum_i n_{ij}$, $n = \sum_i \sum_j n_{ij}$. If $n_{ij} = n_{i.}n_{.j}/n$, the least squares equations show that the $A$, $C$, and $AC$ effects are orthogonal and the usual analysis-of-variance methods apply.

However, if the subclass numbers are not proportional, the $A$, $C$, and $AC$ effects are confounded, requiring a complete least-squares solution of the type presented in Chap. 15. This solution is simplified if it can be assumed that there is no interaction, that is, the only effects are those for $A$ and $C$. Several alternative computing procedures have been outlined by Yates,[7] Snedecor and Cox,[8] and Snedecor.[4] The simplest procedure is to compute the mean yield for each of the $pq$ subclasses and to run an analysis of variance of these means. An estimate of the error variance to test for $A$, $C$, and $AC$ effects is obtained from the sum of squares within subclasses with $n - pq$ degrees of freedom. First compute $s^2 = \text{SS(within)}/(n - pq)$. Since the first analysis is based on means, $s^2$ must be divided by the average number of entries per subclass. The average used is the harmonic mean, $\bar{n}_h$, where

$$\bar{n}_h = \frac{pq}{\sum_i \sum_j \frac{1}{n_{ij}}}.$$

The appropriate error variance to use with the analysis of the means is $s'^2 = s^2/\bar{n}_h$.

The analysis of variance is:

| Source of variation | Degrees of freedom | Mean square |
|---|---|---|
| $A$ | $p - 1$ | MSA |
| $C$ | $q - 1$ | MSC |
| $AC$ | $(p - 1)(q - 1)$ | MS($AC$) |
| Error | $n - pq$ | $s'^2 = s^2/\bar{n}_h$ |

If some of the subclasses have no entries ($n_{ij} = 0$), this *method of unweighted means* cannot be used. Hence it has limited usefulness for the analysis of many social data, for which empty subclasses are common. However, if it can be used, the method has a minimum of computation and furnishes a short-cut procedure of testing for the existence of interactions. This is important information in applying other methods.

If the $n_{ij}$ are almost proportional, an approximate method, called the *method of proportional subclass numbers,* is probably better than the method of unweighted means. However, the authors doubt that the gain is often worth the extra computing time required. (See references 4 and 8 for the computing details.)

A third alternative is the *method of weighted squares of means,* advanced by Yates[7] and also described in references 4 and 8. This method provides exact tests of the main effects when interaction is present and for $p = 2$ also provides an exact test of the interaction.

The method of least squares furnishes an exact test for interactions regardless of the size of $p$ and, if there is no interaction, an exact test of the main effects. First we assume no interaction and use the following model:

$$Y_{ijk} = \mu + \alpha_i + \gamma_j + \epsilon'_{ijk}, \quad i = 1, 2, \ldots, p; j = 1, 2, \ldots, q; \quad k = 1, 2, \ldots, n_{ij},$$

where $\alpha_i$ is the added effect of the $i$th $A$ treatment, $\gamma_j$ the added effect of the $j$th $C$ treatment, and $k$ the $k$th entry in the $(i,j)$ subclass. In order to have $\mu \doteq \bar{Y}$, we set $\sum_{i=1}^{p} n_{i.}\alpha_i = 0$, $\sum_{j=1}^{q} n_{.j}\gamma_j = 0$. The error sum of squares (SSE′) for this model is compared with the within subclass sum of squares (SSE) for the complete model

$$Y_{ijk} = \mu + \tau_{ij} + \epsilon_{ijk},$$

where $\tau_{ij}$ represents the effect of the $(i,j)$ subclass. The error variance will be $s^2 = \text{SSE}/(n - pq)$.

The first model is used to determine $m$, $a_i$, and $c_j$, using

$$\hat{Y}_{ij} = n_{ij}(m + a_i + c_j),$$

where $\hat{Y}_{ij}$ is the predicted total yield for the $(i,j)$ subclass with $n_{ij}$ entries and $\sum_i n_{i.}a_i = 0 = \sum_j n_{.j}c_j$. The least-squares equations can be written as follows:

$$m\colon nm + \sum_{i=1}^{p} n_{i.}a_i + \sum_{j=1}^{q} n_{.j}c_j = G,$$

$$a_i\colon n_{i.}m + n_{i.}a_i + \sum_{l=1}^{q} n_{il}c_l = A_i,$$

$$c_j\colon n_{.j}m + \sum_{i=1}^{p} n_{ij}a_i + n_{.j}c_j = C_j,$$

where $A_i$ and $C_j$ are respective treatment totals. Since

$$\sum_i n_{i.}a_i = 0 = \sum_j n_{.j}c_j,$$

$m = G/n = \bar{Y}$. In order to solve for the $\{a_i\}$ and $\{c_j\}$, a method of matrix inversion or the forward solution of the abbreviated Doolittle method can be used (see Chap. 15).

However, a short-cut procedure is available if the inverse matrix is not wanted. This short cut is the same as the method of adjusting for block effects in an incomplete-blocks design (see Sec. 19.2) and is frequently called the *sweep-out method.* The $c_j$ are adjusted for the $a_i$ by multiplying the $a_i$ equation by $(n_{ij}/n_{i.})$ and subtracting the sum of all these altered $a_i$ equations from the $c_j$ equation. The resultant equation is

$$n'_{j1}c_1 + n'_{j2}c_2 + \cdots + n'_{jj}c_j + \cdots + n'_{jq}c_q = C'_j,$$

where

$$n'_{jl} = \begin{cases} n_{.j} - \sum_{i=1}^{p} n_{ij}^2/n_{i.}, & l = j, \\ -\sum_{i=1}^{p} n_{ij}n_{il}/n_{i.}, & l \neq j, \end{cases}$$

$$C'_j = C_j - \sum_{i=1}^{p} n_{ij}A_i/n_{i.}.$$

These $q$ equations in the $\{c_j\}$ can then be handled by the forward solution of the abbreviated Doolittle method to determine SSC (adjusted for $A$) and the $\{c_j\}$. Since $\sum_j n_{.j}c_j = 0$, the constants in the $c_q$ row will be zero. Hence the $C'_q$ equation is often omitted and the effect $c_q$ from the other equations. However, it might be advisable to retain $c_q$ and the $C'_q$ equation as a check on the computations. The shortest computing time is achieved when $p \geq q$; if $p < q$, reverse the $A$ and $C$ treatments in the analysis.

The analysis of variance can now be set up.

$$\text{SSA (unadjusted for } C) = \sum_i \frac{A_i^2}{n_{i.}} - \frac{G^2}{n},$$

and SSC (adjusted for $A$) is computed from the $y$ column of the abbreviated Doolittle computations. Hence the total sum of squares for $A$ and $C$ is

$$\text{SS}(A + C) = \text{SSA(unadj)} + \text{SSC(adj)}.$$

The total sum of squares for all $pq$ subclasses is

$$\sum_i \sum_j \frac{T_{ij}^2}{n_{ij}} - \frac{G^2}{n},$$

where $T_{ij}$ is the total yield in the $(i,j)$ subclass. Hence the residual, due to interaction, is

$$\text{SS}(AC) = \sum_i \sum_j \frac{T_{ij}^2}{n_{ij}} - \sum_i \frac{A_i^2}{n_{i.}} - \text{SSC(adj)}.$$

Also SSA(adjusted for $C$) can be computed by subtraction as follows:

$$\text{SSA(adj)} = \text{SS}(A + C) - \text{SSC(unadj)},$$

$$\text{where SSC(unadj)} = \sum_j \frac{C_j^2}{n_{.j}} - \frac{G^2}{n}.$$

The analysis of variance is:

| Source of variation | Degrees of freedom | Sum of squares | Mean square |
|---|---|---|---|
| $A$(unadj) | $p - 1$ | | |
| $C$(adj) | $q - 1$ | SSC(adj) | MSC |
| $C$(unadj) | $q - 1$ | | |
| $A$(adj) | $p - 1$ | SSA(adj) | MSA |
| $AC$ | $(p - 1)(q - 1)$ | SS($AC$) | MS($AC$) |
| Error | $n - pq$ | SSE | $s^2$ |

**Example 20.4.** Some data were presented in Exercise 18.5 on the gain in weight of 149 rats for four successive generations, both male and female.[8] In order to test for generation and sex effects and the (generation $\times$ sex) interaction, an analysis for unequal subclass numbers is needed. The analysis of variance for the unweighted means is as follows:

| Source of variation | Degrees of freedom | Mean square |
|---|---|---|
| Generations | 3 | 42.08 |
| Sex | 1 | 6,394.67 |
| $G \times S$ | 3 | 58.22 |
| Error | 141 | 26.27 |

In computing the error mean square, $\bar{n}_h = 15.576$ and

$$s^2 = 57{,}695/141 = 409.2.$$

The only significant effect is sex, but the $F$ value for interaction of 2.22 is slightly larger than the $F_{.10}$ value for 3 and 141 degrees of freedom. Hence one might be hesitant about concluding there was no interaction; apparently the main differences were sex differences with the possibility that these differences were not the same from one generation to another.

In order to make the test for interaction more exact, we present the least-squares solution. The least-squares equations, omitting the interaction constants, are ($a_i$ for generation and $c_j$ for sex effects):

$$\begin{array}{llllllll}
m: & 149m + 48a_1 & + 40a_2 & + 35a_3 & + 26a_4 & + 55c_1 & + 94c_2 & = 19{,}537, \\
a_1: & 48m + 48a_1 & & & & + 21c_1 & + 27c_2 & = 6{,}673, \\
a_2: & 40m & + 40a_2 & & & + 15c_1 & + 25c_2 & = 5{,}274, \\
a_3: & 35m & & + 35a_3 & & + 12c_1 & + 23c_2 & = 4{,}364, \\
a_4: & 26m & & & + 26a_4 & + 7c_1 & + 19c_2 & = 3{,}226, \\
c_1: & 55m + 21a_1 & + 15a_2 & + 12a_3 & + 7a_4 & + 55c_1 & & = 9{,}203, \\
c_2: & 94m + 27a_1 & + 25a_2 & + 23a_3 & + 19a_4 & & + 94c_2 & = 10{,}334.
\end{array}$$

The restrictions are

$$48a_1 + 40a_2 + 35a_3 + 26a_4 = 0; \qquad 55c_1 + 94c_2 = 0.$$

The $a$ effects are swept out of the $c$ equations as follows:

$$n'_{11} = 55 - \left[\frac{(21)^2}{48} + \cdots + \frac{(7)^2}{26}\right] = 34.18860,$$

$$n'_{12} = n'_{21} = -\left[\frac{(21)(27)}{48} + \cdots + \frac{(7)(19)}{26}\right] = -34.18860,$$

$$n'_{22} = 94 - \left[\frac{(27)^2}{48} + \cdots + \frac{(19)^2}{26}\right] = 34.18860,$$

$$C'_1 = 9{,}203 - \left[\frac{(21)(6{,}673)}{48} + \cdots + \frac{(7)(3{,}226)}{26}\right] = 1{,}941.045,$$

$$C'_2 = 10{,}334 - \left[\frac{(27)(6{,}673)}{48} + \cdots + \frac{(19)(3{,}226)}{26}\right] = -1{,}941.045.$$

Hence the adjusted $c$ equations are

$$34.18860(c_1 - c_2) = 1{,}941.045,$$
$$-34.18860(c_1 - c_2) = -1{,}941.045.$$

If we neglect the $C_2$ equation and $c_2$ (or set $c'_1 = c_1 - c_2$), we have

$$c'_1 = 56.77463$$

and

$$\text{SSC(adj)} = c'_1(1{,}941.045) = 110{,}202.1.$$

Also

$$\text{SSA(unadj)} = \frac{(6{,}673)^2}{48} + \cdots + \frac{(3{,}226)^2}{26} - \frac{(19{,}537)^2}{149} = 5{,}756.4,$$

and

$$\text{SSC(unadj)} = \frac{(9{,}203)^2}{55} + \frac{(10{,}334)^2}{94} - \frac{(19{,}537)^2}{149} = 114{,}286.1.$$

The total sum of squares for all eight subclasses was

$$\frac{(3{,}716)^2}{21} + \cdots + \frac{(2{,}029)^2}{19} - \frac{(19{,}537)^2}{149} = 119{,}141.0.$$

Hence the interaction sum of squares is

$$119{,}141.0 - 110{,}202.1 - 5{,}756.4 = 3{,}182.5.$$

The analysis of variance is:

| Source of variation | Degrees of freedom | Mean square |
|---|---|---|
| Generations | 3 | |
| Sex(adj) | 1 | 110,202 |
| | | |
| Sex | 1 | |
| Generation(adj) | 3 | 557 |
| | | |
| Sex × generation | 3 | 1,061 |
| | | |
| Error | 141 | 409.2 |

The $F$ value to test for interaction is

$$F = 1{,}061/409.2 = 2.59,$$

with 3 and 141 degrees of freedom, which is not quite significant at the 5 per cent probability level ($F_{.05} = 2.67$). Note that the exact $F$ is slightly larger than the $F$ using the method of unweighted means. This is generally true, as the exact method is somewhat more powerful.

If we conclude that there is no real interaction, we can use the error mean square (409.2) to test for the adjusted sex and generation effects, showing a highly significant sex difference but no real difference in gains for the four generations. If we want a more exact test of over-all sex effects without neglecting the interaction than the test using the unweighted means, interaction constants can be inserted in the model and the main effects adjusted for the interaction, or the method of weighted squares of means can be used. However, the average main effect has little meaning if interaction is present, because a real interaction indicates that the sex difference is not the same from one generation to another. Hence it would appear better to test for sex difference in each generation, using either the pooled $s^2$ or a separate $s^2$ for each generation. Pooling is justified only if the within subclass variance is constant from one subclass to another. We have assumed the constancy of these variances, but the reasonableness of the assumption should be checked.

It might be mentioned that a significant interaction is often evidence of a multiplicative relationship. In this case if we analyzed $Z = \log Y$, the assumption of additivity would be more nearly correct. However, it should be cautioned that if we analyze $Z = \log Y$, we must assume that the errors in $Y$ also multiply so they become additive for $Z$.

**20.6. The Use of Incomplete-blocks Designs for Factorial Experiments.** As mentioned in Chap. 19, when all the treatments are not used in each block, the treatment and block effects become *confounded*. Since the factorial designs are constructed to obtain information on single comparisons, it seems reasonable to attempt to confound some of the less important comparisons and leave the more important comparisons free of block effects. For example, if we use a $2 \times 2 \times 2$ factorial experiment and only 4 plots are available per block, it would be desirable to confound the $ACD$ three-factor interaction and leave the other effects free of block effects.

Designate the 8 treatment combinations as

$$111,\ 211,\ 121,\ 221,\ 112,\ 212,\ 122,\ 222,$$

where the first number refers to the $A$ treatment (1 or 2), the second to the $C$ treatment, and the third to the $D$ treatment. If we put treatments

(111, 221, 212, 122) in one block and (211, 121, 112, 222) in the second block, the main effects and two factor interactions will be clear of block effects and $ACD$ will be completely confounded with block effects. However, if we repeat the experiment several times so that we have $r$ replications ($2r$ blocks), a test can be made of $ACD$, using methods to be discussed in Chap. 23 for split-plot designs. We shall defer a discussion of this point until then and simply indicate the analysis-of-variance degrees of freedom as follows:

| Source of Variation | Degrees of Freedom |
|---|---|
| Blocks | $2r - 1$ |
| $A$ | 1 |
| $C$ | 1 |
| $D$ | 1 |
| $AC$ | 1 |
| $AD$ | 1 |
| $CD$ | 1 |
| Error | $6(r - 1)$ |

The general procedure of confounding in factorial experiments is extensively discussed in references 1 to 3. The reader is encouraged to read these references if he is interested in setting up factorial experiments with more treatment conbinations than plots per block. Some exercises are included at the end of the chapter.

**20.7. Construction of Experimental Designs.** In all of the theoretical discussions in this and previous chapters, we have assumed that the design was known and have proceeded to set up an analysis for this design. The reader might be interested in knowing how to construct designs in the first place so that the analysis will be relatively simple.

(*a*) There is no difficulty in setting up completely randomized or randomized complete blocks or complete Latin-square designs, except to remember that randomization is necessary.

(*b*) In planning confounded factorial designs, the main principle is to restrict the confounding to high-order interactions, if this is possible. One principle must always be remembered with $2^n$ designs: if two interactions are confounded, then a third effect is also confounded—this third effect is formed by casting out all like letters in the first two. For example, if $ABC$ and $ABD$ are confounded, $CD$ will be also. Hence it is often necessary to adjust the confounding so as to protect main effects and two-factor interactions. For more than two levels, the principles of confounding are much more complicated. We shall present a few examples of how to construct confounded factorials (see Yates[3] for the details of other examples).

**Example 20.5.** If a design is of the $2^n$ character ($n$ factors each at two levels), the construction of a confounded design is simplified by the use of the $(+,-)$ system. For example if we wish to use $2^4$ $(=16)$ treatments in 4 blocks of 4 treatments each, we are led to confound 3 degrees of freedom (the number of degrees of freedom between blocks in a replication). Let us designate the 4 factors as $A$, $B$, $C$, and $D$, with 1 standing for the low level and 2 the high level of a factor. We cannot confound on $ABCD$, because if we select any 3-factor interaction, we shall automatically confound a main effect by the above rule. Hence we consider confounding two of the four 3-factor interactions and one 2-factor interaction, for example, $ABC$, $ABD$, and $CD$. We set up the $(+,-)$ system for each of these three effects as in Table 20.1. We note that

TABLE 20.1

| Treatment | $ABC$ | $ABD$ | $CD$ | Block 1 | Block 2 | Block 3 | Block 4 |
|---|---|---|---|---|---|---|---|
| 1111 | − | − | + | | | | x |
| 2111 | + | + | + | x | | | |
| 1211 | + | + | + | x | | | |
| 2211 | − | − | + | | | | x |
| 1121 | + | − | − | | x | | |
| 2121 | − | + | − | | | x | |
| 1221 | − | + | − | | | x | |
| 2221 | + | − | − | | x | | |
| 1112 | − | + | − | | | x | |
| 2112 | + | − | − | | x | | |
| 1212 | + | − | − | | x | | |
| 2212 | − | + | − | | | x | |
| 1122 | + | + | + | x | | | |
| 2122 | − | − | + | | | | x |
| 1222 | − | − | + | | | | x |
| 2222 | + | + | + | x | | | |

there is a + for the treatment having the high level of all the factors in a particular interaction, − for one low level and the remainder high levels, etc. Also, $CD = (ABC)(ABD)$. The treatments with the same combination of $(+,-)$ signs are assigned to the same block. This method can be used for all $2^n$ designs.

**Example 20.6.** Consider a $3^2$ design with the levels designated as 1, 2, and 3. The 9 treatments can be arranged in a $3 \times 3$ table.

| | | |
|---|---|---|
| 11 | 12 | 13 |
| 21 | 22 | 23 |
| 31 | 32 | 33 |

The $AB$ interaction (4 degrees of freedom) can be split into two components, each with 2 degrees of freedom. We compute

$$I_0 = (11 + 22 + 33), \quad I_1 = (12 + 23 + 31), \quad I_2 = (13 + 21 + 32).$$
$$J_0 = (11 + 23 + 32), \quad J_1 = (12 + 21 + 33), \quad J_2 = (13 + 22 + 31).$$

The two components are

$$I = \frac{\sum_i I_i^2}{3} - \frac{G^2}{9}, \qquad J = \frac{\sum_i J_i^2}{3} - \frac{G^2}{9}.$$

If we wanted to use only 3 treatments per block, we could confound either the $I$ or the $J$ part of the $AB$ interaction by planting the $I$ or $J$ combination of treatments in blocks. We note that these combinations do not confound the main effects, since all 3 levels of each factor are present in each combination. (See reference 3 for the rules when $n > 2$.)

**20.8. Summary.** We have presented only an introduction to factorial designs in this chapter, but it is hoped that the reader has been able to see the usefulness of these designs. Yates[3] and Cochran and Cox[1] have an extensive amount of material on factorial designs, but even they do not present an exhaustive list; more needs to be done in developing confounded factorial designs for the engineers and the physical scientists, who require three or more levels of each treatment and often more sets of treatments than are used by the natural scientists. Too little attention has been paid to encouraging experimenters to use three or more levels of each treatment in an experiment in order to discover whether or not there is curvilinearity in the response curves. The $2^n$ factorials have been used because of their simplicity, but they furnish little information on the response surface.

Some work has been done on *fractional replication*[1,11–14] in which only part of the treatment combinations are used. Fractional replication is needed in industrial experimentation, especially in destructive testing. Too little attention has been paid to the development of these designs, especially for mixed series, such as a $2 \times 3 \times 4$ experiment.

## EXERCISES

**20.1.** (*a*) In Sec. 20.3, show that

$$E(L_2^2)/4r = E(\text{SSA}), \qquad E(L_3^2)/4r = E(\text{SSC}), \qquad E(L_4^2)/4r = E[\text{SS}(AC)].$$

HINT: Remember that $\alpha_1 + \alpha_2 = 0$, $\gamma_1 + \gamma_2 = 0$, etc.

(b) In Example 20.3, show that

$$E\left[\frac{F_l^2}{24} + \frac{F_q^2}{72}\right] = E(\mathrm{SSF}).$$

**20.2.** (a) In Example 20.1, what was the estimated efficiency of the randomized complete-blocks design as compared with a completely randomized design? Would you consider this to be significantly greater than 1?

(b) Reanalyze the data, using the following orthogonal sets: $V_1 - V_2$; $V_1 + V_2 - 2V_3$; $N_2 - N_1$; $2N_3 - (N_1 + N_2)$; interactions of the $V$ and $N$ comparisons. What does this analysis reveal?

**20.3.** An experiment was designed to compare five varieties of cowpeas, at three different spacings, 4, 8, and 12 inches apart in row, with rows 3 feet apart.[5] For the data, see the accompanying table.

DATA OF EXERCISE 20.3
Yield of Cowpea Hay (Pounds per $\frac{1}{100}$ Morgen Plot)

| Variety × spacings | | Blocks I | II | III | IV | Total | Subtotal |
|---|---|---|---|---|---|---|---|
| New Era | 4″ | 56 | 45 | 43 | 46 | 190 | |
| | 8″ | 60 | 50 | 45 | 48 | 203 | 616 |
| | 12″ | 66 | 57 | 50 | 50 | 223 | |
| 34 C 361 | 4″ | 61 | 58 | 55 | 56 | 230 | |
| | 8″ | 60 | 59 | 54 | 54 | 227 | 674 |
| | 12″ | 59 | 55 | 51 | 52 | 217 | |
| 34 C 395 | 4″ | 63 | 53 | 49 | 48 | 213 | |
| | 8″ | 65 | 56 | 50 | 50 | 221 | 665 |
| | 12″ | 66 | 58 | 52 | 55 | 231 | |
| 34 C 402 | 4″ | 65 | 61 | 60 | 63 | 249 | |
| | 8″ | 60 | 58 | 56 | 60 | 234 | 692 |
| | 12″ | 53 | 53 | 48 | 55 | 209 | |
| 34 C 408 | 4″ | 60 | 61 | 50 | 53 | 224 | |
| | 8″ | 62 | 68 | 67 | 60 | 257 | 773 |
| | 12″ | 73 | 77 | 77 | 65 | 292 | |
| Block totals | | 929 | 869 | 807 | 815 | 3,420 | |

(a) Set up a table of means.

(b) Set up the analysis of variance.

(c) Derive the linear and quadratic components of the spacing effect and the interaction. Graph these results, using spacing as the $X$ variate and drawing separate lines for each variety.

(*d*) What is the standard error to compare any 2 of the 15 treatment means?

(*e*) Discuss the results.

**20.4.** A fertility test was made on the growth of grass on Philadelphia Flat soils in the Manti National Forest with three levels of nitrogen ($N$) and three levels of phosphate ($P$) with two samples of each treatment. For the data, see the accompanying table. Note that this is not a

DATA OF EXERCISE 20.4

| | Grams of grass | | | Total |
|---|---|---|---|---|
| | $N_0$ | $N_1$ | $N_2$ | |
| $P_0$ | 18.7 | 20.8 | 22.3 | |
| | 17.5 | 20.5 | 22.9 | |
| | 36.2 | 41.3 | 45.2 | 122.7 |
| $P_1$ | 19.2 | 18.8 | 24.9 | |
| | 21.3 | 23.5 | 24.2 | |
| | 40.5 | 42.3 | 49.1 | 131.9 |
| $P_2$ | 20.8 | 22.0 | 25.6 | |
| | 20.5 | 24.0 | 27.1 | |
| | 41.3 | 46.0 | 52.7 | 140.0 |
| Total | 118.0 | 129.6 | 147.0 | 394.6 |

randomized-blocks experiment but is analyzed as a completely randomized design of the type discussed in Sec. 18.2.

(*a*) Set up the table of means, and make the analysis of variance.

(*b*) Show that the only important effects are the linear for both $N$ and $P$.

(*c*) Draw a graph similar to Fig. 20.2, and discuss the results.

**20.5.** Suppose you wish to set up an experiment to test the effectiveness of 2 levels of nitrogen, 2 levels of phosphate, and 2 levels of potash on the yield of potatoes and had enough land to plant 80 plots.

(*a*) Show how you would set up this experiment.

(*b*) Set up the analysis-of-variance table.

(*c*) Indicate what kind of information can be obtained from such an experiment.

(*d*) If you wanted to know something about the maximum level of the three fertilizers to use, what changes have to be made in planning another experiment?

(*e*) How would you take account of the cost of the fertilizers in making your recommendations to the farmer?

**20.6.** A 6 × 6 Latin-square experiment was run at the North Carolina Agricultural Experiment Station to determine the effect of nitrogen and phosphate fertilizers on potato yields. The following treatments were used:

| Nitrogen | Phosphate | | |
|---|---|---|---|
| | Low | Medium | High |
| Low | *A* | *B* | *C* |
| High | *D* | *E* | *F* |

The field arrangement and yields (pounds per plot) were:

| | | | | | | Row totals |
|---|---|---|---|---|---|---|
| | *E* 633 | *B* 527 | *F* 652 | *A* 390 | *C* 504 | *D* 416 | 3,122 |
| | *B* 489 | *C* 475 | *D* 415 | *E* 488 | *F* 571 | *A* 282 | 2,720 |
| | *A* 384 | *E* 481 | *C* 483 | *B* 422 | *D* 334 | *F* 646 | 2,750 |
| | *F* 620 | *D* 448 | *E* 505 | *C* 439 | *A* 323 | *B* 384 | 2,719 |
| | *D* 452 | *A* 432 | *B* 411 | *F* 617 | *E* 594 | *C* 466 | 2,972 |
| | *C* 500 | *F* 505 | *A* 259 | *D* 366 | *B* 326 | *E* 420 | 2,376 |
| Col. totals | 3,078 | 2,868 | 2,725 | 2,722 | 2,652 | 2,614 | 16,659 |

(*a*) Make a complete analysis of this experiment, indicating the treatment means and effects and linear and quadratic effects. Graph the results with nitrogen as the $X$ variate and using separate lines for each phosphate.

(*b*) What recommendations should be made if it costs \$2 per plot extra for high instead of low nitrogen and \$1 per plot extra for each jump in the amount of phosphate and potatoes sold for \$.03 a pound?

(*c*) Was the Latin square better than a randomized complete-blocks design?

**20.7.** An experiment was conducted by C. H. Li to study the effect of electrolytic chromium plate as a source for the chromium impregnation of low-carbon steel wire.[6] Eighteen treatments were considered, using all combinations of three diffusion temperatures (2200°F, 2350°F, 2500°F), three diffusion times (4, 8, and 12 hours), and two degassing treatments [no degassing (0) and degassing (1)]. Each treatment was used on 4 wires, giving a total of 72 wires used. The variable studied was average resistivity in microhms per cubic centimeter. The average resistivities are shown in the accompanying table.

DATA OF EXERCISE 20.7

| Temperature | 2200° | | 2350° | | 2500° | |
|---|---|---|---|---|---|---|
| Degassing | 0 | 1 | 0 | 1 | 0 | 1 |
| | 4 hours | | | | | |
| | 18.1 | 17.9 | 22.1 | 21.2 | 22.9 | 22.8 |
| | 18.9 | 18.0 | 20.2 | 20.4 | 24.0 | 22.3 |
| | 18.6 | 18.7 | 21.3 | 21.2 | 23.0 | 22.7 |
| | 19.1 | 19.0 | 22.6 | 21.2 | 23.0 | 23.3 |
| | 74.7 | 73.6 | 86.2 | 84.0 | 92.9 | 91.1 |
| | 8 hours | | | | | |
| | 19.2 | 19.2 | 23.2 | 22.7 | 25.5 | 26.9 |
| | 19.3 | 19.0 | 21.8 | 22.7 | 26.6 | 26.9 |
| | 20.7 | 20.4 | 22.9 | 22.5 | 25.9 | 26.3 |
| | 20.4 | 19.2 | 22.3 | 22.5 | 26.8 | 26.9 |
| | 79.6 | 77.8 | 90.2 | 90.4 | 104.8 | 107.0 |
| | 12 hours | | | | | |
| | 20.0 | 19.9 | 23.9 | 23.3 | 27.0 | 26.5 |
| | 20.2 | 20.1 | 23.6 | 23.5 | 26.2 | 26.8 |
| | 20.1 | 20.0 | 23.2 | 23.5 | 25.9 | 25.4 |
| | 20.5 | 20.8 | 23.7 | 22.9 | 26.9 | 27.2 |
| | 80.8 | 80.8 | 94.4 | 93.2 | 106.0 | 105.9 |

(*a*) Set up a table of means for the 18 treatment combinations and for each of the main effects.

(*b*) Make an analysis of variance with single degrees of freedom ($Sy^2 = 524.2550$).

(*c*) Determine the standard error for the difference between any 2 of the 18 treatments.

(*d*) What are your conclusions regarding these treatments?

**20.8.** A randomized blocks experiment was set up to test the performance of 16 treatment combinations in two different blocks, each block having 4 rows with 4 treatments per row. The original setup was a factorial experiment. It turned out that only 2 of the main treatments, designated as $L$ and $O$, were important. It also became evident that the blocks were badly placed, since there were marked differences in fertility between the 4 rows, which ran across both blocks. In the analysis of the difference between the effects of $L$ and $O$, we are confronted with the difficulty that $L$ and $O$ did not each appear twice in each row of each block but sometimes $L$ would appear 3 times and $O$ once, or vice versa. The yields are presented below:

| Row | Block I | | Block II | | Total | | |
|---|---|---|---|---|---|---|---|
| | $L$ | $O$ | $L$ | $O$ | $L$ | $O$ | $L + O$ |
| 1 | 84, 70, 81 | 66 | 63, 97 | 56, 64 | 395 | 186 | 581 |
| 2 | 146, 171 | 148, 137 | 189 | 168, 158, 152 | 506 | 763 | 1,269 |
| 3 | 247 | 179, 218, 228 | 195, 189 | 191, 179 | 631 | 995 | 1,626 |
| 4 | 177, 153 | 123, 166 | 145, 141, 130 | 133 | 746 | 422 | 1,168 |
| Total | 1,129 | 1,265 | 1,149 | 1,101 | 2,278 | 2,366 | 4,644 |
| | 2,394 | | 2,250 | | | | |

(*a*) Set up the least-squares equations to test whether or not there was a real difference between $L$ and $O$ after adjusting for row effects and neglecting the other treatments.

(*b*) Show that the following analysis of variance is obtained:

| Source of Variation | Sum of Squares |
|---|---|
| Blocks | 648.00 |
| Rows | 70,542.25 |
| Treatments (adj.) | 1,313.21 |
| Error | 8,006.04 |

(*c*) Fill in the appropriate degrees of freedom in (*b*), and make a test of the treatment differences.

(*d*) Is there any feature of the error which might cause you to doubt the validity of the analysis?

**20.9.** Use the method presented in Sec. 15.3 (page 198) to solve for the values of $m$, $\{a_i\}$, and $\{c_j\}$ in Example 20.4.

**20.10.** C. B. Ratchford[9] investigated the differences in average man work units per farm for 114 nontractor farms in the coastal plains counties of North Carolina (1949). He studied three factors which might have influenced the number of man work units per farm: size of farm (small, medium, or large), type of farming (tobacco or general), and three types of rental arrangements. The total man work units were as shown in the accompanying table (number of farms in parentheses). The total sum of squares within classes was 1,201,641.

DATA OF EXERCISE 20.10

| Type of farming | Size of farm | Type of rental arrangement 1 | 2 | 3 | Total |
|---|---|---|---|---|---|
| Tobacco | Small | 7,770.7(26) | 2,837.1 (9) | 5,410.7(19) | 16,018.5 (54) |
| | Medium | 2,492.5 (8) | 1,239.6 (3) | 359.6 (1) | 4,091.7 (12) |
| | Large | 1,654.6 (4) | 403.3 (1) | (0) | 2,057.9 (5) |
| | Total | 11,917.8(38) | 4,480.0(13) | 5,770.3(20) | 22,168.1 (71) |
| General | Small | 2,081.1 (9) | 1,443.7 (4) | 2,252.3(13) | 5,777.1 (26) |
| | Medium | 1,256.6 (4) | 1,179.0 (3) | 2,142.7 (5) | 4,578.3 (12) |
| | Large | 680.8 (2) | 958.7 (2) | 361.1 (1) | 2,000.6 (5) |
| | Total | 4,018.5(15) | 3,581.4 (9) | 4,756.1(19) | 12,356.0 (43) |
| Grand total | | 15,936.3(53) | 8,061.4(22) | 10,526.4(39) | 34,524.1(114) |

(*a*) Derive the total sum of squares due to the main effects of size, type, and rental arrangement, not adjusted for interaction. Write the variables in this order in the matrix: rental arrangement, type, size. Sweep out the rental constants, and solve for the type and size constants: type (adjusted for rental) and size (adjusted for rental and type).

(*b*) Derive the interaction sum of squares, and show that there was no significant interaction. What does this tell you about the separate two-factor and three-factor interactions?

(*c*) Test the effect of size adjusted for rental arrangement and type of farming.

(*d*) How would you go about testing the other two adjusted main effects?

**20.11.** Read an article by Anderson and Manning[10] for a more complete discussion of matrix methods with unequal frequencies.

**20.12.** Use the observation equations for each of the eight subclasses to set up the normal equations in Example 20.4 and Exercise 20.10.

**20.13.** Show that the method of least squares produces exact tests for the main effects, even when interaction is present, if $n_{ij} = n_{i.}n_{.j}/n$.

**20.14.** Suppose you studied only small and medium-sized farms in Exercise 20.10.

(*a*) Make an analysis by the method of unweighted means in this case.

(*b*) Does this analysis give you any clue to the separate interactions of Exercise 20.10?

(*c*) Why could you not use this method for all farms?

**20.15.** Given the following data on the number of plants emerging in an experiment with two levels each of nitrogen ($N$), phosphate ($P$), and potash ($K$). Four treatments were used per block, with a total of 8 blocks (4 replications), and the *NPK* interaction was confounded. The stands were as follows:

| *NPK* | 1*a* | 2*a* | 3*a* | 4*a* | Total |
|---|---|---|---|---|---|
| 211 | 31 | 30 | 33 | 28 | 122 |
| 121 | 25 | 24 | 30 | 19 | 98 |
| 112 | 21 | 21 | 30 | 24 | 96 |
| 222 | 66 | 39 | 41 | 36 | 182 |
| Total | 143 | 114 | 134 | 107 | 498 |

| *NPK* | 1*b* | 2*b* | 3*b* | 4*b* | Total |
|---|---|---|---|---|---|
| 111 | 11 | 7 | 19 | 13 | 50 |
| 212 | 33 | 31 | 36 | 31 | 131 |
| 122 | 29 | 27 | 31 | 26 | 113 |
| 221 | 43 | 39 | 36 | 35 | 153 |
| Total | 116 | 104 | 122 | 105 | 447 |

(*a*) Show that the following analysis is correct:

| Source of variation | Degrees of freedom | Mean square |
|---|---|---|
| Blocks | 7 | 50.10 |
| *N* | 1 | 1,667.53 |
| *P* | 1 | 675.28 |
| *K* | 1 | 306.28 |
| *NP* | 1 | 9.03 |
| *NK* | 1 | 16.53 |
| *PK* | 1 | 3.78 |
| Error | 18 | 32.05 |

(*b*) Test the significance of the main effects. What about the interactions?

(*c*) Show that the main effects and two-factor interactions are not confounded with block effects and that *NPK* is completely confounded.

**20.16.** Two different cultivation methods were also used in the experiment presented in Example 20.3, giving a total of 12 treatments, but only 6 treatments were planted per block. The treatment effects can be divided as follows, with the number of degrees of freedom per effect in parentheses: $F(2)$, $V(1)$, $FV(2)$, $C(1)$, $FC(2)$, $VC(1)$, $FVC(2)$. The two cultivation methods ($c_1$ and $c_2$) were assigned in the following order for each block (see the example for $F$ and $V$):

| $F$ | $V$ | Block 1 | 2 | 3 | 4 | 5 | 6 |
|---|---|---|---|---|---|---|---|
| 1 | 1 | 2 | 1 | 1 | 2 | 1 | 2 |
| 1 | 2 | 1 | 2 | 2 | 1 | 2 | 1 |
| 2 | 1 | 1 | 2 | 2 | 1 | 1 | 2 |
| 2 | 2 | 2 | 1 | 1 | 2 | 2 | 1 |
| 3 | 1 | 1 | 2 | 1 | 2 | 2 | 1 |
| 3 | 2 | 2 | 1 | 2 | 1 | 1 | 2 |

We note that there are three complete replications of the 12 treatments. The total yields of three plots for each of the 12 treatments were:

| Treatment | 111 | 112 | 121 | 122 | 211 | 212 | 221 | 222 | 311 | 312 | 321 | 322 | Total |
|---|---|---|---|---|---|---|---|---|---|---|---|---|---|
| Yield | 411 | 444 | 561 | 657 | 479 | 578 | 659 | 645 | 451 | 517 | 546 | 601 | 6,549 |

($a$) Check that the above treatment totals are correct.

($b$) Write out 11 treatment effects, using $F_l$ and $F_q$ as before. Show that 8 of these are independent of block effects, and show that the sum of squares attributable to these 8 effects is 25,977.84.

($c$) Show that $VC$, $F_lVC$, and $F_qVC$ are not independent of block effects; these effects are confounded with block effects.

($d$) Show that the sums of squares for the effects in ($c$) adjusted for blocks are 40.5, 154.1, and 129.6, respectively.

($e$) Compute the new error mean square, and make the necessary tests of significance.

**References Cited**

1. Cochran, W. G., and G. M. Cox, *Experimental Designs*, John Wiley & Sons, Inc., New York, 1950.
2. Fisher, R. A., *Design of Experiments*, 4th ed., Oliver & Boyd, Ltd., Edinburgh & London, 1947.
3. Yates, F., "The Design and Analysis of Factorial Experiments," *Imp. Bur. Soil Sci., Tech. Commun.* 35 (1937).
4. Snedecor, G. W., *Statistical Methods*, 4th ed., Collegiate Press, Inc., of Iowa State College, Ames, Iowa, 1946.
5. Saunders, A. R., and A. A. Rayner, "Statistical Methods with Special References to Field Experiments," 3d ed., *S. Africa Dept. Agr. Sci. Bull.* 200 (1951).
6. Li, C. H., *Steel Chromizing and Master Charts for Diffusion in Cylindrical Media*, unpublished thesis, Library, Purdue University, 1951.
7. Yates, F., "The Analysis of Multiple Classifications with Unequal Numbers in the Different Subclasses," *J. Am. Stat. Assoc.*, **29**:51–66 (1934).

8. SNEDECOR, G. W., and G. M. COX, "Disproportionate Subclass Numbers in Tables of Multiple Classification," *Iowa State Coll., Agr. Expt. Sta. Bull.* 180 (1935).
9. RATCHFORD, C. B., *Rental Arrangements in a Developing Economy*, unpublished thesis, Duke University, Durham, N.C., 1951.
10. ANDERSON, R. L., and H. L. MANNING, "An Experimental Design Used to Estimate the Optimum Planting Date for Cotton," *Biometrics*, **4**:171–196 (1948).
11. FINNEY, D. J., "The Fractional Replication of Factorial Arrangements," *Ann. Eugenics*, **12**: 291–301 (1945).
12. FINNEY, D. J., "Recent Developments in the Design of Field Experiments. III. Fractional Replication," *J. Agr. Sci.*, **36**: 184–191 (1946).
13. KEMPTHORNE, O., "A Simple Approach to Confounding and Fractional Replication in Factorial Experiments," *Biometrika*, **34**:255–272 (1947).
14. DAVIES, O. L., and W. A. HAY, "The Construction and Use of Fractional Factorial Designs in Industrial Research," *Biometrics*, **6**:233–249 (1950).

**Other Reading**

BARNARD, M. M., "An Enumeration of the Confounded Arrangements in the $2^n$ Factorial Designs," *J. Roy. Stat. Soc. Suppl.*, **3**:195–202 (1936).

BLISS, C. I., "Factorial Design and Covariance in the Biological Assay of Vitamin D," *J. Am. Stat. Assoc.*, **35**:498–506 (1940).

BOSE, R. C., "Mathematical Theory of the Symmetrical Factorial Design," *Sankhyā*, **8**:107–166 (1947).

CAMERON, J. M., and W. J. YOUDEN, "The Selection of a Limited Number from Many Possible Conditioning Treatments for Alloys to Achieve Best Coverage and Statistical Evaluation," *Proc. ASTM*, **50**:951–960 (1950).

FINNEY, D. J., "The Construction of Confounded Arrangements," *Empire J. Exptl. Agr.*, **15**:107–112 (1947).

FISHER, R. A., "The Theory of Confounding in Factorial Experiments in Relation to the Theory of Groups," *Ann. Eugenics*, **11**:341–353 (1942).

LI, J. C. R., "Design and Statistical Analysis of Some Confounded Factorial Experiments," *Iowa State Coll. Agr. Expt. Sta. Bull.* 333 (1944).

NAIR, K. R., "On a Method of Getting Confounded Arrangements in the General Symmetrical Type of Experiments," *Sankhyā*, **4**:121–138 (1938).

NAIR, K. R., "Balanced Confounded Arrangements for the $5^n$ Type of Experiments," *Sankhyā*, **5**:57–70 (1940).

YATES, F., "The Analysis of Replicated Experiments When the Field Results Are Incomplete," *Empire J. Exptl. Agr.*, **1**:129–142 (1933).

# CHAPTER 21

# THE ANALYSIS OF COVARIANCE

**21.1. Introduction.** In Chaps. 18 to 20, we considered various types of experimental designs to estimate treatment effects and to test for differences among these treatments. Frequently the experimenter wishes to make these estimates and tests on some dependent variate after adjusting for the effects of one or more fixed variates. For example, he might wish to test the effectiveness of various rations on the gains in weight of hogs after adjustments have been made for the initial weights of the hogs. Other fixed variates may be used in order to study the effect of the rations adjusted for the effects of such external factors as temperature of the pens or sunlight. An agronomic experiment might be improved by adjusting crop yield for weather and soil conditions or for unequal stand. In an educational experiment to test for differences between teaching methods, it might be advisable to adjust the results for the mental age or for some test score secured before the experiment started. Cochran has discussed the theoretical and practical aspects of the analysis of covariance in references 1 and 2. R. A. Fisher first introduced the method in reference 3.

## 21.2. The Use of Simple Covariance for a Randomized Complete-blocks Experiment

(i) We shall not attempt to present the theory of covariance for all of the experimental designs of Chap. 18, since it is believed that the method can be adequately demonstrated with the randomized complete-blocks type of experiment. As in Sec. 18.3, we shall assume that the experimenter has $p$ treatments, each assigned at random to an individual plot in each of $r$ blocks. The variate to be estimated is designated as $Y$, and the fixed variate for which $Y$ is to be adjusted is designated as $X$. The experimental model for the yield of the $i$th treatment in the $j$th block is

$$Y_{ij} = \mu + \tau_i^* + \beta_j^* + \beta x_{ij} + \epsilon_{ij} = m + t_i^* + b_j^* + bx_{ij} + e_{ij},$$

where $x_{ij} = X_{ij} - \bar{X}$, and $\tau_i^*$ and $\beta_j^*$ are the treatment and block effects adjusted for the effect of the $X$'s. Since $Sx = 0$, it is obvious that $\mu^* = \mu$; hence, we shall use $\mu$ and its estimate, $m$, in the theory which follows. As usual

$$\sum_i \tau_i^* = \sum_j \beta_j^* = 0.$$

The $X$'s are assumed to be fixed, and hence not influenced by the treatments. In case $X$ has some effect on the yield ($Y$) and the experimenter was not able to maintain the same value of $X$ for all treatments, it is desirable to estimate the treatment effects after the yields have been adjusted for the effect of $X$. If the values of $X$ are actually influenced by the treatments but can be measured without error, an analysis of covariance can still be run but interpretations are often quite difficult. As indicated in Chap. 15, if we estimate $\mu$, $\tau_i^*$, $\beta_j^*$, and $\beta$ by the method of least squares, each of the first three estimates will be adjusted for the linear effect of $X$. It should be emphasized at this point that we are here considering only the linear effect of $X$; however, any other function of $X$ could be used as the fixed variate, and we might consider several fixed variates in a multiple covariance.

(ii). The least-squares equations for $m$, $t_i^*$, $b_j^*$, and $b$, respectively, are

$$\begin{aligned} rpm \qquad\qquad\qquad\qquad &= SY, \\ rm + rt_i^* \qquad\quad + bx_{i\cdot} &= T_i, \\ pm \qquad + pb_j^* + bx_{\cdot j} &= B_j, \\ \sum_i t_i^* x_{i\cdot} + \sum_j b_j^* x_{\cdot j} + bSx^2 &= SxY = Sxy, \end{aligned}$$

where $x_{i\cdot} = \underset{j}{S} x_{ij} = X_{i\cdot} - r\bar{X}$, $x_{\cdot j} = \underset{i}{S} x_{ij} = X_{\cdot j} - p\bar{X}$, and $T_i$ and $B_j$ were defined in Sec. 18.3. In other words, $x_{i\cdot}$ and $x_{\cdot j}$ are treatment and block sums for $x$. It is seen that $\sum_i x_{i\cdot} = \sum_j x_{\cdot j} = 0$.

The solutions to the least-squares equations are

$$m = \frac{SY}{rp} = \bar{Y},$$

$$b = \frac{Sxy - p\sum_j \bar{B}_j \bar{x}_{\cdot j} - r\sum_i \bar{T}_i \bar{x}_{i\cdot}}{Sx^2 - p\sum_j \bar{x}_{\cdot j}^2 - r\sum_i \bar{x}_{i\cdot}^2} \equiv \frac{E_{xy}}{E_{xx}},$$

$$\begin{aligned} t_i^* &= (\bar{T}_i - \bar{Y}) - b\bar{x}_{i\cdot} = t_i - b\bar{x}_{i\cdot}, \\ b_j^* &= (\bar{B}_j - \bar{Y}) - b\bar{x}_{\cdot j} = b_j - b\bar{x}_{\cdot j}, \end{aligned}$$

where $E_{xx}$ and $E_{xy}$ are similar to SSE but applied to $x^2$ and $xy$, $\bar{x}_{i\cdot} = x_{i\cdot}/r$, $\bar{x}_{\cdot j} = x_{\cdot j}/p$, and similarly for $T$ and $B$.

We see that an adjusted treatment effect ($t^*$) is estimated by subtracting an adjustment factor from the unadjusted effect ($t$). The adjustment factor, $b\bar{x}_{i\cdot}$, is simply the average change in $Y$ for a unit change in $X$ multiplied by the difference between the treatment mean of $X$ and

$\bar{X}(\bar{x}_{i\cdot} = \bar{X}_{i\cdot} - \bar{X})$. Hence each treatment effect is adjusted to the average effect if all treatments had operated with the mean value of X.

It can be shown that

$$E_{xy} = S(x_{ij} - \bar{x}_{\cdot j} - \bar{x}_{i\cdot})(y_{ij} - \bar{B}_j - \bar{T}_i),$$
$$E_{xx} = S(x_{ij} - \bar{x}_{\cdot j} - \bar{x}_{i\cdot})^2.$$

(iii) The above estimates can be put in terms of the parameters and $\{\epsilon_{ij}\}$ as follows:

$$\bar{Y} = \mu + \bar{\epsilon},$$
$$y_{ij} = \tau_i^* + \beta_j^* + \beta x_{ij} + \epsilon_{ij} - \bar{\epsilon},$$
$$\bar{B}_j = \mu + \beta_j^* + \beta\bar{x}_{\cdot j} + \bar{\epsilon}_{\cdot j},$$
$$\bar{T}_i = \mu + \tau_i^* + \beta\bar{x}_{i\cdot} + \bar{\epsilon}_{i\cdot},$$
$$b = \frac{E_{xy}}{E_{xx}} = \beta + \frac{S(x_{ij} - \bar{x}_{\cdot j} - \bar{x}_{i\cdot})(\epsilon_{ij} - \bar{\epsilon}_{\cdot j} - \bar{\epsilon}_{i\cdot} - \bar{\epsilon})}{E_{xx}}$$
$$= \beta + \frac{S(x_{ij} - \bar{x}_{\cdot j} - \bar{x}_{i\cdot})\epsilon_{ij}}{E_{xx}} \equiv \beta + \epsilon_b,$$
$$t_i^* = \tau_i^* + \bar{\epsilon}_{i\cdot} - \bar{\epsilon} - \bar{x}_{i\cdot}\epsilon_b,$$
$$b_j^* = \beta_j^* + \bar{\epsilon}_{\cdot j} - \bar{\epsilon} - \bar{x}_{\cdot j}\epsilon_b,$$

where $\bar{\epsilon} = S\epsilon/rp$, $\bar{\epsilon}_{\cdot j} = \underset{i}{S}\epsilon_{ij}/p$, and $\bar{\epsilon}_{i\cdot} = \underset{j}{S}\epsilon_{ij}/r$.

Hence $\bar{Y}$, $b$, $t_i^*$, and $b_j^*$ are unbiased estimates of $\mu$, $\beta$, $\tau_i^*$, and $\beta_j^*$, respectively.

An unbiased estimate of an adjusted treatment mean is

$$t_i^* + \bar{Y} = \tau_i^* + \mu + \bar{\epsilon}_{i\cdot} - \bar{x}_{i\cdot}\epsilon_b.$$

Similarly the estimate of the difference, $\delta^*$, between two treatment means is

$$d^* = t_i^* - t_l^* = (\tau_i^* - \tau_l^*) + (\bar{\epsilon}_{i\cdot} - \bar{\epsilon}_{l\cdot}) - (\bar{x}_{i\cdot} - \bar{x}_{l\cdot})\epsilon_b.$$

The variance of the difference between two treatment means is

$$\sigma^2(d^*) = \sigma^2\left[\frac{2}{r} + \frac{(\bar{x}_{i\cdot} - \bar{x}_{l\cdot})^2}{E_{xx}}\right].$$

In computing this variance, we use $\bar{X}_{i\cdot} - \bar{X}_{l\cdot} = \bar{x}_{i\cdot} - \bar{x}_{l\cdot}$. It might be noted that in computing this variance, we computed $\sigma^2(b) = \sigma^2/E_{xx}$.

(iv) From least-squares theory, we know that the residual sum of squares is given by

$$\text{SSE}^* = Sy^2 - \sum_i t_i^* T_i - \sum_j b_j^* B_j - bSxy$$
$$= Sy^2 - \frac{1}{r}\left[\sum_i T_i^2 - rC\right] - \frac{1}{p}\left[\sum_j B_j^2 - pC\right] - bE_{xy},$$

where $C = (SY)^2/rp$ and $Sy^2 = SY^2 - C$. But this is the usual error sum of squares for the analysis of variance (Sec. 18.3),

$$\text{SSE} = Sy^2 - \text{SSB} - \text{SST},$$

minus the reduction due to regression when $x$ and $y$ are adjusted for block and treatment effects. We see that

$$\hat{Y}_{ij} = \bar{Y} + t_i^* + b_j^* + bx_{ij} = \mu + \tau_i^* + \beta_j^* + \beta x_{ij} + \bar{\epsilon}_{i\cdot} + \bar{\epsilon}_{\cdot j} - \bar{\epsilon} + \epsilon_b(x_{ij} - \bar{x}_{i\cdot} - \bar{x}_{\cdot j}).$$

Hence the residual $e_{ij}$ is

$$e_{ij} = Y_{ij} - \hat{Y}_{ij} = (\epsilon_{ij} - \bar{\epsilon}_{i\cdot} - \bar{\epsilon}_{\cdot j} + \bar{\epsilon}) - \epsilon_b(x_{ij} - \bar{x}_{i\cdot} - \bar{x}_{\cdot j}).$$

The expected value of $\text{SSE}^* = Se_{ij}^2$ is

$$(r-1)(p-1)\sigma^2 - \sigma^2 = [(r-1)(p-1) - 1]\sigma^2.$$

Therefore $s^{*2} = \text{SSE}^*/[(r-1)(p-1) - 1]$ is an unbiased estimate of $\sigma^2$.† This estimated variance can be used to set up confidence limits for differences between adjusted treatment means.

The added reduction due to treatments is found by omitting the treatment constants from the model equation. The new residual variance is

$$(\text{SSE}^*)' = Sy^2 - \text{SSB} - b'E'_{xy},$$

where

$$b' = \frac{E'_{xy}}{E'_{xx}} = \frac{S(x_{ij} - \bar{x}_{\cdot j})(y_{ij} - \bar{B}_j)}{S(x_{ij} - \bar{x}_{\cdot j})^2}.$$

This is simply $\text{SSE}'(= Sy^2 - \text{SSB})$ minus the reduction due to regression when $x$ and $y$ are adjusted for block effects only. The added reduction due to treatments is

$$\text{SST}^* = (\text{SSE}^*)' - \text{SSE}^*.$$

Also,

$$\begin{aligned} {}'_{ij} &= \bar{Y} + b_j^* + b'x_{ij}, \\ e'_{ij} &= \tau_i^* + (\epsilon_{ij} - \bar{\epsilon}_{\cdot j} + \bar{\epsilon}) - \epsilon'_b(x_{ij} - \bar{x}_{\cdot j}), \end{aligned}$$

where $\epsilon'_b = S(x_{ij} - \bar{x}_{\cdot j})\epsilon_{ij}/S(x_{ij} - \bar{x}_{\cdot j})^2$. Hence the expected value of $(\text{SSE}^*)'$ is

$$r\sum_i (\tau_i^*)^2 + [r(p-1) - 1]\sigma^2.$$

Since $\text{SST}^* = (\text{SSE}^*)' - \text{SSE}^*$, the expected value of $\text{SST}^*$ is

$$r\sum_i (\tau_i^*)^2 + (p-1)\sigma^2.$$

† $s^{*2}$ is usually designated as $s^2_{y\cdot x}$.

Hence

$$E(\text{MST}^*) = \frac{r\sum_i (\tau_i^*)^2}{(p-1)} + \sigma^2.$$

Under the null hypothesis $\{\tau_i^* = 0\}$, SST* is distributed as $\chi^2\sigma^2$ with $(p-1)$ degrees of freedom and independently of SSE*, which is distributed as $\chi^2\sigma^2$ with $(rp - r - p)$ degrees of freedom. Hence

$$F = \frac{\text{SST}^*/(p-1)}{\text{SSE}^*/(rp-r-p)} = \frac{\text{MST}^*}{s^{*2}},$$

with $(p-1,\ rp-r-p)$ degrees of freedom, can be used to test the above null hypothesis.

(v) The analysis of covariance table is:

| Source of variation | Degrees of freedom | Original sums | | | Adjusted results | | |
|---|---|---|---|---|---|---|---|
| | | $y^2$ | $xy$ | $x^2$ | d.f. | SS | MS |
| Total | $rp-1$ | $Sy^2$ | $Sxy$ | $Sx^2$ | | | |
| Blocks | $r-1$ | SSB | $B_{xy}$ | $B_{xx}$ | | | |
| Treatments | $p-1$ | SST | $T_{xy}$ | $T_{xx}$ | | | |
| Error | $(r-1)(p-1)$ | SSE | $E_{xy}$ | $E_{xx}$ | $(r-1)(p-1)-1$ | SSE* | $s^{*2}$ |
| (Error)′ | $r(p-1)$ | SSE′ | $E'_{xy}$ | $E'_{xx}$ | $r(p-1)-1$ | (SSE*)′ | |
| Adjusted treatments = (error)′ − (error) | | | | | $p-1$ | SST* | MST* |

In this analysis,

$$(\text{Error})' = \text{error} + \text{treatments},$$

$$B_{xy} = p\sum_j \bar{B}_j\bar{x}_{.j} = \frac{\sum_j B_j X_{.j}}{p} - \frac{(SY)(SX)}{rp},$$

$$T_{xy} = r\sum_i \bar{T}_i\bar{x}_{i.} = \frac{\sum_i T_i X_{i.}}{r} - \frac{(SY)(SX)}{rp},$$

and similarly $B_{xx}$ and $T_{xx}$ are block and treatment sums of squares for $x$.

(vi) The analysis of covariance has two main uses:

(*a*) To reduce the error variance by eliminating the plot-to-plot variation attributable to fluctuations in the fixed variate,

(*b*) To eliminate any bias in treatment comparisons caused by an uneven distribution of the fixed variate to the various treatments.

The efficiency ($I$) of covariance in reducing the error variance is given by the ratio of the variance of the difference between two unadjusted treatment means ($2s^2/r$) to the average variance of the difference between two adjusted treatment means.† Finney[4] shows that the average variance of the difference between two adjusted means is

$$\overline{s^2(d^*)} = \frac{2s^{*2}}{r}\left[1 + \frac{T_{xx}}{(p-1)E_{xx}}\right].$$

Hence

$$I = \frac{s^2}{s^{*2}\left[1 + \dfrac{T_{xx}}{(p-1)E_{xx}}\right]}.$$

It is rather difficult to assess the effectiveness of covariance in eliminating the effect of $X$ on the treatment means. It has sometimes been stated that one might test for treatment differences in $X$ by use of $F_x = (r-1)T_{xx}/E_{xx}$. If $F_x$ is not significant, the experimenter is told that he can attribute adjusted yield differences to the treatments; however, if $F_x$ is significant, he is advised to be cautious, because adjusted yield differences might be attributed to differences in $X$. Actually the experimenter should consider whether treatment differences in $X$ were inherent in the treatments (such as poor germination resulting in a low stand) or were the result of external circumstances. If the latter is the case, then covariance should be used to eliminate a bias in estimating treatment differences. But if the treatments actually produce differences in $X$, the experimenter should take this into account in making recommendations.

**Example 21.1.** Snedecor[5] presents an example of the analysis of covariance of the yield of sugar beets ($Y$) adjusted for stand ($X$). The yields in tons per acre and the stand in numbers of beets per plot are presented in Table 21.1.

† Since there is a loss of only 1 degree of freedom in adjusting for $X$, we need not worry about this feature unless there are very few degrees of freedom for error.

TABLE 21.1

| Fertilizer applied | (*i*) | Stand and yield | Block (*j*) 1 | 2 | 3 | 4 | 5 | 6 | Treatment sums and means $X_{i.}/T_i$ | $\bar{X}_{i.}/\bar{T}_i$ |
|---|---|---|---|---|---|---|---|---|---|---|
| None | 1 | Stand | 183 | 176 | 291 | 254 | 225 | 249 | 1,378 | 229.7 |
| | | Yield | 2.45 | 2.25 | 4.38 | 4.35 | 3.42 | 3.27 | 20.12 | 3.353 |
| Superphosphate, *P* | 2 | Stand | 356 | 300 | 301 | 271 | 288 | 258 | 1,774 | 295.7 |
| | | Yield | 6.71 | 5.44 | 4.92 | 5.23 | 6.74 | 4.74 | 33.78 | 5.630 |
| Muriate of potash, *K* | 3 | Stand | 224 | 258 | 244 | 217 | 192 | 236 | 1,371 | 228.5 |
| | | Yield | 3.22 | 4.14 | 2.32 | 4.42 | 3.28 | 4.00 | 21.38 | 3.563 |
| $P + K$ | 4 | Stand | 329 | 283 | 308 | 326 | 318 | 318 | 1,882 | 313.7 |
| | | Yield | 6.34 | 5.44 | 5.22 | 8.00 | 6.96 | 6.96 | 38.92 | 6.487 |
| $P +$ sodium nitrate, *N* | 5 | Stand | 371 | 354 | 352 | 331 | 290 | 410 | 2,108 | 351.3 |
| | | Yield | 6.48 | 7.11 | 5.88 | 7.54 | 6.61 | 8.86 | 42.48 | 7.080 |
| $K + N$ | 6 | Stand | 230 | 221 | 237 | 193 | 247 | 250 | 1,378 | 229.7 |
| | | Yield | 3.70 | 3.24 | 2.82 | 2.15 | 5.19 | 4.13 | 21.23 | 3.538 |
| $P + K + N$ | 7 | Stand | 322 | 367 | 400 | 333 | 314 | 385 | 2,121 | 353.5 |
| | | Yield | 6.10 | 7.68 | 7.37 | 7.83 | 7.75 | 7.39 | 44.12 | 7.353 |
| Block sums | | $X_{.j}$ | 2,015 | 1,959 | 2,133 | 1,925 | 1,874 | 2,106 | 12,012 | 286.0 |
| | | $B_j$ | 35.00 | 35.30 | 32.91 | 39.52 | 39.95 | 39.35 | 222.03 | 5.286 |

The computations are as follows:

$$SX^2 = 3{,}587{,}590 \qquad SXY = 67{,}664.27 \qquad SY^2 = 1{,}316.1479$$

$$\frac{(SX)^2}{42} = 3{,}435{,}432 \qquad \frac{(SX)(SY)}{42} = 63{,}500.58 \qquad \frac{(SY)^2}{42} = 1{,}173.7457$$

$$Sx^2 = 152{,}158 \qquad Sxy = 4{,}163.69 \qquad Sy^2 = 142.4022$$

$$E_{xy} = 4{,}163.69 - \left[\frac{(2{,}015)(35.00) + \cdots + (2{,}106)(39.35)}{7} - 63{,}500.58\right]$$

$$- \left[\frac{(1{,}378)(20.12) + \cdots + (2{,}121)(44.12)}{6} - 63{,}500.58\right]$$

$$= 4{,}163.69 + 116.56 - 3{,}598.05 = 682.20.$$

$$E_{xx} = 28{,}665.10, \qquad b = \frac{E_{xy}}{E_{xx}} = .023799.$$

$$\text{SSE}^* = Sy^2 - \text{SSB} - \text{SST} - bE_{xy}$$

$$= 142.4022 - 6.3134 - 112.8562 - 16.2357 = 6.9969.$$

The results are presented in the following analysis-of-covariance table:

| Source of variation | Degrees of freedom | Original sums | | | Adjusted results | | |
|---|---|---|---|---|---|---|---|
| | | $Sy^2$ | $Sxy$ | $Sx^2$ | SS | d.f. | MS |
| Total | 41 | 142.4022 | 4,163.69 | 152,158.00 | | | |
| Blocks | 5 | 6.3134 | −116.56 | 7,472.57 | | | |
| Treatments | 6 | 112.8562 | 3,598.05 | 116,020.33 | | | |
| Error | 30 | 23.2326 | 682.20 | 28,665.10 | 6.9969 | 29 | .2413 |
| (Error)′ | 36 | 136.0888 | 4,280.25 | 144,685.43 | 9.4655 | 35 | |
| Adjusted treatments = (error)′ − error | | | | | 2.4686 | 6 | .4114 |

$$F = \frac{.4114}{.2413} = 1.70, \quad \alpha > .10.$$

Since $F$ is not significant, we conclude that the treatments did not differ in their mean yields after adjusting for stand. This experiment falls in the uncertain class, because the stand is a result of the experiment and hence may be a treatment characteristic. For example, a given treatment may produce a good germination or a good start on the part of the plant so that its main contribution to yield may be in producing a good stand. If this is so, an adjustment for stand will cancel out the treatment effects. A test of $T_{xx} = 116{,}020.33$ against $E_{xx} = 28{,}665.10$ gives $F_x = 20.24$, a highly significant value. This indicates that there were actually differences in stand from one treatment to another. Furthermore we note that a test of the treatment effects on yield not adjusted for stand gives

$$F = \frac{112.8562/6}{23.2326/30} = 24.29,$$

also a highly significant value. Hence we conclude that there were definite treatment effects on yield but that these effects probably were arrived at indirectly through different stands, which then resulted in different yields. One further complication might be mentioned. Yields for low stand are often higher per plant than for high stand because of less competition for the available plant food and moisture. This apparently did not happen in our sugar beet example but in general should be considered. Also, it should be noted again that we considered only the linear effect of stand on yield; often the effect may be curvilinear. A final point is that although the treatments did affect the stand, the stand could be measured without error.

In this case, there is little need to set up the average variance of adjusted treatment differences, but we present it to complete the example:

$$\overline{s^2(d^*)} = \frac{.4826}{6}\left(1 + \frac{19{,}337}{28{,}665}\right) = .135.$$

The exact variance for $(t_1^* - t_2^*)$, for example, is

$$.2413\left[\frac{2}{6} + \frac{(66)^2}{28{,}665}\right] = .117.$$

The unadjusted and adjusted treatment means are:

| Means | Treatment 1 | 2 | 3 | 4 | 5 | 6 | 7 | All |
|---|---|---|---|---|---|---|---|---|
| Unadjusted | 3.353 | 5.630 | 3.563 | 6.487 | 7.080 | 3.538 | 7.353 | 5.286 |
| Adjusted | 4.693 | 5.399 | 4.931 | 5.828 | 5.526 | 4.878 | 5.746 | 5.286 |

The variance of an unadjusted mean difference would have been

$$\left(\frac{2}{6}\right)\left(\frac{23.2326}{30}\right) = .258.$$

Hence $I = .258/.135 = 1.91$.

**21.3. The Use of Simple Covariance for Other Experimental Designs.** No attempt will be made in this book to outline in detail the computational procedures for the use of simple covariance with other experimental designs. The computing procedure for other complete-blocks designs is exactly the same as for randomized blocks, namely:

(i) Set up the usual analysis of variance given in Chap. 18, but include the sum of squares for $x$ and the sum of cross products as well as the sum of squares for $y$ for each line in the analysis.

(ii) Compute the error line by subtraction for SSE, $E_{xy}$, and $E_{xx}$.

(iii) Compute $\text{SSE}^* = \text{SSE} - bE_{xy} = \text{SSE} - E_{xy}^2/E_{xx}$. $\text{MSE}^* = s^{*2}$.

(iv) Compute the (error + treatment) = (error)′ line by adding the treatment line to the error line.

(v) $(\text{SSE}^*)' = \text{SSE}' - b'E'_{xy}$.

(vi) Compute the adjusted sum of squares for treatments,

$$\text{SST}^* = (\text{SSE}^*)' - \text{SSE}^*.$$
$$\text{MST}^* = \text{SST}^*/(p - 1).$$

(vii) $F = \text{MST}^*/s^{*2}$.

(viii) $t_i^* + \bar{Y} = \bar{T}_i - b(\bar{X}_{i.} - \bar{X})$.

(ix) $\overline{s^2(d^*)} = \dfrac{2s^{*2}}{r}\left[1 + \dfrac{T_{xx}}{(p-1)E_{xx}}\right]$.

If the experimenter wishes to test a single degree of freedom of the $(p - 1)$ treatment degrees of freedom, he must go through the same procedure as outlined above with this one degree of freedom replacing the treatment line in the computations. If several of these single components are desired, an approximate method of computation has been suggested by Cochran and Cox.[1] Compute

$$S(y - bx)^2 = Sy^2 - 2bSxy + b^2Sx^2$$

for each component of the treatment sum of squares. This computation would give the correct value of SSE but overestimates each of the components of SST. However, the bias is generally small, and if the experiment is a complicated factorial, much labor is saved in testing the various main effects and interactions.

See reference 6 for the use of covariance with lattice designs.

## 21.4. The Use of Multiple Covariance.

$$Y_{ij} = \mu + \tau_i^* + \beta_j^* + \sum_{k=1}^{m} \beta_k x_{kij} + \epsilon_{ij}.$$

Snedecor[5] presents an example of a randomized blocks experiment on wheat yields in Great Britain with two fixed variates (height of shoots at ear emergence and number of plants at tillering). The treatments were 6 different places, and the blocks were 3 different years. The computing procedure is as follows for $m$ fixed variates:

(i) Derive a table of sums of squares and cross-products for total, blocks, and treatments (and any other component in the analysis, such as columns in a Latin square).

(ii) Compute the error line for each sum of squares and cross products by subtracting blocks, treatments, and any other component from the total. Use these error values to compute the $\{b_k\}$ and $R_e^2$, the squared multiple correlation coefficient for the error line.

(iii) Compute an (error + treatment) line and $R_{e+t}^2$.

(iv) $\text{SSE}^* = \text{SSE} - R_e^2\text{SSE} = \text{SSE}(1 - R_e^2)$.

$(\text{SSE}^*)' = \text{SSE}'(1 - R_{e+t}^2)$.

(v) $s^{*2} = \text{SSE}^* \div$ (error d.f. − number of fixed variates).
$\text{MST}^* = [(\text{SSE}^*)' - \text{SSE}^*]/(p - 1)$.
$F = \text{MST}^*/s^{*2}$.

(vi) $t_i^* + \bar{Y} = \bar{T}_i - \sum_{k=1}^{m} b_k(\bar{X}_{ki\cdot} - \bar{X}_k)$, where $b_k$ is estimated in (ii).

(vii) If estimates of the variances of adjusted treatment differences are wanted, the $b$'s should be derived by a matrix-inversion method in order to obtain the variances and covariances of the $b$'s.

$$s^2(t_i^* - t_l^*) = s^{*2}\left[\frac{2}{r} + \sum_k \sum_{k'} c_{kk'}(\bar{X}_{ki\cdot} - \bar{X}_{kl\cdot})(\bar{X}_{k'i\cdot} - \bar{X}_{k'l\cdot})\right],$$

where $c_{kk'}$ is the element in the inverse matrix of the error line. The average variance of adjusted treatment differences is

$$\frac{2s^{*2}}{r}\left[1 + \sum_k \sum_{k'} \frac{c_{kk'}T_{kk'}}{p - 1}\right],$$

where $T_{kk'}$ is the sum of cross products for $(x_k x_{k'})$ in the treatment line of (i),

$$T_{kk'} = \frac{\underset{i}{S}(X_{ki} - \bar{X}_k)(X_{k'i} - \bar{X}_{k'})}{r}.$$

## EXERCISES

**21.1.** Derive these relationships for $E_{xy}$ and $E_{xx}$:

$$E_{xy} = S(x_{ij} - \bar{x}_{\cdot j} - \bar{x}_{i\cdot})(y_{ij} - \bar{B}_j - \bar{T}_i),$$
$$E_{xx} = S(x_{ij} - \bar{x}_{\cdot j} - \bar{x}_{i\cdot})^2.$$

**21.2.** (*a*) Derive Finney's result for the average variance of the difference between two adjusted treatment means, presented in Sec. 21.2. (*b*) Also, derive the result for multiple covariance given in Sec. 21.4.

**21.3.** (*a*) Make a complete least-squares solution of a simple covariance analysis for a Latin-square design.

(*b*) Illustrate the results in (*a*) by analyzing the following 5 × 5 Latin-square experiment on the yield in bags per acre of No. 1 Irish potatoes ($Y$), adjusted for the percentage of No. 1's ($X$). The treatments were different amounts (pounds) of $P_2O_5$ per acre: $a = 0$, $b = 40$, $c = 80$, $d = 120$, $e = 160$.

| Rows | Columns | | | | | | | | | | | | | | | Total | |
|---|---|---|---|---|---|---|---|---|---|---|---|---|---|---|---|---|---|
| | 1 | | | 2 | | | 3 | | | 4 | | | 5 | | | | |
| | *t* | *Y* | *X* | *t* | *Y* | *X* | *t* | *Y* | *X* | *t* | *Y* | *X* | *t* | *Y* | *X* | *Y* | *X* |
| 1 | *a* | 134.0 | 91 | *b* | 149.1 | 88 | *c* | 141.3 | 87 | *d* | 161.3 | 91 | *e* | 149.2 | 91 | 734.9 | 448 |
| 2 | *b* | 148.5 | 90 | *d* | 148.5 | 91 | *e* | 199.3 | 94 | *a* | 148.5 | 90 | *c* | 152.7 | 93 | 797.5 | 458 |
| 3 | *c* | 145.2 | 93 | *e* | 149.5 | 95 | *a* | 119.9 | 90 | *b* | 149.2 | 94 | *d* | 145.8 | 90 | 709.6 | 462 |
| 4 | *d* | 171.1 | 91 | *c* | 169.0 | 94 | *b* | 144.9 | 89 | *e* | 170.8 | 95 | *a* | 130.4 | 88 | 786.2 | 457 |
| 5 | *e* | 175.8 | 91 | *a* | 153.4 | 94 | *d* | 168.9 | 92 | *c* | 167.6 | 96 | *b* | 141.5 | 93 | 807.2 | 466 |
| Total | | 774.6 | 456 | | 769.5 | 462 | | 774.3 | 452 | | 797.4 | 466 | | 719.6 | 455 | 3,835.4 | 2,291 |

$$SY^2 = 595{,}038.38, \qquad SXY = 351{,}944.8, \qquad SX^2 = 210{,}085.$$

Show that $b = 2.0616$ and $s^{*2} = 127.18$.

(*c*) Analyze the linear component of the treatment mean square by the exact method and by the Cochran and Cox approximation presented in Sec. 21.3. Then show that the deviations from a linear trend are not significant.

**21.4.** Consider a single degree of freedom to test for the adjusted effect of phosphate in the sugar beet example (Example 21.1):

$$t = -t_1 + t_2 - t_3 + t_4 - t_6 + t_7.$$

(*a*) Use the exact procedure to show that the effect of phosphate is significant even after adjusting for stand.

(*b*) Show that the approximate procedure presented in Sec. 21.3 cannot be used in this case.

**21.5.** The vitamin $B_2$ example used in Chap. 15 and Exercise 18.6 can also be analyzed by covariance.

(*a*) Analyze the effects of the three soil moistures on the amount of vitamin $B_2$ after adjusting for the effect of $X_1$.

(*b*) Analyze the effect of these three soil moistures after adjusting for $X_1$ and $X_3$.

(*c*) Can the fixed variates be considered independent of the soil moistures?

**21.6.** Johnson and Tsao[7] analyzed the influence of sex, scholastic standing, individual order, and grade on education development as measured by the *Iowa Tests of Education Development*. There were 3 of each of the last 3 variables and the 2 sexes, giving a total of 54 treatment combinations. An initial score and the mental age of each student were determined before the development tests were administered. Only one student was tested for each treatment combination. The final scores ($Y$), initial scores ($X_1$), and mental age ($X_2$) were as shown in the accompanying table:

DATA OF EXERCISE 21.6

| Sex | Scholastic standing | Individual order | Grade 10 | | | Grade 11 | | | Grade 12 | | |
|---|---|---|---|---|---|---|---|---|---|---|---|
| | | | $Y$ | $X_1$ | $X_2$ | $Y$ | $X_1$ | $X_2$ | $Y$ | $X_1$ | $X_2$ |
| Male | Good | 1 | 30 | 28 | 45 | 26 | 22 | 62 | 29 | 25 | 60 |
| | | 2 | 25 | 22 | 58 | 26 | 21 | 57 | 29 | 24 | 88 |
| | | 3 | 22 | 19 | 46 | 24 | 21 | 65 | 22 | 19 | 64 |
| | Average | 1 | 26 | 22 | 56 | 24 | 25 | 54 | 23 | 21 | 64 |
| | | 2 | 17 | 14 | 19 | 23 | 18 | 55 | 20 | 17 | 47 |
| | | 3 | 14 | 14 | 29 | 15 | 13 | 24 | 19 | 17 | 75 |
| | Poor | 1 | 18 | 18 | 34 | 18 | 17 | 40 | 17 | 16 | 29 |
| | | 2 | 17 | 14 | 17 | 16 | 13 | 24 | 15 | 15 | 38 |
| | | 3 | 12 | 9 | 19 | 13 | 12 | 23 | 14 | 12 | 28 |
| Female | Good | 1 | 21 | 16 | 44 | 26 | 22 | 60 | 33 | 29 | 94 |
| | | 2 | 21 | 21 | 44 | 25 | 22 | 57 | 29 | 29 | 89 |
| | | 3 | 19 | 17 | 6 | 23 | 19 | 52 | 25 | 22 | 78 |
| | Average | 1 | 20 | 18 | 38 | 22 | 19 | 54 | 23 | 21 | 50 |
| | | 2 | 18 | 16 | 27 | 21 | 19 | 54 | 18 | 19 | 57 |
| | | 3 | 14 | 14 | 18 | 17 | 16 | 52 | 17 | 17 | 43 |
| | Poor | 1 | 14 | 9 | 18 | 19 | 17 | 40 | 15 | 13 | 36 |
| | | 2 | 12 | 7 | 18 | 15 | 12 | 28 | 15 | 14 | 35 |
| | | 3 | 9 | 7 | 5 | 13 | 12 | 48 | 10 | 9 | 14 |

$$SY = 1068, \quad SX_1 = 944, \quad SX_2 = 2{,}379,$$
$$SY^2 = 22{,}730, \quad SX_1^2 = 17{,}926, \quad SX_2^2 = 127{,}639,$$
$$SX_1Y = 20{,}116, \quad SX_2Y = 52{,}005, \quad SX_1X_2 = 46{,}227.$$

(*a*) Set up an analysis of simple covariance on $Y$, using $X_2$ as the fixed variate with the main effects of sex, scholastic standing, order, and grade pulled out plus all two-factor interactions. Pool the three-factor and four-factor interactions as error (see Sec. 20.2).

(*b*) Repeat (*a*), but with both dependent variates.

**21.7.** Covariance was used to reduce the experimental error in a randomized blocks experiment on scuppernong grapes.[8] Four blocks and 5 magnesium treatments were used. Four plants were used per plot. The yields were in terms of pounds per plant. Two fixed variates were used to estimate yielding ability prior to treatment: $X_1$ = a score of 1 to 5 given by the investigators as to the vigor and size of each of the eight arms on each plant; $X_2$ = diameter of each arm at a point 18 inches from the crown. For both $X$'s, the individual arm measurements were cumulated for each plant. The sum of squares and cross products were as follows:

| | d.f. | $Sy^2$ | $Sx_1y$ | $Sx_2y$ | $Sx_1x_2$ | $Sx_1^2$ | $Sx_2^2$ |
|---|---|---|---|---|---|---|---|
| Total | 19 | 1,001.90 | 306.25 | 629.55 | 308.64 | 154.52 | 963.44 |
| Blocks | 3 | 223.50 | 39.81 | −85.95 | 9.07 | 20.64 | 77.19 |
| Treatments | 4 | 144.60 | 64.54 | 246.90 | 113.11 | 32.89 | 436.32 |

(*a*) Complete the analysis of covariance using only $X_1$. What was the efficiency of the covariance analysis?

(*b*) Repeat (*a*) using $X_2$ also.

(*c*) The treatment means per plant were as follows:

| | I | II | III | IV | V | Total |
|---|---|---|---|---|---|---|
| $Y$ | 13.79 | 20.28 | 17.77 | 19.75 | 14.33 | 17.18 |
| $X_1$ | 19.56 | 22.88 | 22.56 | 22.56 | 20.81 | 21.67 |
| $X_2$ | 64.44 | 75.06 | 72.56 | 73.69 | 64.31 | 70.01 |

Derive the adjusted treatment means in (*a*) and (*b*) and the average standard error of the difference between two adjusted means.

**21.8.** Covariance can also be used to make an analysis of variance when one or more of the plots are missing: this is necessary only when a double or higher restriction is made on the design, as with a randomized complete-blocks or a Latin-square design. The procedure is to set $Y = 0$ and $X = -1$ for the missing plot and $X = 0$ elsewhere. If there are several missing plots, multiple covariance must be used, with $X_1 = -1$ for the first one, $X_2 = -1$ for the second, etc. Use the method of covariance to make the analysis of Exercise 18.12. For the application of these methods to other designs, see reference 9.

**21.9.** For the application of covariance techniques to disproportionate frequency problems, see reference 10.

**21.10.** The analysis of covariance is often used to determine whether or not the same regression coefficient ($\beta$) applies to all treatments. Snedecor[5] presents an example of this type of analysis. Use the vitamin $B_2$ data [Exercise 21.5(*a*)] to compute a separate $b$ (for $X_1$) for each of the three soil moistures. Then set up the following analysis, where $b_i$ is the regression coefficient of $Y$ on $X_1$ for each of the three treatments ($i = 1,2,3$).

| Source of variation | Degrees of freedom | SS | MS |
|---|---|---|---|
| Deviations from average regression ($b$) | 23 | SSE* | |
| Deviations from individual regressions | 21 | (SSE)″ | $s''^2$ |
| Differences among individual regressions | 2 | SSE* − (SSE)″ | $\frac{\text{SSE}^* - (\text{SSE})''}{2}$ |

$$F = [\text{SSE}^* - (\text{SSE})'']/2s''^2,$$

$$(\text{SSE})'' = Sy^2 - \text{SST} - [b_1 \underset{1}{S} x_1 y + b_2 \underset{2}{S} x_1 y + b_3 \underset{3}{S} x_1 y],$$

where $\underset{i}{S}$ applies to summation over treatment $i$.

**21.11.** In Example 21.1, neglect the block effects and apply the methods of Exercise 21.10 to determine a separate regression line for each treatment. Graph these data, and draw in each regression line and the over-all regression line.

### References Cited

1. Cochran, W. G., and G. M. Cox, *Experimental Designs*, John Wiley & Sons, Inc., New York, 1950.
2. Cochran, W. G., "The Analysis of Covariance," *Inst. Stat. Mim. Ser.* 6 (1946).
3. Fisher, R. A., *Statistical Methods for Research Workers*, 4th ed., Oliver & Boyd, Ltd., Edinburgh and London, 1932. Sec. 49.1.
4. Finney, D. J., "Standard Errors of Yields Adjusted for Regression on an Independent Measurement," *Biometrics Bull.*, **2**:53–55 (1946).
5. Snedecor, G. W., *Statistical Methods*, 4th ed., Collegiate Press, Inc., of Iowa State College, Ames, Iowa, 1946.
6. Cox, G. M., R. C. Eckhardt, and W. G. Cochran, "The Analysis of Lattice and Triple Lattice Experiments in Corn Varietal Tests," *Iowa State Coll. Agr. Expt. Sta. Research Bull.* 281 (1940).
7. Johnson, P. O., and F. Tsao, "Factorial Design and Covariance in the Study of Individual Educational Development," *Psychometrika*, **10**:133–162 (1945).
8. Rigney, J. A., E. B. Morrow, and W. L. Lott, "A Method of Controlling Experimental Error for Perennial Horticultural Crops," *Proc. Am. Soc. Hort. Sci.*, **54**:209–212 (1949).
9. Anderson, R. L., "Missing Plot Techniques," *Biometrics Bull.*, **2**:41–47 (1946).
10. Hazel, L. N., "The Covariance Analysis of Multiple Classification Tables with Unequal Subclass Numbers," *Biometrics Bull.*, **2**:21–25 (1946).

### Other Reading

Bartlett, M. S., "An Examination of the Value of Covariance in Dairy Cow Nutrition Experiments," *J. Agr. Sci.*, **25**:238–244 (1935).

Cochran, W. G., and C. I. Bliss, "Discriminant Functions with Covariance," *Ann. Math. Stat.*, **19**:151–176 (1948).

Cornish, E. A., "The Analysis of Covariance in Quasi-factorial Designs," *Ann. Eugenics*, **10**:269–279 (1940).

DeLury, D. B., "The Analysis of Covariance," *Biometrics*, **4**:153–170 (1948).

Fisher, R. A., *Design of Experiments*, 4th ed., Oliver & Boyd, Ltd., Edinburgh and London, 1947.

Fisher, R. A., "The Analysis of Covariance Method for the Relation between a Part and the Whole," *Biometrics*, **3**:65–68 (1947).

Jackson, R. W. B., "Application of the Analysis of Variance and Covariance Method to Educational Problems," *Univ. Toronto Dept. Ed. Research Bull.* 11 (1940).

Johnson, P. O., *Statistical Methods in Research*, Prentice-Hall, Inc., New York, 1949.

Lindquist, E. F., *Statistical Analysis in Educational Research*, Houghton Mifflin Company, Boston, 1940.

Mood, A. M., *Introduction to the Theory of Statistics*, McGraw-Hill Book Company, Inc., New York, 1950.

Nair, K. R., "The Application of Covariance Techniques to Field Experiments with Missing or Mixed Up Yields," *Sankhyā*, **4**:581–588 (1940).

Quenouille, M. H., "The Analysis of Covariance and Non-orthogonal Comparisons," *Biometrics*, **4**:240–246 (1948).

Wilks, S. S., "The Analysis of Variance and Covariance in Non-orthogonal Data," *Metron*, **13**: 141–158 (1938).

Wishart, J., "Tests of Significance in the Analysis of Covariance," *J. Roy. Stat. Soc. Suppl.*, **3**:79–82 (1936).

# CHAPTER 22

## VARIANCE COMPONENTS: ALL RANDOM COMPONENTS, EXCEPT THE MEAN

**22.1. Introduction.** The regression models used in the previous chapters of Part II assumed that all variates were fixed except for a single random error term. Most experiments are designed so that several components are random instead of all except one being fixed. That is, the blocks in a randomized-blocks design may be assumed to be randomly selected from a large population of blocks, so that the block-to-block part of the analysis of variance is also a random component. And in sampling experiments and surveys and in genetics experiments, the model almost always postulates several random components: for example, (i) a sample of soils to determine the basic sources of variability, such as plot-to-plot differences, sample-to-sample differences in the same plot, and laboratory determination errors; (ii) a sample survey covering an entire region with a few counties selected from the large number of counties in the region, then a few areas selected from each sample county, and perhaps only one or two families from each selected area; (iii) a corn-breeding experiment with parents taken from a population produced by random mating, the progeny randomly assigned to plots, and a random selection of plants from each plot.

The regression model using several sources of random variation can take on one of two forms: (*a*) every variate, except the general mean, is a random variate, or (*b*) there is a mixture of random and fixed variates. Eisenhart[1] has presented the basic difference between (*a*) and the model used in the previous chapters of Part II and has indicated the importance of (*b*) without delving into the many theoretical difficulties involved in its use. Crump[2] presents the basic theory for (*a*) and includes an extensive bibliography of the use of components of variance. Crump[3] presents a more recent bibliography of articles on variance components and discusses problems which merit further investigation. R. A. Fisher[4] indicated the additive properties of variances in the first edition of his *Statistical Methods for Research Workers.* Yates and Zacopanay[5] indicated the application of these methods to field sampling; among others, Cochran[6] extended them to enumerative surveys. Much of the recent development in the field of quantitative genetics has been built on a variance-components model, as discussed in references 7 and 8.

One of the authors of this book has presented the basic theory required for the mixed model (*b*) in an article on the analysis of price data.[9] The reader is cautioned that this last article has many drawbacks from an economic point of view, but the difficulties encountered in the use of a mixed model are adequately outlined therein. This article drew much of its theory from articles by Daniels[10] and Satterthwaite.[11] The mixed model is also required in the analysis of a series of experiments, such as those conducted over several years and at several places. Cochran and Cox[12] indicate some of the difficulties for this type of experimentation.

We shall discuss general uses of model (*a*) in this chapter, mixed models in Chap. 23, and the use of variance components for balanced incomplete-blocks designs and lattice designs in Chap. 24 and shall give a general summary in Chap. 25.

**22.2. A Randomized-blocks Model.** Let us assume that we have $p$ treatments, each allocated to each of $r$ blocks, and $q$ samples taken from each of the $pr$ plots, assuming that in each case the particular treatment, block, and sample are random samples from infinite (at least, very large) populations.† Hence there are $prq$ samples. The model for the yield of the $k$th sample from the $i$th treatment on the $j$th block is

$$Y_{ijk} = \mu + \tau_i + \beta_j + (\tau\beta)_{ij} + \epsilon_{ijk},$$

where $\tau_i$, $\beta_j$, $(\tau\beta)_{ij}$, and $\epsilon_{ijk}$ are all assumed to be NID with means 0 and variances, $\sigma_t^2$, $\sigma_b^2$, $\sigma_{tb}^2$, and $\sigma_e^2$, respectively. Again it should be made clear that for purposes of estimation, the assumption of normality is not needed. This assumption is required, however, if the usual tests of significance and confidence limits are used. These variances are called *variance components.* Hence

$$E(Y_{ijk}) = \mu, \qquad \sigma^2(Y_{ijk}) = \sigma_t^2 + \sigma_b^2 + \sigma_{tb}^2 + \sigma_e^2.$$

An experiment of this kind is set up to estimate the mean, $\mu$, and the variance of this estimate and/or to obtain estimates of the variance components themselves. The statistical geneticists, for example, are interested mainly in the variance components. If the experiment was set up to obtain an estimate of $\mu$, it is understood that the estimate, $\bar{Y}$, will deviate from $\mu$ because only a sample of treatments, blocks, and plots (or samples from the subclasses) is used in the experiment. In other words, from one experiment to another, one could expect different values of the

† Or we might consider $r$ blocks with $pq$ plots per block, each treatment being assigned at random to $q$ plots per block. Although the two types of experiments are analyzed the same, the interpretations are different. The procedure given in the body of the text produces an estimate of sample-to-sample fluctuation in the same plot, while the one mentioned in this footnote produces an estimate of the plot-to-plot variation within a block.

$\{\tau_i\}$, $\{\beta_j\}$, $\{\tau\beta_{ij}\}$, and $\{\epsilon_{ijk}\}$ to appear. The results of the experiment can be used to estimate the variability of these random variables and hence to furnish an estimate of the variance of $\bar{Y}$. This estimate of $\sigma^2(\bar{Y})$ can be used to construct confidence limits for $\mu$ and to indicate how changes in future experimental plans might affect the precision of the estimate. The reader will note that this type of experimentation is fundamentally different from that described in the previous four chapters, even though the same analysis is used. In those chapters we were interested in estimating certain treatment effects under very limited experimental conditions and in making tests regarding the differences between these effects. Here we want to estimate a single mean with application to a wider area than that of the experimental plots used in the experiment.

If the experimenter is interested only in the variance components, the problem is certainly much different from that of estimating a mean. In this case he wants confidence limits for the variance components, or functions of the variance components. We have stated previously that nonnormality was probably not too serious for estimating the confidence limits for means, and if it were serious, some simple transformation would generally remedy the situation. However, the situation is not so simple for variance components. As we shall see later, the only estimates of the variances of these estimated variance components will be in terms of the components themselves, a satisfactory condition if normality holds. However, slight deviations from normality may require a knowledge of other data than that furnished by the analysis of variance (such as higher moments) in order to estimate these variances. As will be shown later, the problem of setting up confidence limits for variance components is far from solved.

The estimates of the variance components will be designated as $\sigma^2 \doteq s^2$ with the same subscripts. Obviously $\mu \doteq \bar{Y}$. Since we have more than one component of variation in this model, the method of least squares cannot be used in the estimation process. Instead we must utilize a more general estimation procedure, such as the method of maximum likelihood. In order to present this material in its practical connection with the analysis-of-variance problems discussed previously, we shall assume that the data have been summarized in an analysis-of-variance table and then proceed to derive the expected values of the mean squares, using our variance-components model. Then the estimates of these variance components are found by equating the mean squares and their expectations, where each $\sigma^2$ is replaced by its corresponding $s^2$ in the expectations. These analysis-of-variance estimates are the same as the maximum-likelihood estimates for an orthogonal model such as the randomized complete-blocks model, if the errors are normally distributed. For non-orthogonal models, such as a disproportionate frequency factorial, the maximum-likelihood equations are very difficult to solve (requiring iterative procedures in many cases), and the two sets of estimates would not be the same. We can derive unbiased estimates of the variance components from the analysis of variance, but there is no guarantee that these estimates are the most efficient which could be devised; in fact it is often doubtful that they are even moderately efficient for multiple-classification data with unequal numbers in the subclasses.

The analysis of variance pertaining to the randomized complete-blocks model is:

| Source of variation | Degrees of freedom | Sum of squares | Mean square† | $E(V)$† |
|---|---|---|---|---|
| Blocks | $r-1$ | SSB | $\text{MSB} = V_1$ | $\sigma_e^2 + q\sigma_{tb}^2 + pq\sigma_b^2 \equiv \sigma_1^2$ |
| Treatments | $p-1$ | SST | $\text{MST} = V_2$ | $\sigma_e^2 + q\sigma_{tb}^2 + rq\sigma_t^2 \equiv \sigma_2^2$ |
| $T \times B$ | $(r-1)(p-1)$ | SS($TB$) | $\text{MS}(TB) = V_3$ | $\sigma_e^2 + q\sigma_{tb}^2 \equiv \sigma_3^2$ |
| Sampling error | $(q-1)rp$ | SSE | $\text{MSE} = V_4$ | $\sigma_e^2 \equiv \sigma_4^2$ |

† We shall use $V$ to stand for a mean square.

$$\text{SSB} = \frac{\sum_j (B_j - G/r)^2}{pq} = \frac{\sum_j [(B_j - pq\mu) - (G - rpq\mu)/r]^2}{pq}$$

$$= \frac{\sum_{j=1}^{r} (B_j - pq\mu)^2}{pq} - \frac{(G - rpq\mu)^2}{rpq},$$

$$B_j - pq\mu = q \sum_i \tau_i + pq\beta_j + q \sum_i (\tau\beta)_{ij} + \sum_i \sum_k \epsilon_{ijk},$$

$$G - rpq\mu = rq \sum_i \tau_i + pq \sum_j \beta_j + q \sum_i \sum_j (\tau\beta)_{ij} + \sum_i \sum_j \sum_k \epsilon_{ijk}.$$

Hence

$$E(\text{SSB}) = r\left[\frac{pq^2\sigma_t^2 + p^2q^2\sigma_b^2 + pq^2\sigma_{tb}^2 + pq\sigma_e^2}{pq}\right] - \left[\frac{r^2pq^2\sigma_t^2 + rp^2q^2\sigma_b^2 + rpq^2\sigma_{tb}^2 + rpq\sigma_e^2}{rpq}\right]$$

$$= (r-1)pq\sigma_b^2 + (r-1)q\sigma_{tb}^2 + (r-1)\sigma_e^2,$$

$$E(V_1) = \frac{E(\text{SSB})}{r-1} = pq\sigma_b^2 + q\sigma_{tb}^2 + \sigma_e^2 \equiv \sigma_1^2.$$

Since SST will be the same as SSB except for $p$ and $r$ and $\sigma_t^2$ and $\sigma_b^2$ interchanged, it is evident that

$$\text{SST} = \frac{\sum_i (T_i - rq\mu)^2}{rq} - \frac{(G - rpq\mu)^2}{rpq},$$

$$T_i - rq\mu = rq\tau_i + q\sum_j \beta_j + q\sum_j (\tau\beta)_{ij} + \sum_j\sum_k \epsilon_{ijk},$$

$$E(\text{SST}) = (p-1)(rq\sigma_t^2 + q\sigma_{tb}^2 + \sigma_e^2),$$

$$E(V_2) = rq\sigma_t^2 + q\sigma_{tb}^2 + \sigma_e^2 \equiv \sigma_2^2.$$

Also, we know that

$$\text{SS}(TB) = \frac{\sum_i\sum_j \left[(TB)_{ij} - \frac{T_i}{r} - \frac{B_j}{p} + \frac{G}{rp}\right]^2}{q}$$

$$= \frac{\sum_i\sum_j \left[(TB)_{ij} - q\mu - \frac{T_i - rq\mu}{r} - \frac{B_j - pq\mu}{p} + \frac{G - rpq\mu}{rp}\right]^2}{q}$$

$$= \frac{\sum_i\sum_j [(TB)_{ij} - q\mu]^2}{q} - \frac{\sum_i (T_i - rq\mu)^2}{rq} - \frac{\sum_j (B_j - pq\mu)^2}{pq} + \frac{(G - rpq\mu)^2}{rpq}$$

where $(TB)_{ij} - q\mu = q[\tau_i + \beta_j + (\tau\beta)_{ij}] + \sum_k \epsilon_{ijk}$.

Hence

$$\begin{aligned} E[\text{SS}(TB)] &= rp[q(\sigma_t^2 + \sigma_b^2 + \sigma_{tb}^2) + \sigma_e^2] - p[rq\sigma_t^2 + q\sigma_b^2 + q\sigma_{tb}^2 + \sigma_e^2] \\ &\quad - r[q\sigma_t^2 + pq\sigma_b^2 + q\sigma_{tb}^2 + \sigma_e^2] + [rq\sigma_t^2 + pq\sigma_b^2 + q\sigma_{tb}^2 + \sigma_e^2] \\ &= q(rp - p - r + 1)\sigma_{tb}^2 + (rp - p - r + 1)\sigma_e^2 \\ &= (r-1)(p-1)(q\sigma_{tb}^2 + \sigma_e^2), \end{aligned}$$

$$E(V_3) = q\sigma_{tb}^2 + \sigma_e^2 \equiv \sigma_3^2.$$

Finally we know that the total sum of squares is

$$Sy^2 = S(Y - G/rpq)^2 = S[Y - rpq\mu]^2 - [G - rpq\mu]^2/rpq.$$

The expected value of this total is

$$rq(p-1)\sigma_t^2 + pq(r-1)\sigma_b^2 + q(rp-1)\sigma_{tb}^2 + (rpq-1)\sigma_e^2.$$

It is easy to show that

$$E(V_4) = \sigma_e^2 \equiv \sigma_4^2.$$

The residual also can be expressed as†

$$e_{ijk} = Y_{ijk} - (TB)_{ij}/q = \epsilon_{ijk} - \sum_k \epsilon_{ijk}/q,$$

$$E(e_{ijk}^2) = (q-1)\sigma_e^2/q, \qquad E(\text{SSE}) = rp(q-1)\sigma_e^2.$$

Since

$$\bar{Y} = \mu + \frac{\sum_i \tau_i}{p} + \frac{\sum_j \beta_j}{r} + \frac{\sum_i\sum_j (\tau\beta)_{ij}}{rp} + \frac{\sum_i\sum_j\sum_k \epsilon_{ijk}}{rpq},$$

$$E(\bar{Y}) = \mu \qquad \text{and } \sigma^2(\bar{Y}) = \frac{\sigma_t^2}{p} + \frac{\sigma_b^2}{r} + \frac{\sigma_{tb}^2}{rp} + \frac{\sigma_e^2}{rpq} = \frac{\sigma_1^2 + \sigma_2^2 - \sigma_3^2}{rpq}.$$

If a particular treatment mean is of importance,

$$\bar{T}_i = \frac{\underset{jk}{S} Y_{ijk}}{rq} = \mu + \tau_i + \frac{\sum_j \beta_j}{r} + \frac{\sum_j (\tau\beta)_{ij}}{r} + \frac{\sum_j\sum_k \epsilon_{ijk}}{rq},$$

$$E(\bar{T}_i) = \mu + \tau_i,$$

$$\sigma^2(\bar{T}_i) = \frac{\sigma_b^2}{r} + \frac{\sigma_{tb}^2}{r} + \frac{\sigma_e^2}{rq} = \frac{\sigma_1^2 + (p-1)\sigma_3^2}{rpq}.$$

This assumes $\tau_i$ is now a fixed variate (see Chap. 23).

The relative importance of various components can be assessed in $\sigma^2(\bar{Y})$ or $\sigma^2(\bar{T}_i)$ and compared with the costs of obtaining the sample to enable the experimenter better to plan his future experiments to estimate $\mu$ or $\tau_i$. For example, if it costs $C_e$ for each sample in a plot and $C_p$ for each plot, then the total cost per treatment is

$$C_i = r'q'C_e + r'C_p,$$

where $r'$ plots are sampled and $p'$ samples per plot. Suppose now that the total cost per treatment is fixed at $C$. We are then led to minimize $\sigma^2(\bar{T}_i)$ subject to the restriction $C_i = C$, in other words, to select $r'$ and $q'$ so as to minimize

$$\sigma^2(\bar{T}_i) + \lambda(C_i - C).$$

$$-\frac{\sigma_e^2}{r'q'^2} + \lambda(r'C_e) = 0, \qquad -\frac{1}{r'^2}\left(\sigma_b^2 + \sigma_{tb}^2 + \frac{\sigma_e^2}{q'}\right) + \lambda(q'C_e + C_p) = 0,$$

$$C_i = C.$$

The solutions are

$$q' = \sqrt{\frac{C_p\sigma_e^2}{C_e(\sigma_b^2 + \sigma_{tb}^2)}}, \qquad r' = \frac{C}{q'C_e + C_p}.$$

† See the footnote on page 314 for a discussion of this residual. $\epsilon$ may represent either sampling error or plot-to-plot error, depending on the randomization plan.

Of course $q'$ and $r'$ must be integers, and so the exact minimum in general will not be reached.

In order to make the estimates of the variance components ($\sigma_e^2, \sigma_{tb}^2, \sigma_t^2$, and $\sigma_b^2$) unbiased, we merely replace the components by their estimates ($s_e^2, s_{tb}^2, s_t^2$, and $s_b^2$, respectively) in the $E(V)$ column and equate respective rows in the $V$ and $E(V)$ columns. Hence $\sigma_e^2 \doteq s_e^2 = V_4$, and

$$\sigma_{tb}^2 \doteq s_{tb}^2 = \frac{V_3 - V_4}{q},$$

$$\sigma_t^2 \doteq s_t^2 = \frac{V_2 - V_3}{rq},$$

$$\sigma_b^2 \doteq s_b^2 = \frac{V_1 - V_3}{pq}.$$

It can be shown that all of the quantities $[B_j - G/r]$, $[T_i - G/p]$, $[Y_{ijk} - (TB)_{ij}/q]$, and $[(TB)_{ij} - T_i/r - B_j/p + G/rp]$ are orthogonal to one another. Hence the various mean squares are noncorrelated. Since any $V_i$ is a sum of squared linear functions of NID variates, it is independently distributed as $\chi^2\sigma_i^2$ with $f_i$ degrees of freedom, where $i$ stands for some particular line in the analysis-of-variance table with $f_i$ degrees of freedom in that line and $\sigma_i^2 = E(V_i)$. Also,

$$\sigma^2(V_i) = \frac{2\sigma_i^4}{f_i} \doteq \frac{2V_i^2}{f_i + 2}.\dagger$$

In order to use the method of maximum likelihood to estimate the variance components, some preliminary transformations are needed. When the only random effect is $\epsilon$($\tau$, $\beta$, and $\tau\beta$ are fixed effects), the $Y_{ijk}$ are

$$\text{NID}(\mu + \tau_i + \beta_j + \tau\beta_{ij};\, \sigma_e^2).$$

However, when some of tbe other effects are also random, the $Y_{ijk}$ are correlated. For example when everything is random except $\mu$, the covariance between $Y_{ijk}$ and $Y_{ijk'}$ is

$$\sigma_t^2 + \sigma_b^2 + \sigma_{tb}^2.$$

Hence the simultaneous distribution of the $Y$'s is a multivariate normal distribution with nonzero covariance elements. This distribution can be simplified by splitting $(Y_{ijk} - \bar{Y})$ into the sum of orthogonal parts as follows:

$$Y_{ijk} - \bar{Y} = (qY_{ijk} - TB_{ij})/q + (TB_{ij} - T_i/r - B_j/p + G/rp)/q$$
$$+ (pT_i - G)/rpq + (rB_j - G)/rpq,$$

† Some attention needs to be paid to the use of the fourth moment of the observations in estimating $\sigma_i^4$. In some sampling problems, it may be possible to obtain several independent samples, determining $V_i$ from each, and then estimating $\sigma^2(V_i)$ from the sample-to-sample fluctuations.

where each quantity in parentheses is orthogonal to every other such quantity and has an expectation of zero.†

Therefore

$$\underset{ijk}{S}(Y_{ijk} - \bar{Y})^2 = \underset{ijk}{S}(Y_{ijk} - TB_{ij}/q)^2 + \underset{ij}{S}(TB_{ij} - T_i/r - B_j/p + G/rp)^2/q + \underset{i}{S}(T_i - G/p)^2/rq + \underset{j}{S}(B_j - G/r)^2/pq$$
$$= (q-1)rpV_4 + (r-1)(p-1)V_3 + (p-1)V_2 + (r-1)V_1.$$

If the components are NID, these four sums of squares are independently distributed as $\chi_i^2\sigma_i^2$ with $f_i$ degrees of freedom, where the successive $\sigma_i^2$ are

$$\sigma_4^2 = \sigma_e^2, \qquad \sigma_3^2 = (\sigma_e^2 + q\sigma_{tb}^2), \qquad \sigma_2^2 = (\sigma_e^2 + q\sigma_{tb}^2 + rq\sigma_t^2),$$
$$\sigma_1^2 = (\sigma_e^2 + q\sigma_{tb}^2 + pq\sigma_b^2).$$

The respective $f_i$ are

$$f_4 = rp(q-1), \qquad f_3 = (r-1)(p-1), \qquad f_2 = (p-1), \qquad f_1 = (r-1).$$

Since the above sums of squares are independently distributed as $\chi_i^2\sigma_i^2$, their joint frequency distribution is that of four $\chi^2$ distributions.† By transforming from the distributions of $\chi^2$ to those of the $V$'s, it can be shown that the logarithmn of the likelihood function ($L$) is

$$L = -\frac{1}{2}\left[\text{constant} + \Sigma f_i \log \sigma_i^2 + \sum \frac{f_i V_i}{\sigma_i^2}\right].$$

Hence the ML estimates are

$$\widehat{\sigma_i^2} = V_i, \qquad i = 1, 2, 3, 4.$$

And by subtraction we find that

$$\widehat{\sigma_{tb}^2} = \frac{V_3 - V_4}{q}, \qquad \widehat{\sigma_t^2} = \frac{V_2 - V_3}{rq}, \qquad \widehat{\sigma_b^2} = \frac{V_1 - V_3}{pq}.$$

Since the mean squares are orthogonal, the variance of an estimate of a variance component is simply a multiple of the sums of the variances of the mean squares used in estimating this variance component. That is, a variance component can be written in the form

$$s^2 = \sum_i a_i V_i / c,$$

† Note that we are studying only deviations from the sample mean. This is equivalent to studying the likelihood of the four parts of the analysis of variance, neglecting any information which $\bar{Y}$ furnishes about the variance components.

where $a_i = \pm 1$. Hence

$$\sigma^2(s^2) = \frac{\sum_i \sigma^2(V_i)}{c^2} \doteq \frac{2}{c^2}\left[\sum_i \frac{V_i^2}{f_i + 2}\right] \equiv s'^2.$$

For example,

$$s_b^2 = \frac{V_1 - V_3}{pq},$$

$$\sigma^2(s_b^2) = \frac{\sigma^2(V_1) + \sigma^2(V_3)}{(pq)^2}$$

$$\doteq \frac{2}{(pq)^2}\left[\frac{V_1^2}{r+1} + \frac{V_3^2}{(r-1)(p-1)+2}\right] \equiv s_b'^2.$$

The problem of estimating confidence limits for $\sigma_b^2$ is still not completely solved. Some of the available procedures are indicated by Bross.[13] These are:

(i) When $r$ and $p$ are large, the distribution of $s_b^2$ approaches normality. In this case the $(1 - \alpha)$ confidence limits are

$$s_b^2 - T_\alpha s_b' < \sigma_b^2 < s_b^2 + T_\alpha s_b',$$

where $\mathcal{P}(|T| > T_\alpha) = \alpha$ and $T$ is a normal deviate.

(ii) Satterthwaite[11] suggested that $s^2$ was approximately distributed as $\chi^2\sigma^2/f'$, with $f'$ degrees of freedom, where

$$f' = (\Sigma a_i V_i)^2 / \Sigma(a_i^2 V_i^2 / f_i).$$

Presumably it is best to use the nearest integer for $f'$. In example 10.2 it was shown that the $(1 - \alpha)$ confidence limits for $\sigma^2$ are

$$\frac{f's^2}{\chi_2^2} < \sigma^2 < \frac{f's^2}{\chi_1^2},$$

where $\mathcal{P}(\chi^2 > \chi_2^2) = \mathcal{P}(\chi^2 < \chi_1^2) = \alpha/2$. For $\sigma_b^2$,

$$f_b' = (V_1 - V_3)^2 / [(V_1^2/f_1) + (V_3^2/f_3)].$$

Satterthwaite warned that when some of the $a$'s are negative, as in our case, caution must be exercised in the use of this $\chi^2$ approximation.

(iii) If $s^2 = (V_i - V_j)/c$ and $\sigma^2 = E(s^2) > 0$,

$$F_0 = \frac{V_i}{V_j} = F\frac{\sigma_i^2}{\sigma_j^2} = F\left[1 + \frac{c\sigma^2}{\sigma_j^2}\right], \qquad \text{or} \qquad F = \frac{F_0}{[1 + (c\sigma^2/\sigma_j^2)]},$$

where $\sigma^2$ is the variance component under consideration.

Let $F_2$ and $F_1$ be tabular values of $F$, with $f_i$ and $f_j$ degrees of freedom, such that

$$\mathcal{P}(F > F_2) = \mathcal{P}(F < F_1) = \alpha/2.$$

Hence

$$\frac{\alpha}{2} = \mathcal{P}\left[F_0 > F_2\left(1 + c\frac{\sigma^2}{\sigma_j^2}\right)\right] = \mathcal{P}\left[F_0 < F_1\left(1 + c\frac{\sigma^2}{\sigma_j^2}\right)\right].$$

If we solve inside the brackets for $\sigma^2$, we find that

$$\frac{\alpha}{2} = \mathcal{P}\left[\sigma^2 < \left(\frac{F_0}{F_2} - 1\right)\frac{\sigma_j^2}{c}\right] = \mathcal{P}\left[\sigma^2 > \left(\frac{F_0}{F_1} - 1\right)\frac{\sigma_j^2}{c}\right].$$

Hence

$$\mathcal{P}\left[\left(\frac{F_0}{F_2} - 1\right)\frac{\sigma_j^2}{c} < \sigma^2 < \left(\frac{F_0}{F_1} - 1\right)\frac{\sigma_j^2}{c}\right] = 1 - \alpha.$$

If we replace $\sigma_j^2/c$ by its estimate, $V_j/c = s^2/(F_0 - 1)$, the confidence limits for $\sigma^2$ are

$$\frac{(F_0/F_2) - 1}{F_0 - 1}\, s^2 < \sigma^2 < \frac{(F_0/F_1) - 1}{F_0 - 1}\, s^2.$$

(iv) Using the fiducial probability concepts of R. A. Fisher,[14] Bross[13] derived the following $(1 - \alpha)$ fiducial limits for $\sigma^2$:

$$\left[\frac{(F_0/F_2) - 1}{F_2'(F_0/F_2) - 1}\right] s^2 < \sigma^2 < \left[\frac{(F_0/F_1) - 1}{F_1'(F_0/F_1) - 1}\right] s^2,$$

where $F_i' = F_i$ for ($f_i$ and $\infty$) degrees of freedom.

In (iii) and (iv), $F_1 = 1/F_2(f_j,f_i)$, where $F_2 = F_2(f_i,f_j)$ (see Exercise 7.29). In all cases, if the lower limit is negative, it is replaced by zero. This will occur when $F_0$ is nonsignificant at the $\alpha/2$ significance level ($F_0 < F_2$).

The problem of setting confidence limits for $\mu$ is also complicated, because one does not know how many degrees of freedom to use for $t$. The Satterthwaite approximation[11] presumably can also be used here. For the given experiment,

$$\sigma^2(\bar{Y}) = (\sigma_1^2 + \sigma_2^2 - \sigma_3^2)/rpq.$$

Hence $s^2(\bar{Y}) = (V_1 + V_2 - V_3)/rpq$, with approximately $f'$ degrees of freedom, where

$$f' = \frac{(V_1 + V_2 - V_3)^2}{\dfrac{V_1^2}{r - 1} + \dfrac{V_2^2}{p - 1} + \dfrac{V_3^2}{(r - 1)(p - 1)}}.$$

Of course, if $r$ and $p$ are large, it is safe to use $t_{.05} = 2$.

The problem for a single treatment mean is slightly different, because

$$\sigma^2(\bar{T}_i) = [\sigma_1^2 + (p - 1)\sigma_3^2]/rpq.$$

Hence $s^2(\bar{T}_i) = [V_1 + (p-1)V_3]/rpq$ with $f''$ degrees of freedom, where

$$f'' = \frac{[V_1 + (p-1)V_3]^2}{\frac{V_1^2}{r-1} + \frac{[(p-1)V_3]^2}{(r-1)(p-1)}} = \frac{(r-1)[V_1 + (p-1)V_3]^2}{V_1^2 + (p-1)V_3^2}.$$

**Example 22.1.** Let us consider the example presented by Crump[2] of a series of genetic experiments by J. W. Gowen on the number of eggs laid by each of 12 females, from 25 races of *Drosophila melanogaster* on the fourth day of laying, the whole experiment being carried out 4 times ($r = 4$, $p = 25$, $q = 12$). The analysis of variance was as follows:

| Source of variation | Degrees of freedom | Mean square | $E$(MS) |
|---|---|---|---|
| Experiments (blocks) | 3 | $V_1 = 46{,}659$ | $\sigma_1^2 = \sigma_e^2 + 12\sigma_{tb}^2 + 300\sigma_b^2$ |
| Races (treatments) | 24 | $V_2 = 3{,}243$ | $\sigma_2^2 = \sigma_e^2 + 12\sigma_{tb}^2 + 48\sigma_t^2$ |
| $T \times B$ | 72 | $V_3 = 459$ | $\sigma_3^2 = \sigma_e^2 + 12\sigma_{tb}^2$ |
| Females in subclasses | 1100 | $V_4 = 231$ | $\sigma_4^2 = \sigma_e^2$ |

$$s_e^2 = 231, \qquad s_e'^2 = \frac{2(231)^2}{1{,}102} = 97,$$

$$s_{tb}^2 = \frac{459 - 231}{12} = 19, \qquad s_{tb}'^2 = \frac{2}{144}\left[\frac{(231)^2}{1{,}102} + \frac{(459)^2}{74}\right] = 40,$$

$$s_t^2 = \frac{3{,}243 - 459}{48} = 58, \qquad s_t'^2 = \frac{2}{2{,}304}\left[\frac{(459)^2}{74} + \frac{(3{,}243)^2}{26}\right] = 354,$$

$$s_b^2 = \frac{46{,}659 - 459}{300} = 154, \quad s_b'^2 = \frac{2}{90{,}000}\left[\frac{(459)^2}{74} + \frac{(46{,}659)^2}{5}\right] = 9{,}676.$$

The estimated variances of a general mean and a race mean with $r'$ experiments, $p'$ races, and $q'$ females per subclass are

$$s^2(\bar{Y}) = \frac{231}{r'p'q'} + \frac{19}{r'p'} + \frac{58}{p'} + \frac{154}{r'},$$

$$s^2(\bar{T}_i) = \frac{231}{r'q'} + \frac{19}{r'} + \frac{154}{r'} = \frac{231}{r'q'} + \frac{173}{r'}.$$

The most important component appears to be the variation from experiment to experiment ($\sigma_b^2$). Hence, in order materially to cut down the variance of a race mean, it is necessary to increase the number of experiments ($r$), since increasing $r$ decreases both parts of $s^2(\bar{T}_i)$.

Since $\sigma_b^2$ is so important, let us consider the different methods of setting 90 per cent confidence limits for it.

| Method | 5% lower limit | 5% upper limit | 10% upper limit |
|---|---|---|---|
| Normal (i) | 0 | 316 | |
| $\chi^2$ (ii) | 59 | 1,313 | 791 |
| $F$ (iii) | 55 | 1,331 | 801 |
| Fiducial (iv) | 58 | 1,325 | 797 |

Some of the data needed for the above results were:

$$s'_b = 98.4, \quad f'_b = 3, \quad F_0 = 101.65,$$
$$\chi^2_{.05} = 7.81, \quad \chi^2_{.95} = .352, \quad \chi^2_{.90} = .584,$$
$$F_{.05} = 2.74, \quad F_{.95} = \frac{1}{8.57}, \quad F_{.90} = \frac{1}{5.15},$$
$$F'_{.05} = 2.60, \quad F'_{.95} = \frac{1}{8.53}, \quad F'_{.90} = \frac{1}{5.13}.$$

We computed the 10 per cent upper limit for the last three methods, assuming that the lower limit would be zero. Actually, when all the probability is put on the upper tail, the lower limit will be slightly negative for (iii) and (iv), but we have postulated that $\sigma_b^2 \geq 0$. When there are so few degrees of freedom for estimating a component such as $\sigma_b^2$, the confidence limits should be quite wide. The normal approximation is definitely unsatisfactory in this case. The other three estimates are remarkedly close together. Bross[13] gives some examples where this is not the case. He criticizes the $\chi^2$ method in one case of a nonsignificant $F_0$, for which methods (iii) and (iv) will give negative lower limits (assumed 0 since $\sigma_b^2 \geq 0$), whereas the $\chi^2$ lower limit is greater than zero. It might be advisable, when $F_0$ is nonsignificant, to put all of the probability on the upper tail. This procedure should be considered from a theoretical standpoint.

For this particular sample, $s^2(\bar{Y}) = 41.20$, and

$$f' = \frac{(49,443)^2}{\frac{(46,659)^2}{3} + \frac{(3,243)^2}{24} + \frac{(459)^2}{72}} = 3.4;$$

also, $s^2(\bar{T}_i) = 48.06$, and

$$f'' = \frac{3(57,675)^2}{(46,659)^2 + (24)(459)^2} = 4.6.$$

Hence the 95 per cent confidence limits would be

$$\bar{Y} - (2.3)(6.4) < \mu < \bar{Y} + (2.3)(6.4),$$
$$\bar{T}_i - (2.1)(6.9) < \tau_i < \bar{T}_i + (2.1)(6.9).$$

**22.3. Repeated Subsampling with Equal Numbers in the Subclasses.** A sampling technique ordinarily used in sample surveys and in many sampling experiments in the physical and biological sciences is that of *repeated subsampling,* sometimes called *nested sampling* (see references 15 and 16). We shall assume that there are four tiers in the universe: $A$, $B$ in $A$, $C$ in $B$, $D$ in $C$. Obviously there may be more or less, but we shall illustrate the methods with four. Assume that the number of possible samples from $A$ is large enough so that the sample represents only a small segment of the tier; hence, regardless of the sampling rate within the selected $A$ units, the sampling rate for all $B$, $C$, and $D$ units will be small. Suppose that $a$ $A$ units are selected, $b$ $B$ units from each of the $A$ units, $c$ $C$ units from each $B$ unit, and $d$ $D$ units from each $C$ unit, the total number of samples being $n = abcd$.

$$Y_{ijkm} = \mu + \alpha_i + \beta_{ij} + \gamma_{ijk} + \delta_{ijkm},$$

where $i = 1, 2, \ldots, a$; $j = 1, 2, \ldots, b$; $k = 1, 2, \ldots, c$; $m = 1, 2, \ldots, d$. All of the effects, except $\mu$, are assumed NID$(0,\sigma_e^2)$, where $\sigma_e^2 = \sigma_a^2, \sigma_b^2, \sigma_c^2$, or $\sigma_d^2$, respectively. Hence

$$\bar{Y} = \frac{SY_{ijkm}}{abcd} \quad \text{and} \quad \sigma^2(\bar{Y}) = \frac{\sigma_a^2}{a} + \frac{\sigma_b^2}{ab} + \frac{\sigma_c^2}{abc} + \frac{\sigma_d^2}{abcd}.$$

The analysis of variance is as follows:

| Source of variation | Degrees of freedom | Mean square | $E$(MS) |
|---|---|---|---|
| $A$ | $a - 1$ | $V_1$ | $\sigma_1^2 = \sigma_d^2 + d\sigma_c^2 + cd\sigma_b^2 + bcd\sigma_a^2$ |
| $B$ in $A$ | $a(b - 1)$ | $V_2$ | $\sigma_2^2 = \sigma_d^2 + d\sigma_c^2 + cd\sigma_b^2$ |
| $C$ in $B$ | $ab(c - 1)$ | $V_3$ | $\sigma_3^2 = \sigma_d^2 + d\sigma_c^2$ |
| $D$ in $C$ | $abc(d - 1)$ | $V_4$ | $\sigma_4^2 = \sigma_d^2$ |
| Total | $abcd - 1$ | | |

The sum of squares for $A$ is computed like the block and treatment sums of squares in Sec. 22.2. The remaining sums are simply within sums of squares. Hence,

$$\text{SSA} = \frac{\sum_i A_i^2}{bcd} - \frac{G^2}{abcd},$$

$$\text{SSB} = \frac{\sum_i \sum_j B_{ij}^2}{cd} - \frac{\sum_i A_i^2}{bcd},$$

etc.,

where $A_i = \sum_j \sum_k \sum_m Y_{ijkm}$, $B_{ij} = \sum_k \sum_m Y_{ijkm}$, etc. The expected values of the mean squares are computed as in Sec. 22.2. All of the theory presented in that section pertaining to the estimates of the variance components and their variances and confidence limits carries over here, except that each variance component is estimated from its mean square and the one just below. For example

$$s_a^2 = \frac{V_1 - V_2}{bcd}.$$

However, the confidence limits for $\mu$ are easier to compute, because $s^2(\bar{Y}) = V_1/n$ with $(a - 1)$ degrees of freedom.

**Example 22.2.** Suppose we had a sample of 40 townships with 4 areas per township and 2 farms from each area, giving a total of 320 farms, to estimate the average number of acres of corn per farm. The mean corn yield was 40 bushels per acre. The analysis of variance for the sample data was:

| Division | Degrees of freedom | Mean square | $E$(MS) |
|---|---|---|---|
| Townships | 39 | 320 | $\sigma_f^2 + 2\sigma_a^2 + 8\sigma_t^2$ |
| Areas in townships | 120 | 240 | $\sigma_f^2 + 2\sigma_a^2$ |
| Farms in areas | 160 | 100 | $\sigma_f^2$ |
| Total | 319 | | |

The expectations of the mean squares are given on the right, where $\sigma_f^2$ is the farm-to-farm variance component, $\sigma_a^2$ the area component, and $\sigma_t^2$ the township component. The estimates of these variance components are

$$s_f^2 = 100, \qquad s_a^2 = \frac{140}{2} = 70, \qquad s_t^2 = \frac{320 - 240}{8} = 10.$$

The estimated variance of the mean corn yield for $b'$ townships, $c'$ areas per township, and $d'$ farms per area would be

$$s^2(\bar{Y}) = \frac{10}{b'} + \frac{70}{b'c'} + \frac{100}{b'c'd'}.$$

For the given sample, $s^2(\bar{Y}) = 1.00$. Hence the 95 per cent confidence limits for $\mu$ are

$$40 - 2.0 < \mu < 40 + 2.0$$

or

$$38 < \mu < 42.$$

**22.4. Repeated Subsampling with Unequal Numbers in the Subclasses.**† Ganguli[15] presents the requisite formulas for the expected values of the mean squares when there are unequal numbers in the various subclasses. Assume there are $a$ $A$ units, each with $n_i$ samples $\left(\sum_i n_i = n\right)$; each $A$ unit has $b_i$ $B$ units, each $B$ unit having $n_{ij}$ samples; each $B$ unit has $c_{ij}$ $C$ units, each $C$ unit having $n_{ijk}$ samples; each $C$ unit has $d_{ijk}$ $D$ units, each $D$ unit being a sample. The analysis of variance is as follows:

| Source of variation | Degrees of freedom | Coefficients of variance components in $E$(MS) | | | |
|---|---|---|---|---|---|
| | | $\sigma_d^2$ | $\sigma_c^2$ | $\sigma_b^2$ | $\sigma_a^2$ |
| $A$ | $a - 1$ | 1 | $\sum_i\sum_j\sum_k n_{ijk}^2 f_i$ | $\sum_i\sum_j n_{ij}^2 f_i$ | $\sum_i n_i^2 f_i$ |
| $B$ in $A$ | $\sum_i b_i - a$ | 1 | $\sum_i\sum_j\sum_k n_{ijk}^2 f_{ij}$ | $\sum_i\sum_j n_{ij}^2 f_{ij}$ | |
| $C$ in $B$ | $\sum_i\sum_j c_{ij} - \sum_i b_i$ | 1 | $\sum_i\sum_j\sum_k n_{ijk}^2 f_{ijk}$ | | |
| $D$ in $C$ | $n - \sum_i\sum_j c_{ij}$ | 1 | | | |

$$f_i = \frac{(1/n_i) - (1/n)}{a - 1}, \quad f_{ij} = \frac{(1/n_{ij}) - (1/n_i)}{\sum_i b_i - a}, \quad \text{and } f_{ijk} = \frac{(1/n_{ijk}) - (1/n_{ij})}{\sum_i\sum_j c_{ij} - \sum_i b_i}.$$

The sums of squares in the analysis of variance are computed as follows:

$$\text{SSA} = \sum_i \frac{A_i^2}{n_i} - \frac{G^2}{n},$$

$$\text{SSB} = \sum_i\sum_j \frac{B_{ij}^2}{n_{ij}} - \sum_i \frac{A_i^2}{n_i},$$

$$\text{SSC} = \sum_i\sum_j\sum_k \frac{C_{ijk}^2}{n_{ijk}} - \sum_i\sum_j \frac{B_{ij}^2}{n_{ij}},$$

etc.

A systematic computing procedure can be set up to determine the coefficients of the variance components in the expected values of the mean squares. This will be demonstrated in Example 22.3 below.

† This section may be omitted without upsetting the continuity of the book.

**Example 22.3.** Cochran[6] presents the analysis of a 1937 enumeration of commercial wheat fields in 6 districts of Great Britain. The sampling plan was to select a number of farms from each district, 1 or 2 fields per farm and 2 paths per field, each path having 6 bulked samples. In addition, from the only farm in district III, 2 varieties were sampled in each of the 3 fields (2 paths per variety per field). The number of farms and fields per farm for each district were:

| District | No. farms | No. fields per farm† | Totals | |
|---|---|---|---|---|
| | | | Fields | Paths |
| I | 2 | 2(2) | 4 | 8 |
| II | 2 | 2, 1 | 3 | 6 |
| III‡ | 1 | 3 | 3 | 12 |
| IV | 9 | 2(2), 1(7) | 11 | 22 |
| V | 1 | 2 | 2 | 4 |
| VI | 10 | 2(3), 1(7) | 13 | 26 |
| Total | 25 | | 36 | 78 |

† Numbers in parentheses refer to number of farms with this many fields; those without parentheses have one farm with this many fields.
‡ Two varieties were sampled in each field.

The analysis of variance, excluding the 3 degrees of freedom for varieties, is presented below in terms of hundredweights (112 pounds) per acre (based on the means of the six bulked samples).†

| Source of variation | Degrees of freedom | Mean square | $E(\text{MS})$ |
|---|---|---|---|
| Districts ($A$) | 5 | 10.28 | $\sigma_1^2 = \sigma_d^2 + 2.34\sigma_c^2 + 4.90\sigma_b^2 + 11.96\sigma_a^2$ |
| Farms ($B$) in $A$ | 19 | 6.59 | $\sigma_2^2 = \sigma_d^2 + 2.00\sigma_c^2 + 2.58\sigma_b^2$ |
| Fields ($C$) in $B$ | 11 | 3.03 | $\sigma_3^2 = \sigma_d^2 + 2.36\sigma_c^2$ |
| Paths ($D$) in $C$ | 39 | .825 | $\sigma_4^2 = \sigma_d^2$ |

Set up a diagram like the following to help in computing the coefficients of the variance components in $E(\text{MS})$:

† Cochran presents his analysis in terms of the sum of four sets of 3 samples each, each set being a mean of the 3 samples in the set; hence his mean squares are eight times as large as those above.

| | No. units | No. samples | Distribution of the samples† | | | | | | | | |
|---|---|---|---|---|---|---|---|---|---|---|---|
| Total | 1 | $n$ | 78 | | | | | | | | |
| Districts | 6 | $n_i$ | 8 | 6 | | 12 | 22 | | 4 | 26 | |
| Farms | 25 | $n_{ij}$ | 4(2) | 4(1) | 2(1) | 12(1) | 4(2) | 2(7) | 4(1) | 4(3) | 2(7) |
| Fields | 36 | $n_{ijk}$ | 2(4) | 2(2) | 2(1) | 4(3) | 2(4) | 2(7) | 2(2) | 2(6) | 2(7) |

† Numbers in parentheses are number of farms or fields having this many samples.

This diagram reads as follows for, say, the last district: there are 26 samples from this district, 4 from each of 3 farms and 2 from each of 7 farms; there are 13 fields each with 2 samples.

The expectations of the various sums of squares are handled as follows:

| Sum of squares | $\sigma_a^2$ | $\sigma_b^2$ | $\sigma_c^2$ |
|---|---|---|---|
| $\dfrac{G^2}{n}$ | $\dfrac{\sum_i n_i^2}{n} = \dfrac{1{,}420}{78} = 18.21$ | $\dfrac{\sum_i \sum_j n_{ij}^2}{n} = \dfrac{348}{78} = 4.46$ | $\dfrac{\sum_i \sum_j \sum_k n_{ijk}^2}{n} = \dfrac{180}{78} = 2.31$ |
| $\sum_i \dfrac{A_i^2}{n_i}$ | $\sum_i n_i = 78$ | $\sum_i \sum_j \dfrac{n_{ij}^2}{n_i} = 28.98$ | $\sum_i \sum_j \sum_k \dfrac{n_{ijk}^2}{n_i} = 14.00$ |
| $\sum_i \sum_j \dfrac{B_{ij}^2}{n_{ij}}$ | $\sum_i \sum_j n_{ij} = 78$ | $\sum_i \sum_j n_{ij} = 78$ | $\sum_i \sum_j \sum_k \dfrac{n_{ijk}^2}{n_{ij}} = 52.00$ |
| $\sum_i \sum_j \sum_k \dfrac{C_{ijk}^2}{n_{ijk}}$ | 78 | 78 | 78 |

To illustrate the computing procedure, consider a few examples:

$$(a)\quad \sum_i \sum_j \frac{n_{ij}^2}{n_i} = \frac{(16)(2)}{8} + \frac{(16)(1) + (4)(1)}{6} + \frac{144}{12} + \frac{(16)(2) + (4)(7)}{22} + \frac{16}{4} + \frac{(16)(3) + (4)(7)}{26} = 28.98,$$

$$(b)\quad \sum_i \sum_j \sum_k \frac{n_{ijk}^2}{n_{ij}} = \frac{(4)(18)}{4} + \frac{(4)(15)}{2} + \frac{(16)(3)}{12} = 52.$$

It should be noted that, for unequal subclass numbers, the mean squares are no longer distributed as simply $\chi^2\sigma_i^2/f_i$, but as sums like $\lambda_1\chi_1^2 + \lambda_2\chi_2^2 + \cdots$, where $\lambda$'s are functions of the variance components and the number of observations. Hence the confidence limits presented in Sec. 22.2 cannot be used here. The theory applicable to this problem is beyond this book.

## EXERCISES

**22.1.** In Example 22.1, suppose that $C_e = 10$, $C_p = 120$, and $C = 960$. Solve for $r'$ and $q'$ to minimize $s^2(\bar{T}_i)$. What is $s^2(\bar{T}_i)$ using these values of $r'$ and $q'$? Compare this result with that obtained in the actual experiment ($r = 4$, $q = 12$).

**22.2.** An experiment was run on the average stem length (in inches) per plant of snapdragons. Seven soil types were used in each of 3 replications, 18 plants being selected at random from each plot. The analysis of variance was as follows:

| Source of variation | Degrees of freedom | Sum of squares |
|---|---|---|
| Replications | | 39.04 |
| Soil types | | 103.15 |
| Interaction | | 19.74 |
| Sampling error | | 507.30 |

(*a*) Fill in the degrees of freedom, and compute the mean squares.

(*b*) If these replications and soil types can be assumed to be randomly selected from large populations, what are the expectations of the mean squares?

(*c*) Compute the estimates of the variance components in (*b*).

(*d*) The sample mean height was 32.56 inches per plant. What is the variance of this mean and the 95 per cent confidence limits for the true mean, under the assumptions of (*b*)?

(*e*) What is the estimated variance of a mean if $p'$ soil types, $r'$ replications, and $q'$ plants per plot were used?

**22.3.** An experiment was conducted to estimate the genetic and environmental variances in corn,[7] using 192 progenies produced from 48 males with 192 females (4 females per male). The field layout was in 12 blocks of 32 plots each, each block having 4 male parents, each crossed with 4 different females, and each cross duplicated. The yields were based on the pounds of grain for 10 guarded plants per plot (plants having another plant on each side of the row). An estimate of the plant-to-plant variability was obtained from 23 of the plots (230 plants). The analysis of variance was as follows:

| Source of variation | Degrees of freedom | Mean square | $E$(MS)† |
|---|---|---|---|
| Blocks | 11 | .153 | |
| Duplications in blocks | 12 | .063 | |
| Males in blocks | 36 | .167 | $\sigma^2 + 10\sigma_p^2 + 20\sigma_f^2 + 80\sigma_m^2$ |
| Females in males in blocks | 144 | .069 | $\sigma^2 + 10\sigma_p^2 + 20\sigma_f^2$ |
| Parents × duplications in blocks | 180 | .031 | $\sigma^2 + 10\sigma_p^2$ |
| Plants in plots | 207 | .0153 | $\sigma^2$ |

† $\sigma^2$ is the plant-to-plant variance, $\sigma_p^2$ the plot-to-plot variance (parent × duplicate interaction), $\sigma_f^2$ the added variance due to females, and $\sigma_m^2$ the added variance due to males.

(a) Derive the coefficients of the variance components in $E$(MS).
(b) Compute estimates of these variance components.
(c) How would you test the hypothesis that $\sigma_m^2 = \sigma_f^2$?
(d) Derive approximate confidence limits for $\sigma_f^2$ and $\sigma_m^2$.

**22.4.** Assume we have $p$ treatments and $r$ blocks with $a_i b_j$ samples for the $i$th treatment and the $j$th block, with all effects random except the mean.
(a) Set up the analysis-of-variance table.
(b) Derive formulas for the expectations of the mean squares in terms of the $a_i$ and $b_j$.
(c) Suppose that $a_i b_j = c_i$. How does this affect the results in (b)?

**22.5.** Prove that

$$\sum_i \sum_j \left[ (TB)_{ij} - q\mu - \frac{T_i - rq\mu}{r} - \frac{B_j - pq\mu}{p} + \frac{G - rpq\mu}{rp} \right]^2$$

$$= \sum_i \sum_j [(TB)_{ij} - q\mu]^2 - \frac{\sum_i (T_i - rq\mu)^2}{r} - \frac{\sum_j (B_j - pq\mu)^2}{p} + \frac{(G - rpq\mu)^2}{rp}.$$

**22.6.** (a) Prove that $(B_j - G/r)$ and $(T_i - G/p)$ are not correlated. (b) Prove that each is not correlated with $[(TB)_{ij} - T_i/r - B_j/p + G/rp]$.

**22.7.** Show that $E(V_i^2) = (f_i + 2)\sigma_i^4/f_i$.

**22.8.** Show that the ML solution in Sec. 22.2 is correct. What happens if you consider $S(Y - \mu)^2$ instead of $S(Y - \bar{Y})^2$?

**22.9.** (a) Given $V_i - V_j = c\chi^2\sigma^2/f'$, where $V_i = \chi_i^2\sigma_i^2/f_i$, $V_j = \chi_j^2\sigma_j^2/f_j$, $c\sigma^2 = \sigma_i^2 - \sigma_j^2$, and each chi-square has as degrees of freedom its denominator. Show by equating the variances of the two sides of this equation that

$$f' = \frac{(c\sigma^2)^2}{(\sigma_i^4/f_i) + (\sigma_j^4/f_j)}.$$

Also, show that $E(V_i - V_j) = E(c\chi^2\sigma^2/f')$.

(*b*) How does this result connect with Satterthwaite's approximation for confidence limits on $\sigma^2$?

**22.10.** Marcuse[17] presents the following data on the moisture content of 2 sample cheeses from each of 3 different lots with 2 subsamples per sample (remember samples 1 and 2 are not the same for the different lots):

| Sample | Lot | | |
|---|---|---|---|
| | I | II | III |
| 1 | 39.02 | 35.74 | 37.02 |
| | 38.79 | 35.41 | 36.00 |
| 2 | 38.96 | 35.58 | 35.70 |
| | 39.01 | 35.52 | 36.04 |

(*a*) Set up the analysis of variance for these data with the expected values of the mean squares, assuming everything random except the mean.

(*b*) Estimate the values of the variance components.

(*c*) Determine 90 per cent confidence limits for the "lots" component by the four methods outlined above.

(*d*) Given that the costs are 10 per lot, 3 per cheese per lot, and 1 per subsample. Assume that 2 subsamples per cheese are to be used and that the total cost is approximately 100, and determine the number of lots and cheeses per lot to minimize the variance of the general mean. Could a lower variance be obtained by using other than 2 subsamples per cheese?

(*e*) What are the 95 per cent confidence limits for the mean?

**22.11.** Show that the expected values of the mean squares in Sec. 22.3 are correct.

**22.12.** Derive the ML estimates for nested sampling with equal numbers taken from each class.

**22.13.** In a 1940 Iowa AAA corn-acreage study, 2 sections were selected from each of 1,617 townships. The analysis of variance of the corn acreage per section was:

| Source of variation | Degrees of freedom | Mean square |
|---|---|---|
| Between townships | | 6,511.9 |
| Within townships | | 1,954.3 |

(*a*) Fill in the degrees of freedom, and determine the expectations of the mean squares.

(*b*) Estimate the variance components.

(*c*) What is the variance of a sample mean if $r'$ townships and $q'$ sections per township were sampled?

(*d*) Determine 90 per cent confidence limits for the variance components.

**22.14.** Rigney and Reed[18] studied some of the factors affecting the variability of estimates of various soil properties. They took samples from 20 fields ($A$), 2 sections ($B$) from each field, 2 samples ($C$) consisting of a composite of 20 borings from each section, and then 2 subsamples ($D$) from each sample. ($a = 20$, $b = 2$, $c = 2$, $d = 2$.) The analysis of variance for several of the properties is presented below:

| Source of variation | Degrees of freedom | Mean squares | | | |
|---|---|---|---|---|---|
| | | Calcium | Magnesium | Potash | Organic matter |
| $A$ | | 19.19 | .1809 | .0405 | 12.003 |
| $B$ in $A$ | | 3.59 | .0545 | .0076 | 7.674 |
| $C$ in $B$ | | .30 | .0080 | .0011 | .275 |
| $D$ in $C$ | | .01 | .0005 | .0001 | .002 |

(*a*) Fill in the degrees-of-freedom column.

(*b*) Set up the model for this sample and then the expectations of the mean squares in terms of the variance components.

(*c*) Estimate the variance components for one of the properties and the variance of the general mean for this sample. What is the variance of a mean of $a'$ fields, $b'$ sections per field, $c'$ samples per section, and $d'$ subsamples per sample?

**22.15.** (*a*) In Example 22.2, suppose it cost \$2.70 on the average to get to a given township, \$2.10 extra to cover each area in the townships selected, and \$3 extra to secure and analyze the data from each farm selected in the sample. Determine values of $b'$, $c'$, and $d'$ to minimize $s^2(\bar{Y})$ if the total cost is fixed at \$1,890. What is $s^2(\bar{Y})$ for this sampling plan?

(*b*) Suppose it was decided to set $d = 2$. Determine values of $b'$ and $c'$ to minimize $s^2(\bar{Y})$ under this condition, and compute $s^2(\bar{Y})$.

**22.16.** For a discussion of sampling from finite populations, see references 19 and 20.

**22.17.** (*a*) In Example 22.3, show how the expectations of the mean squares are computed from the expectations of the sums of squares.

(*b*) Compute the estimates of the variance components in this example.

(*c*) In this example, the six districts constituted the population. Hence what would you say regarding $\sigma_a^2$?

(*d*) What would be the expected value and the variance of the general mean from these data? Of the mean for district I?

(*e*) The six bulked samples actually consisted of two sets of three samples each. Show how the analysis would change if the computations were based on the means of the three bulked samples per set and a component for sets was put into the model. The actual sum of squares between sets in paths was 99.31.

**22.18.** In Exercise 18.4, suppose that the 13 markets were chosen at random from a large population of markets.

(*a*) Set up the mathematical model for this sample and the expected values of the mean squares in the analysis of variance. Show that the expected value of the mean square for markets is $\sigma_e^2 + k\sigma_m^2$, where $\sigma_m^2$ is the variance component for markets and

$$k = \frac{1}{12}\left[69 - \frac{8^2 + 6^2 + \cdots + 9^2}{69}\right].$$

(*b*) Estimate the variance components.

(*c*) What would be the estimated variance of the mean of a sample from $r'$ markets with $q'$ sellers at each market?

(*d*) Suppose it costs $10 to visit a market and $1 to enumerate each seller, what is the optimum number of markets and sellers if it is desired to obtain 100 schedules? How much will it cost to obtain this many schedules?

**22.19.** An experiment was to be designed to test various molds for their efficiency in the production of streptomycin. Before setting up an overall experiment, a preliminary experiment was set up to examine the various sources of variability in the production and assay process. There are five stages in this process: the initial *incubation stage* in a test tube (or *slant*, as it is generally called), a *primary inoculation period* in a petri dish, a *secondary inoculation period*, a *fermentation period* in a bath, and the *final assay* of the amount of streptomycin produced. Several sampling plans could be devised to estimate the amount of variability contributed at each stage. Two of these plans are as follows:

(i) Consider 5 test tubes, draw 2 samples from each test tube for the primary inoculation, 2 samples from each primary for the secondary inoculation, 2 samples from each secondary for the fermentation, and assay 2 samples from each fermentation bath.

(ii) Use 2 test tubes as in (i); 2 test tubes the same, except only 1 assay per fermentation; 4 test tubes the same, except only one fermentation per secondary and one assay per fermentation; 8 test tubes, with two primaries each and one of each stage henceforth.

(*a*) Show that there are 80 assays for each plan.

(*b*) Set up the analysis of variance for both plans, and determine the expected values of the mean squares, assuming all effects are random.

(*c*) Which of these two plans would you recommend if one did not know in advance the relative magnitude of the variance components?

## References Cited

1. EISENHART, C., "The Assumptions Underlying the Analysis of Variance," *Biometrics*, **3**:1–21 (1947).
2. CRUMP, S. L., "The Estimation of Variance Components in Analysis of Variance," *Biom. Bull.*, **2**:7–11 (1946).
3. CRUMP, S. L., "The Present Status of Variance Component Analysis," *Biometrics*, **7**:1–16 (1951).
4. FISHER, R. A., *Statistical Methods for Research Workers*, 1st ed., Oliver & Boyd, Ltd., Edinburgh and London, 1925.
5. YATES, F., and I. ZACOPANAY, "The Estimation of the Efficiency of Sampling, with Special Reference to Sampling for Yield in Cereal Experiments," *J. Agr. Sci.*, **25**: 545–577 (1935).
6. COCHRAN, W. G., "The Use of the Analysis of Variance in Enumeration by Sampling," *J. Am. Stat. Assoc.*, **34**:492–510 (1939).
7. COMSTOCK, R. E., and H. F. ROBINSON, "The Components of Genetic Variance in Populations of Biparental Progenies and Their Use in Estimating the Average Degree of Dominance," *Biometrics*, **4**:254–266 (1948).
8. COMSTOCK, R. E., and H. F. ROBINSON, "Consistency of Estimates of Variance Components," *Biometrics*, **7**:75–82 (1951).
9. ANDERSON, R. L., "Use of Variance Components in the Analysis of Hog Prices in Two Markets," *J. Am. Stat. Assoc.*, **42**:612–634 (1947).
10. DANIELS, H. E., "The Estimation of Components of Variance," *J. Roy. Stat. Soc. Suppl.*, **6**:186–197 (1939).
11. SATTERTHWAITE, F. E., "An Approximate Distribution of Estimates of Variance Components," *Biom. Bull.*, **2**:110–114 (1946).
12. COCHRAN, W. G., and G. M. COX, *Experimental Designs*, John Wiley & Sons, Inc., New York, 1950.
13. BROSS, I., "Fiducial Intervals for Variance Components," *Biometrics*, **6**:136–144 (1950).
14. FISHER, R. A., "The Fiducial Argument in Statistical Inference," *Ann. Eugenics*, **6**:391–398 (1935).
15. GANGULI, M., "A Note on Nested Sampling," *Sankhyā*, **5**:449–452 (1941).
16. MAHALANOBIS, P. C., "On Large Scale Sample Surveys," *Phil. Trans. Roy. Soc., Ser. B, Biol. Sci.*, **23**: 329–451 (1944).
17. MARCUSE, S., "Optimum Allocation and Variance Components in Nested Sampling with an Application to Chemical Analysis," *Biometrics*, **5**:189–206 (1949).
18. RIGNEY, J. A., and J. F. REED, "Some Factors Affecting the Accuracy of Soil Sampling," *Proc. Soil. Sci. Soc. Am.*, **10**:257–259 (1945).
19. HANSEN, M. H., and W. N. HURWITZ, "On the Theory of Sampling for Finite Populations," *Ann. Math. Stat.*, **14**:333–362 (1943).
20. COCHRAN, W. G., "Sample Survey Techniques," *Inst. Stat. Mim. Ser.* 7 (1950).

## Other Reading

*Experimental*

BROWNLEE, K. A., *Industrial Experimentation*, Chemical Publishing Company, Inc., Brooklyn, 1947.

FEDERER, W. T., and G. F. SPRAGUE, "A Comparison of Variance Components in Corn Yield Trials," *J. Am. Soc. Agron.*, **39**:453–463 (1947).

FISHER, R. A., *The Design of Experiments*, 4th ed., Oliver & Boyd, Ltd., Edinburgh and London, 1947.

HOMEYER, P. G., and G. A. BLACK, "Sampling Replicated Field Experiments on Oats for Yield Determination," *Soil. Sci. Proc.*, **11**:341–344 (1946).

MATHER, K., *Statistical Analysis of Biology*, 2d ed., Interscience Pub., Inc., New York, 1946.

McNEMAR, Q., *Psychological Statistics*, John Wiley & Sons, Inc., New York, 1949.

MOOD, A. M., *Introduction to the Theory of Statistics*, McGraw-Hill Book Company, Inc., New York, 1950.

*Proceedings of the Auburn Conference on Statistics Applied to Research in the Social Sciences, Plant Sciences, and Animal Sciences*, Alabama Polytechnic Institute, Auburn, Ala. (1948).

RIGNEY, J. A., and R. E. BLASER, "Sampling Alyce Clover for Chemical Analysis," *Biometrics*, **4**:234–239 (1948).

TIPPETT, L. H. C., *Technological Applications of Statistics*, John Wiley & Sons., Inc., New York, 1950.

WALD, A., "On the Analysis of Variance in Case of Multiple Classifications with Unequal Class Frequencies," *Ann. Math. Stat.*, **12**:346–350 (1941).

WINSOR, C. P., and G. L. CLARK, "A Statistical Study of Variation in the Catch of Plankton Nets," *J. Marine Research*, **3**:1–34 (1940).

*Sample Surveys*

DEMING, W. E., *Some Theory of Sampling*, John Wiley & Sons, Inc., New York (1950).

FINKNER, A. L., J. J. MORGAN, and R. J. MONROE, "Methods of Estimating Farm Employment from Sample Data in North Carolina," *N. Carolina Agr. Expt. Sta. Tech. Bull.* 75 (1943).

HENDRICKS, W. A., "The Theory of Sampling," *Inst. Stat. Mim. Ser.* 1 (1942).

HENDRICKS, W. A., "The Relative Efficiencies of Groups of Farms as Sampling Units," *J. Am. Stat. Assoc.*, **39**:367–376 (1944).

HENDRICKS, W. A., "Mathematics of Sampling," *Virginia Agr. Expt. Sta. Special Tech. Bull.* (1948).

HOUSEMAN, E. E., C. R. WEBER, and W. T. FEDERER, "Pre-harvest Sampling of Soyb ans for Yield and Quality," *Iowa State Coll., Agr. Exp. Sta., Research Bull.* 341 (1946).

JESSEN, R. J., "Statistical Investigation of a Sample Survey for Obtaining Farm Fact ," *Iowa State Coll., Agr. Expt. Sta., Research Bull.* 304 (1942).

JESSEN, R. J., and E. E. HOUSEMAN, "Statistical Investigations of Farm Sample Surveys Taken in Iowa, Florida and California," *Iowa State Coll., Agr. Expt. Sta., Research Bull.* 329 (1944).

JOHNSON, F. A., "A Statistical Study of Sampling Methods for the Nursery Inventories," *J. Forestry*, **41**:674–679 (1943).

KING, A. J., and E. H. JEBE, "An Experiment in the Pre-harvest Sampling of Wheat Fields," *Iowa State Coll., Agr. Expt. Sta., Research Bull.* 273 (1940).

KING, A. J., and D. E. McCARTY, "Application of Sampling to Agricultural Statistics with Emphasis on Stratified Samples," *J. Marketing*, **5**:462–474 (1941).

KING, A. J., D. E. McCARTY, and M. McPEEK, "An Objective Method of Sampling Wheat Fields to Estimate Production and Quality of Wheat," *U.S. Dept. Agr. Tech. Bull.* 814 (1942).

MADOW, W. G., and L. H. MADOW, "On the Theory of Systematic Sampling," *Ann. Math. Stat.*, **15**: 1–24 (1944).

REED, J. F., and J. A. RIGNEY, "Soil Sampling from Fields of Uniform and Nonuniform Appearances and Soil Types," *J. Am. Soc. Agron.*, **39**:26–40 (1947).

SUKHATME, P. V., "The Problem of Plot-size in Large-scale Yield Surveys," *J. Am. Stat. Assoc.*, **42**:297–310 (1947).

YATES, F., *Sampling Methods for Census and Surveys*, Charles Griffin & Co., Ltd., London, 1949.

# CHAPTER 23

## ANALYSIS OF DATA WITH BOTH RANDOM AND FIXED EFFECTS (MIXED MODEL)

**23.1. Randomized Complete Blocks.** In this section we shall consider the same model as in Sec. 22.2 except that the $\{\tau_i\}$ are assumed to be fixed; in other words, inferences are to be made regarding only these particular $p$ treatments. We have made a basic change from the model of Sec. 18.3, in that the blocks are assumed to be representative of a larger universe of environmental conditions than those of the particular experiment being analyzed and we have added a (treatment $\times$ block) effect to the model.

In Sec. 18.3, it was necessary to assume that there was no real $TB$ interaction if the blocks were assumed fixed and MS($TB$) was to be used as the error mean square. If the true model for Sec. 18.3 was

$$Y_{ij} = \mu + \tau_i + \beta_j + (\tau\beta)_{ij} + \epsilon_{ij},$$

with fixed block and interaction effects, the expected value of the error mean square, $s^2$, would have been $\sigma_e^2 + \theta_1(\tau\beta)$, where

$$\theta_1(\tau\beta) = \Sigma\Sigma(\tau\beta)^2/(r-1)(p-1).$$

Hence since $E(\text{MST}) = \sigma_e^2 + \theta(\tau)$, there would have been no real error term to test $H_0$: $\{\tau_i = 0\}$, because under $H_0$ the expected value of the denominator of $F$ would have been greater than the expected value of the numerator; in other words, $F$ would have been too small, and too few significant results would have been posted.

If the experimenter is willing to assume that the block effects are random, he finds that

$$E(s^2) = \sigma_e^2 + \sigma_{tb}^2, \qquad E(\text{MST}) = \sigma_e^2 + \sigma_{tb}^2 + r\theta(\tau).$$

Hence MST$/s^2$ is distributed as F under the null hypothesis, $H_0$: $\{\tau_i = 0\}$, and it is not necessary to assume a nonexistent interaction.

But if more than one sample is secured for each treatment in each block, that is, $q$ samples, the experimenter can assume fixed block effects and still have a legitimate error term even if there is a fixed interaction. In this case, we have an estimate of the sampling error, $\sigma_e^2$. This estimate is MSE, with $rp(q-1)$ degrees of freedom. Hence MST/MSE is distributed as $F$ under the null hypothesis of no treatment effects.

Let us summarize these statements with a table showing the expectations of the treatment ($T$), treatment $\times$ block ($TB$), and sampling ($E$) mean squares for various experimental conditions and assumptions.†

| Mean square | Assumptions | | |
|---|---|---|---|
| | $(\tau\beta) = 0$ | $(\tau\beta) \neq 0$ | |
| | | Blocks fixed | Blocks random |
| One sample per treatment per block ($q = 1$) | | | |
| $T$ | $\sigma_e^2 + r\theta(\tau)$ | $\sigma_e^2 + r\theta(\tau)$ | $\sigma_e^2 + \sigma_{tb}^2 + r\theta(\tau)$ |
| $TB$ | $(\sigma_e^2)$ | $\sigma_e^2 + \theta_1(\tau\beta)$ | $(\sigma_e^2 + \sigma_{tb}^2)$ |
| $q$ samples per treatment per block | | | |
| $T$ | $\sigma_e^2 + rq\theta(\tau)$ | $\sigma_e^2 + rq\theta(\tau)$ | $\sigma_e^2 + q\sigma_{tb}^2 + rq\theta(\tau)$ |
| $TB$ | $\sigma_e^2$ } (pool) | $\sigma_e^2 + q\theta_1(\tau\beta)$ | $(\sigma_e^2 + q\sigma_{tb}^2)$ |
| $E$ | $\sigma_e^2$ } (pool) | $(\sigma_e^2)$ | $\sigma_e^2$ |

The proper error term is indicated in parentheses. Note that for $(\tau\beta) = 0$ and $q > 1$, $TB$ and $E$ are both estimates of $\sigma_e^2$ and should be pooled to obtain the error mean square; however, if the experimenter is not sure that $(\tau\beta) = 0$, he had better use $TB$ as the error mean square. For $(\tau\beta) \neq 0$ and blocks fixed, there is no error term unless $q > 1$.

As mentioned before, few experimenters wish to confine their conclusions to the particular blocks used in the experiment. Hence they wish to assume random block effects. But if they assume random block effects and do not wish to assume nonexistent interactions, they can obtain an error term to test treatments even if only one sample is obtained for each treatment per block. And this error term is the same error term we have used all the time in Chaps. 17 to 21, the $TB$ interaction. But if the particular blocks used in the experiment cannot be considered to be representative of a wider area, the experimenter must have more than one sample per treatment per block in order to obtain an error term.

Now let us proceed with an experiment using the model for this section:

$$Y_{ijk} = \mu + \tau_i + \beta_j + (\tau\beta)_{ij} + \epsilon_{ijk},$$

with random block, interaction, and sampling effects and fixed treatment effects ($p$ treatments, $r$ blocks, and $q$ samples per treatment per

† It does not make any difference whether blocks are fixed or not if $(\tau\beta) = 0$. There is no sampling mean square if $q = 1$.

block). Such an experiment is designed to estimate treatment differences and confidence limits for the true differences and to make tests of these differences, as well as to assess several sources of variability which cause fluctuations in the yields of a given treatment. We are seldom interested in the general mean, contrary to the importance of this mean in Sec. 22.2. And we generally are interested in only the variance components which affect treatment comparisons, because we want to plan experiments to minimize the variance of treatment differences for fixed costs or amount of experimental material.

We have presented the expectations of the $T$, $TB$, and $E$ mean squares for our present model [blocks random and $(\tau\beta) \neq 0$]. There is some controversy over the expectation of the blocks mean square, but we shall proceed as follows:

$$(B_j - pq\mu) = q \sum_i \tau_i + pq\beta_j + q \sum_i (\tau\beta)_{ij} + \sum_i \sum_k \epsilon_{ijk} = pq\beta_j + \sum_i \sum_k \epsilon_{ijk}.$$

We know that $\sum_i \tau_i = 0$ from the assumption of fixed treatment effects.

It seems reasonable to also assume that

$$\sum_i (\tau\beta)_{ij} = 0,$$

since all the $(\tau\beta)_{ij}$ (for a fixed $j$) in the population are in the sample. (See reference 1 for a similar approach.) Naturally the sum over $j$ for a fixed $i$ is not zero, because the $r$ blocks in this experiment are assumed to be a random sample from a larger population. Similarly

$$(G - rpq\mu) = pq \sum_j \beta_j + \sum_i \sum_j \sum_k \epsilon_{ijk}.$$

Now

$$\text{SSB} = \frac{\sum_j (B_j - pq\mu)^2}{pq} - \frac{(G - rpq\mu)^2}{rpq}.$$

Hence

$$E(\text{SSB}) = pq(r-1)\sigma_b^2 + (r-1)\sigma_e^2, \qquad \text{and} \qquad E(\text{MSB}) = pq\sigma_b^2 + \sigma_e^2.$$

Because of the above restriction on the $(\tau\beta)$ effects, we shall use the same definition used for nested sampling from a finite population, for example, reference 2, to define $\sigma_{ib}^2$ as follows:

$$\sigma_{ib}^2 = \sum_i (\tau\beta)_{ij}^2/(p-1).$$

Using this definition of $\sigma_{ib}^2$, it is easy to show that the expectations of

MS($TB$) and MSE are the same as in Sec. 22.2, as stated earlier in this section. We see, for example, that

$$E[\underset{ijk}{S}(Y - \mu - \tau_i)^2] = rpq\sigma_b^2 + (p - 1)rq\sigma_{ib}^2 + rpq\sigma_e^2.$$

There are certain difficulties about the variance of $\bar{Y}$ when the treatments are finite; presumably the finite population correction should be used here, but we shall neglect it in the discussion which follows. Perhaps some of these theoretical difficulties would be resolved if we used the intraclass correlation concept, which is used by Hansen and Hurwitz[3] in considering finite populations for nested sampling.

Since the $\{\tau_i\}$ are assumed fixed,

$$E(\text{SST}) = rq \sum_i \tau_i^2 + (p - 1)(q\sigma_{ib}^2 + \sigma_e^2),$$

$$E(\text{MST}) = rq\theta(\tau) + \sigma_3^2,$$

where $\theta(\tau) = rq \sum_i \tau_i^2/(p - 1)$ and $\sigma_3^2 = q\sigma_{ib}^2 + \sigma_e^2$, as in Sec. 22.2, and $\sigma_3^2 \doteq \text{MS}(TB)$.

Hence the analysis of variance for this mixed model is as follows:

| Source of variation | Degrees of freedom | Mean square | $E$(MS) |
|---|---|---|---|
| Blocks | $r - 1$ | MSB $= V_1$ | $\sigma_e^2 + pq\sigma_b^2 = \sigma_1^2$ |
| Treatments | $p - 1$ | MST $= V_2$ | $\sigma_e^2 + q\sigma_{ib}^2 + rq\theta(\tau)$ |
| $T \times B$ | $(r - 1)(p - 1)$ | MS($TB$) $= V_3$ | $\sigma_e^2 + q\sigma_{ib}^2 = \sigma_3^2$ |
| Samples | $rp(q - 1)$ | MSE $= V_4$ | $\sigma_e^2 = \sigma_4^2$ |

Since the $\tau$'s are fixed,

$$\sigma^2(\bar{Y}) = \frac{\sigma_b^2}{r} + \frac{\sigma_{ib}^2}{rp} + \frac{\sigma_e^2}{rpq} = \frac{\sigma_1^2 + \sigma_3^2 - \sigma_4^2}{rpq} \doteq \frac{V_1 + V_3 - V_4}{rpq}.$$

The variance of a given treatment mean, $\bar{T}_i$, is

$$\sigma^2(\bar{T}_i) = \frac{\sigma_b^2}{r} + \frac{\sigma_{ib}^2}{r} + \frac{\sigma_e^2}{rq} = \frac{\sigma_1^2 + p\sigma_3^2 - \sigma_4^2}{rpq} \doteq \frac{V_1 + pV_3 - V_4}{rpq}.$$

But the principal comparison desired in this experiment is the difference, $d$, between two treatment means,

$$\sigma^2(d) = 2\left(\frac{\sigma_e^2}{rq} + \frac{\sigma_{ib}^2}{r}\right) = \frac{2\sigma_3^2}{rq} \doteq \frac{2V_3}{rq}.$$

The first two comparisons have the degree-of-freedom complication mentioned in Sec. 22.2, but not $\sigma^2(d)$. The importance of the variance components can be assessed as in Sec. 22.2 and confidence limits approximated by any of the four methods mentioned in that section.

In the above analysis, $V_2$ is not distributed as $\chi^2\sigma_2^2/f_2$, because

$$E(T_i - rq\mu) = rq\tau_i \neq 0.$$

$V_2$ is distributed as a noncentral $\chi^2[E(V_2) = \sigma_3^2 + \text{constant}]$ with a variance of

$$\frac{4\sigma_3^2}{f_2}[\sigma_3^2 + rq\theta(\tau)] - \frac{2\sigma_3^4}{f_2}.\dagger$$

It can be shown that an unbiased estimate of the variance of $V_2$, which consists of both random and fixed components, is

$$s^2(V_2) = \frac{4}{f_2}V_2V_3 - \frac{2f_3V_3^2}{(f_3+2)f_2}.$$

In general, if the random component consists of several sources of variation, which must be estimated from more than one mean square, we can write for the mean square ($V$) with both random and fixed components

$$E(V) = \sigma_r^2 + \lambda\theta,$$

where $\sigma_r^2$ is the random and $\theta$ the fixed component. We can write

$$\sigma_r^2 = \sum_j a_j\sigma_j^2,$$

where $a_j = \pm 1$ and $\sigma_j^2 \doteq V_j$. That is, $\sigma_r^2$ can be thought of as the sum and difference of several independent random variances, each estimated by a single mean square in the analysis of variance. Let $V = V_r + V_s$, where $\sigma_r^2 \doteq V_r$ and $\lambda\theta \doteq V_s$. Since the $V$'s are all independent,

$$V_r = \Sigma a_jV_j \qquad \text{and} \qquad E(VV_r) = E(V_r)E(V) = \sigma_r^2(\sigma_r^2 + \lambda\theta).$$

Also, since $E(V_j^2) = \sigma_j^4\dfrac{f_j+2}{f_j}$ and $E(V_jV_k) = \sigma_j^2\sigma_k^2$,

$$\sigma_r^4 = \sum_j \sigma_j^4 + 2\sum_{j<k}\sum a_ja_k\sigma_j^2\sigma_k^2 \doteq \sum_j \frac{f_j}{f_j+2}V_j^2 + 2\sum_{j<k}\sum a_ja_kV_jV_k.$$

Collecting terms, we find that an unbiased estimate of the variance of a mean square $V$, consisting of both random and fixed components, is

$$\frac{4}{f}VV_r - \frac{2}{f}\left[\sum_j \frac{f_j}{f_j+2}V_j^2 + 2\sum_{j<k}\sum a_ja_kV_jV_k\right],$$

with $V_r = \sum_j a_jV_j$ and $f$ degrees of freedom for $V$.

† See references 4 and 5.

**Example 23.1.** An experiment was run to test the effectiveness of 9 different spray materials on cherry trees with 9 blocks (81 trees) and four 1-pound random samples of fruit from each of the 81 trees in the experiment. The variable studied was the number of fruit per 1-pound sample, and it is assumed that block and sample effects are random. The totals of four samples for each of the trees were as shown in Table 23.1:

TABLE 23.1

| Blocks | Treatments | | | | | | | | | Total |
|---|---|---|---|---|---|---|---|---|---|---|
| | 0 | 1 | 2 | 3 | 4 | 5 | 6 | 7 | 8 | |
| 1 | 506 | 471 | 580 | 438 | 497 | 514 | 468 | 455 | 494 | 4,423 |
| 2 | 444 | 464 | 718 | 478 | 483 | 484 | 515 | 451 | 507 | 4,544 |
| 3 | 452 | 417 | 638 | 485 | 474 | 526 | 495 | 445 | 506 | 4,438 |
| 4 | 453 | 443 | 503 | 437 | 500 | 539 | 476 | 457 | 469 | 4,277 |
| 5 | 468 | 459 | 596 | 417 | 493 | 516 | 462 | 436 | 470 | 4,517 |
| 6 | 427 | 428 | 559 | 457 | 531 | 496 | 442 | 479 | 430 | 4,249 |
| 7 | 460 | 468 | 583 | 482 | 509 | 427 | 470 | 468 | 462 | 4,329 |
| 8 | 395 | 506 | 571 | 414 | 457 | 452 | 475 | 418 | 486 | 4,174 |
| 9 | 455 | 454 | 718 | 429 | 515 | 511 | 406 | 425 | 484 | 4,397 |
| Total | 4,060 | 4,110 | 5,466 | 4,037 | 4,459 | 4,465 | 4,209 | 4,034 | 4,308 | 39,148 |
| Mean | 112.8 | 114.2 | 151.8 | 112.1 | 123.9 | 124.0 | 116.9 | 112.1 | 119.7 | 120.8 |

The total sum of squares between samples for the same tree was 4,610. The other computations are as follows:

$$C = \frac{(39{,}148)^2}{324},$$

$$\text{SST} = \frac{(4{,}060)^2 + (4{,}110)^2 + \cdots + (4{,}308)^2}{36} - C = 45{,}326,$$

$$\text{SSB} = \frac{(4{,}423)^2 + (4{,}544)^2 + \cdots + (4{,}397)^2}{36} - C = 2{,}804,$$

$$\text{SS}(TB) = \frac{(506)^2 + (471)^2 + \cdots + (484)^2}{4} - C - \text{SST} - \text{SSB}$$

$$= 19{,}722.$$

The analysis of variance is as follows:

| Source of variation | Degrees of freedom | Sum of squares | Mean square | $E$(MS) |
|---|---|---|---|---|
| Blocks | 8 | 2,804 | 350.5 | $\sigma_e^2 + 36\sigma_b^2$ |
| Treatments | 8 | 45,326 | 5,665.7 | $\sigma_e^2 + 4\sigma_{tb}^2 + 36\theta(\tau)$ |
| $T \times B$ | 64 | 19,722 | 308.1 | $\sigma_e^2 + 4\sigma_{tb}^2$ |
| Samples in trees | 243 | 4,610 | 18.97 | $\sigma_e^2$ |

The error term to test for treatment differences is MS($TB$) = 308.1 with 64 degrees of freedom. Hence the $F$ value to make this test is

$$F = \frac{5{,}665.7}{308.1} = 18.39,$$

which is highly significant [$F_{.01}(8,64) = 2.80$].

The estimate of $\sigma_{tb}^2$ is

$$s_{tb}^2 = \frac{308.1 - 19.0}{4} = \frac{289.1}{4} = 72.3.$$

The variance of $s_{tb}^2$ is

$$\frac{2}{16}\left[\frac{V_{tb}^2}{66} + \frac{V_e^2}{245}\right] = 180.$$

Hence the 95 per cent normal two-tailed confidence limits for $\sigma_{tb}^2$ are

$$72.3 - 26.3 < \sigma_{tb}^2 < 72.3 + 26.3$$

or

$$46.0 < \sigma_{tb}^2 < 98.6.$$

It is obvious that this is the important source of variation, the sample-to-sample fluctuations being quite small.

The variance of the difference, $d$, between two treatment means is

$$\sigma^2(d) = 2\left[\frac{\sigma_e^2}{36} + \frac{\sigma_{tb}^2}{9}\right] = \frac{2}{36}(\sigma_e^2 + 4\sigma_{tb}^2)$$

and is estimated by

$$s^2(d) = 2\text{MS}(TB)/36 = 17.1.$$

Hence the 95 per cent confidence limits for the true difference, $\delta$, is

$$d - 8.3 < \delta < d + 8.3.$$

The limits for $\bar{T}_4 - \bar{T}_0$ are

$$2.8 < \delta < 19.4.$$

Again the experimenter is cautioned against use of these confidence limits to test the greatest mean against the smallest, unless he has decided to compare these particular treatments (regardless of their ultimate standing) before running the experiment. If the results of the experiment are used to decide on the comparison to make, the probability levels are upset. The reader is again advised to read an article by Tukey[6] on this topic.

**23.2. Split-plot Designs.** A special type of incomplete-blocks design is the *split-plot design*, in which one set of $p$ treatments ($T$) is arranged in a randomized complete-blocks design with $r$ blocks $(B)$ and a second set of $q$ treatments $(A)$ is assigned at random to one of $q$ subplots in each of the $pr$ whole plots. The mathematical model for this experiment is

$$Y_{ijk} = \mu + \tau_i + \beta_j + (\tau\beta)_{ij} + \alpha_k + (\tau\alpha)_{ik} + \epsilon_{ijk},$$

where $\alpha$, $\tau$, and $(\tau\alpha)$ are fixed treatment effects, $(\tau\beta)_{ij}$ and $\epsilon_{ijk}$ are random sources of error, and $\beta_j$ is a random block effect.† The analysis of variance for this model is:

| Source of variation | Degrees of freedom | Sum of squares | Mean square | $E$(MS)† |
|---|---|---|---|---|
| Blocks $(B)$ | $r - 1$ | SSB | $V_b$ | $\sigma_e^2 + pq\sigma_b^2$ |
| $T$ | $p - 1$ | SST | $V_t$ | $\sigma_e^2 + q\sigma_{tb}^2 + rq\theta_1(\tau)$ |
| $T \times B$ | $(r - 1)(p - 1)$ | SS$(TB)$ | $V_{tb}$ | $\sigma_e^2 + q\sigma_{tb}^2$ |
| $A$ | $q - 1$ | SSA | $V_a$ | $\sigma_e^2 + rp\theta_2(\alpha)$ |
| $T \times A$ | $(p - 1)(q - 1)$ | SS$(TA)$ | $V_{ta}$ | $\sigma_e^2 + r\theta_3(\tau\alpha)$ |
| Subplot error | $p(r - 1)(q - 1)$ | SSE | $V_e$ | $\sigma_e^2$ |

† $\theta_1(\tau)$, $\theta_2(\alpha)$, and $\theta_3(\tau\alpha)$ are sums of squares of fixed effects divided by the degrees of freedom.

The first five sums of squares are computed in the usual manner for main effects and interactions (see Chap. 20) and the subplot error (SSE) by subtraction. Note that we have omitted $\sigma_{tb}^2$ from the expectation of the blocks mean square.

In making tests of significance of the differences among fixed effects, SSE is the error sum of squares for $A$ and $TA$ and SS$(TB)$ for $T$. The problem of determining confidence limits for differences between various treatment means is slightly complicated. We know that

$$(TA)_{ik} = r\mu + r\tau_i + \sum_j \beta_j + \sum_j (\tau\beta)_{ij} + r\alpha_k + r(\tau\alpha)_{ik} + \sum_j \epsilon_{ijk}.$$

We have the following types of means to compare:

(i) *Two $T$ treatments*

$$d_t = \bar{T}_i - \bar{T}_{i'} = (\tau_i - \tau_{i'}) + \sum_j [(\tau\beta)_{ij} - (\tau\beta)_{i'j}]/r + \sum_j \sum_k (\epsilon_{ijk} - \epsilon_{i'jk})/rq,$$

$$E(d_t) = (\tau_i - \tau_{i'}), \qquad \sigma^2(d_t) = \frac{2}{rq}[q\sigma_{tb}^2 + \sigma_e^2] \doteq \frac{2V_{tb}}{rq}.$$

† In this case we assume that there is no real $(\alpha\beta)$ or $(\tau\alpha\beta)$ interaction but that the only deviation in the subplot is a single random error, $\epsilon_{ijk}$.

(ii) *Two A treatments*

$$d_a = \bar{A}_k - \bar{A}_{k'} = (\alpha_k - \alpha_{k'}) + \sum_i \sum_j (\epsilon_{ijk} - \epsilon_{ijk'})/rp,$$

$$E(d_a) = \alpha_k - \alpha_{k'}, \qquad \sigma^2(d_a) = 2\sigma_e^2/rp \doteq 2V_e/rp.$$

(iii) *Two T treatments with the same A treatment*

$$d_{tk} = (\overline{TA})_{ik} - (\overline{TA})_{i'k} = (\tau_i - \tau_{i'}) + \sum_j [(\tau\beta)_{ij} - (\tau\beta)_{i'j}]/r$$
$$+ [(\tau\alpha)_{ik} - (\tau\alpha)_{i'k}] + \sum_j (\epsilon_{ijk} - \epsilon_{i'jk})/r,$$

$$E(d_{tk}) = (\tau_i - \tau_{i'}) + [(\tau\alpha)_{ik} - (\tau\alpha)_{i'k}],$$
$$\sigma^2(d_{tk}) = 2(\sigma_{tb}^2 + \sigma_e^2)/r \doteq 2[V_{tb} + (q-1)V_e]/rq.$$

(iv) *Two A treatments with the same T treatment*

$$d_{ia} = (\overline{TA})_{ik} - (\overline{TA})_{ik'} = (\alpha_k - \alpha_{k'}) + [(\tau\alpha)_{ik} - (\tau\alpha)_{ik'}]$$
$$+ \sum_j (\epsilon_{ijk} - \epsilon_{ijk'})/r,$$

$$E(d_{ia}) = (\alpha_k - \alpha_{k'}) + [(\tau\alpha)_{ik} - (\tau\alpha)_{ik'}], \qquad \sigma^2(d_{ia}) = 2\sigma_e^2/r.$$

(v) *Two different A treatments and two different T treatments*

$$d_{ta} = (\overline{TA})_{ik} - (\overline{TA})_{i'k'} = (\tau_i - \tau_{i'}) + \sum_j [(\tau\beta)_{ij} - (\tau\beta)_{i'j}]/r$$
$$+ (\alpha_k - \alpha_{k'}) + [(\tau\alpha)_{ik} - (\tau\alpha)_{i'k'}] + \sum_j (\epsilon_{ijk} - \epsilon_{i'jk'})/r,$$

$$E(d_{ta}) = (\tau_i - \tau_{i'}) + (\alpha_k - \alpha_{k'}) + [(\tau\alpha)_{ik} - (\tau\alpha)_{i'k'}],$$
$$\sigma^2(d_{ta}) = 2(\sigma_{tb}^2 + \sigma_e^2)/r \doteq 2[V_{tb} + (q-1)V_e]/rq.$$

It should be mentioned that if the experimenter wants to use (iii) or (v) to test the difference between two treatment means, he does not know how many degrees of freedom to use, since two error terms are involved. The number of degrees of freedom will fall between $(r-1)(p-1)$ and $p(r-1)(q-1)$. Hence, if the difference is significant using $(r-1)(p-1)$ degrees of freedom, it will be significant for the correct degrees of freedom; and, conversely, if it is not significant using $p(r-1)(q-1)$ degrees of freedom, we can conclude it is not significant. However, if it is not significant for the smaller and is significant for the larger number of degrees of freedom, the test is inconclusive. A rather good approximation to the correct number of degrees of freedom is furnished by Satterthwaite:[7]

$$f' = \frac{[V_{tb} + (q-1)V_e]^2}{\dfrac{V_{tb}^2}{(r-1)(p-1)} + \dfrac{[(q-1)V_e]^2}{p(r-1)(q-1)}}.$$

A more complete description of the split-plot design can be found in references 8 and 9. This design enables the experimenter to obtain quite accurate information on the $A$ treatments and on the interaction between $T$ and $A$ at the expense of less accurate information on the $T$ treatments as compared with a factorial design (Chap. 20), since the error mean square for the $T$ treatments has an added component of variation and is estimated with fewer degrees of freedom. Also, with this design, the experimenter can allocate the $T$ treatments to rather large plots and reserve the small subplots for the $A$ treatments. If one set of treatments is cultivation methods and a second set is fertilizer treatments, it would be advantageous to put the former on the larger whole plots because of the difficulty of handling machinery on small plots.

Also, this design is useful if the $A$ treatments are successive years in a long-term experiment. Unfortunately the years cannot be randomized, but it is not the year itself, but the effect of the year which we want to randomize. And it seems reasonable to assume that nature does a fairly good job of randomizing the year-to-year effects. But in this case it seems more reasonable to regard the subplot treatments (years) as random effects, and not fixed. And since they are random, the assumption that the $(\alpha\beta)$ interaction is zero seems somewhat unrealistic. Hence for this case we would advocate using the following model:

$$Y_{ijk} = \mu + \tau_i + \beta_j + (\tau\beta)_{ij} + \alpha_k + (\tau\alpha)_{ik} + (\beta\alpha)_{jk} + \epsilon_{ijk},$$

with everything random except $\mu$ and $\tau_i$. Of course, all interactions with $\tau_i$ are assumed random in one direction only. Also, we still assume $(\tau\alpha\beta)$ is zero, an assumption which does not strike us as being too bad even when the $\alpha$'s are random effects.

**Example 23.2.** A corn-yield experiment was conducted to compare four methods of primary seedbed preparation ($T$) and four methods of planting ($A$), using four blocks ($B$). The seedbed preparations were used on the whole plots, and each whole plot was divided into four subplots for the four planting methods. The corn yields in bushels per acre were as shown in Table 23.2.

TABLE 23.2

| Replication | Planting methods | | | | Total | |
|---|---|---|---|---|---|---|
| | $a_1$ | $a_2$ | $a_3$ | $a_4$ | | |
| | $t_1$ plowed 7″ | | | | | |
| 1 | 81.8 | 46.2 | 78.6 | 77.7 | 284.3 | |
| 2 | 72.2 | 51.6 | 70.9 | 73.6 | 268.3 | |
| 3 | 72.9 | 53.6 | 69.8 | 70.3 | 266.6 | |
| 4 | 74.6 | 57.0 | 69.6 | 72.3 | 273.5 | |
| Total | 301.5 | 208.4 | 288.9 | 293.9 | 1,092.7 | |
| | $t_2$ plowed 4″ | | | | | |
| 1 | 74.1 | 49.1 | 72.0 | 66.1 | 261.3 | |
| 2 | 76.2 | 53.8 | 71.8 | 65.5 | 267.3 | |
| 3 | 71.1 | 43.7 | 67.6 | 66.2 | 248.6 | |
| 4 | 67.8 | 58.8 | 60.6 | 60.6 | 247.8 | |
| Total | 289.2 | 205.4 | 272.0 | 258.4 | 1,025.0 | |
| | $t_3$ blank basin listed | | | | | |
| 1 | 68.4 | 54.5 | 72.0 | 70.6 | 265.5 | |
| 2 | 68.2 | 47.6 | 76.7 | 75.4 | 267.9 | |
| 3 | 67.1 | 46.4 | 70.7 | 66.2 | 250.4 | |
| 4 | 65.6 | 53.3 | 65.6 | 69.2 | 253.7 | |
| Total | 269.3 | 201.8 | 285.0 | 281.4 | 1,037.5 | |
| | $t_4$ disk-harrowed | | | | | |
| 1 | 71.5 | 50.9 | 76.4 | 75.1 | 273.9 | |
| 2 | 70.4 | 65.0 | 75.8 | 75.8 | 287.0 | |
| 3 | 72.5 | 54.9 | 67.6 | 75.2 | 270.2 | |
| 4 | 67.8 | 50.2 | 65.6 | 63.3 | 246.9 | |
| Total | 282.2 | 221.0 | 285.4 | 289.4 | 1,078.0 | 4,233.2 |

The four planting methods were surface drill ($a_1$), list ($a_2$), basin list ($a_3$), and list with bedding sweeps ($a_4$). The $T$ and $A$ totals are:

| | Sum | Mean | | Sum | Mean |
|---|---|---|---|---|---|
| $T_1$ | 1092.7 | 68.29 | $A_1$ | 1142.2 | 71.39 |
| $T_2$ | 1025.0 | 64.06 | $A_2$ | 836.6 | 52.29 |
| $T_3$ | 1037.5 | 64.84 | $A_3$ | 1131.3 | 70.71 |
| $T_4$ | 1078.0 | 67.38 | $A_4$ | 1123.1 | 70.19 |

The analysis of variance is as follows:

| Source of variation | Degrees of freedom | Sum of squares | Mean square | E(MS) |
|---|---|---|---|---|
| Blocks | 3 | 223.81 | 74.60 | $\sigma_e^2 + 16\sigma_b^2$ |
| Seedbed methods ($T$) | 3 | 194.56 | 64.85 | $\sigma_e^2 + 4\sigma_{tb}^2 + 16\theta_1(\tau)$ |
| $T \times B$ | 9 | 158.25 | 17.58 | $\sigma_e^2 + 4\sigma_{tb}^2$ |
| Planting methods ($A$) | 3 | 4,107.39 | 1,369.13 | $\sigma_e^2 + 16\theta_2(\alpha)$ |
| $T \times A$ | 9 | 221.74 | 24.64 | $\sigma_e^2 + 4\theta_3(\tau\alpha)$ |
| Subplot error | 36 | 608.47 | 16.90 | $\sigma_e^2$ |

There are highly significant differences between the planting methods ($F = 1{,}369.13/16.90$ with 3 and 36 degrees of freedom) but not between the seedbed methods (although the $F = 64.85/17.58 = 3.69$ is almost significant, since $F_{.05} = 3.86$ for 3 and 9 degrees of freedom). There is no evidence of any interaction between the two sets of treatments. An examination of the planting means shows that only $a_2$ is really different from the rest. In order to adjust for the fact that we have selected the smallest from a set of four means, which can be done in 4 ways, the significance probability assuming random choice might be multiplied by 4 to obtain an estimate of the true significance probability. If we take the linear form $l = A_1 + A_3 + A_4 - 3A_2 = 886.8$, we find that $\sigma^2(l) = 192\sigma_e^2 \doteq 3{,}244.80$. Hence

$$t = 886.8/\sqrt{3{,}244.80} = 15.6,$$

for which the estimated significance probability is much less than $4(.0005) = .002$. And we see that this 1 degree of freedom accounts for almost all of SSA. The sum of squares for $l$ is $(886.8)^2/192 = 4{,}095.91$, leaving only 11.48 for the other 2 degrees of freedom, a decidedly non-significant amount.

The variance of the difference between two $T$ means is

$$2(17.58)/16 = 2.20.$$

The variance of the mean difference between two $T$ treatments with the same $A$ treatment is $2[17.58 + 3(16.90)]/16 = 8.54$. This would apply to testing $t_1$ versus $t_2$ when planting method $a_1$ was used, the mean difference being 3.075 in this case. And finally the variance to compare two $A$ treatments with the same $T$ treatment is $2(16.90)/4 = 8.45$. This would apply to $a_1$ versus $a_2$ for $t_1$, the mean difference being 23.275.

**Example 23.3.** Wilm[11] presents some data on soil moisture deficits (in inches of water) as affected by timber cutting with 4 blocks, 5 $T$ treatments (amount of cutting), and 3 years as subplot treatments. The $T$ treatments were in terms of volume of board feet of trees larger than 9.6 inches in diameter which were left in the forest after treatment: uncut (11,900 feet); 6,000 feet; 4,000 feet; 2,000 feet; all cut. The years were 1941, 1942, and 1943. In this case it might be reasonable to regard the years as random and add the (year × block) random effect to the model. The analysis of variance for these data was:

| Source of variation | Degrees of freedom | Mean square | $E$(MS) |
|---|---|---|---|
| Blocks ($B$) | 3 | 1.4832 | $\sigma_e^2 + 5\sigma_{ba}^2 + 15\sigma_b^2$ |
| Treatments ($T$) | 4 | 1.3333 | $\sigma_e^2 + 3\sigma_{tb}^2 + 4\sigma_{ta}^2 + 12\theta(\tau)$ |
| $T \times B$ | 12 | .3909 | $\sigma_e^2 + 3\sigma_{tb}^2$ |
| Years ($A$) | 2 | 6.5418 | $\sigma_e^2 + 5\sigma_{ba}^2 + 20\sigma_a^2$ |
| $T \times A$ | 8 | .2554 | $\sigma_e^2 + 4\sigma_{ta}^2$ |
| $B \times A$ | 6 | .1294 | $\sigma_e^2 + 5\sigma_{ba}^2$ |
| Remainder ($E$) | 24 | .1053 | $\sigma_e^2$ |

Using $F = .1294/.1053$, we see that $\sigma_{ba}^2$ does not test significantly greater than zero; and using $F = .2554/.1053 = 2.43$, we see that $\sigma_{ta}^2$ tests significant at the $\alpha = .05$ probability level. The test of $\sigma_a^2$ is not too good, since there are only 6 degrees of freedom for error, but $F = 6.5418/.1294$ is significant at the $\alpha = .001$ level. The difficult test to make involves $\theta(\tau)$. There is no single error term to make this test. Two different tests have been proposed. Both tests are based on the Satterthwaite approximation.[4,7] In the first case, we use an estimate of $(\sigma_e^2 + 3\sigma_{tb}^2 + 4\sigma_{ta}^2)$ as the error term for MST. This estimate is $V_{tb} + V_{ta} - V_e \equiv V_r$ with $f_r'$ degrees of freedom, where

$$f_r' = \frac{V_r^2}{(V_{tb}^2/f_{tb}) + (V_{ta}^2/f_{ta}) + (V_e^2/f_e)}$$

and the $f$'s are the corresponding degrees of freedom. Then we assume that $F' = V_t/V_r$ is approximately distributed as $F$ with ($f_t$ and $f_r'$) degrees of freedom. Cochran[12] suggests that we add $V_e$ to $V_t$ and use

$$F'' = \frac{V_t + V_e}{V_{tb} + V_{ta}}$$

with $f_t''$ and $f_r''$ degrees of freedom. $f_t''$ and $f_r''$ would have to be computed as $f_r'$. There is some indication that $F''$ is more powerful than $F'$ in detecting real treatment effects, but there is some doubt that it is enough better to afford to compute 2 estimated degrees of freedom instead of 1.

In the Wilm problem, $V_r = .5410$, and $F' = 1.3333/.5410 = 2.46$ with degrees of freedom 4 and

$$f'_r = \frac{(.5410)^2}{\frac{(.3909)^2}{12} + \frac{(.2554)^2}{8} + \frac{(.1053)^2}{24}} = 14.$$

$F'$ is not significant at the 5 per cent level; actually $\alpha$ is about .10 in this case. Similarly

$$F'' = 1.4386/.6463 = 2.23$$

with (5,20) degrees of freedom. Again $\alpha$ is about .10.

The variance of the difference between any two $T$ treatment means is

$$\sigma^2(d) = 2\left[\frac{\sigma_{tb}^2}{q} + \frac{\sigma_{ta}^2}{r} + \frac{\sigma_e^2}{rq}\right] \doteq 2V_r/rq,$$

$$s^2(d) = \frac{2(.5410)}{12} = .0902.$$

Hence the 95 per cent confidence limits for $\delta$ will be

$$d - (2.15)(.30) < \delta < d + (2.15)(.30),$$

where we use a $t$ value with $f'_r = 14$ degrees of freedom.

## EXERCISES

**23.1.** Prove that the expected value of $s^2$ in Sec. 18.3 is actually $\sigma_e^2 + \sigma_{tb}^2$ if there is an interaction.

**23.2.** Reexamine the examples and exercises in Sec. 18.3 and Chap. 20 to see in which experiments it is logical to assume the blocks are representative of a wider set of experimental conditions than in the given experiment.

(*a*) How would the cities in Exercise 18.9 and the plants in Exercise 18.10 have to be selected to make this condition true?

(*b*) How can you rationalize that consecutive days or consecutive years might have random effects on crop yields or other experimental results, such as in Example 18.3?

(*c*) Where does this rationale fall down in the analysis of economic data, such as market prices?

**23.3.** What assumptions must be made concerning the effects in a Latin-square design in order to extend the results to a wider horizon than the given experiment?

**23.4.** Determine the four approximate 90 per cent confidence intervals for $\sigma_{tb}^2$ in Example 23.1.

**23.5.** (*a*) In Exercise 20.3, what changes should be made in the analysis if the four blocks and five varieties constituted representative samples from large universes of blocks and varieties?

(*b*) What are the expectations of the mean squares under this assumption?

(*c*) Determine estimates of the random variance components, and make the necessary tests of significance.

(*d*) Make a test of spacing differences, and determine the standard error of the difference between two spacing means if $p'$ varieties and $r'$ blocks were used.

**23.6.** A field experiment was conducted to determine an acceptable lower limit on the size of similar future experiments. The analysis of variance was:

| Source of variation | Degrees of freedom | Mean square |
|---|---|---|
| Blocks | 2 | 4,399 |
| Treatments | 4 | 4,429 |
| $T \times B$ | 8 | 866 |
| Samples in plots | 15 | 239 |
| Determinations in samples | 30 | 7 |

(*a*) Assuming everything random, except treatments, set up the expectations of the mean squares, and determine estimates of the random components.

(*b*) What is the standard error of the difference between two treatment means with *b* blocks, *s* samples per plot, and *d* determinations per sample? Which of these three sampling plans (which cost the same) would be favored: $b = 6, s = 2, d = 1; b = 3, s = 5, d = 1; b = 4, s = 2, d = 2$?

(*c*) Determine the 90 per cent confidence limits for $\sigma^2_{tb}$.

**23.7.** Show how the variance components in Example 23.3 were obtained, and also $\sigma^2(d)$.

**23.8.** Derive an approximate test for Example 23.2 to test whether the average yield for $t_1$ and $t_4$ was significantly greater than the average of $t_2$ and $t_3$.

**23.9.** Johnson and Tsao[13] conducted a psychological experiment to determine the *difference limen* (DL) of subjects for weights increasing at constant rates. Two classes of people were chosen as to sight—normal ($A$) and congenitally blind ($B$). Two males and two females were selected to represent each class, giving a total of 8 people. Then the average of five DL values was determined for each subject for each of 28 rate-weight combinations, 7 weights and 4 rates. The entire experiment was repeated at a later date with different people. Hence there was a total of $28 \times 8 \times 2 = 448$ average DL's. The order of presentation of the 28 combinations was randomized for each subject at each date.

(*a*) Set up the analysis of variance as to sources of variation, degrees of freedom, and expectations of the mean squares.

(*b*) How would the analysis be changed if each of the five DL values was recorded instead of a single average being reported?

(*c*) A portion of the data (for 3 weights and 2 rates) is reproduced in the accompanying table for computational purposes.

DATA OF EXERCISE 23.9

| Weight | | | | 1 | | 2 | | 3 | |
|---|---|---|---|---|---|---|---|---|---|
| Rate | | | | *a* | *b* | *a* | *b* | *a* | *b* |
| Sex | Sight | Date | Individual | | | | | | |
| | | 1 | 1 | 4.5 | 10.9 | 4.5 | 10.1 | 4.5 | 8.6 |
| *M* | *A* | | 2 | 14.0 | 30.5 | 13.9 | 25.5 | 12.2 | 29.3 |
| | | 2 | 1 | 3.1 | 6.2 | 3.3 | 6.8 | 3.5 | 7.0 |
| | | | 2 | 13.4 | 26.2 | 12.8 | 23.5 | 12.8 | 27.8 |
| | | 1 | 1 | 24.2 | 48.1 | 25.3 | 41.2 | 25.1 | 31.4 |
| *M* | *B* | | 2 | 19.3 | 41.0 | 21.1 | 30.1 | 19.6 | 35.0 |
| | | 2 | 1 | 41.2 | 59.1 | 29.8 | 59.7 | 28.5 | 48.7 |
| | | | 2 | 19.9 | 44.1 | 18.3 | 28.5 | 15.9 | 31.8 |
| | | 1 | 1 | 18.5 | 22.3 | 10.2 | 25.2 | 11.4 | 19.7 |
| | | | 2 | 3.1 | 7.0 | 3.9 | 5.4 | 3.6 | 7.3 |
| *F* | *A* | 2 | 1 | 11.2 | 21.8 | 8.8 | 14.0 | 8.1 | 21.8 |
| | | | 2 | 3.9 | 11.4 | 5.1 | 10.2 | 3.7 | 8.7 |
| | | 1 | 1 | 9.6 | 17.9 | 7.3 | 18.2 | 6.5 | 15.8 |
| | | | 2 | 9.0 | 16.1 | 6.4 | 15.9 | 6.9 | 12.9 |
| *F* | *B* | 2 | 1 | 6.1 | 13.9 | 6.0 | 12.5 | 6.4 | 12.1 |
| | | | 2 | 8.6 | 14.5 | 6.9 | 14.2 | 5.3 | 12.0 |

**23.10.** Professor J. Wishart[10] furnishes us this example. "The seed mixtures denoted by *A*, *B*, *C*, *D* below were sown under wheat in 1938, the treatments being randomized over the plots of each block. In the summer of 1939, Blocks I, IV, VI and VII were grazed and Blocks II, III, V and VIII were cut for hay (each successive *pair* of blocks was taken as a unit and a random choice made as to which block should be grazed and which cut for hay). The table below gives the estimated weights, in pounds, of clover (green) in the May 1940 cut. Analyze these weights fully and draw attention to the significant results. The sum of the 32 weights is 527.4 and the sum of their squares is 9,410.18."

| I | | II | | III | | IV | |
|---|---|---|---|---|---|---|---|
| *C* 8.7 | *B* 14.1 | *B* 15.2 | *A* 14.8 | *C* 16.3 | *D* 22.4 | *D* 25.1 | *B* 25.3 |
| *A* 8.8 | *D* 13.2 | *C* 8.7 | *D* 9.4 | *A* 9.4 | *B* 13.9 | *C* 19.6 | *A* 18.1 |

| V | | VI | | VII | | VIII | |
|---|---|---|---|---|---|---|---|
| *C* 22.2 | *A* 21.9 | *C* 22.4 | *B* 16.6 | *C* 19.6 | *B* 18.6 | *D* 19.9 | *A* 17.4 |
| *B* 21.5 | *D* 20.6 | *A* 16.0 | *D* 13.6 | *D* 13.3 | *A* 13.3 | *B* 14.4 | *C* 13.1 |

**23.11.** Suppose in Example 20.2 that the plot yields were available for each of the 12 years with the following sums of squares for years and interactions with years:

| | |
|---|---|
| Years ($Y$) | 165,808 |
| Years $\times$ treatments ($YT$) | 6,185 |
| Years $\times$ replications ($YR$) | 19,554 |
| Remainder ($E$) | 44,490 |

(*a*) Set up the complete analysis of variance for this experiment. Remember that the analysis in Example 20.2 was based on the total yields for 12 years, while the above sums of squares are based on annual yields.

(*b*) What conclusions would you draw from this analysis?

(*c*) What aspects of these data might violate the assumptions behind the use of the analysis of variance in making tests of significance? Do you have any suggestions for improving the analysis?

**23.12.** In Exercise 22.4, assume that the treatment effects are fixed.

(*a*) Derive the expectation of the treatment mean square.

(*b*) How would you test for treatment differences?

**23.13.** In a bee experiment conducted by E. Oertel in Louisiana, the honey was collected from 32 colonies randomly assigned to 4 rows of 8 colonies each for each of 5 years. It seems reasonable to assume that colony and year effects are random and row effects are fixed. We note that this is a completely randomized design for the whole plots (rows are $T$ treatments). The analysis of variance for the yields in pounds of honey per year was:

| Source of variation | Degrees of freedom | Mean square | $E$(MS) |
|---|---|---|---|
| Rows ($T$) | | 15,593 | $\sigma_{ca}^2 + 8\sigma_{ta}^2 + 5\sigma_c^2 + 40\theta(\tau)$ |
| Colonies in rows ($C$) | | 2,529 | $\sigma_{ca}^2 + 5\sigma_c^2$ |
| Years ($A$) | | 107,297 | $\sigma_{ca}^2 + 32\sigma_a^2$ |
| $T \times A$ | | 3,019 | $\sigma_{ca}^2 + 8\sigma_{ta}^2$ |
| $C \times A$ | | 2,589 | $\sigma_{ca}^2$ |

(*a*) Set up a mathematical model for this experiment.

(*b*) Fill in the degrees-of-freedom column, and show that the $E$(MS) column is correct.

(*c*) What do you conclude regarding the colony-to-colony variation in the same row?

(*d*) Is there much evidence of a real row-by-year interaction in this problem?

(*e*) What is the most important source of variation? What are approximate 90 per cent confidence limits for this component?

(*f*) How would you test for row differences?

(*g*) The mean productions per colony per year for each row were: 182.5, 149.2, 158.9, and 135.6. Show that the standard error for the difference between any two row means is 12.6.

**23.14.** Suppose data were available on the average sales price per pound of tobacco for a period of $y$ years at each of $m$ markets. These markets are divided into 4 geographical areas with $m_1$, $m_2$, $m_3$, and $m_4$ markets per area $\left(\sum_i m_i = m\right)$.

(*a*) Set up an analysis of variance to reflect the sources of variation in the marketing picture, assuming that areas are fixed and the remaining components are random.

(*b*) Determine the expectations of the mean squares.

(*c*) What is the variance of a mean over all 4 areas with $m'$ markets per area and $y'$ years?

**23.15.** A randomized complete-blocks experiment was conducted on the percentage of acid in orange juice with 4 blocks and 5 fertilizers, each plot having 3 trees. Two samples were taken from each tree, one sample being picked by one man and the second sample by another man. The basic analysis of variance was as follows:

| Source of variation | Degrees of freedom | Mean square | $E$(MS) |
|---|---|---|---|
| Blocks ($B$) | 3 | .002315 | |
| Fertilizers ($T$) | 4 | .042064 | |
| $T \times B$ | 12 | .009133 | |
| Trees in plots ($E$) | 40 | .004735 | |
| Men ($A$) | 1 | .012813 | |
| $T \times A$ | 4 | .003924 | |
| $A \times B$ | 3 | .003449 | |
| Remainder | 52 | .002749 | |

(*a*) Set up a model for this experiment, assuming we want to make inferences about only these fertilizers, but that all other effects are representative of large populations.

(*b*) Compute the expectations of the mean squares for your model.

(*c*) Compute estimates of the variance components.

(*d*) How would you test for fertilizer differences?

(*e*) What is the variance of the mean amount of acid for any one fertilizer if $r'$ blocks, $q'$ trees per plot, and $m'$ samples are used? Compute this variance for $r' = 4$, $q' = 3$, $m' = 2$; $r' = 6$, $q' = 1$, $m' = 4$.

**23.16.** (*a*) In Sec. 20.6, show that if the replication effects are assumed to be random, we can obtain the following analysis for the $(2r - 1)$ degrees of freedom between blocks:

| Source of variation | Degrees of freedom | Mean square | $E$(MS) |
|---|---|---|---|
| Replications ($R$) | $r - 1$ | MSR | |
| $ACD$ | 1 | MS($ACD$) | $\sigma_e^2 + 4\sigma_{e'}^2 + 4r\theta(\tau)$ |
| $(ACD) \times R$ | $r - 1$ | MSE′† | $\sigma_e^2 + 4\sigma_{e'}^2$ |

† MSE′ is the whole-plot error mean square, and $\sigma_{e'}^2$ is the variance for the (replication) $\times$ ($ACD$) error.

(*b*) Apply this result to test the $NPK$ interaction in Exercise 20.15.

**References Cited**

1. NORDSKOG, A. W., and S. L. CRUMP, "Systematic and Random Sampling for Estimating Egg Production in Poultry," *Biometrics*, **4**:223–233 (1948).
2. COCHRAN, W. G., "Sample Survey Techniques," *Inst. Stat. Mim. Ser.* 7 (1950).
3. HANSEN, M. H., and W. N. HURWITZ, "On the Theory of Sampling for Finite Populations," *Ann. Math. Stat.*, **14**:333–362 (1943).

4. ANDERSON, R. L. "Use of Variance Components in the Analysis of Hog Prices in Two Markets," *J. Am. Stat. Assoc.*, **42**:612–634 (1947).
5. DANIELS, H. E., "The Estimation of Components of Variance," *J. Roy. Stat. Soc. Suppl.*, **6**:186–197 (1939).
6. TUKEY, J. W., "Comparing Individual Means in the Analysis of Variance," *Biometrics*, **5**:99–114 (1949).
7. SATTERTHWAITE, F. E., "An Approximate Distribution of Estimates of Variance Components," *Biom. Bull.*, **2**:110–114 (1946).
8. COCHRAN, W. G., and G. M. COX, *Experimental Designs*, John Wiley & Sons, Inc., New York, 1950.
9. SNEDECOR, G. W., *Statistical Methods*, 4th ed., Collegiate Press, Inc., of Iowa State College, Ames, Iowa, 1946.
10. WISHART, J., "Design of Experiments," *Inst. Stat. Mim. Ser.* 15 (1949).
11. WILM, H. G., "Notes on Analysis of Experiments Replicated in Time," *Biom. Bull.*, **1**:16–20 (1945).
12. COCHRAN, W. G., "Testing a Linear Relation among Variances," *Biometrics*, **7**:17–32 (1951).
13. JOHNSON, P. O., and F. TSAO, "Factorial Design in the Determination of Differential Limen Values," *Psychometrika*, **9**:107–144 (1944).

### Other Reading†

COCHRAN, W. G., "Problems Arising in the Analysis of a Series of Similar Experiments," *J. Roy. Stat. Soc. Suppl.*, **4**:102–118 (1937).

CROWTHER, F., and W. G. COCHRAN, "Rotation Experiments with Cotton in the Sudan Gezira," *J. Agr. Sci.*, **32**:390–405 (1942).

SMITH, H. F., "Analysis of Variance with Unequal but Proportionate Numbers of Observations in the Sub-classes of a Two-way Classification," *Biometrics*, **7**: 70–74 (1951).

YATES, F., and W. G. COCHRAN, "The Analysis of Groups of Experiments," *J. Agr. Sci.*, **28**:556–580 (1938).

† Also see the references given in Chap. 22.

# CHAPTER 24

# THE RECOVERY OF INTERBLOCK INFORMATION IN INCOMPLETE-BLOCKS DESIGNS

**24.1. Balanced Incomplete-blocks Designs.** It was mentioned in Sec. 19.3 that *Yates*[1] introduced a new computing technique for balanced incomplete-blocks designs which utilized the so-called *interblock information* on treatment effects. The basic change in the model is that the $\beta$'s are assumed to be random effects with the same variance, $\sigma_b^2$, the plot-to-plot (intrablock) error being designated by $\sigma_e^2$. From Sec. 19.3 we know that the intrablock estimate, $t_i$, of $\tau_i$ had a variance

$$\sigma^2(t_i) = \frac{k-1}{kE_f}\,\frac{1}{rE_fW_1} = \frac{p-1}{p}\,\frac{1}{rE_fW_1},$$

where $W_1 = 1/\sigma_e^2$. We can obtain a second estimate of $\tau_i$ (the interblock estimate) from $\sum_j n_{ij}B_j \equiv T_{bi}$ (see Sec. 19.3).

$$T_{bi} - \frac{k}{p}G = (r-\lambda)\tau_i + k\sum_j n_{ij}\beta_j - \frac{k^2}{p}\sum_j \beta_j + \sum_{i'}\sum_j n_{i'j}n_{ij}\epsilon_{i'j} - \frac{k}{p}\sum_{i'}\sum_j n_{i'j}\epsilon_{i'j}.$$

$$\tau_i \doteq \frac{T_{bi} - \dfrac{k}{p}G}{r-\lambda} \equiv t_{bi}.$$

$$\sigma^2(t_{bi}) = \frac{rk(p-k)}{p}\,\frac{(k\sigma_b^2 + \sigma_e^2)}{(r-\lambda)^2} = \frac{p-1}{p}\,\frac{k}{(r-\lambda)W_2},$$

where $W_2 = 1/(k\sigma_b^2 + \sigma_e^2)$.

If we have two independent estimates ($t_1$ and $t_2$) of the same quantity, $\tau$, the combined estimate with minimum variance is given by

$$t = \frac{W_1't_1 + W_2't_2}{W_1' + W_2'},$$

where $W'_i = 1/\sigma^2(t_i)$. Hence the combined estimate of $\tau'_i (= \tau_i + \mu)$ is

$$t'_{ic} = t_{ic} + m = \frac{rE_fW_1t_i + \frac{(r-\lambda)W_2}{k}t_{bi}}{rE_fW_1 + \frac{(r-\lambda)W_2}{k}} + \frac{G}{rp}$$

$$= \frac{\frac{(kT_i - T_{bi})W_1}{k} + \frac{T_{bi}W_2}{k} - \frac{kGW_2}{pk}}{rE_fW_1 + \frac{(r-\lambda)W_2}{k}} + \frac{G}{rp}$$

$$= \frac{T_i}{r} + \theta D_i = \frac{T_i + r\theta D_i}{r},$$

where $\theta = (W_1 - W_2)/r[p(k-1)W_1 + (p-k)W_2]$ and $D_i = [(p-k)T_i - (p-1)T_{bi} + (k-1)G]$.

Certain identities are useful in making the above simplification:

$$(r-\lambda)(p-1) = r(p-k) \qquad \text{and} \qquad kE_f(p-1) = p(k-1).$$

The variance of the difference between two adjusted means, using interblock information, is

$$\frac{2k(p-1)}{r[p(k-1)W_1 + (p-k)W_2]}.$$

The computations needed to estimate $W_1$ and $W_2$ are the following:

(i) SSB(unadj) in the usual manner.

(ii) $$\frac{\sum_i T_{bi}^2}{k(r-\lambda)} - \frac{\left(\sum_i T_{bi}\right)^2}{pk(r-\lambda)} = \text{SST}_b.$$

(iii) $$\frac{\sum_i D_i^2}{N(p-k)(k-1)} = \text{SSD}.$$

(iv) SSB(adj) = SSD + SSB(unadj) − $\text{SST}_b$, with $(q-1)$ degrees of freedom. $V_b$ = MSB(adj).

(v) SSE = $Sy^2$ − SSB(adj) − SST(unadj), with $N - p - q + 1$ degrees of freedom. $V_e$ = MSE.

(vi) It can be shown that $E(V_b) = \sigma_e^2 + \frac{N-p}{q-1}\sigma_b^2$. Hence

$$W_2 \doteq \frac{N-p}{k(q-1)V_b - (p-k)V_e}.$$

(vii) Compute $r\theta$ and then $t'_{ic} = (T_i + r\theta D_i)/r$.

In general it is also advisable to compute SST(adj) as a check on the computation and to make a test of the differences among the treatment means. If the experiment is large enough so that we can replace $W_1$ and $W_2$ by their estimates in the formula for $t'_{ic}$, the problem is solved. If there are fewer than 15 degrees of freedom in $V_b$, the authors do not recommend using this weighted analysis; instead, they advise using the unweighted analysis of Sec. 19.3 (using no interblock information). And with 15 to 25 degrees of freedom, the weights are not too stable.

If groups of blocks form $c$ complete replications, the sum of squares for replications with $(c-1)$ degrees of freedom is removed from SSB(adj) and the expected value for $V_b$ [with $(q-c)$ degrees of freedom] is

$$E(V_b) = \sigma_e^2 + \frac{N-p-k(c-1)}{q-c}\sigma_b^2.$$

Hence

$$W_2 \doteq \frac{N-p-k(c-1)}{k(q-c)V_b - (p-k)V_e}.$$

If $c = r$,

$$E(V_b) = \sigma_e^2 + \frac{k(r-1)}{r}\sigma_b^2 \quad \text{and} \quad W_2 \doteq \frac{r-1}{rV_b - V_e}.$$

This is the result for balanced lattices with $d = 1$.

**Example 24.1.** Suppose we estimate $\sigma_b^2$ from the balanced-lattice experiment of Example 19.1. The values of $D_i = 6T_i - 8T_{bi} + 2G$ are 242, −6, −276, 118, 74, −28, −80, −76, and 32.

$$\text{SST}_b = \frac{(152)^2 + \cdots + (188)^2}{9} - \frac{(1{,}512)^2}{81} = 127,$$

$$\text{SSD} = \frac{(242)^2 + \cdots + (32)^2}{432} = 389,$$

$$\text{SSB(adj)} = 389,$$

since $\text{SST}_b = \text{SSB(unadj)} - \text{SS(replications)}$.

$$V_b = \tfrac{389}{8} = 48.63, \qquad V_e = 28.57.$$

$$W_2 \doteq \frac{3}{4V_b - V_e} = \frac{3}{4(48.63) - 28.57} = .01808, \qquad W_1 \doteq \frac{1}{V_e} = .03500.$$

$$\theta = \frac{W_1 - W_2}{4(18W_1 + 6W_2)} \doteq \frac{V_b - V_e}{72V_b} = \frac{20.06}{3{,}501} = .00573.$$

The adjusted treatment means, $t'_{ic} = (T_i/r) + \theta D_i$, are 20.13, 11.72, 2.92, 22.93, 14.17, 11.34, 13.54, 7.06, 22.18. The variance and standard error of the difference between two adjusted means are

$$\sigma^2(d) = \frac{48}{4(18W_1 + 6W_2)} = \frac{2}{3W_1 + W_2} \doteq 16.25, \qquad \sigma(d) \doteq 4.03.$$

Using recovery of interblock information, the relative efficiency of this design compared with randomized complete blocks is

$$I = 17.64/16.25 = 1.09.$$

Hence the recovery resulted in a gain of 16 per cent over no recovery. However, with only 8 degrees of freedom to estimate $\sigma_b^2$, we believe that this is a rather fictitious gain since the estimates of the weights ($W_1$ and $W_2$) have considerable error.

**24.2. Simple Lattice Designs.** In Sec. 19.4, we indicated that most analyses of lattice designs also make use of interblock information to increase the efficiency of the estimates of treatment effects. Since the blocks are arranged in complete replications, a constant $\gamma$ is introduced into the model for fixed replication effects, with random $\beta$ effects within replications. As before, we assume that we have $p = k^2$ treatments in $k$ blocks of $k$ treatments per block. Since the simple lattice has 2 replications, we have $2k$ blocks and $2k^2$ plots.

The first replication is designated as $X$ and the second as $Y$ with individual yields $X_{ij}$ and $Y_{ij}$, where $(i,j) = 1, 2, \ldots, k$. The mathematical model for $X_{ij}$ and $Y_{ij}$ is

$$X_{ij} = \mu + \gamma_x + \beta_{xi} + \tau_{ij} + \epsilon_{ij},$$
$$Y_{ij} = \mu + \gamma_y + \beta_{yj} + \tau_{ij} + \epsilon'_{ij},$$

where $\beta$, $\epsilon$, and $\epsilon'$ are independent random effects and the others are fixed. $\{\beta\}$ are NID$(0,\sigma_b^2)$ and $\{\epsilon,\epsilon'\}$ are NID$(0,\sigma_e^2)$. Hence

$$G = 2k^2\mu + k\left(\sum_i \beta_{xi} + \sum_j \beta_{yj}\right) + \sum_i\sum_j (\epsilon_{ij} + \epsilon'_{ij}),$$

$$X_{..} = k^2(\mu + \gamma_x) + k\sum_i \beta_{xi} + \sum_i\sum_j \epsilon_{ij},$$

$$Y_{..} = k^2(\mu + \gamma_y) + k\sum_j \beta_{yj} + \sum_i\sum_j \epsilon'_{ij},$$

$$X_{i.} = k(\mu + \gamma_x) + k\beta_{xi} + \sum_j \tau_{ij} + \sum_j \epsilon_{ij},$$

$$Y_{i.} = k(\mu + \gamma_y) + \sum_j \beta_{yj} + \sum_j \tau_{ji} + \sum_j \epsilon'_{ij},$$

$$D_{i.} \equiv X_{i.} - Y_{i.} = k(\gamma_x - \gamma_y) + k\beta_{xi} - \sum_j \beta_{yj} + \sum_j (\epsilon_{ij} - \epsilon'_{ij}),$$

$$D_{..} = k^2(\gamma_x - \gamma_y) + k\left(\sum_i \beta_{xi} - \sum_j \beta_{yj}\right) + \sum_i\sum_j (\epsilon_{ij} - \epsilon'_{ij}),$$

where $D_{i.}$ is a linear function of the block effects adjusted for treatment effects. Similarly we can compute $D_{.j}$, using $X_{.j}$ and $Y_{.j}$. These $(2k)$ $D$'s could be used to solve for the $\beta$'s, adjusted for the $\tau$'s.

We can use $G$, $X..$, and $Y..$ to estimate $\mu$, $\gamma_x$, and $\gamma_y$. The replication sum of squares in the analysis of variance (with 1 degree of freedom) is

$$\frac{X_{..}^2 + Y_{..}^2}{k^2} - \frac{G^2}{2k^2} = \frac{(X.. - Y..)^2}{2k^2},$$

with an expected value of $\dfrac{k^2(\gamma_x - \gamma_y)^2}{2} + k\sigma_b^2 + \sigma_e^2$.

A block sum of squares, adjusted for treatments, with $2(k-1)$ degrees of freedom, can be computed from

$$\text{SSB(adj)} = \frac{\Sigma D_{i.}^2 + \Sigma D_{.j}^2}{2k} - \frac{2D_{..}^2}{2k^2}.$$

$$E[\text{SSB(adj)}] = 2(k-1)\left(\frac{k}{2}\sigma_b^2 + \sigma_e^2\right).$$

Hence if we designate $V_b = \text{SSB(adj)}/2(k-1)$,

$$E(V_b) = \frac{k}{2}\sigma_b^2 + \sigma_e^2.$$

It can be shown that

$$\text{SSE} = Sx^2 + Sy^2 - \text{SST(unadj)} - \text{SSB(adj)},$$

with $2(k^2-1) - (k^2-1) - 2(k-1) = (k-1)^2$ degrees of freedom. Also,

$$E(V_e) = E(\text{MSE}) = \sigma_e^2,$$

so that

$$\sigma_e^2 \doteq V_e \quad \text{and} \quad \sigma_b^2 \doteq 2(V_b - V_e)/k.$$

In order to estimate a treatment effect, $t_{ij}$, we shall write†

$$\begin{aligned} t_{ij} &\equiv \bar{t}_{i.} + \bar{t}_{.j} + (t_{ij} - \bar{t}_{i.} - \bar{t}_{.j}) \\ &= (\bar{t}'_{i.} + \bar{t}'_{.j} - 2m) + (t'_{ij} - \bar{t}'_{i.} - \bar{t}'_{.j} + m) \equiv t + v. \end{aligned}$$

In Sec. 19.4, we used $\bar{Y}_{i.}$ as an estimate of $\bar{t}'_{i.}$ and $\bar{X}_{.j}$ as an estimate of $\bar{t}'_{.j}$, since these two estimates were free of block effects. However, now that we have a means of handling the block effects, it seems reasonable to utilize this interblock information.

It turns out that the part in the second parentheses ($v$) is independent of block effects, even when we use all of the data to estimate $\bar{t}'_{i.}$ and $\bar{t}'_{.j}$.

† This method is suggested by the similarity between this design and a factorial with $k$ levels of two treatments. The effect of the $i$th level of one and $j$th level of a second is generally written in this form. Let $t$ stand for the main effects (first parentheses) and $v$ for the interaction (second parentheses).

That is, if we use all of the data,

$$\bar{t}'_{i.} = \frac{Y_{i.} + X_{i.}}{2k} = \mu + \bar{\tau}_{i.} + \frac{\beta_{xi} + \bar{\beta}_{y.}}{2} + \frac{\bar{\epsilon}_{i.} + \bar{\epsilon}'_{i.}}{2},$$

$$\bar{t}'_{.j} = \frac{X_{.j} + Y_{.j}}{2k} = \mu + \bar{\tau}_{.j} + \frac{\bar{\beta}_{x.} + \beta_{yj}}{2} + \frac{\bar{\epsilon}_{.j} + \bar{\epsilon}'_{.j}}{2},$$

$$t'_{ij} = \frac{X_{ij} + Y_{ij}}{2} = \mu + \tau_{ij} + \frac{\beta_{xi} + \beta_{yj}}{2} + \frac{\epsilon_{ij} + \epsilon'_{ij}}{2},$$

$$m = \frac{G}{2k^2} = \mu + \frac{\bar{\beta}_{x.} + \bar{\beta}_{y.}}{2} + \frac{\bar{\epsilon}_{..} + \bar{\epsilon}'_{..}}{2},$$

where $\bar{\epsilon}_{i.} = \sum_j \epsilon_{ij}/k$, $\bar{\epsilon}_{..} = \Sigma\Sigma\epsilon_{ij}/k^2$, etc. Hence

$$v \equiv (t'_{ij} - \bar{t}'_{i.} - \bar{t}'_{.j} + m) = \tau_{ij} - \bar{\tau}_{i.} - \bar{\tau}_{.j} + \epsilon_v,$$

where $\epsilon_v = \frac{1}{2}[\epsilon_{ij} + \epsilon'_{ij} - (\bar{\epsilon}_{i.} + \bar{\epsilon}'_{i.} + \bar{\epsilon}_{.j} + \bar{\epsilon}'_{.j}) + (\bar{\epsilon}_{..} + \bar{\epsilon}'_{..})]$.

However, if we use all of the data to estimate $t \equiv (\bar{t}'_{i.} + \bar{t}'_{.j} - 2m)$, block effects will be involved. Hence it is proposed that we obtain two different estimates of $t$, one free of block effects ($t_1$) and one involving block effects ($t_2$), and form a weighted average of the two.

$$t = \frac{W'_1 t_1 + W'_2 t_2}{W'_1 + W'_2},$$

where $W'_i = 1/\sigma_i^2$. Then we shall have

$$t_1 = \frac{Y_{i.} + X_{.j}}{k} - \frac{G}{k^2} = \bar{\tau}_{.j} + \bar{\tau}_{i.} + \epsilon_1,$$

$$t_2 = \frac{X_{i.} + Y_{.j}}{k} - \frac{G}{k^2} = \bar{\tau}_{.j} + \bar{\tau}_{i.} + \beta_2 + \epsilon_2,$$

where $\epsilon_1 = (\bar{\epsilon}_{.j} + \bar{\epsilon}'_{i.} - \bar{\epsilon}_{..} - \bar{\epsilon}'_{..})$, $\epsilon_2 = (\bar{\epsilon}_{i.} + \bar{\epsilon}'_{.j} - \bar{\epsilon}_{..} - \bar{\epsilon}'_{..})$, and $\beta_2 = \beta_{xi} + \beta_{yj} - \bar{\beta}_{x.} - \bar{\beta}_{y..}$ Hence

$$\sigma_1^2 = \frac{2(k-1)}{k^2}\sigma_e^2,$$

and

$$\sigma_2^2 = \frac{2(k-1)}{k^2}\sigma_e^2 + \frac{2(k-1)}{k}\sigma_b^2 = \frac{2(k-1)}{k^2}[\sigma_e^2 + k\sigma_b^2].$$

Therefore $t = [W_1 t_1 + W_2 t_2]/(W_1 + W_2)$, where $W_1 = 1/\sigma_e^2$, and $W_2 = 1/(k\sigma_b^2 + \sigma_e^2)$.

Again we caution against the use of a weighted analysis if there are less than 15 degrees of freedom for estimating $\sigma_b^2$ (and we have grave doubts when there are less than 25 degrees of freedom). It is better to duplicate the experiment to obtain more information on $\sigma_b^2$ if weighting is to be used.

In computing adjusted treatment means, some simplification can be made. We note that

$$t'_{ij} = \frac{X_{ij} + Y_{ij}}{2} - \frac{X_{i.} + Y_{i.} + X_{.j} + Y_{.j}}{2k} + \frac{W_1(Y_{i.} + X_{.j}) + W_2(X_{i.} + Y_{.j})}{k(W_1 + W_2)}$$

$$= \frac{T_{ij}}{2} - \frac{W_1 - W_2}{2k(W_1 + W_2)} (D_{i.} - D_{.j}).$$

Note that $(D_{i.} - D_{.j})$ is the same as $\delta_{ij}$ given in Sec. 19.4. The only difference in $t'_{ij}$ is that $\delta_{ij}$ is multiplied by the weighting factor

$$\theta = \frac{(W_1 - W_2)}{2k(W_1 + W_2)}$$

instead of $1/2k$. If $\sigma_b^2 = 0$, so that $W_1 = W_2$, no adjustment at all is made for blocks: $t'_{ij} = T_{ij}/2$. If $\sigma_e^2$ is small compared with $\sigma_b^2$, $\theta$ approaches $1/2k$, the value used without recovery of interblock information.

It can be shown that the variance of the difference between two adjusted treatment means, which appear in the same block, is

$$\frac{1}{kW_1}\left[(k - 1) + \frac{2W_1}{W_1 + W_2}\right].$$

And for varieties not in the same block, this variance is

$$\frac{1}{kW_1}\left[(k - 2) + \frac{4W_1}{W_1 + W_2}\right].$$

The average variance is

$$\frac{1}{(k + 1)W_1}\left[(k - 1) + \frac{4W_1}{W_1 + W_2}\right] = \frac{1}{W_1}\left[1 + \frac{4k\theta}{k + 1}\right].$$

Also, the efficiency of the simple lattice, relative to randomized complete blocks, is

$$I = \frac{k + W_1/W_2}{(k - 1) + 4W_1/(W_1 + W_2)}.$$

The reader is advised to read references 2 and 3 for more details on lattice designs.

If the simple lattice is duplicated several times (Sec. 19.4) so that $2d$ replications ($2kd$ blocks) are used, it can be shown that the expected value of the "block-effect" mean square with $2(d - 1)(k - 1)$ degrees of freedom is $(\sigma_e^2 + k\sigma_b^2)$. The expected value of the other mean square with $2(k - 1)$ degrees of freedom is, as above, $(\sigma_e^2 + \frac{1}{2}k\sigma_b^2)$. Hence, if the two mean squares are pooled to obtain the adjusted-blocks mean square with $2d(k-1)$ degrees of freedom, the expected value of this mean square is $\left(\sigma_e^2 + \frac{2d-1}{2d} k\sigma_b^2\right)$. In this latter case,

$$W_2 \doteq \frac{2d-1}{2dV_b - V_e} \quad \text{and} \quad \theta \doteq \frac{d(V_b - V_e)}{2k[dV_b + (d-1)V_e]}.$$

The variances of adjusted mean differences will be divided by $d$.

**Example 24.2.** In order to illustrate only the computing procedure for the recovery of interblock information, we shall use Example 19.2. Actually one should not contemplate any recovery with so few degrees of freedom for blocks.

| $D_{i\cdot}$ | $D_{\cdot j}$ |
|---|---|
| −22 | 2 |
| −21 | −16 |
| −3 | −32 |
| −46 | −46 |

$$\text{SSB(adj)} = \frac{\Sigma(D_{i\cdot}^2 + D_{\cdot j}^2)}{6} - \frac{(-46)^2}{9} = 134.$$

As a check, SSB(unadj) + SST(adj) should be equal to SSB(adj) + SST (unadj). We note that

$$68 + 593 = 134 + 527 = 661.$$

It is advisable to make this check on the computing. The analysis of variance is:

| Source of variation | Degrees of freedom | Mean square | $E$(MS) |
|---|---|---|---|
| Replications | 1 | 118 | |
| Treatments(adj) | 8 | 74 | |
| Blocks(adj) | 4 | $34 = V_b$ | $\sigma_e^2 + 1.5\sigma_b^2$ |
| Error | 4 | $47 = V_e$ | $\sigma_e^2$ |

The estimate of $\sigma_b^2$ would be negative, and so we assume $\sigma_b^2 = 0$. Hence, no adjustments would be made even if there were sufficient degrees of freedom to estimate the weights. This raises a rather critical issue regarding incomplete-blocks designs, namely, that we do not take the loss in efficiency which we really suffered by using such a design with a negative estimate of $\sigma_b^2$. Instead we use $t'_{ij} = T_{ij}/2$, with the variance of a mean equal to $\frac{47}{2} = 24$.

If $V_b > V_e$ so we could obtain a positive estimate of $\sigma_b^2$ and if there were sufficient degrees of freedom to warrant weighting, we would compute

$\delta_{ij} = D_{i\cdot} - D_{\cdot j}$. Then $\theta = (W_1 - W_2)/6(W_1 + W_2)$, where $W_1 \doteq 1/V_e$ and $W_2 \doteq 1/(2V_b - V_e)$. (Here we assume that $\theta = 0$.) An adjusted treatment mean is

$$t'_{ij} = \frac{T_{ij}}{2} - \theta\delta_{ij}.$$

The estimated average variance of the difference between two adjusted means is

$$\frac{V_e}{2}\left[1 + \frac{2V_b - V_e}{V_b}\right]$$

**24.3. Other Lattice Designs.** Reference 3 contains the theory and computing details for a triple lattice and reference 2 the computing procedures for rectangular lattices. One of the present authors presented the method of analysis for $d$ duplications of any orthogonal square lattice design.† If there are $r$ replications in the basic design ($rd$ total replications) and if the two parts of the adjusted-blocks sum of squares are pooled with $rd(k - 1)$ degrees of freedom,

$$W_2 \doteq \frac{rd - 1}{rdV_b - V_e} \quad \text{and} \quad \theta = \frac{W_1 - W_2}{rk[(r - 1)W_1 + W_2]}.$$

The average variance of the difference between two adjusted means is

$$\frac{2}{rdW_1}\left[1 + \frac{r^2k}{k + 1}\theta\right].$$

## EXERCISES

**24.1.** (*a*) Prove that, if we have two unbiased independent estimates, $t_1$ and $t_2$, of a parameter $\tau$ with respective variances $1/W'_1$ and $1/W'_2$, the combined linear unbiased estimate with lowest variance will be

$$t = \frac{W'_1t_1 + W'_2t_2}{W'_1 + W'_2}.$$

HINT: remember that $E(t) = \tau$.

(*b*) Show that $t_1$ and $t_2$ are independent estimates of $\tau$ in Sec. 24.1.

**24.2.** (*a*) Derive the formula for $\sigma^2(t_{bi})$, and show that $t'_{ic} = (T_i/r) + \theta D_i$.

(*b*) Also derive the variance of the difference between two adjusted means.

(*c*) Show that SSB(adj) is independent of treatment effects.

(*d*) Show that $E(V_b)$ and the estimate of $W_2$ are correct in (vi) above.

† Presented by R. L. Anderson at a meeting of the Biometrics Section of the American Statistical Association, March, 1946. An abstract is presented in the June, 1946, issue of the *Biometrics Bulletin* (p. 58).

**24.3.** As a computing exercise only, analyze the data in Exercise 19.1, using recovery of interblock information. Why is it dangerous in practice to use recovery for this example?

**24.4.** Analyze the data in Exercises 19.2 and 19.3, using recovery of interblock information.

**24.5.** Prove that $V_e$ is an unbiased estimate of $\sigma_e^2$. In other words, show that SSE $= Sx^2 + Sy^2 -$ SST(unadj) $-$ SSB(adj).

**24.6.** On page 363, show that the results for $\sigma_1^2$ and $\sigma_2^2$ are correct. Why is $(2V_b - V_e)$ an unbiased estimate of $(\sigma_e^2 + k\sigma_b^2)$?

**24.7.** Derive the formulas for the variances of the differences between two adjusted means, using a simple lattice design. Also, derive the formula for relative efficiency, $I$.

**24.8.** (*a*) Analyze the data in Exercise 19.4, using recovery of interblock information.

(*b*) What is the relative efficiency of this design compared with a randomized complete-blocks design?

**References Cited**

1. YATES, F., "The Recovery of Inter-block Information in Balanced Incomplete Block Designs," *Ann. Eugenics*, **10**:317–325 (1940).
2. COCHRAN, W. G., and G. M. COX, *Experimental Designs*, John Wiley & Sons, Inc., New York, 1950.
3. COX, G. M., R. C. ECKHARDT, and W. G. COCHRAN, "The Analyses of Lattice and Triple Lattice Experiments in Corn Varietal Tests," *Iowa State Coll., Agr. Expt. Sta., Research Bull.*, 281 (1940).

**Other Reading**†

BANCROFT, T. A., and A. L. SMITH, "Efficiency of the Simple Lattice Design Relative to Randomized Complete Blocks Design in Cotton Variety and Strain Testing," *Agron. J.*, **41**:157–160 (1949).

BLISS, C. I., and R. B. DEARBORN, "The Efficiency of Lattice Squares in Corn Selection Tests in New England and Pennsylvania," *Proc. Am. Soc. Hort. Sci.*, **41**: 324–342 (1942).

COCHRAN, W. G., "An Examination of the Accuracy of Lattice and Lattice Square Experiments in Corn," *Iowa State Coll., Agr. Expt. Sta., Research Bull.* 289 (1941).

COMSTOCK, R. E., W. J. PETERSON, and H. A. STEWART, "An Application of the Balanced Lattice Design in a Feeding Trial with Swine," *J. Animal Sci.*, **7**:320–331 (1948).

CORNISH, E. A., "The Recovery of Inter-block Information in Quasi-factorial Designs with Incomplete Data," *Australian Council Sci. Ind. Research Bul.* 158, 175 (1943, 1944).

HARSHBARGER, BOYD, "On the Analysis of a Certain Six-by-six-four-group Lattice Design, Using the Recovery of Inter-block Information," *Ann. Math. Stat.*, **16**:387–390 (1945).

JAMES, E., and T. A. BANCROFT, "The Use of Half-plants in a Balanced Incomplete Block in Investigating the Effect of Calcium, Phosphorus and Potassium, at

† Also see the following references in Chap. 19: 6, 9, 10, 11, and 12.

Two Levels Each, on the Production of Hard Seed in Crimson Clover," *Agron. J.*, **43**:96–98 (1951).

NAIR, K. R., "The Recovery of Inter-block Information in Incomplete Block Designs," *Sankhyā*, **6**:383–390 (1944).

*Proceedings of the Auburn Conference on Statistics Applied to Research in the Social Sciences, Plant Sciences, and Animal Sciences*, Alabama Polytechnic Institute, Auburn, Ala., 1948.

RAO, C. R., "General Methods of Analysis for Incomplete Block Designs," *J. Am. Stat. Assoc.*, **42**:541–561 (1947).

YATES, F., "The Recovery of Inter-block Information in Variety Trials Arranged in Three-dimensional Lattices," *Ann. Eugenics*, **9**:136–156 (1939).

ZUBER, M. S., "Relative Efficiency of Incomplete Block Designs Using Corn Uniformity Trial Data," *J. Am. Soc. Agron.*, **34**:30–47 (1942)

# CHAPTER 25

## OTHER TOPICS CONCERNING COMPONENTS OF VARIANCE: SUMMARY OF NEEDED RESEARCH

**25.1. Covariance.** Cochran[1] considered the following covariance model for a sampling design with $p$ plots and $r$ samples per plot,

$$Y_{ij} = \mu + \tau_i^* + \beta x_{ij} + \epsilon_{ij},$$

where the $\tau$'s and $\epsilon$'s are assumed NID with zero means and respective variances $\sigma_t^2$ and $\sigma_e^2$, and $\mu$, $\beta$, and the $x$'s are assumed fixed. The maximum-likelihood estimate of $\beta$ is a weighted mean of the $b$'s derived from the plots ($b_t$) and error ($b_e$) lines of the analysis of covariance [see Sec. 21.2 (v) with treatments corresponding to plots].

If information about $\beta$ in the plots line is disregarded, the procedure is as follows:

(i) $s^{*2}$ is an unbiased estimate of $\sigma_e^2$ and SSE* is distributed as

$$\sigma_e^2 \chi^2_{p(r-1)-1}.$$

(ii) $\text{SST}^* = r \sum_i (\bar{Y}_{i\cdot} - \bar{Y} - b_t \bar{x}_{i\cdot})^2 + (b_t - b_e)^2 \dfrac{T_{xx}E_{xx}}{T_{xx} + E_{xx}}$, where

$$\bar{Y}_{i\cdot} = \mu + \tau_i^* + \beta \bar{x}_{i\cdot} + \bar{\epsilon}_{i\cdot}.$$

The first term is distributed as $(\sigma_e^2 + r\sigma_t^2)\chi^2_{(p-2)}$. Since

$$b_t = \beta + \frac{r\Sigma(\tau_i^* + \bar{\epsilon}_{i\cdot})\bar{x}_{i\cdot}}{T_{xx}}, \qquad b_e = \beta + \frac{\Sigma\Sigma \epsilon_{ij}(x_{ij} - \bar{x}_{i\cdot})}{E_{xx}},$$

the second term is distributed as $(\sigma_e^2 + \lambda r \sigma_t^2)\chi_1^2$, where $\lambda = E_{xx}/(T_{xx} + E_{xx})$.

(iii) All three chi-squares are independent.

(iv) $\sigma_\tau^2 \doteq \dfrac{(\text{MST}^* - s^{*2})}{r} \dfrac{p-1}{(p-2+\lambda)}$.

The estimate of $\sigma_\tau^2$ in (iv) involves some loss of information because plot information about $\beta$ is ignored, and the single degree of freedom in SST* is presumably given too much weight.

If the estimate of $\beta$ from the error line is used, parallel results can be obtained for a two-way classification, for example, randomized blocks.

**25.2. The Use of Components of Variance in Regression Problems.** Variance components are also used to evaluate methods of estimating regression coefficients. The experimenter often obtains several values of $Y$ for each value of $X$ in order to determine the sampling or observational error (see Example 13.1 and Fig. 13.3). The model for $r$ independent variates with $p$ samples of $Y$ for each set of $\{X_i\}$ values is

$$Y_{jk} = \mu + \sum_{i=1}^{r} \beta_i x_{ij} + \epsilon_j + \delta_{jk}, \qquad j = 1, 2, \ldots, n; \; k = 1, 2, \ldots, p,$$

where $\epsilon$ and $\delta$ are NID with zero means and respective variances $\sigma_e^2$ and $\sigma_d^2$. $\sigma_e^2$ measures the failure of the regression line to go through the average $Y$ values ($\bar{Y}_{j.}$), while $\sigma_d^2$ measures the fluctuation of individual values $Y_{jk}$ about their means $\bar{Y}_{j.}$.

The analysis of variance of the residuals will have the following appearance:

| Error | Degrees of freedom | Mean square | $E$(MS) |
|---|---|---|---|
| Deviations from regression | $n - r - 1$ | $V_e$ | $\sigma^2 = \sigma_d^2 + p\sigma_e^2$ |
| Observations | $n(p - 1)$ | $V_d$ | $\sigma_d^2$ |

In this case the experimenter can determine whether he should add more sets of $X$'s or collect more values of $Y$ for each set, basing his conclusions on the relative size of $\sigma_d^2$ and $\sigma_e^2$ as compared with the relative costs of obtaining more sets or more observations per set.

Very few examples are available of planned experiments with the same number of observations per set (other than one observation). In many cases, there will be experiments with several values of $Y$ for a given $X_1$, but the values of $X_2$, $X_3$, . . . vary as well as $Y$ (see the vitamin $B_2$ example in Chap. 15). Hence we are led to use the one-error regression equation. Another difficulty often arises, namely, that the observation error tends to increase with increasing $\bar{Y}$. This difficulty is not avoided when we use only one observation per set, but it is usually neglected (see Sec. 14.4). If several observations were taken for each set of $X$ values, the experimenter would have some information as to the uniformity of his variation as $\bar{Y}$ increased.

The factorial design is an example of several observations for each set of $X$'s; however, the $X$ values are often qualitative rather than quantitative (different varieties, cultivation methods, teaching methods, etc.). When a factorial is used with different levels of the factors, the principle of multiple regression with several observations for each set of $X$ values is being applied. However, there are seldom enough levels of the various factors to estimate the deviation error (for example, see Exercises 20.4, 20.6, and 20.7). The article referred to in Exercise 20.11 was based on estimating a quadratic regression of yield on planting date of cotton with 10 equally spaced planting dates. In this case $\sigma_d^2 \doteq .3606$ and $\sigma_d^2 + p\sigma_e^2 \doteq .3357$, a value less than the estimate of $\sigma_d^2$. This is an all too common result—the estimate of $\sigma_e^2$ is negative. This indicates a need for a more thorough investigation for many regression problems of the accuracy of the assumptions of homogeneous variance from point to point and independence of the true residuals.

**Example 25.1.** A survey was conducted in eastern North Carolina in 1949 to estimate the relationship between per cent dry weight ($Y$) of Irish potatoes (Cobbler variety) and $X = 200$ (specific gravity $-$ 1.045). The values of $X$ were $-1, 0, 1, \ldots, 11$, with 8 samples and 2 determinations per sample for many samples. If there had been potatoes for each of the 13 $X$ classes for each sample and determination, there would have been 104 samples and 208 determinations. Unfortunately, there were few samples for $X = -1$ and $X = 11$ and many blanks in other places, so that only 127 determinations were obtained. The data were as shown in Table 25.1.

TABLE 25.1

| Sample | $X$ | | | | | | | | | | | |
|---|---|---|---|---|---|---|---|---|---|---|---|---|
| | 0 | 1 | 2 | 3 | 4 | 5 | 6† | 7 | 8 | 9 | 10 | 11 |
| 1 | 14.34 | 14.73 | 16.30 | 17.46 | 18.82 | 19.48 | 20.40 | 20.67 | 21.75 | | | |
| | 14.66 | 14.87 | 16.79 | 17.23 | 17.68 | 19.16 | 19.90 | 21.27 | 22.70 | | | |
| 2 | 14.12 | 15.04 | 16.50 | 16.75 | 17.90 | 18.91 | 20.35 | 20.72 | 22.28 | 23.45 | 24.98 | |
| | 14.82 | 15.88 | 16.43 | 17.08 | 18.39 | | 19.32 | 20.89 | 22.28 | 23.31 | 24.53 | |
| | | | | | | | 19.68 | | | | | |
| 3 | 13.58 | 15.48 | 15.80 | 17.38 | 17.86 | 18.81 | 19.68 | 20.78 | 21.83 | 23.50 | 24.60 | |
| | 13.68 | 14.07 | 15.60 | 16.80 | 18.30 | 18.84 | 19.90 | 20.86 | 22.17 | 23.39 | 24.80 | |
| 4 | 13.83 | 15.04 | 16.17 | 17.63 | 17.90 | 19.15 | 20.11 | 20.69 | | | | |
| | 13.92 | 15.36 | 16.10 | 16.68 | 17.88 | 20.18 | 21.14 | 21.05 | | | | |
| 5 | 13.53 | 14.34 | 15.60 | 16.78 | 17.66 | | 19.08 | 20.88 | 21.71 | 23.25 | 24.80 | |
| 6 | | 15.30 | 15.60 | 16.63 | 17.98 | | 19.38 | 20.56 | 22.78 | | 24.80 | |
| 7 | 14.09 | 14.10 | 15.50 | 16.48 | 17.63 | | 19.10 | 20.34 | 21.71 | 22.73 | 23.60 | 25.56 |
| 8‡ | 13.86 | 14.63 | 15.14 | 16.49 | 17.10 | 18.51 | 19.18 | 20.26 | 21.44 | 22.43 | | |
| | 13.61 | 14.63 | 14.90 | 16.27 | 17.20 | 17.97 | 19.08 | 20.80 | 21.64 | | | |

† Three determinations on the second sample.

‡ There was 1 determination = 13.05 for $X = -1$.

The analysis for the third sample is as follows:

| Source of variation | Degrees of freedom | Mean square | $E$(MS) |
|---|---|---|---|
| Regression | 1 | 253.593 | |
| Deviations | 9 | .1086 | $\sigma_d^2 + 2\sigma_e^2$ |
| Determinations | 11 | .1269 | $\sigma_d^2$ |

Again we note a negative estimate of $\sigma_e^2$. For the 5 samples with duplicate determinations, 2 had negative estimates of $\sigma_e^2$, 2 had positive estimates, and 1 was almost zero (slightly positive).

An over-all regression analysis for all 8 samples gave $\sigma_d^2 \doteq .1362$ and $\sigma_d^2 + \lambda\sigma_e^2 \doteq .1804$. The value of $\lambda$ is somewhere between 1 and 2. A rough approximation is the number of determinations divided by the number of samples $= \frac{127}{79} = 1.6$.

**Example 25.2.** In Example 13.1, we used the total error sum of squares to estimate the error mean square to test whether or not $\beta$ was zero. If we disregard the fact that the error variance tended to increase with increasing $X$, we could subdivide the error sum of squares into two parts as follows:

| Error | Degrees of freedom | Sum of squares | Mean square | $E$(MS) |
|---|---|---|---|---|
| Deviations from regression | 47 | 407 | 8.66 | $\sigma_d^2 + \lambda\sigma_e^2$† |
| Between families for a given $X$ | 860 | 1,139 | 1.32 | $\sigma_d^2$ |

† $\lambda$ is the average number of families for each $X$.

A rough approximation for $\lambda$ would be $\frac{909}{49} = 18.6$. A more accurate estimate of $\lambda$ is given by use of the formulas given in Sec. 22.4 (see Exercise 22.18).

$$\lambda = \frac{1}{47}\left[909 - \frac{\sum_i n_i^2}{909}\right],$$

where the $n_i$ are the number of families for $X = X_i$ (see Table 13.1). In this case $\sum_i n_i^2 = 33{,}161$ and

$$\lambda = \frac{1}{47}(909 - 36.5) = \frac{872.5}{47} = 18.6,$$

which is the same as above (to one decimal place).

If $Z = \log (Y + 1)$ is used in the regression equation, the error splits up as follows:

| Error | Degrees of freedom | Sum of squares | Mean square |
|---|---|---|---|
| Deviations from regression | 47 | 2.121 | .0451 |
| Between families for a given $X$ | 860 | 22.429 | .0261 |

In this case we have reduced the $\sigma_e^2$ part substantially by making the $\sigma_d^2$ more nearly equal. But notice what happens for the incomes less than $4,000 when a log transformation is used. In this case $\sigma_d^2 \doteq .0214$, and $\sigma_d^2 + \lambda\sigma_e^2 \doteq .0233$, indicating that $\sigma_e^2$ is practically zero. It would appear that extremely large estimates of $\sigma_e^2$ may be caused by unequal sampling variability along the regression line. Some theoretical study should be made on this point.

**25.3. Other Topics in Relation to Variance Components.** The industrial and engineering research men have need for variance components in studying the precision of measurements. This topic is still in the exploratory stage and is too complicated to be discussed here. If the reader is interested in precision of measurements, he is advised to read references 2 to 4. Cameron[5] considers the use of variance components in determining the precision of estimating the clean content of wool, where several cores are taken from each of a number of bales of wool (see Exercises 25.4 and 25.5 for his technique).

Tukey[6] considers the problems of estimating regression coefficients and variance components when both variates ($X$ and $Y$) are subject to error, that is, each observed quantity = (steady part) + (fluctuation). In most practical cases, a third variate (an *instrumental variate*) with special properties is required. These special properties are that its covariance with the fluctuations in both $X$ and $Y$ vanish, but its covariance with the steady parts shall not vanish. The three fields of application where these problems have been most prevalent are indicated to be precision of measurements, psychology, and econometrics. We have not discussed problems of this nature in this book, because they are too complicated for an elementary treatment. However, the reader is advised to read Tukey's article at least to obtain some insight into the nature of the problem. He provides a list of references, which should also be useful.

Some recent articles have been written on the power of current tests of significance for variance components (see, for example, references 7 and 8). Cochran[9] also discusses the power of his $F''$ statistic, mentioned in Chap. 23.

**25.4. Summary of Needed Research.** In these last four chapters, we have presented a rather extensive treatment of a relatively new statistical tool—components of variance. However, this is actually the basis of all statistical concepts, because it deals with that particular aspect of data which requires statistical treatment—*variability*. We have here a method of identifying separate sources of variability and using estimates of these variances to plan future experiments, to make tests of significance, and to set confidence limits on a treatment or a general mean.

Since this statistical tool is so new, adequate statistical theory has not been developed to apply it to all problems where it should be applied. Some of the problems in variance component analysis which should be studied are:

(1) In a randomized complete-blocks model with all effects random except the mean, the assumption of independence of the main effects and interactions frequently does not appear to be justified. The assumption of additivity needs to be explored in detail, especially with interactions and main effects. Why do large main effects more often produce significant interactions than do small main effects? Can anything be done to correct this difficulty?

(2) A clear statement is needed of how to determine whether the interaction in a two-way classification is fixed or random.

(3) A better method of handling finite populations is needed.

(4) More exact methods of assigning confidence limits for variance components should be developed.

(5) Better agreement is needed on how to handle the mixed model, which probably is the most important of all the models.

(6) How can we detect correlated errors? And if we find that the errors are correlated, what should be done?

(7) A study needs to be made of the efficiency of various methods of analyzing multiple classifications with unequal numbers in the subclasses. Also, short-cut computing techniques are needed, especially some which can be used with card-punching and electronic equipment.

(8) What can be done to simplify the analysis of data with unequal variances?

(9) What are the effects of various types of nonnormality on the consistency and efficiency of estimates?

(10) What is the best test in a mixed model where the error must be estimated from several mean squares?

(11) Some study needs to be made of the proper allocation of samples in a nested sampling problem with limited resources and a need for good estimates of all components (see, for example, Exercise 22.19).

## EXERCISES

**25.1.** (*a*) Prove Cochran's results for the use of variance components in a covariance analysis, and apply them to Exercise 21.5.

(*b*) Derive the same results for a randomized complete-blocks experiment.

**25.2.** (*a*) In Example 25.1, determine the value of $\lambda$ by use of the regression model, as was done in Example 25.2.

(*b*) Estimate $\sigma_d^2$ for the other four samples with duplicate determinations.

(*c*) Show how the over-all estimates of $\sigma_d^2$ and $\lambda\sigma_e^2$ were obtained.

(*d*) What is the proper error term to use in testing for the significance of a single regression line?

(*e*) How would you set up a computing procedure to test the over-all regression and the deviations of sample regressions from the over-all regression?

(*f*) Is there much evidence that $\sigma_d^2$ was not constant from one sample to another?

**25.3.** (*a*) In Example 13.1, assuming $\sigma_d^2$ constant from $X$ to $X$, what is the expectation of SSR? Hence, how should you test the hypothesis that $\beta = 0$?

(*b*) If a weighted analysis is used, what happens to the expectations of the mean squares?

(*c*) On the basis of (*b*), what advantages do you see in the use of a transformation instead of a weighted analysis, if the transformation can make the variances reasonably stable?

**25.4.** Given the model

$$Y_{ijk} = \mu + \alpha_i + \beta_{ij} + \gamma_{ijk},$$

where $\alpha_i$ represents the $i$th lot, $\beta_{ij}$ the $j$th bale in the $i$th lot, and $\gamma_{ijk}$ the $k$th core in the $(ij)$ bale. We shall assume all effects, except $\mu$, are NID with respective variances $\sigma_a^2$, $\sigma_b^2$, and $\sigma_c^2$. Assume we have $2M$ lots with $n$ bales per lot and $k_1$ cores per bale for $M$ lots and $k_2$ cores per bale for the other $M$ lots. All cores for each lot are composited.

(*a*) Show that the variances per lot mean are

$$\sigma_a^2 + \frac{\sigma_b^2}{n} + \frac{\sigma_c^2}{nk_1} \quad \text{and} \quad \sigma_a^2 + \frac{\sigma_b^2}{n} + \frac{\sigma_c^2}{nk_2}.$$

(*b*) Given that $V_1$ is the mean square between the $M$ lots with $nk_1$ cores per lot and $V_2$ for the other $M$ lots. Show that, if $k_2 > k_1$,

$$\sigma_c^2 \doteq \frac{nk_1k_2}{k_2 - k_1}(V_1 - V_2),$$

$$(n\sigma_a^2 + \sigma_b^2) \doteq \frac{n}{k_2 - k_1}(k_2V_2 - k_1V_1).$$

(*c*) How could you design a sample to estimate both $\sigma_a^2$ and $\sigma_b^2$?

**25.5.** Use the same model as in Exercise 25.4. Assume that $n_i$ bales are selected from the *i*th of the first $M$ lots with 2 cores per bale, 1 core from each bale being composited to give 2 composite samples per lot. Call the difference between these 2 samples $d_i$. For the other $M$ bales, $2n_k$ bales are taken from each, and again 2 cores per bale; both cores from $n_k$ of the bales are composited, and similarly for the other $n_k$ bales, again giving 2 composite samples per lot. Call the difference between these two samples $d_k$.

(*a*) Show that $\sigma^2(d_i) = 2\sigma_c^2/n_i$ and $\sigma^2(d_k) = (2\sigma_b^2 + \sigma_c^2)/n_k$.

(*b*) Show that

$$\sigma_c^2 \doteq \frac{\sum_{i=1}^{M} n_i d_i^2}{2M},$$

$$(2\sigma_b^2 + \sigma_c^2) \doteq \frac{\sum_{k=1}^{M} n_k d_k^2}{M}.$$

(*c*) What is the estimate of $\sigma_b^2$?

(*d*) What are the variances of the estimates of $\sigma_c^2$ and $\sigma_b^2$?

### References Cited

1. Cochran, W. G., "The Analysis of Covariance," *Inst. Stat. Mim. Ser.* 6 (1946).
2. Grubbs, F. E., "On Estimating Precision of Measuring Instruments and Product Variability," *J. Am. Stat. Assoc.*, **43**:247–264 (1948).
3. Smith, H. F., "Estimating Precision of Measuring Instruments," *J. Am. Stat. Assoc.*, **45**:447–451 (1950).
4. Whitwell, J. C., "Estimating Precision of Textile Instruments," *Biometrics*, **7**:102–112 (1951).
5. Cameron, J. M., "Use of Components of Variance in Preparing Schedules for the Sampling of Baled Wool," *Biometrics*, **7**:83–96 (1951).
6. Tukey, J. W., "Components in Regression," *Biometrics*, **7**:33–69 (1951).
7. Johnson, N. L., "Alternative Systems in the Analysis of Variance," *Biometrika*, **35**:80–87 (1948).
8. Patnaik, P. B., "The Non-central $\chi^2$ and F-distributions and Their Applications," *Biometrika*, **36**:202–232 (1949).

9. Cochran, W. G., "Testing a Linear Relation among Variances," *Biometrics*, **7**:17–32 (1951).

### Other Reading

Crump, S. L., *The Estimation of Components of Variance in Multiple Classifications*, unpublished thesis, Iowa State College Library, Ames, Iowa, 1947.

Federer, W. T., *Evaluation of Variance Components from a Group of Experiments with Multiple Classifications*, unpublished thesis, Iowa State College Library, Ames, Iowa, 1948.

Geary, R. C., "Determination of Linear Relations between Systematic Parts of Variables with Errors of Observation the Variances of Which Are Unknown," *Econometrica*, **17**:30–58 (1949).

Hammersly, J. M., "The Unbiased Estimate and Standard Error of the Interclass Variance," *Metron*, **15**:189–205 (1949).

Hendricks, W. A., "Variance Components as a Tool for the Analysis of Sample Data," *Biometrics*, **7**:97–101 (1951).

Tanner, L., and W. E. Deming, "Some Problems in the Sampling of Bulk Materials," *Proc., ASTM*, 49 (1949).

Tukey, J. W., "Dyadicanova, an Analysis of Variance for Vectors," *Human Biol.*, **21**:65–110 (1949).

Tukey, J. W., "Some Sampling Simplified," *J. Am. Stat. Assoc.*, **45**:501–519 (1950).

Wald, A., "A Note on Regression Analysis," *Ann. Math. Stat.*, **18**:586–588 (1947).

Welch, B. L., "The Generalization of Student's Problem When Several Different Population Variances Are Involved," *Biometrika*, **34**:28–35 (1947).

# APPENDIX

## Explanation of the Tables

I*a*. *Ordinates of the Normal Distribution.* This table gives values of

$$f(x) = \frac{1}{\sqrt{2\pi}} e^{-x^2/2}$$

for values of $x$ between 0 and 4 at intervals of .01. For negative values of $x$, one uses the relation $f(-x) = f(x)$.

I*b*. *Area under the Normal Curve, $F(y)$.* This table gives values of

$$F(y) = 1 - \frac{\alpha}{2} = \int_{-\infty}^{y} \frac{1}{\sqrt{2\pi}} e^{-x^2/2}\, dx$$

for values of $y$ between 0 and 3.5 at intervals of .01. For negative values of $y$, one uses the relation $F(-y) = 1 - F(y) = \alpha/2$.

Values of $y$ corresponding to a few selected values of $\alpha$ are presented beneath the main table. These are useful in making tests of significance for a specified significance probability, $\alpha$, or in setting up confidence intervals with confidence probability $(1 - \alpha)$, as in Sec. 7.2 for the statistic $T_\alpha$.

II. *Percentage Points of the $\chi^2$ Distribution.* This table gives values of $\chi^2_\alpha$ for selected values of $\alpha$ and for the number of degrees of freedom, $\nu$, ranging from 1 to 30, plus $\nu = 40, 50, 60$, where

$$\alpha = \int_{\chi_\alpha^2}^{\infty} \frac{1}{\Gamma(\nu/2)} \left(\frac{\chi^2}{2}\right)^{(\nu-2)/2} e^{-\chi^2/2}\, d\left(\frac{\chi^2}{2}\right).$$

For larger values of $\nu$, a normal approximation is quite accurate. The quantity $\sqrt{2\chi^2} - \sqrt{2\nu - 1}$ is nearly normally distributed with zero mean and unit variance. Hence $\chi^2_\alpha$ may be computed as

$$\chi^2_\alpha = \tfrac{1}{2}(T_{2\alpha} + \sqrt{2\nu - 1})^2$$

where we use $T_{2\alpha}$ because the probability for $\chi^2$ corresponds to a single tail of the normal curve (see Sec. 7.2 and Table I*b*). For example consider $\chi'^2_{.05}$ for $\nu = 40$. The exact value is $\chi^2_{.05} = 55.8$, and the approximate value would be

$$\tfrac{1}{2}(1.645 + \sqrt{79})^2 = 55.5.$$

III. *Percentage Points of the t Distribution.* This table gives values of $t_\alpha$ for selected values of $\alpha$ and for the following number of degrees of freedom, $n$: 1, 2, . . . , 30, 40, 60, 120, $\infty$, where

$$\alpha = 2 \int_{\alpha}^{\infty} \frac{\Gamma\left(\frac{n+1}{2}\right)}{\sqrt{\pi n}\, \Gamma(n/2)} \left(1 + \frac{t^2}{n}\right)^{-(n+1)/2} dt.$$

If a percentage point is needed for some $n$ not given in the table, linear interpolation can be used between tabulated percentage points, but the reciprocals of $n$ should be used. For example, the value of $t_{.05}$ for 50 degrees of freedom would be

$$2.021 - \frac{\frac{1}{40} - \frac{1}{50}}{\frac{1}{40} - \frac{1}{60}} (.021) = 2.008.$$

IV. *Percentage Points of the F Distribution.* This table gives values of $F_\alpha$ for $\alpha = .01$ and $.05$; $n_1 = 1\ (1)\ 10, 12, 16, 20, 24, 30, 50, 100, \infty$; and $n_2 = 1\ (1)\ 20\ (2)\ 28\ (4)\ 40, 60, 100, 200, \infty$. $F_\alpha$ is defined as follows:

$$\alpha = \int_{F_\alpha}^{\infty} \frac{(n_1/n_2)^{n_1/2}}{B\left(\frac{n_1}{2}, \frac{n_2}{2}\right)} F^{\frac{1}{2}n_1 - 1} \left(1 + \frac{n_1}{n_2} F\right)^{-(n_1+n_2)/2} dF.$$

$F = s_1^2/s_2^2$, where $s_1^2$ is a sample variance with $n_1$ degrees of freedom and $s_2^2$ a sample variance with $n_2$ degrees of freedom. The table also can be used to determine $F_{1-\alpha}$ by use of the formula

$$F_{(1-\alpha)}(n_1,n_2) = \frac{1}{F_\alpha(n_2,n_1)},$$

where the first $n$ indicates the number of degrees of freedom in the numerator and the second $n$ the number of degrees of freedom in the denominator. For example

$$F_{.95}(3,75) = \frac{1}{F_{.05}(75,3)} = \frac{1}{8.57}.$$

One should interpolate on the reciprocals of $n_1$ and $n_2$ as in Table III.

TABLE I*a*
Ordinates of the Normal Distribution

| x | .00 | .01 | .02 | .03 | .04 | .05 | .06 | .07 | .08 | .09 |
|---|---|---|---|---|---|---|---|---|---|---|
| .0 | .3989 | .3989 | .3989 | .3988 | .3986 | .3984 | .3982 | .3980 | .3977 | .3973 |
| .1 | .3970 | .3965 | .3961 | .3956 | .3951 | .3945 | .3939 | .3932 | .3925 | .3918 |
| .2 | .3910 | .3902 | .3894 | .3885 | .3876 | .3867 | .3857 | .3847 | .3836 | .3825 |
| .3 | .3814 | .3802 | .3790 | .3778 | .3765 | .3752 | .3739 | .3725 | .3712 | .3697 |
| .4 | .3683 | .3668 | .3653 | .3637 | .3621 | .3605 | .3589 | .3572 | .3555 | .3538 |
| .5 | .3521 | .3503 | .3485 | .3467 | .3448 | .3429 | .3410 | .3391 | .3372 | .3352 |
| .6 | .3332 | .3312 | .3292 | .3271 | .3251 | .3230 | .3209 | .3187 | .3166 | .3144 |
| .7 | .3123 | .3101 | .3079 | .3056 | .3034 | .3011 | .2989 | .2966 | .2943 | .2920 |
| .8 | .2897 | .2874 | .2850 | .2827 | .2803 | .2780 | .2756 | .2732 | .2709 | .2685 |
| .9 | .2661 | .2637 | .2613 | .2589 | .2565 | .2541 | .2516 | .2492 | .2468 | .2444 |
| 1.0 | .2420 | .2396 | .2371 | .2347 | .2323 | .2299 | .2275 | .2251 | .2227 | .2203 |
| 1.1 | .2179 | .2155 | .2131 | .2107 | .2083 | .2059 | .2036 | .2012 | .1989 | .1965 |
| 1.2 | .1942 | .1919 | .1895 | .1872 | .1849 | .1826 | .1804 | .1781 | .1758 | .1736 |
| 1.3 | .1714 | .1691 | .1669 | .1647 | .1626 | .1604 | .1582 | .1561 | .1539 | .1518 |
| 1.4 | .1497 | .1476 | .1456 | .1435 | .1415 | .1394 | .1374 | .1354 | .1334 | .1315 |
| 1.5 | .1295 | .1276 | .1257 | .1238 | .1219 | .1200 | .1182 | .1163 | .1145 | .1127 |
| 1.6 | .1109 | .1092 | .1074 | .1057 | .1040 | .1023 | .1006 | .0989 | .0973 | .0957 |
| 1.7 | .0940 | .0925 | .0909 | .0893 | .0878 | .0863 | .0848 | .0833 | .0818 | .0804 |
| 1.8 | .0790 | .0775 | .0761 | .0748 | .0734 | .0721 | .0707 | .0694 | .0681 | .0669 |
| 1.9 | .0656 | .0644 | .0632 | .0620 | .0608 | .0596 | .0584 | .0573 | .0562 | .0551 |
| 2.0 | .0540 | .0529 | .0519 | .0508 | .0498 | .0488 | .0478 | .0468 | .0459 | .0449 |
| 2.1 | .0440 | .0431 | .0422 | .0413 | .0404 | .0396 | .0387 | .0379 | .0371 | .0363 |
| 2.2 | .0355 | .0347 | .0339 | .0332 | .0325 | .0317 | .0310 | .0303 | .0297 | .0290 |
| 2.3 | .0283 | .0277 | .0270 | .0264 | .0258 | .0252 | .0246 | .0241 | .0235 | .0229 |
| 2.4 | .0224 | .0219 | .0213 | .0208 | .0203 | .0198 | .0194 | .0189 | .0184 | .0180 |
| 2.5 | .0175 | .0171 | .0167 | .0163 | .0158 | .0154 | .0151 | .0147 | .0143 | .0139 |
| 2.6 | .0136 | .0132 | .0129 | .0126 | .0122 | .0119 | .0116 | .0113 | .0110 | .0107 |
| 2.7 | .0104 | .0101 | .0099 | .0096 | .0093 | .0091 | .0088 | .0086 | .0084 | .0081 |
| 2.8 | .0079 | .0077 | .0075 | .0073 | .0071 | .0069 | .0067 | .0065 | .0063 | .0061 |
| 2.9 | .0060 | .0058 | .0056 | .0055 | .0053 | .0051 | .0050 | .0048 | .0047 | .0046 |
| 3.0 | .0044 | .0043 | .0042 | .0040 | .0039 | .0038 | .0037 | .0036 | .0035 | .0034 |
| 3.1 | .0033 | .0032 | .0031 | .0030 | .0029 | .0028 | .0027 | .0026 | .0025 | .0025 |
| 3.2 | .0024 | .0023 | .0022 | .0022 | .0021 | .0020 | .0020 | .0019 | .0018 | .0018 |
| 3.3 | .0017 | .0017 | .0016 | .0016 | .0015 | .0015 | .0014 | .0014 | .0013 | .0013 |
| 3.4 | .0012 | .0012 | .0012 | .0011 | .0011 | .0010 | .0010 | .0010 | .0009 | .0009 |
| 3.5 | .0009 | .0008 | .0008 | .0008 | .0008 | .0007 | .0007 | .0007 | .0007 | .0006 |
| 3.6 | .0006 | .0006 | .0006 | .0005 | .0005 | .0005 | .0005 | .0005 | .0005 | .0004 |
| 3.7 | .0004 | .0004 | .0004 | .0004 | .0004 | .0004 | .0003 | .0003 | .0003 | .0003 |
| 3.8 | .0003 | .0003 | .0003 | .0003 | .0003 | .0002 | .0002 | .0002 | .0002 | .0002 |
| 3.9 | .0002 | .0002 | .0002 | .0002 | .0002 | .0002 | .0002 | .0002 | .0001 | .0001 |

TABLE I*b*

Area under the Normal Curve, $F(y)$†

| $y$ | .00 | .01 | .02 | .03 | .04 | .05 | .06 | .07 | .08 | .09 |
|---|---|---|---|---|---|---|---|---|---|---|
| .0 | .5000 | .5040 | .5080 | .5120 | .5160 | .5199 | .5239 | .5279 | .5319 | .5359 |
| .1 | .5398 | .5438 | .5478 | .5517 | .5557 | .5596 | .5636 | .5675 | .5714 | .5753 |
| .2 | .5793 | .5832 | .5871 | .5910 | .5948 | .5987 | .6026 | .6064 | .6103 | .6141 |
| .3 | .6179 | .6217 | .6255 | .6293 | .6331 | .6368 | .6406 | .6443 | .6480 | .6517 |
| .4 | .6554 | .6591 | .6628 | .6664 | .6700 | .6736 | .6772 | .6808 | .6844 | .6879 |
| .5 | .6915 | .6950 | .6985 | .7019 | .7054 | .7088 | .7123 | .7157 | .7190 | .7224 |
| .6 | .7257 | .7291 | .7324 | .7357 | .7389 | .7422 | .7454 | .7486 | .7517 | .7549 |
| .7 | .7580 | .7611 | .7642 | .7673 | .7704 | .7734 | .7764 | .7794 | .7823 | .7852 |
| .8 | .7881 | .7910 | .7939 | .7967 | .7995 | .8023 | .8051 | .8078 | .8106 | .8133 |
| .9 | .8159 | .8186 | .8212 | .8238 | .8264 | .8289 | .8315 | .8340 | .8365 | .8389 |
| 1.0 | .8413 | .8438 | .8461 | .8485 | .8508 | .8531 | .8554 | .8577 | .8599 | .8621 |
| 1.1 | .8643 | .8665 | .8686 | .8708 | .8729 | .8749 | .8770 | .8790 | .8810 | .8830 |
| 1.2 | .8849 | .8869 | .8888 | .8907 | .8925 | .8944 | .8962 | .8980 | .8997 | .9015 |
| 1.3 | .9032 | .9049 | .9066 | .9082 | .9099 | .9115 | .9131 | .9147 | .9162 | .9177 |
| 1.4 | .9192 | .9207 | .9222 | .9236 | .9251 | .9265 | .9279 | .9292 | .9306 | .9319 |
| 1.5 | .9332 | .9345 | .9357 | .9370 | .9382 | .9394 | .9406 | .9418 | .9429 | .9441 |
| 1.6 | .9452 | .9463 | .9474 | .9484 | .9495 | .9505 | .9515 | .9525 | .9535 | .9545 |
| 1.7 | .9554 | .9564 | .9573 | .9582 | .9591 | .9599 | .9608 | .9616 | .9625 | .9633 |
| 1.8 | .9641 | .9649 | .9656 | .9664 | .9671 | .9678 | .9686 | .9693 | .9699 | .9706 |
| 1.9 | .9713 | .9719 | .9726 | .9732 | .9738 | .9744 | .9750 | .9756 | .9761 | .9767 |
| 2.0 | .9772 | .9778 | .9783 | .9788 | .9793 | .9798 | .9803 | .9808 | .9812 | .9817 |
| 2.1 | .9821 | .9826 | .9830 | .9834 | .9838 | .9842 | .9846 | .9850 | .9854 | .9857 |
| 2.2 | .9861 | .9864 | .9868 | .9871 | .9875 | .9878 | .9881 | .9884 | .9887 | .9890 |
| 2.3 | .9893 | .9896 | .9898 | .9901 | .9904 | .9906 | .9909 | .9911 | .9913 | .9916 |
| 2.4 | .9918 | .9920 | .9922 | .9925 | .9927 | .9929 | .9931 | .9932 | .9934 | .9936 |
| 2.5 | .9938 | .9940 | .9941 | .9943 | .9945 | .9946 | .9948 | .9949 | .9951 | .9952 |
| 2.6 | .9953 | .9955 | .9956 | .9957 | .9959 | .9960 | .9961 | .9962 | .9963 | .9964 |
| 2.7 | .9965 | .9966 | .9967 | .9968 | .9969 | .9970 | .9971 | .9972 | .9973 | .9974 |
| 2.8 | .9974 | .9975 | .9976 | .9977 | .9977 | .9978 | .9979 | .9979 | .9980 | .9981 |
| 2.9 | .9981 | .9982 | .9982 | .9983 | .9984 | .9984 | .9985 | .9985 | .9986 | .9986 |
| 3.0 | .9987 | .9987 | .9987 | .9988 | .9988 | .9989 | .9989 | .9989 | .9990 | .9990 |
| 3.1 | .9990 | .9991 | .9991 | .9991 | .9992 | .9992 | .9992 | .9992 | .9993 | .9993 |
| 3.2 | .9993 | .9993 | .9994 | .9994 | .9994 | .9994 | .9994 | .9995 | .9995 | .9995 |
| 3.3 | .9995 | .9995 | .9995 | .9996 | .9996 | .9996 | .9996 | .9996 | .9996 | .9997 |
| 3.4 | .9997 | .9997 | .9997 | .9997 | .9997 | .9997 | .9997 | .9997 | .9997 | .9998 |

Percentage Points of the Normal Distribution†

| $F(y)$ | .75 | .90 | .95 | .975 | .99 | .995 | .999 | .9995 | .99995 | .999995 |
|---|---|---|---|---|---|---|---|---|---|---|
| $\alpha = 2[1 - F(y)]$ | .50 | .20 | .10 | .05 | .02 | .01 | .002 | .001 | .0001 | .00001 |
| $T_\alpha$ | 0.674 | 1.282 | 1.645 | 1.960 | 2.326 | 2.576 | 3.090 | 3.291 | 3.891 | 4.417 |

† $F(y)$ is the area under the normal curve from $-\infty$ to $y$; $\alpha$ is twice the area from $y$ to $\infty$ (area from $-\infty$ to $-y$ plus the area from $y$ to $\infty$).

## Table II
### Percentage Points of the $\chi^2$ Distribution†

| $\nu$ \ $\alpha$ | .995 | .990 | .975 | .950 | .900 | .750 | .500 | .250 | .100 | .050 | .025 | .010 | .005 |
|---|---|---|---|---|---|---|---|---|---|---|---|---|---|
| 1 | $.0^4393$ | $.0^3157$ | $.0^3982$ | $.0^2393$ | .0158 | .102 | .455 | 1.32 | 2.71 | 3.84 | 5.02 | 6.63 | 7.88 |
| 2 | .0100 | .0201 | .0506 | .103 | .211 | .575 | 1.39 | 2.77 | 4.61 | 5.99 | 7.38 | 9.21 | 10.6 |
| 3 | .0717 | .115 | .216 | .352 | .584 | 1.21 | 2.37 | 4.11 | 6.25 | 7.81 | 9.35 | 11.3 | 12.8 |
| 4 | .207 | .297 | .484 | .711 | 1.06 | 1.92 | 3.36 | 5.39 | 7.78 | 9.49 | 11.1 | 13.3 | 14.9 |
| 5 | .412 | .554 | .831 | 1.15 | 1.61 | 2.67 | 4.35 | 6.63 | 9.24 | 11.1 | 12.8 | 15.1 | 16.7 |
| 6 | .676 | .872 | 1.24 | 1.64 | 2.20 | 3.45 | 5.35 | 7.84 | 10.6 | 12.6 | 14.4 | 16.8 | 18.5 |
| 7 | .989 | 1.24 | 1.69 | 2.17 | 2.83 | 4.25 | 6.35 | 9.04 | 12.0 | 14.1 | 16.0 | 18.5 | 20.3 |
| 8 | 1.34 | 1.65 | 2.18 | 2.73 | 3.49 | 5.07 | 7.34 | 10.2 | 13.4 | 15.5 | 17.5 | 20.1 | 22.0 |
| 9 | 1.73 | 2.09 | 2.70 | 3.33 | 4.17 | 5.90 | 8.34 | 11.4 | 14.7 | 16.9 | 19.0 | 21.7 | 23.6 |
| 10 | 2.16 | 2.56 | 3.25 | 3.94 | 4.87 | 6.74 | 9.34 | 12.5 | 16.0 | 18.3 | 20.5 | 23.2 | 25.2 |
| 11 | 2.60 | 3.05 | 3.82 | 4.57 | 5.58 | 7.58 | 10.3 | 13.7 | 17.3 | 19.7 | 21.9 | 24.7 | 26.8 |
| 12 | 3.07 | 3.57 | 4.40 | 5.23 | 6.30 | 8.44 | 11.3 | 14.8 | 18.5 | 21.0 | 23.3 | 26.2 | 28.3 |
| 13 | 3.57 | 4.11 | 5.01 | 5.89 | 7.04 | 9.30 | 12.3 | 16.0 | 19.8 | 22.4 | 24.7 | 27.7 | 29.8 |
| 14 | 4.07 | 4.66 | 5.63 | 6.57 | 7.79 | 10.2 | 13.3 | 17.1 | 21.1 | 23.7 | 26.1 | 29.1 | 31.3 |
| 15 | 4.60 | 5.23 | 6.26 | 7.26 | 8.55 | 11.0 | 14.3 | 18.2 | 22.3 | 25.0 | 27.5 | 30.6 | 32.8 |
| 16 | 5.14 | 5.81 | 6.91 | 7.96 | 9.31 | 11.9 | 15.3 | 19.4 | 23.5 | 26.3 | 28.8 | 32.0 | 34.3 |
| 17 | 5.70 | 6.41 | 7.56 | 8.67 | 10.1 | 12.8 | 16.3 | 20.5 | 24.8 | 27.6 | 30.2 | 33.4 | 35.7 |
| 18 | 6.26 | 7.01 | 8.23 | 9.39 | 10.9 | 13.7 | 17.3 | 21.6 | 26.0 | 28.9 | 31.5 | 34.8 | 37.2 |
| 19 | 6.84 | 7.63 | 8.91 | 10.1 | 11.7 | 14.6 | 18.3 | 22.7 | 27.2 | 30.1 | 32.9 | 36.2 | 38.6 |
| 20 | 7.43 | 8.26 | 9.59 | 10.9 | 12.4 | 15.5 | 19.3 | 23.8 | 28.4 | 31.4 | 34.2 | 37.6 | 40.0 |
| 21 | 8.03 | 8.90 | 10.3 | 11.6 | 13.2 | 16.3 | 20.3 | 24.9 | 29.6 | 32.7 | 35.5 | 38.9 | 41.4 |
| 22 | 8.64 | 9.54 | 11.0 | 12.3 | 14.0 | 17.2 | 21.3 | 26.0 | 30.8 | 33.9 | 36.8 | 40.3 | 42.8 |
| 23 | 9.26 | 10.2 | 11.7 | 13.1 | 14.8 | 18.1 | 22.3 | 27.1 | 32.0 | 35.2 | 38.1 | 41.6 | 44.2 |
| 24 | 9.89 | 10.9 | 12.4 | 13.8 | 15.7 | 19.0 | 23.3 | 28.2 | 33.2 | 36.4 | 39.4 | 43.0 | 45.6 |
| 25 | 10.5 | 11.5 | 13.1 | 14.6 | 16.5 | 19.9 | 24.3 | 29.3 | 34.4 | 37.7 | 40.6 | 44.3 | 46.9 |
| 26 | 11.2 | 12.2 | 13.8 | 15.4 | 17.3 | 20.8 | 25.3 | 30.4 | 35.6 | 38.9 | 41.9 | 45.6 | 48.3 |
| 27 | 11.8 | 12.9 | 14.6 | 16.2 | 18.1 | 21.7 | 26.3 | 31.5 | 36.7 | 40.1 | 43.2 | 47.0 | 49.6 |
| 28 | 12.5 | 13.6 | 15.3 | 16.9 | 18.9 | 22.7 | 27.3 | 32.6 | 37.9 | 41.3 | 44.5 | 48.3 | 51.0 |
| 29 | 13.1 | 14.3 | 16.0 | 17.7 | 19.8 | 23.6 | 28.3 | 33.7 | 39.1 | 42.6 | 45.7 | 49.6 | 52.3 |
| 30 | 13.8 | 15.0 | 16.8 | 18.5 | 20.6 | 24.5 | 29.3 | 34.8 | 40.3 | 43.8 | 47.0 | 50.9 | 53.7 |
| 40 | 20.7 | 22.2 | 24.4 | 26.5 | 29.1 | 33.7 | 39.3 | 45.6 | 51.8 | 55.8 | 59.3 | 63.7 | 66.8 |
| 50 | 28.0 | 29.7 | 32.4 | 34.8 | 37.7 | 42.9 | 49.3 | 56.3 | 63.2 | 67.5 | 71.4 | 76.2 | 79.5 |
| 60 | 35.5 | 37.5 | 40.5 | 43.2 | 46.5 | 52.3 | 59.3 | 67.0 | 74.4 | 79.1 | 83.3 | 88.4 | 92.0 |

† This table is abridged from "Tables of Percentage Points of the $\chi^2$ Distribution," by Catherine M. Thompson in *Biometrika*, **32**:188–189 (1941), and is published here with the kind permission of the author and the editor of *Biometrika*. $\nu$ is the number of degrees of freedom and $\alpha$ the probability of exceeding the tabular value.

TABLE III
Percentage Points of the $t$ Distribution†

| $n$ \ $\alpha$ | .50 | .40 | .30 | .20 | .10 | .05 | .02 | .01 | .001 |
|---|---|---|---|---|---|---|---|---|---|
| 1 | 1.000 | 1.376 | 1.963 | 3.078 | 6.314 | 12.706 | 31.821 | 63.657 | 636.619 |
| 2 | .816 | 1.061 | 1.386 | 1.886 | 2.920 | 4.303 | 6.965 | 9.925 | 31.598 |
| 3 | .765 | .978 | 1.250 | 1.638 | 2.353 | 3.182 | 4.541 | 5.841 | 12.941 |
| 4 | .741 | .941 | 1.190 | 1.533 | 2.132 | 2.776 | 3.747 | 4.604 | 8.610 |
| 5 | .727 | .920 | 1.156 | 1.476 | 2.015 | 2.571 | 3.365 | 4.032 | 6.859 |
| 6 | .718 | .906 | 1.134 | 1.440 | 1.943 | 2.447 | 3.143 | 3.707 | 5.959 |
| 7 | .711 | .896 | 1.119 | 1.415 | 1.895 | 2.365 | 2.998 | 3.499 | 5.405 |
| 8 | .706 | .889 | 1.108 | 1.397 | 1.860 | 2.306 | 2.896 | 3.355 | 5.041 |
| 9 | .703 | .883 | 1.100 | 1.383 | 1.833 | 2.262 | 2.821 | 3.250 | 4.781 |
| 10 | .700 | .879 | 1.093 | 1.372 | 1.812 | 2.228 | 2.764 | 3.169 | 4.587 |
| 11 | .697 | .876 | 1.088 | 1.363 | 1.796 | 2.201 | 2.718 | 3.106 | 4.437 |
| 12 | .695 | .873 | 1.083 | 1.356 | 1.782 | 2.179 | 2.681 | 3.055 | 4.318 |
| 13 | .694 | .870 | 1.079 | 1.350 | 1.771 | 2.160 | 2.650 | 3.012 | 4.221 |
| 14 | .692 | .868 | 1.076 | 1.345 | 1.761 | 2.145 | 2.624 | 2.977 | 4.140 |
| 15 | .691 | .866 | 1.074 | 1.341 | 1.753 | 2.131 | 2.602 | 2.947 | 4.073 |
| 16 | .690 | .865 | 1.071 | 1.337 | 1.746 | 2.120 | 2.583 | 2.921 | 4.015 |
| 17 | .689 | .863 | 1.069 | 1.333 | 1.740 | 2.110 | 2.567 | 2.898 | 3.965 |
| 18 | .688 | .862 | 1.067 | 1.330 | 1.734 | 2.101 | 2.552 | 2.878 | 3.922 |
| 19 | .688 | .861 | 1.066 | 1.328 | 1.729 | 2.093 | 2.539 | 2.861 | 3.883 |
| 20 | .687 | .860 | 1.064 | 1.325 | 1.725 | 2.086 | 2.528 | 2.845 | 3.850 |
| 21 | .686 | .859 | 1.063 | 1.323 | 1.721 | 2.080 | 2.518 | 2.831 | 3.819 |
| 22 | .686 | .858 | 1.061 | 1.321 | 1.717 | 2.074 | 2.508 | 2.819 | 3.792 |
| 23 | .685 | .858 | 1.060 | 1.319 | 1.714 | 2.069 | 2.500 | 2.807 | 3.767 |
| 24 | .685 | .857 | 1.059 | 1.318 | 1.711 | 2.064 | 2.492 | 2.797 | 3.745 |
| 25 | .684 | .856 | 1.058 | 1.316 | 1.708 | 2.060 | 2.485 | 2.787 | 3.725 |
| 26 | .684 | .856 | 1.058 | 1.315 | 1.706 | 2.056 | 2.479 | 2.779 | 3.707 |
| 27 | .684 | .855 | 1.057 | 1.314 | 1.703 | 2.052 | 2.473 | 2.771 | 3.690 |
| 28 | .683 | .855 | 1.056 | 1.313 | 1.701 | 2.048 | 2.467 | 2.763 | 3.674 |
| 29 | .683 | .854 | 1.055 | 1.311 | 1.699 | 2.045 | 2.462 | 2.756 | 3.659 |
| 30 | .683 | .854 | 1.055 | 1.310 | 1.697 | 2.042 | 2.457 | 2.750 | 3.646 |
| 40 | .681 | .851 | 1.050 | 1.303 | 1.684 | 2.021 | 2.423 | 2.704 | 3.551 |
| 60 | .679 | .848 | 1.046 | 1.296 | 1.671 | 2.000 | 2.390 | 2.660 | 3.460 |
| 120 | .677 | .845 | 1.041 | 1.289 | 1.658 | 1.980 | 2.358 | 2.617 | 3.373 |
| $\infty$ | .674 | .842 | 1.036 | 1.282 | 1.645 | 1.960 | 2.326 | 2.576 | 3.291 |

† This table is abridged from Table III of *Statistical Tables for Biological, Agricultural and Medical Research*, 3d ed., by R. A. Fisher and Frank Yates, published by Oliver & Boyd, Ltd., London and Edinburgh, 1949. It is reproduced here with the kind permission of the authors and their publishers. $n$ is the number of degrees of freedom and $\alpha$ twice the probability of exceeding the tabular value (or the probability of being more than the tabular value or less than the negative of the tabular value).

TABLE IV
Percentage Points of the $F$ Distribution†
$\alpha = .05$

| $n_2$ \ $n_1$ | 1 | 2 | 3 | 4 | 5 | 6 | 7 | 8 | 9 | 10 | 12 | 16 | 20 | 24 | 30 | 50 | 100 | ∞ |
|---|---|---|---|---|---|---|---|---|---|---|---|---|---|---|---|---|---|---|
| 1 | 161 | 200 | 216 | 225 | 230 | 234 | 237 | 239 | 241 | 242 | 244 | 246 | 248 | 249 | 250 | 252 | 253 | 254 |
| 2 | 18.51 | 19.00 | 19.16 | 19.25 | 19.30 | 19.33 | 19.36 | 19.37 | 19.38 | 19.39 | 19.41 | 19.43 | 19.44 | 19.45 | 19.46 | 19.47 | 19.49 | 19.50 |
| 3 | 10.13 | 9.55 | 9.28 | 9.12 | 9.01 | 8.94 | 8.88 | 8.84 | 8.81 | 8.78 | 8.74 | 8.69 | 8.66 | 8.64 | 8.62 | 8.58 | 8.56 | 8.53 |
| 4 | 7.71 | 6.94 | 6.59 | 6.39 | 6.26 | 6.16 | 6.09 | 6.04 | 6.00 | 5.96 | 5.91 | 5.84 | 5.80 | 5.77 | 5.74 | 5.70 | 5.66 | 5.63 |
| 5 | 6.61 | 5.79 | 5.41 | 5.19 | 5.05 | 4.95 | 4.88 | 4.82 | 4.78 | 4.74 | 4.68 | 4.60 | 4.56 | 4.53 | 4.50 | 4.44 | 4.40 | 4.36 |
| 6 | 5.99 | 5.14 | 4.76 | 4.53 | 4.39 | 4.28 | 4.21 | 4.15 | 4.10 | 4.06 | 4.00 | 3.92 | 3.87 | 3.84 | 3.81 | 3.75 | 3.71 | 3.67 |
| 7 | 5.59 | 4.74 | 4.35 | 4.12 | 3.97 | 3.87 | 3.79 | 3.73 | 3.68 | 3.63 | 3.57 | 3.49 | 3.44 | 3.41 | 3.38 | 3.32 | 3.28 | 3.23 |
| 8 | 5.32 | 4.46 | 4.07 | 3.84 | 3.69 | 3.58 | 3.50 | 3.44 | 3.39 | 3.34 | 3.28 | 3.20 | 3.15 | 3.12 | 3.08 | 3.03 | 2.98 | 2.93 |
| 9 | 5.12 | 4.26 | 3.86 | 3.63 | 3.48 | 3.37 | 3.29 | 3.23 | 3.18 | 3.13 | 3.07 | 2.98 | 2.93 | 2.90 | 2.86 | 2.80 | 2.76 | 2.71 |
| 10 | 4.96 | 4.10 | 3.71 | 3.48 | 3.33 | 3.22 | 3.14 | 3.07 | 3.02 | 2.97 | 2.91 | 2.82 | 2.77 | 2.74 | 2.70 | 2.64 | 2.59 | 2.54 |
| 11 | 4.84 | 3.98 | 3.59 | 3.36 | 3.20 | 3.09 | 3.01 | 2.95 | 2.90 | 2.86 | 2.79 | 2.70 | 2.65 | 2.61 | 2.57 | 2.50 | 2.45 | 2.40 |
| 12 | 4.75 | 3.88 | 3.49 | 3.26 | 3.11 | 3.00 | 2.92 | 2.85 | 2.80 | 2.76 | 2.69 | 2.60 | 2.54 | 2.50 | 2.46 | 2.40 | 2.35 | 2.30 |
| 13 | 4.67 | 3.80 | 3.41 | 3.18 | 3.02 | 2.92 | 2.84 | 2.77 | 2.72 | 2.67 | 2.60 | 2.51 | 2.46 | 2.42 | 2.38 | 2.32 | 2.26 | 2.21 |
| 14 | 4.60 | 3.74 | 3.34 | 3.11 | 2.96 | 2.85 | 2.77 | 2.70 | 2.65 | 2.60 | 2.53 | 2.44 | 2.39 | 2.35 | 2.31 | 2.24 | 2.19 | 2.13 |
| 15 | 4.54 | 3.68 | 3.29 | 3.06 | 2.90 | 2.79 | 2.70 | 2.64 | 2.59 | 2.55 | 2.48 | 2.39 | 2.33 | 2.29 | 2.25 | 2.18 | 2.12 | 2.07 |
| 16 | 4.49 | 3.63 | 3.24 | 3.01 | 2.85 | 2.74 | 2.66 | 2.59 | 2.54 | 2.49 | 2.42 | 2.33 | 2.28 | 2.24 | 2.20 | 2.13 | 2.07 | 2.01 |
| 17 | 4.45 | 3.59 | 3.20 | 2.96 | 2.81 | 2.70 | 2.62 | 2.55 | 2.50 | 2.45 | 2.38 | 2.29 | 2.23 | 2.19 | 2.15 | 2.08 | 2.02 | 1.96 |
| 18 | 4.41 | 3.55 | 3.16 | 2.93 | 2.77 | 2.66 | 2.58 | 2.51 | 2.46 | 2.41 | 2.34 | 2.25 | 2.19 | 2.15 | 2.11 | 2.04 | 1.98 | 1.92 |
| 19 | 4.38 | 3.52 | 3.13 | 2.90 | 2.74 | 2.63 | 2.55 | 2.48 | 2.43 | 2.38 | 2.31 | 2.21 | 2.15 | 2.11 | 2.07 | 2.00 | 1.94 | 1.88 |
| 20 | 4.35 | 3.49 | 3.10 | 2.87 | 2.71 | 2.60 | 2.52 | 2.45 | 2.40 | 2.35 | 2.28 | 2.18 | 2.12 | 2.08 | 2.04 | 1.96 | 1.90 | 1.84 |
| 22 | 4.30 | 3.44 | 3.05 | 2.82 | 2.66 | 2.55 | 2.47 | 2.40 | 2.35 | 2.30 | 2.23 | 2.13 | 2.07 | 2.03 | 1.98 | 1.91 | 1.84 | 1.78 |
| 24 | 4.26 | 3.40 | 3.01 | 2.78 | 2.62 | 2.51 | 2.43 | 2.36 | 2.30 | 2.26 | 2.18 | 2.09 | 2.02 | 1.98 | 1.94 | 1.86 | 1.80 | 1.73 |
| 26 | 4.22 | 3.37 | 2.98 | 2.74 | 2.59 | 2.47 | 2.39 | 2.32 | 2.27 | 2.22 | 2.15 | 2.05 | 1.99 | 1.95 | 1.90 | 1.82 | 1.76 | 1.69 |
| 28 | 4.20 | 3.34 | 2.95 | 2.71 | 2.56 | 2.44 | 2.36 | 2.29 | 2.24 | 2.19 | 2.12 | 2.02 | 1.96 | 1.91 | 1.87 | 1.78 | 1.72 | 1.65 |
| 32 | 4.15 | 3.30 | 2.90 | 2.67 | 2.51 | 2.40 | 2.32 | 2.25 | 2.19 | 2.14 | 2.07 | 1.97 | 1.91 | 1.86 | 1.82 | 1.74 | 1.67 | 1.59 |
| 36 | 4.11 | 3.26 | 2.86 | 2.63 | 2.48 | 2.36 | 2.28 | 2.21 | 2.15 | 2.10 | 2.03 | 1.93 | 1.87 | 1.82 | 1.78 | 1.69 | 1.62 | 1.55 |
| 40 | 4.08 | 3.23 | 2.84 | 2.61 | 2.45 | 2.34 | 2.25 | 2.18 | 2.12 | 2.07 | 2.00 | 1.90 | 1.84 | 1.79 | 1.74 | 1.66 | 1.59 | 1.51 |
| 60 | 4.00 | 3.15 | 2.76 | 2.52 | 2.37 | 2.25 | 2.17 | 2.10 | 2.04 | 1.99 | 1.92 | 1.81 | 1.75 | 1.70 | 1.65 | 1.56 | 1.48 | 1.39 |
| 100 | 3.94 | 3.09 | 2.70 | 2.46 | 2.30 | 2.19 | 2.10 | 2.03 | 1.97 | 1.92 | 1.85 | 1.75 | 1.68 | 1.63 | 1.57 | 1.48 | 1.39 | 1.28 |
| 200 | 3.89 | 3.04 | 2.65 | 2.41 | 2.26 | 2.14 | 2.05 | 1.98 | 1.92 | 1.87 | 1.80 | 1.69 | 1.62 | 1.57 | 1.52 | 1.42 | 1.32 | 1.19 |
| ∞ | 3.84 | 2.99 | 2.60 | 2.37 | 2.21 | 2.09 | 2.01 | 1.94 | 1.88 | 1.83 | 1.75 | 1.64 | 1.57 | 1.52 | 1.46 | 1.35 | 1.24 | 1.00 |

TABLE IV. (*Continued*)

$\alpha = .01$

| $n_2$ \ $n_1$ | 1 | 2 | 3 | 4 | 5 | 6 | 7 | 8 | 9 | 10 | 12 | 16 | 20 | 24 | 30 | 50 | 100 | ∞ |
|---|---|---|---|---|---|---|---|---|---|---|---|---|---|---|---|---|---|---|
| 1 | 4,052 | 4,999 | 5,403 | 5,625 | 5,764 | 5,859 | 5,928 | 5,981 | 6,022 | 6,056 | 6,106 | 6,169 | 6,208 | 6,234 | 6,258 | 6,302 | 6,334 | 6,366 |
| 2 | 98.49 | 99.00 | 99.17 | 99.25 | 99.30 | 99.33 | 99.34 | 99.36 | 99.38 | 99.40 | 99.42 | 99.44 | 99.45 | 99.46 | 99.47 | 99.48 | 99.49 | 99.50 |
| 3 | 34.12 | 30.82 | 29.46 | 28.71 | 28.24 | 27.91 | 27.67 | 27.49 | 27.34 | 27.23 | 27.05 | 26.83 | 26.69 | 26.60 | 26.50 | 26.35 | 26.23 | 26.12 |
| 4 | 21.20 | 18.00 | 16.69 | 15.98 | 15.52 | 15.21 | 14.98 | 14.80 | 14.66 | 14.54 | 14.37 | 14.15 | 14.02 | 13.93 | 13.83 | 13.69 | 13.57 | 13.46 |
| 5 | 16.26 | 13.27 | 12.06 | 11.39 | 10.97 | 10.67 | 10.45 | 10.27 | 10.15 | 10.05 | 9.89 | 9.68 | 9.55 | 9.47 | 9.38 | 9.24 | 9.13 | 9.02 |
| 6 | 13.74 | 10.92 | 9.78 | 9.15 | 8.75 | 8.47 | 8.26 | 8.10 | 7.98 | 7.87 | 7.72 | 7.52 | 7.39 | 7.31 | 7.23 | 7.09 | 6.99 | 6.88 |
| 7 | 12.25 | 9.55 | 8.45 | 7.85 | 7.46 | 7.19 | 7.00 | 6.84 | 6.71 | 6.62 | 6.47 | 6.27 | 6.15 | 6.07 | 5.98 | 5.85 | 5.75 | 5.65 |
| 8 | 11.26 | 8.65 | 7.59 | 7.01 | 6.63 | 6.37 | 6.19 | 6.03 | 5.91 | 5.82 | 5.67 | 5.48 | 5.36 | 5.28 | 5.20 | 5.06 | 4.96 | 4.86 |
| 9 | 10.56 | 8.02 | 6.99 | 6.42 | 6.06 | 5.80 | 5.62 | 5.47 | 5.35 | 5.26 | 5.11 | 4.92 | 4.80 | 4.73 | 4.64 | 4.51 | 4.41 | 4.31 |
| 10 | 10.04 | 7.56 | 6.55 | 5.99 | 5.64 | 5.39 | 5.21 | 5.06 | 4.95 | 4.85 | 4.71 | 4.52 | 4.41 | 4.33 | 4.25 | 4.12 | 4.01 | 3.91 |
| 11 | 9.65 | 7.20 | 6.22 | 5.67 | 5.32 | 5.07 | 4.88 | 4.74 | 4.63 | 4.54 | 4.40 | 4.21 | 4.10 | 4.02 | 3.94 | 3.80 | 3.70 | 3.60 |
| 12 | 9.33 | 6.93 | 5.95 | 5.41 | 5.06 | 4.82 | 4.65 | 4.50 | 4.39 | 4.30 | 4.16 | 3.98 | 3.86 | 3.78 | 3.70 | 3.56 | 3.46 | 3.36 |
| 13 | 9.07 | 6.70 | 5.74 | 5.20 | 4.86 | 4.62 | 4.44 | 4.30 | 4.19 | 4.10 | 3.96 | 3.78 | 3.67 | 3.59 | 3.51 | 3.37 | 3.27 | 3.16 |
| 14 | 8.86 | 6.51 | 5.56 | 5.03 | 4.69 | 4.46 | 4.28 | 4.14 | 4.03 | 3.94 | 3.80 | 3.62 | 3.51 | 3.43 | 3.34 | 3.21 | 3.11 | 3.00 |
| 15 | 8.68 | 6.36 | 5.42 | 4.89 | 4.56 | 4.32 | 4.14 | 4.00 | 3.89 | 3.80 | 3.67 | 3.48 | 3.36 | 3.29 | 3.20 | 3.07 | 2.97 | 2.87 |
| 16 | 8.53 | 6.23 | 5.29 | 4.77 | 4.44 | 4.20 | 4.03 | 3.89 | 3.78 | 3.69 | 3.55 | 3.37 | 3.25 | 3.18 | 3.10 | 2.96 | 2.86 | 2.75 |
| 17 | 8.40 | 6.11 | 5.18 | 4.67 | 4.34 | 4.10 | 3.93 | 3.79 | 3.68 | 3.59 | 3.45 | 3.27 | 3.16 | 3.08 | 3.00 | 2.86 | 2.76 | 2.65 |
| 18 | 8.28 | 6.01 | 5.09 | 4.58 | 4.25 | 4.01 | 3.85 | 3.71 | 3.60 | 3.51 | 3.37 | 3.19 | 3.07 | 3.00 | 2.91 | 2.78 | 2.68 | 2.57 |
| 19 | 8.18 | 5.93 | 5.01 | 4.50 | 4.17 | 3.94 | 3.77 | 3.63 | 3.52 | 3.43 | 3.30 | 3.12 | 3.00 | 2.92 | 2.84 | 2.70 | 2.60 | 2.49 |
| 20 | 8.10 | 5.85 | 4.94 | 4.43 | 4.10 | 3.87 | 3.71 | 3.56 | 3.45 | 3.37 | 3.23 | 3.05 | 2.94 | 2.86 | 2.77 | 2.63 | 2.53 | 2.42 |
| 22 | 7.94 | 5.72 | 4.82 | 4.31 | 3.99 | 3.76 | 3.59 | 3.45 | 3.35 | 3.26 | 3.12 | 2.94 | 2.83 | 2.75 | 2.67 | 2.53 | 2.42 | 2.31 |
| 24 | 7.82 | 5.61 | 4.72 | 4.22 | 3.90 | 3.67 | 3.50 | 3.36 | 3.25 | 3.17 | 3.03 | 2.85 | 2.74 | 2.66 | 2.58 | 2.44 | 2.33 | 2.21 |
| 26 | 7.72 | 5.53 | 4.64 | 4.14 | 3.82 | 3.59 | 3.42 | 3.29 | 3.17 | 3.09 | 2.96 | 2.77 | 2.66 | 2.58 | 2.50 | 2.36 | 2.25 | 2.13 |
| 28 | 7.64 | 5.45 | 4.57 | 4.07 | 3.76 | 3.53 | 3.36 | 3.23 | 3.11 | 3.03 | 2.90 | 2.71 | 2.60 | 2.52 | 2.44 | 2.30 | 2.18 | 2.06 |
| 32 | 7.50 | 5.34 | 4.46 | 3.97 | 3.66 | 3.42 | 3.25 | 3.12 | 3.01 | 2.94 | 2.80 | 2.62 | 2.51 | 2.42 | 2.34 | 2.20 | 2.08 | 1.96 |
| 36 | 7.39 | 5.25 | 4.38 | 3.89 | 3.58 | 3.35 | 3.18 | 3.04 | 2.94 | 2.86 | 2.72 | 2.54 | 2.43 | 2.35 | 2.26 | 2.12 | 2.00 | 1.87 |
| 40 | 7.31 | 5.18 | 4.31 | 3.83 | 3.51 | 3.29 | 3.12 | 2.99 | 2.88 | 2.80 | 2.66 | 2.49 | 2.37 | 2.29 | 2.20 | 2.05 | 1.94 | 1.81 |
| 60 | 7.08 | 4.98 | 4.13 | 3.65 | 3.34 | 3.12 | 2.95 | 2.82 | 2.72 | 2.63 | 2.50 | 2.32 | 2.20 | 2.12 | 2.03 | 1.87 | 1.74 | 1.60 |
| 100 | 6.90 | 4.82 | 3.98 | 3.51 | 3.20 | 2.99 | 2.82 | 2.69 | 2.59 | 2.51 | 2.36 | 2.19 | 2.06 | 1.98 | 1.89 | 1.73 | 1.59 | 1.43 |
| 200 | 6.76 | 4.71 | 3.88 | 3.41 | 3.11 | 2.90 | 2.73 | 2.60 | 2.50 | 2.41 | 2.28 | 2.09 | 1.97 | 1.88 | 1.79 | 1.62 | 1.48 | 1.28 |
| ∞ | 6.64 | 4.60 | 3.78 | 3.32 | 3.02 | 2.80 | 2.64 | 2.51 | 2.41 | 2.32 | 2.18 | 1.99 | 1.87 | 1.79 | 1.69 | 1.52 | 1.36 | 1.00 |

† This table is abridged from Table 10.7 of *Statistical Methods*, 4th ed., by G. W. Snedecor, published by the Collegiate Press, Inc., Iowa State College, Ames, Iowa, 1946. It is reproduced here with the kind permission of the author and the publisher. $n_1$ is the number of degrees of freedom in the numerator and $n_2$ the number of degrees of freedom in the denominator of $F$. $\alpha$ is the probability of exceeding the tabular value.

# INDEX

T



U



V